CORE · GEOGRAPHY

Series Editors:
Michael Naish and
Sue Warn

Authors:
Steve Burton,
John Chaffey,
Jane Entwistle,
Steve Frampton,
Roger Robinson and
Sue Sleep

LONGMAN

Longman Group Limited
Longman House, Burnt Mill, Harlow, Essex CM20 2JE, England

The publisher's policy is to use paper manufactured from sustainable
forests.

First published 1994
ISBN 0 582 059380

Set in 9/10pt Palatino
Printed in Great Britain by Scotprint Limited, Musselburgh

Contents

Introduction

This book is based on two important ideas. The first is that geography is concerned with matters of immediate and critical significance for the quality of life on Earth. The argument is that the ways in which people interact with their environments have very significant impacts on both the environments and on the quality of life. Geographers can help develop our understanding of the nature of these impacts, the processes by which they come about and ways of managing both the processes and the impacts themselves.

The second important idea is that people best learn geography by being actively engaged in enquiry into the questions, issues and problems that arise from the interaction of people with their varied environments. This approach to learning geography helps to develop a wide range of skills from practical activities such as relating to other people and drawing communicative maps and diagrams, thinking in a critically creative manner so as to be able to solve problems, making considered decisions and predicting the possible consequences of implementing such decisions.

The best way to use this book would be to take it section by section, working through the activities suggested, rather than by setting out to read it from cover to cover. The activities will lead on to other areas of enquiry, since more questions are raised than are answered and, in some cases, further activities are suggested.

The book is designed to support study of the Core Modules of the Geography 16–19 Advanced level syllabus, but it is also applicable to all Geography A-levels which have a people–environment focus.

Michael Naish and Sue Warn, Editors

1
Landforms and Environmental Management

Introduction

The first section of this chapter deals with the management of coastal landforms and processes in both the UK and the USA. The second section deals with the management of drainage basin landforms and processes. Also, we consider briefly the question of integrated landform management: how do the coastal and drainage basin systems and processes interact, and what are the main landform management challenges that face us towards the year 2000?

Figure 1.1 The future of the coastal zone without coherent management

The Management of Coastal Systems in the UK

Why is the coastline important?

The coastline is a dynamic boundary zone for the human species between the habitable terrestrial and the inhospitable marine environment. It is an area of recreation, industry, commerce and often dense residential development. It is also one of the most geomorphologically active landscapes, undergoing constant change. Therefore, it is a landform system whose processes must be fully understood in order to produce effective and environmentally sensitive management programmes. Such programmes are designed to alleviate the erosive effect of the sea and to restrict the depositional problems it may create. They are also aimed at reconciling the often conflicting demands of educational, scientific, recreational, agricultural, industrial, fishing and coastal-protection interests.

CASE STUDY *The Dorset Coastal Path*

The issue – a coastal recreational conflict

In September 1974 the 115 km Dorset Coast Path running from Lyme Regis to Poole Harbour was opened. However, its continuity is broken between Lulworth and Kimmeridge by the MOD Lulworth Ranges. The area includes the village of Tyneham and Worbarrow Bay. Conflict centres over whether or not there should be totally unrestricted access to this AONB.

The groups concerned and their viewpoints

The Army and MOD: 'We have been established here since 1916, and the ranges are vital for tank training. We provide important civilian employment opportunities for this part of rural Dorset. All four alternative sites have major disadvantages.'

The Countryside Commission: 'We favour unrestricted access, and see no reason why the flora and fauna should suffer if the Army abandon their exercises. In fact the visual impact will improve if this Dorset site closes.' (The CC are responsible for protecting the outstanding landscape value of the area and are obliged to consider recreational needs and facilities.)

English Nature: 'Restricted access since WWII has had major advantages.' (They are responsible for the preservation and conservation of wildlife and their habitats.)

Dorset County Council: 'We want both the employment generated by the ranges and tanks, and access to an AONB. We must not allow the area to degenerate under severe recreational pressure *and* suffer the same footpath, erosion and litter problems of other west coastal areas.' (A compromise is favoured with partial access at weekends and block periods at Christmas, Easter, Whitsun and in the summer.)

The Ramblers Association: 'We want total open access for walkers.'

Established long-term local residents: 'Maintain the status quo.'

MOD = Ministry of Defence

AONB = Area of Outstanding Natural Beauty

MEDIA ANALYSIS AND ISSUE IDENTIFICATION

Environmental issues now have a very high profile and this is reflected in all aspects of the media. Some of these issues relate to our use and abuse of the coastal zone.

One of the quality national daily newspapers is to produce a special supplement, 'Our Coastline in Conflict', to review the current condition of our national coastal zone.

Write a brief summary of a local or regional coastal conflict between, or even within, different land use categories reflecting various groups with interests in our coastline. The article should be no more than 200 words long, with a headline of not more than five words. Use a local example, or one from further afield which draws on your own fieldwork or the media. Be clear on the nature of the conflict. Attempt to explain the different perceptions of the groups concerned, and why they might hold these views.

Figures 1.2, 1.3 and 1.5 will help you to identify suitable issues. If you cannot find a local issue use the materials from the case study above to construct the newspaper article. If there is a sufficient variety and range of issues you could construct a class newspaper supplement on this topic.

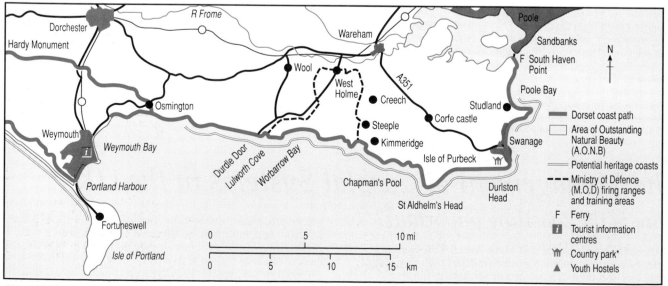

Figure 1.2   Location map for Worbarrow Bay and Tyneham

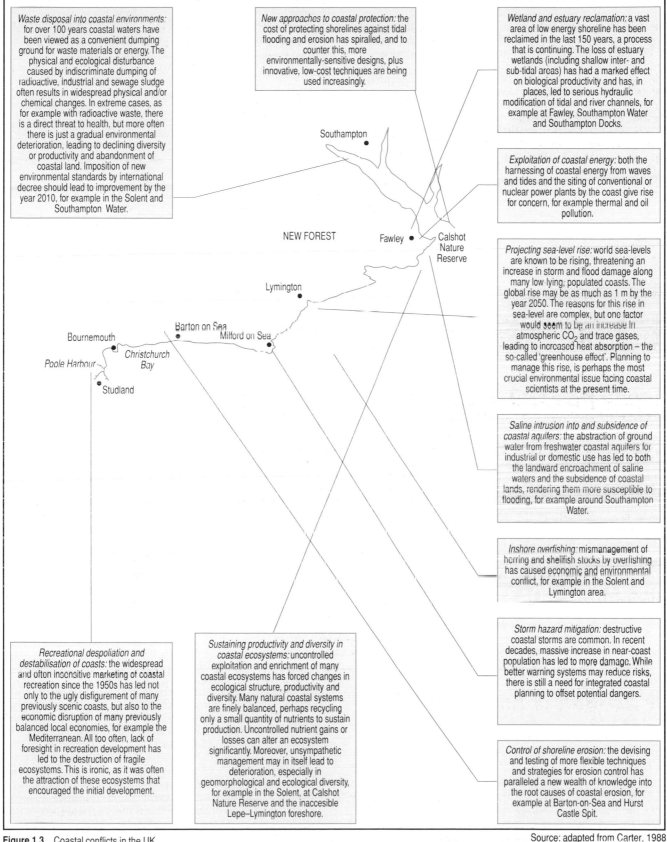

Waste disposal into coastal environments: for over 100 years coastal waters have been viewed as a convenient dumping ground for waste materials or energy. The physical and ecological disturbance caused by indiscriminate dumping of radioactive, industrial and sewage sludge often results in widespread physical and/or chemical changes. In extreme cases, as for example with radioactive waste, there is a direct threat to health, but more often there is just a gradual environmental deterioration, leading to declining diversity or productivity and abandonment of coastal land. Imposition of new environmental standards by international decree should lead to improvement by the year 2010, for example in the Solent and Southampton Water.

New approaches to coastal protection: the cost of protecting shorelines against tidal flooding and erosion has spiralled, and to counter this, more environmentally-sensitive designs, plus innovative, low-cost techniques are being used increasingly.

Wetland and estuary reclamation: a vast area of low energy shoreline has been reclaimed in the last 150 years, a process that is continuing. The loss of estuary wetlands (including shallow inter- and sub-tidal areas) has had a marked effect on biological productivity and has, in places, led to serious hydraulic modification of tidal and river channels, for example at Fawley, Southampton Water and Southampton Docks.

Exploitation of coastal energy: both the harnessing of coastal energy from waves and tides and the siting of conventional or nuclear power plants by the coast give rise for concern, for example thermal and oil pollution.

Projecting sea-level rise: world sea-levels are known to be rising, threatening an increase in storm and flood damage along many low lying, populated coasts. The global rise may be as much as 1 m by the year 2050. The reasons for this rise in sea-level are complex, but one factor would seem to be an increase in atmospheric CO_2 and trace gases, leading to increased heat absorption – the so-called 'greenhouse effect'. Planning to manage this rise, is perhaps the most crucial environmental issue facing coastal scientists at the present time.

Saline intrusion into and subsidence of coastal aquifers: the abstraction of ground water from freshwater coastal aquifers for industrial or domestic use has led to both the landward encroachment of saline waters and the subsidence of coastal lands, rendering them more susceptible to flooding, for example around Southampton Water.

Inshore overfishing: mismanagement of herring and shellfish stocks by overfishing has caused economic and environmental conflict, for example in the Solent and Lymington area.

Storm hazard mitigation: destructive coastal storms are common. In recent decades, massive increase in near-coast population has led to more damage. While better warning systems may reduce risks, there is still a need for integrated coastal planning to offset potential dangers.

Control of shoreline erosion: the devising and testing of more flexible techniques and strategies for erosion control has paralleled a new wealth of knowledge into the root causes of coastal erosion, for example at Barton-on-Sea and Hurst Castle Spit.

Recreational despoliation and destabilisation of coasts: the widespread and often insensitive marketing of coastal recreation since the 1950s has led not only to the ugly disfigurement of many previously scenic coasts, but also to the economic disruption of many previously balanced local economies, for example the Mediterranean. All too often, lack of foresight in recreation development has led to the destruction of fragile ecosystems. This is ironic, as it was often the attraction of these ecosystems that encouraged the initial development.

Sustaining productivity and diversity in coastal ecosystems: uncontrolled exploitation and enrichment of many coastal ecosystems has forced changes in ecological structure, productivity and diversity. Many natural coastal systems are finely balanced, perhaps recycling only a small quantity of nutrients to sustain production. Uncontrolled nutrient gains or losses can alter an ecosystem significantly. Moreover, unsympathetic management may in itself lead to deterioration, especially in geomorphological and ecological diversity, for example in the Solent, at Calshot Nature Reserve and the inaccessible Lepe–Lymington foreshore.

Southampton

NEW FOREST   Fawley   Calshot Nature Reserve

Lymington

Barton on Sea   Milford on Sea

Bournemouth   Christchurch Bay

Poole Harbour

Studland

Figure 1.3   Coastal conflicts in the UK

Source: adapted from Carter, 1988

What types of coast exist?

There have been many attempts at classifying coastal types. Topography decides whether coastlines are bold and high, or low. Their plan-form subdivides into straight and sinuous types. Lithologically, they can be hard rock or soft. According to their degree of human modification they can be regarded as being natural or modified.

Valentin classified coasts on the basis of their sea level variations and dominant marine process (Figure 1.4a). Barnes took an ecological approach based on habitat, flora and fauna (Figure 1.4b). No one system works completely because coastlines are not static features in the landscape; composite classifications based on form and process are most useful.

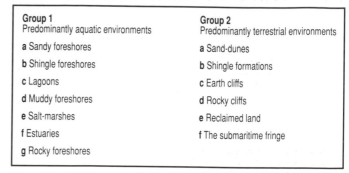

Group 1 Predominantly aquatic environments	Group 2 Predominantly terrestrial environments
a Sandy foreshores	**a** Sand-dunes
b Shingle foreshores	**b** Shingle formations
c Lagoons	**c** Earth cliffs
d Muddy foreshores	**d** Rocky cliffs
e Salt-marshes	**e** Reclaimed land
f Estuaries	**f** The submaritime fringe
g Rocky foreshores	

Figure 1.4b   The Barnes classification of coastal environments

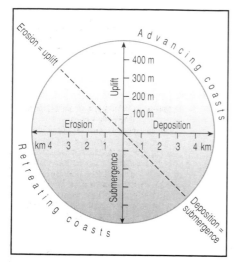

Figure 1.4a   Valentin's system of coastal classification

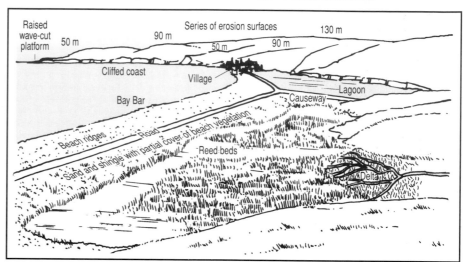

Figure 1.4c   Field sketch of coastal area of south-west England

ACTIVITY: COASTAL CLASSIFICATIONS

Classify the area illustrated in the field sketch of a stretch of coastline in south-west England (Figure 1.4c). Use the ideas of Barnes (Figure 1.4b) and Valentin (Figure 1.4a), as well as topography, plan-form, lithology and degree of human modification. What problems do you encounter when using these classifications?

RESEARCH: COASTAL PROCESSES

Using a suitable text (e.g. Hansom or Clowes and Comfort) research the basic coastal processes responsible for these coastal landforms, and for this area in south-west England suggest how each of the following may have contributed to landform development: changes in sea level; wave action; fluvial deposition; plant colonisation.

The coastline of England and Wales

Accretion

This is a feature of our sheltered coasts and estuaries where low current velocities allow sediment to be deposited. The Royal Commission on Coastal Erosion estimated that through artificial reclamation we may gain up to seven times more land per annum than we lose.

Plants can play a key role in accretionary processes, e.g. in salt marshes and sand dunes. The final elements that make up coastlines of accretion are wave-built ridges or bars of sand and shingle; sand bars, shingle bars and beaches. These features may be due to active processes, or they may be 'fossil' features, the result of higher sea levels in the pleistocene, e.g. Morecambe Bay and the Wash.

Erosion

This process is a feature of exposed coastlines. It can be very slow but continuous, e.g. the great cliffed coastlines of Cornwall and the chalk cliffs of the south and east coasts; or very rapid, e.g. Holderness, where the boulder clay cliffs, which run for 61.5 km north of the Humber, have been retreating at an average rate of approximately 1 m per annum for over 1000 years.

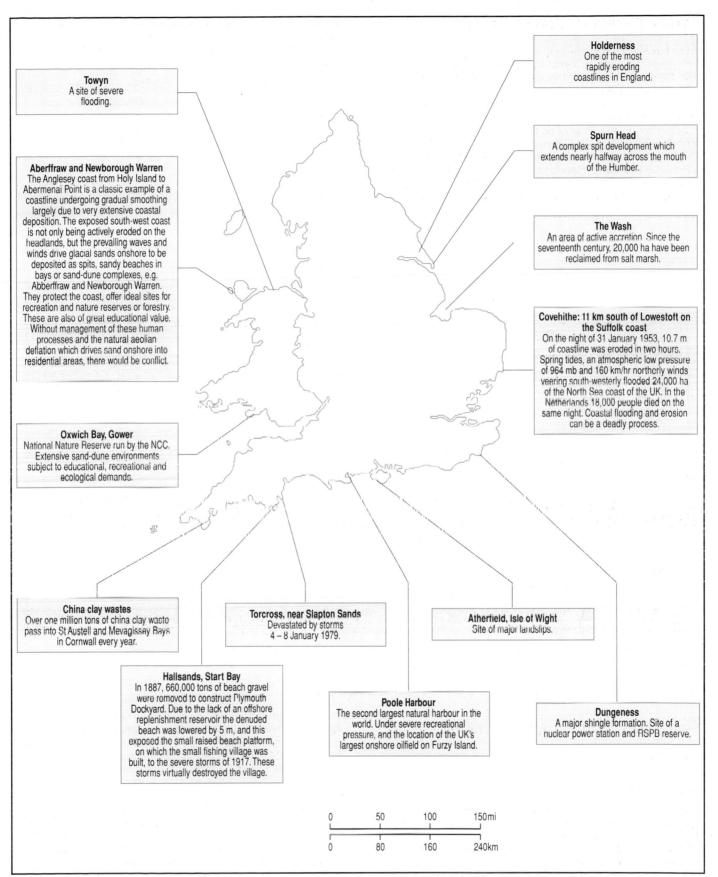

Towyn
A site of severe flooding.

Aberffraw and Newborough Warren
The Anglesey coast from Holy Island to Abermenai Point is a classic example of a coastline undergoing gradual smoothing largely due to very extensive coastal deposition. The exposed south-west coast is not only being actively eroded on the headlands, but the prevailing waves and winds drive glacial sands onshore to be deposited as spits, sandy beaches in bays or sand-dune complexes, e.g. Abberffraw and Newborough Warren. They protect the coast, offer ideal sites for recreation and nature reserves or forestry. These are also of great educational value. Without management of these human processes and the natural aeolian deflation which drives sand onshore into residential areas, there would be conflict.

Oxwich Bay, Gower
National Nature Reserve run by the NCC. Extensive sand-dune environments subject to educational, recreational and ecological demands.

Holderness
One of the most rapidly eroding coastlines in England.

Spurn Head
A complex spit development which extends nearly halfway across the mouth of the Humber.

The Wash
An area of active accretion. Since the seventeenth century, 20,000 ha have been reclaimed from salt marsh.

Covehithe: 11 km south of Lowestoft on the Suffolk coast
On the night of 31 January 1953, 10.7 m of coastline was eroded in two hours. Spring tides, an atmospheric low pressure of 964 mb and 160 km/hr northerly winds veering south-westerly flooded 24,000 ha of the North Sea coast of the UK. In the Netherlands 18,000 people died on the same night. Coastal flooding and erosion can be a deadly process.

China clay wastes
Over one million tons of china clay waste pass into St Austell and Mevagissey Bays in Cornwall every year.

Torcross, near Slapton Sands
Devastated by storms 4 – 8 January 1979.

Atherfield, Isle of Wight
Site of major landslips.

Hallsands, Start Bay
In 1887, 660,000 tons of beach gravel were removed to construct Plymouth Dockyard. Due to the lack of an offshore replenishment reservoir the denuded beach was lowered by 5 m, and this exposed the small raised beach platform, on which the small fishing village was built, to the severe storms of 1917. These storms virtually destroyed the village.

Poole Harbour
The second largest natural harbour in the world. Under severe recreational pressure, and the location of the UK's largest onshore oilfield on Furzy Island.

Dungeness
A major shingle formation. Site of a nuclear power station and RSPB reserve.

0	50	100	150mi
0	80	160	240km

Figure 1.5   The coastline of England and Wales

What factors influence the form of the coastline?

Your research in the previous exercise – using Clowes and Comfort or another standard geomorphological text to consider active coastal processes – should have highlighted the dynamic nature of the coastline. This dynamism is due to four independent controlling influences. Two of these are long-term influences beyond the scope of our study: plate tectonics and relative land–sea levels. A third influence is direct or indirect human intervention, often having a short-term or rapid impact and stemming from activities such as: (1) sea defence; (2) navigation; (3) tidal barrages; (4) reclamation; (5) port development; (6) conservation; (7) mineral extraction; (8) fishing; (9) waste disposal; (10) recreation; (11) industry; (12) residential development.

The fourth group of influences are the natural processes of coastal erosion and accretion due to subaerial, fluvial and marine processes. We will now focus on these short-term natural processes in detail, e.g. waves and mass movement processes on cliff faces that are responsible for the changes in the form of coastal systems within our lifetimes.

SYSTEMS ANALYSIS

Using Figure 1.6 explain how the coastline can be regarded as a system. Clearly identify all the inputs and outputs in this system.

Coasts are subject to inputs of energy and materials that interact within a geological and biological framework to produce landforms.

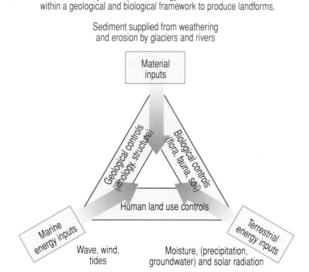

Waves
Waves form when the water surface is disturbed, for example by wind, earthquakes or planetary gravitational forces. During such disturbances energy and momentum are transferred to the water mass and transmitted in the direction of the impelling force. It is important to note that it is the wave form, not the water mass, that is transmitted. A proportion of the wave energy is dispersed by radial, inertial and convective means, but a large amount is not lost until waves encounter shallow coastal waters. This energy 'powers' many coastal processes.

Tides
The regular rise and fall of sealevel is of importance not only through the effects of tidal currents, but also as it spreads the range and influence of marine processes over a wider area. In some cases the latter may be over 20 m (tide plus wave effects) vertically, and several tens of kilometres horizontally. Tidal translation involves large-scale water mass and energy fluxes, resulting in extensive current generation, and attendant sediment transport, bed-form development, faunal and floral diversification and management problems. Extreme high tides can lead to flooding, property damage and loss of life. Periodic rise and fall of oceanic and coastal waters is caused by systematic variations in the relative positions of the Earth, Moon and Sun.

Sediment supplied from weathering and erosion by glaciers and rivers

Material inputs

Geological controls (lithology, structure)

Biological controls (flora, fauna, soil)

Human land use controls

Marine energy inputs

Wave, wind, tides

Terrestrial energy inputs

Moisture, (precipitation, groundwater) and solar radiation

It is important to understand that these factors will not only vary spatially, but also temporally due to changes in climate, sea level and energy and material inputs. Chester-on-Dee in Cheshire and Rye in Sussex, once prosperous coastal ports, have declined in importance due to coastal deposition. Excessive energy inputs can create even more serious problems, for example, in 1421, coastal flooding killed 10,000 people in the UK; the floods of 1953 destroyed 24,000 houses and 307 people were killed in the UK and the damage was even more extensive in the Low Countries.

Figure 1.6   Coastal systems

Waves

Waves are the principal source of energy input into the coastal zone. The irregular and complex surface of the sea actually consists of a number of superimposed wave sizes travelling in different directions. These are called wave trains. These different waves have been caused by winds of varying duration, speed and fetch.

Long waves, with a long wave length proportional to wave height, are known as *swell* waves. They emerge quickly from a distant storm area in advance of short waves. By the time they reach the coast they are well sorted, arriving as fast, flat, regular waves with parallel wave crests of equal velocity. When long waves enter shallow water with steep beaches they break as *surging* breakers.

Short waves are known as *sea* or *storm* waves. They are produced within the storm generation area and often occur with long waves. Thus the sea appears to be a complex mass of wave types. Storm waves tend to have short wave lengths and have increased wave height and steepness. The height and steepness produces the effective erosive energy of these waves.

When storm waves enter shallow water they break as *spilling* breakers on flat beaches, and as *plunging* breakers on steep beaches. Away from source regions, these storm waves will decay to swell waves.

It is waves that produce the currents responsible for the movement of most coastal sediment. These are known as *shore-normal currents* which run on- and offshore and move sediment up and down the beach, and *shore-parallel* or *longshore currents* which move large quantities of sediment along the beach.

DIAGRAM ANNOTATION

Produce your own annotated diagram to highlight the influence of beach gradient on wave form. What wave types might generate the most difficult coastal management problems? It may be helpful to refer to Figure 1.7.

Source: Knapp, 1986

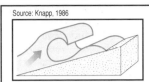

(i) *Plunging breakers* – destructive waves which deposit sediment below low water.

(ii) *Spilling breakers* – strong constructive waves which push material onshore.

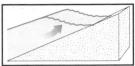

(iii) *Surging breakers* – constructive waves which create a swash ridge by pushing material up the beach.

Figure 1.7 The three main wave types

CASE STUDY – *Coastal Processes in Weymouth Bay*

Furzy Cliff is a Site of Special Scientific Interest (SSSI) 5 km north of Weymouth, Dorset (Figure 1.8a). The cliff, composed of Oxford clay, is 800 m long and 30 m high. It has been subject to rapid erosion averaging 1 m per annum for over a century. The area is developed at the southern and northern extremes (Figures 1.8b and 1.8d) but the bulk of the area above the cliff is public open space used for informal recreation. The main Weymouth–Wareham road is protected by a sea wall dating from 1890 at the Overcombe end of Furzy Cliff. In 1983, a scheme designed to reduce rapid rates of cliff recession was completed at the southern end of Furzy Cliff (Figure 1.8b).

For large parts of the year the beach is gently sloping but at other times shingle and grit deposits are steeply banked at the cliff toe. Offshore, the general direction of shingle circulation is from east to south-west. This is counterbalanced by a wave-induced littoral drift which moves material northwards. The grain size of the beach material tends to be finer in the north around Bowleaze Cove and coarser at Overcombe.

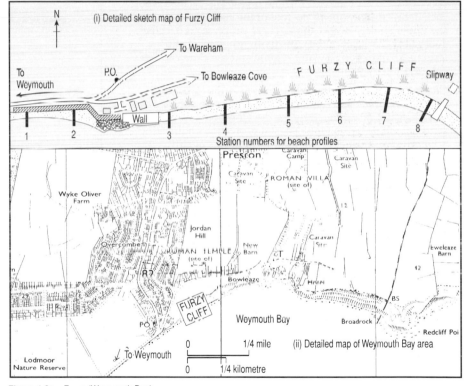

Figure 1.8a Furzy (Weymouth Bay)

Figure 1.8b Furzy cliff (beach in winter from south)

Station number	Beach width in m	Angle
1	15	32°
2	20	15°
3	20	14°
4	21	13°
5	23	16°
6	24	20°
7	31	10°
8	37	11°

Figure 1.8c Data from beach profiles

Figure 1.8d Furzy cliff (beach in summer from north)

ACTIVITY: LOCAL STUDY

To give your local study a context, first research coastal erosional and depositional processes using a standard geomorphological textbook (e.g. Clowes and Comfort).

Study the data from the beach profile transects (Figure 1.8c) and the photographs (Figures 1.8b and 1.8d). What do they tell you about active coastal processes? What hypotheses can you construct from this data? How would you go about trying to test these, considering the sample size of the data?

What is the evidence for changes in beach morphology and volume over time? What factors might help explain this temporal variation?

Why do you think a coastal protection structure was built at the southern end of Furzy Cliff in 1983? How might this influence the active processes you have described above, and with what consequences?

What further primary and secondary data would have been useful in trying to complete these tasks? How would you have organised the collection of this primary data?

Mass movement processes

Figure 1.9 analyses mass and energy movements within earth cliff systems. These are soft, easily eroded cliffs of clays and poorly cemented sandstones that occur extensively around the south and east coasts of England from Black Ven at Lyme Regis to Holderness on Humberside.

Earth cliffs are the result of processes which include:

1 *Cliff face processes.* These weathering and mass movement processes active at the cliff top and on the cliff face transport rock debris downslope to the foot of the cliff, thus reducing the upper slope size and angle. These processes reflect the geological character of the cliffs (both lithological and structural), the ground water regime and the extent of cliff colonisation by plants.

2 *Cliff foot processes.* Marine processes lower the foreshore, erode the cliff toe and remove the base of slope debris. These processes can be inhibited by the development of a stable sand or shingle beach, or by coastal protection engineering schemes. The most effective long-term means of cliff protection is a wide, stable beach which protects the foot of the cliff.

3 *Human processes, e.g. recreational pressure.* Earth cliffs are attractive for recreation and provide a direct route to beaches. Good accessibility leads to increased recreational usage and increased problems of trampling, damage to vegetation by compaction, footpath erosion, and eventual gulleying.

Conclusion

Coastal landforms are the outputs of the coastal system, the type of landform reflecting the particular combination of inputs of energy and materials into the coastal system. Coastal landforms that are well adjusted to the present combination of

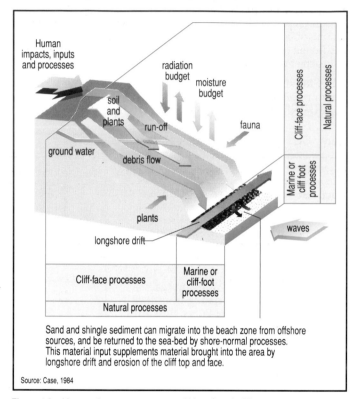

Sand and shingle sediment can migrate into the beach zone from offshore sources, and be returned to the sea-bed by shore-normal processes. This material input supplements material brought into the area by longshore drift and erosion of the cliff top and face.

Source: Case, 1984

Figure 1.9   Mass and energy movements within soft rock cliff systems

coastal processes are in dynamic equilibrium, where small changes in one input source are balanced by small reactive changes elsewhere. Human intervention in the coastal system often disrupts this equilibrium. Over time there may be major changes in the inputs to the system, e.g. climatic change and/or sea level changes.

ACTIVITY: PHOTOGRAPH INTERPRETATION

Study Figure 1.10 and try to explain how natural and human processes interact to produce coastal landforms. Include an annotated sketch of the photograph, similar to Figure 1.4c.

Figure 1.10   Barton-on-Sea

Who is responsible for our coastline?

Unlike the USA, the UK does not yet have a central integrated government body to manage the conflicting demands on the coastline. In the UK there is little formal control, even at a local or regional level, leaving many untackled conflicts and issues, and allowing major environmental problems to mature. Local authorities tend to get involved only after a dramatic decline in environmental or landscape quality, or when there is a proven hazard which affects life, livelihood or property.

'In the UK coastal management is very confused and in disarray' (Carter, 1988). Although the main developed coastline is primarily controlled by local authorities, there is no recognised coastal zone in law. Different authorities have jurisdiction over the sea-bed, the inter-tidal zone, estuaries, and the beach above high-water mark.

1 Cliff-top planning is currently controlled by town and country planning legislation, whereas coastal erosion is controlled by the Coast Protection Act of 1949. Land use zoning, pollution control, provision of recreational facilities, and wildlife and habitat protection may rest with other authorities. In Norway the problem has been resolved by creating a legally recognised coastal zone which restricts all developments within 100 m of the coastal edge. In Sweden the 'set-back' line is 100–300 m inland.

2 Local authority administrative boundaries are not geomorphological ones. Engineering structures constructed by one local authority may create major environmental problems in an adjacent planning area. A classic example of this problem is known as terminal groyne syndrome and is widespread along the Hampshire and Sussex coastlines where downdrift local authorities find their sediment inputs from longshore sources reduced by large groyne structures built by their updrift neighbours.

3 Local authority responsibility for the coast is not continuous. Various elements of our developed coast are managed by independent bodies including British Rail, water authorities, sea defence commissioners and private landowners. This makes co-ordination virtually impossible (Table 1.1).

Table 1.1   Coastal management organisations in the UK in the early 1990s

Organisation	Status and how funded	Name of management project	Management method and purpose
National Trust	Voluntary charity	Enterprise Neptune 1985	At present manage 650 km of coastline in England, Wales and N. Ireland.
Worldwide Fund for Nature	Voluntary charity	Protection of estuaries and wetlands	Conservation of endangered wildlife and habitats
English Nature	Government body that promotes nature conservation in Britain	SSSIs & NNRs Selects, establishes and manages sites	Protect scientific or ecologically important sites for research, education, wildlife and recreation
Friends of the Earth	Voluntary charity	Marine dumping of waste. TBT marine anti-fouling paint	Active pressure group. Raise public awareness
Countryside Commission	Advises on conservation and recreation in England and Wales	Heritage Coasts 1972. AONBs in England and Wales. National Parks, e.g. Pembrokeshire Coast	Heritage Coasts attempt to protect 31 scenically attractive areas which are under heavy visitor pressure. Managed by a consensus of local interested parties
Crown Estate Commissioners		Leases foreshore areas to local authorities, port authorities, harbour commissions	Manage foreshore and inter-tidal areas on behalf of the monarch. The public have common rights of use and access to this land
RSPB	Voluntary charity		Owns coastal nature reserves for protection and conservation of wild birds and their habitats
Marine Conservation Society	Voluntary charity	*UK Good Beach Guide*. Annually every April, featuring approximately 170 beaches. Lundy Island Marine Nature Reserve	Aims to raise public awareness about beach quality as laid down by the EC. Awards are based on sewage, litter, facilities and access
Greenpeace	Voluntary charity	The Beluga Survey. Britain's Threatened Coastline	Active pressure group. Public awareness
Nature Conservation Trusts	Voluntary charity	e.g. Hants and Isle of Wight Naturalists Trust	County level practical conservation projects and public awareness

For a more comprehensive account consult the Greenpeace publication *Coastline*.

CLASS DEBATE: COASTAL MANAGEMENT IN THE UK

The 4800 km coastline of England, Wales and Northern Ireland includes 1600 km of developed coast and 1600 km of coast which is classified as unimportant scenically or scientifically. The National Trust manages 650 km of the important interesting coast, leaving 950 km in private ownership or being managed by responsible trusts. Do you agree that the coast management situation is 'confused and in disarray'?

How is the coastline managed?

ENQUIRY: SIMILAR PROBLEMS, SIMILAR PROCESSES?

Study Figure 1.11 and Table 1.2 depicting the problems of the coast, and the management options and techniques used to tackle these pressures.

Explain how coastal management can be seen to be a three-fold programme based on policy, planning and practice.

Identify the problems which are common to a wide range of coastal habitats, and their appropriate solutions.

Do rocky cliffs and earth cliffs share common problems? Fully explain your answer with reference to the physical and human processes you have studied.

Do any environments suffer from unique pressures? How have these been tackled?

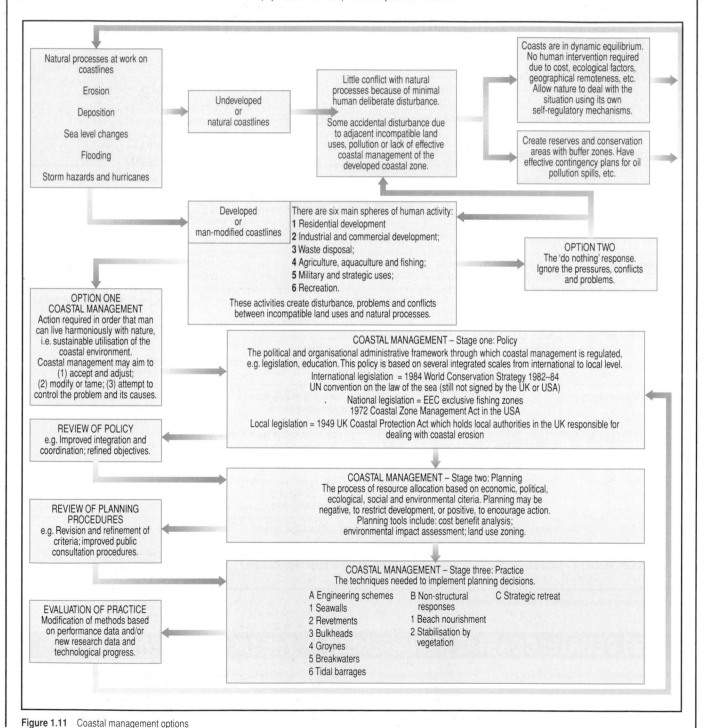

Figure 1.11   Coastal management options

Table 1.2 Management of coastal environments

Environment	Definition	Named example and occurrence	Types of pressures	Conservation and management
1 Shingle foreshore	Coarse sediments greater than 2 mm in diameter which occur along 900 km of the UK coast, as fringing beach spits, bars or barriers, cuspate forelands and offshore barrier islands	Hurst Castle spit. The Loe, Cornwall. Chesil Beach, Dorset. Dungeness, Kent.	Human – coastal protection-schemes, removal of shingle for building, recreational pressure, grazing. Natural – cyclic erosion and progradation	Lack of access and difficulty with walking on shingle is best form of protection. Regular monitoring by aerial photos and ground-based ecological surveys, car-park restrictions, reduction of gravel extraction
2 Lagoons	Shallow bodies of brackish or sea water partially separated from an adjacent coastal sea by a barrier of sand or shingle, which only leaves narrow openings through which sea water can flow	Found on low-lying coasts, e.g. eastern seaboard of the USA and the Gulf of Mexico. Fleet, Weymouth, Dorset. Venice, Italy. Zuider Zee, Netherlands	Human – long history of human usage as harbours and aquaculture, more recently for recreation and industry. Problems include water quality, recreational pressure, land reclamation, coastal protection schemes. Natural – siltation	Reduce dumping of untreated sewage. Reduce agricultural inputs. Reduce industrial pollution. Diverting discharges away from sensitive ecological areas
3 Muddy foreshore	Extensive flat areas of fine-grained sediment in a low energy environment. They are rich in organic debris and possess special ecological significance because they are the main feeding medium for migratory wading birds and wildfowl	Sheltered parts of embayments, inlets or estuaries or behind shingle formations or sand dunes. The Wash. Morecambe Bay. Poole Harbour. Dee Estuary. Southampton Water. Humberside. Solway Firth	Human – shellfish industries, wildfowling, recreation, birdwatching. Main pressures however are from: 1 Land reclamations as they are seen by most planners as a land-use vacuum which must be filled. In the past for agriculture, today for recreation, housing (marina developments), water storage and industry, e.g. oil refineries, power stations, petrochemical refineries. 2 Poor water quality from untreated sewage and industrial effluents. Eutrophication	Reduce land reclamation and marina developments. Creation of more mudland nature reserves. Concentrate access points where they will have least adverse effect on the ecology of the area. Improve treatment of discharges and pipe material further offshore for dumping
4 Salt-marshes	Natural or semi-natural halophytic grassland on alluvial sediments bordering saline water bodies whose water level fluctuates, and whose salinity ranges from 5‰ to 38‰. Various subtypes can be recognised including estuarine, lagoons, bog, polderland and beach plain	Sheltered areas of slow sedimentation and low erosion. New England, USA. Fleet, Weymouth, Dorset. E. Anglian Fens	Natural stress is rare, e.g. increased sedimentation or erosion. Human pressure is extensive. 1 Agriculture – grazing by cattle, sheep, horses. This leads to compaction, turf-layer destruction, ecological regression. Application of nitrogen and phosphorous fertilisers changes the species composition. 2 Turf cutting for covering and reinforcing sea walls. 3 Land reclamation and drainage. 4 Large-scale impoundment of coastal waters, e.g. Delta plan of the Netherlands and proposed tidal barrage projects in the UK, e.g. Cardiff Bay. 5 Pollution – from artificial detritus litter, chemical substances, agricultural wastes, fertiliser outwash, urban sewage and industrial effluents. 6 Recreation	Manage grazing practices by stocking densities. Reduce spraying and the introduction of foreign species. Reduce land reclamation and marina developments. Purify water before discharge.
5 Rocky foreshores and cliffs	Coastal environment dominated by the outcrop of resistant bare rock as inaccessible cliffs with irregular masses of extensive boulder beaches. Cliffs tend to be high, steep, stable, wave or spray-beaten with little vegetation	Occur extensively around mountainous and upland areas, where the harder igneous and metamorphic rocks occur, e.g. S.W. England, Scotland and Wales. Also older resistant sedimentary rocks, e.g. Carboniferous Limestone, Old Red Sandstone. The Lizard and Lands End, Cornwall. Gower Coast. Lindisfarne	Pollution, oil spills, e.g. Torrey Canyon 1967. Outfalls of urban-industrial areas including PCBs. Fishing and shellfish exploitation. Military firing ranges, e.g. Castle Martin, Pembrokeshire. Nuclear power stations, e.g. WYLFA. The lack of agriculture forestry or any other commercial development adds to their appeal. Recreation – exhilarating scenery and wildlife interest, e.g. long distance coastal footpaths, e.g. South-West Way. Limited natural pressures	Naturally protected by their remoteness and inaccessibility. On accessible sites – new paths, resurfacing. Waste treatment and disposal improvements in coastal townships. Improved oil-spill treatments. Protective ownership and establishment of reserves with reduced access, increased education, e.g. National Trust's Enterprise Neptune, AONBs, NCC reserves. Countryside Commission's Heritage Coasts

Environment	Definition	Named example and occurrence	Types of pressures	Conservation and management
6 Sand-dunes	Coarse sediments deposited and transported by wind and stabilised by vegetation. Very important environments ecologically. Very sensitive to human disruption	Oxwich, Gower. Studland, Dorset. Culbin, Moray, Scotland.	Limited natural pressures. Humans can introduce or remove species directly or indirectly by changing environmental factors, e.g. pollution or changing the water table, trampling, industrial and residential development. 1 Afforestation by pines. 2 Rabbit burrowing and grazing. 3 Overgrazing by farm animals. 4 Recreational impacts of trampling, litter, pony-treking, biking. 5 Golf course construction. 6 Military uses	Sand stabilisation using dune stabilising grasses, sand fences. Reducing public access to limit trampling. Construct reinforced artificial walkways. Increase species diversity by turf cutting, grazing, mowing. Reduce afforestation
7 Shingle formations	Large-scale stable shingle formations which are predominantly terrestrial and have sparse but characteristic vegetation. They are of three types. 1 Cuspate forelands made up of a whole series of parallel shingle ridges. 2 Offshore barrier islands. 3 Apposition beaches associated with spits	Type 1 = Dungeness, Kent. Type 2 = Scolt Head, Norfolk. Type 3 = Orfordness. Chesil Beach has a more complex origin	Many man-made pressures. 1 Cattle grazing and rabbits. 2 Surface disturbance from treading or vehicles. 3 Mortar bombs and landmines on military sites. 4 Shingle extraction and excavation. 5 Industrial developments, e.g. nuclear power stations. Limited natural pressures	Difficulty of access is the best form of natural protection. Creation of more nature reserves or extending AONBs. Stop gravel mining in sensitive sites of ecological importance. Permit public access at areas of least ecological significance, to maintain and encourage ecological diversity. Zoning, i.e. leave remote areas untouched and allow public access to those nearer urban centres
8 Earth cliffs	Low, soft, unstable, easily eroded cliffs subject to rapid erosion and frequent change due to mass-movements. These soft and often unconsolidated Mesozoic and Tertiary sedimentary rocks may have a mean annual cliff-top retreat of more than 0.25 m	South and eastern England form Dorset to Yorkshire. Atherfield, Isle of Wight. Lyme Bay, Dorset. Barton on Sea, Hants. Folkestone, Kent. North Kent, Tertiary coast. Holderness. Furzy Cliff, Weymouth	Many natural pressures – at the cliff top and on the cliff face, mass movement processes. At the cliff foot marine erosion. Super-imposed on this are human pressures. 1 Recreation – trampling. 2 Resort development. 3 Educational parties. 4 Access to beaches. 5 Coastal protection schemes to reduce marine erosion and stabilise the cliff face, e.g. sea walls and drainage schemes	The 1949 Coast Protection Act, to control coastal retreat, is the responsibility of the local authority. It may be financed by a grant from central government. Any management requires measures to control marine erosion, soil erosion and damage to vegetation. Sites must be seen in their regional context both in terms of their geomorphological and ecological characteristics *and* recreational usage
9 Reclaimed land	An artificially created coastal environment that ranges from partly ditched high level salt marshes, with little obvious human interference to intensively managed land used for agriculture. Majority consists of an enclosing reclamation bank containing an area with drainage ditches. Reclamation consists of either: 1 simply enclosing a former intertidal land surface. 2 enclosing an area, then it is infilled with sea-bed slurry and pumped dry	Morecambe Bay, Lancashire. The Wash. Calshot, Southampton Water. Delta Plan and Zuider Zee, Netherlands. Land for agriculture, residential development, industry, airports, power stations, ports	Despite its artifical origins historical reclaimed land is often ecologically valuable. This is being threatened by recent agricultural improvements, e.g. conversion to arable land, land drainage, use of fertilisers and herbicides. The habitat is also threatened by urban expansion and recreational activities, e.g. caravaning, birdwatching, wildfowling. Because of its remoteness it provides an ideal venue for military training and weapons training	Protection by preventing drainage, ploughing. Controlled grazing. Cutting down invasive scrub. Creation of new niche habitats. Controlled public access
10 The submaritime fringe	The zone 2 km immediately inland of all the zones under direct marine influence. It is the product of both maritime and terrestrial processes *and* the role of humans	The coast of the UK especially Cornwall, Devon, Hampshire, Sussex and Kent. The costas of Spain. Low Countries bordering the North Sea	1 Industry – large flat transhipment points for bulk materials, e.g. iron ore or crude oil. 2 Recreation – campsites, trampling, motor vehicles, litter, golf courses, promenades, caravan parks. These lead to the physical destruction of environments and the disturbance of animal communities and loss of amenity. 3 Coniferous afforestation, e.g. Scots Pine. 4 Over grazing. 5 Pollution	Positive planning and land use zoning. Higher standards of erosion control

Source: Barnes, 1977

What are coastal management plans?

Ecologically important coastal sites are often managed by management plans. Site management plans should be based on broad, clear and coherent aims, backed up by specific practical objectives. These aims may include such factors as ecology, site stability, access, recreation and education. Specific ecological objectives might include:

1 Maintenance or promotion of habitat or species diversity.

2 Diversifying the habitat.

3 Preservation, increase or introduction of scientifically important species (because they are rare, beautiful, important, or a significant part of a food-chain).

4 Conservation of a diverse range of natural assemblages of plants and animals as representative 'types'.

5 Maintaining or imitating some specific floral or faunal status quo.

6 Elimination of unwanted species.

There also may be similar objectives for such aspects as stability of the site, recreation, access and education.

CASE STUDY *Management Methods at the Oxwich Reserve*

Three broad categories of management can be recognised.

1 Estate management – e.g. day-to-day maintenance of fences, paths, roads, sites, etc.

2 Habitat management – managing the land to support the wildlife population. If the habitat is healthy then the wildlife will be varied and healthy, e.g. combat erosion on frontal dunes, control scrub on dunes in slack areas, combat invasive bracken (see Table 1.3).

3 Visitor management – the main problem of the site is that the prime attraction of Oxwich is the recreation beach and not the natural history of the site. For this reason site protection and information are essential – e.g. explaining to people where and why there is limited or no access, and providing information and education – e.g. signposts, leaflets, displays and trails.

Table 1.3   Methods of dune management at the Countryside Commission for Wales' Oxwich Reserve

		Influencing internal factors	Present management policy	Methods
Frontal dunes	Mobile dunes	These are in a stabilised equilibrium state *but* the delicate balance is easily destroyed through excessive public pressure	Maintain stability and so protect the dune system as a whole	Various degrees of protective fencing. Pathways to localise the public's shore–dune movement 1970–80. Sand traps, marram planting, signs and active wardening
	Fixed dunes	These are stable and are able to withstand public pressure *but* this has reduced the proportion of low herb communities	Accept tall grassland as part of overall diversity to the site	1980–90 Care and maintenance only. Allow status quo
Rear dunes	Dune slack	Early seral stages virtually absent. Effective water table lowering in all slacks due to sand accumulation. *Salix repens* may be overdeveloped. Scrub invasion (birch)	Control scrub development. Create new slack(s)	Cut mature scrub and chemically treat stumps. Use goats to browse developing scrub. Create new slacks by excavation
	Dune grassland	Bracken and fescue domination tend to exclude small or fragile annual plants. Some invasion by scrub, aggressive grasses and weeds, e.g. thistle, ragwort	Remove bracken. Encourage diversity of vegetation structure. Control invasive species	Control bracken through repeated mowing. Introduce large animals for grazing, e.g. ponies. Allow rabbit population to develop. Control invasive species using selective herbicide or pulling
	Dune woodland	Final stage of natural succession for the whole system in the absence of grazing or similar management	Restrict development	Cutting/goat browsing

Source: Hughes, 1990

NATURE CONSERVATION AT OXWICH 1978–1993

The 1978 perspective

If Oxwich NNR is to retain the fascinating and complex variety of habitats which we value so much today, and which is of national importance for its wildlife, it must be continuously and intensively managed.

Many of the very large numbers of holiday makers visiting Oxwich use the dunes for recreation. Unfortunately, the foredunes are fragile and the thin cover of vegetation over the sand is easily broken by trampling feet. Once the vegetation has gone, the loose sand is exposed to the autumn and winter gales which blow it away. To repair the dunes brushwood fences have to be erected to trap sand, eroding areas are thatched with brushwood, and bare sand is planted with marram grass. These methods can be very successful, but only if the area is rested from trampling while the vegetation becomes re-established.

Oxwich dunes were probably used as grazing land for sheep in the past, and in recent times they were heavily grazed by rabbits. Following the drastic fall in the rabbit population due to the myxomatosis epidemic in the late 1950s, the almost complete absence of grazing has allowed the natural succession to move forward once more, and bramble, shrubs and small trees are colonising the fixed dunes and slacks. This succession will, if unchecked, result in the development of a predominantly oak and ash woodland. Bracken has also become established over large areas of the fixed dunes, probably as a consequence of cessation of grazing and perhaps encouraged by accidental fires. The heavy shade and deep acid litter from this invasive fern seriously inhibit the growth of other plants, and control work is being undertaken to eliminate it or at least reduce its rate of spread.

Source: Hughes, 1981

The 1985 perspective

Management of people on frontal dunes

The animal which has the greatest environmental impact on the dunes is Man! The main impact is erosion, particularly in the dunes closest to the sea.

There are some positive aspects to allowing access to the dunes:
- The more people know about their value and attractiveness, the more they will appreciate them.
- Many dune plants are pioneers – species which need open conditions to establish themselves. Trampling creates bare patches which can be used as seedbeds by these plants.

Consequently, we encourage a certain amount of public access, but not so much that the dunes become unstable again.

The trick is to get a balance between the three objectives of maintaining the **stability** of dunes, helping the **diversity** of wildlife and allowing a certain amount of **access**.

Source: Hughes, 1990

The 1993 perspective

Management of the over-stabilised rear dunes – habitat restoration

In the 1960s and 1970s stabilisation had been the main management objective. By the 1980s the site was not only stable but increasing in species diversity.

Meanwhile in the rear dunes another problem was emerging – the lack of burrowing, trampling and grazing in this more remote and very sheltered stable area allowed coarse grasses and bracken to invade and infest the site. Bracken replaces the more floristically diverse previous seral stage dominated by herbaceous plants which provide a rich habitat for a wide variety of insects and other animals which make Oxwich such a special place. Various measures have been considered including using selective herbicides, burning, cutting down the vegetation and rotovating the area. The most successful techniques have involved winter grazing the sites by ponies and goats. Ponies are selective grazers, unlike sheep, so winter grazing not only removes the coarse grasses and brackens but also increases micro-habitat diversity. Goats have been used in overgrown wet slack areas to reduce the growth of invasive shrubs.

Source: Hughes, 1991

Threats to sand dune ecosystems

1	Erosion	In the past the main threat has been from recreational use. Trampling, horse riding, lighting of fires, use of vehicles which break up the vegetation and expose the sand to the action of wind which, unchecked, can form blow-outs.
2	Afforestation	Within the last century, afforestation, which was initiated to help prevent major movements of the mobile sand, has destroyed the entire character of the vegetation in the planted areas, e.g. Newborough Warren, Anglesey.
3	Water abstraction	Lowering of the water table may lead to the drying out of species-rich slacks, which are often breeding grounds for the rare natterjack toads.
4	Over-grazing	Heavy rabbit grazing produces an open, lichen-dominated community. Overgrazing by domestic stock can also be damaging, especially where supplementary feeding is used.
5	Intensive farming	Drainage and fertiliser application reduces plant and animal diversity through soil compaction and nutrient enrichment.
6	Reduction of sediment supply	Direct removal of sand from the beach or dunes, or indirect impact of stabilisation works elsewhere along the coast interrupt the supply of beach material.
7	Scrub and bracken invasion	The extensive development of bracken, coarse herbs or scrubs will reduce plant diversity. This is now the main problem.
8	Tipping of domestic waste	Visual impact. Destruction of vegetation cover. Soil compaction.
9	Reclamation for industry	Complete habitat destruction.
10	Development of adjacent areas	Caravan sites. Golf courses – frequent mowing, use of herbicides, manipulation of water supplies can alter the vegetation.

LOCAL ENQUIRY: HOW ARE SPECIFIC SITES MANAGED?

Study Figures 1.12–1.16, Table 1.3 and the boxes on 'Nature conservation' and 'Threats to sand dune ecosystems', which depict the management of the Oxwich National Nature Reserve, Gower, South Wales.

1 Suggest four reasons why the CCW established a reserve in the area in 1963.

2 What are the key management issues or potential threats to the sand dune system within Oxwich Bay?

3 Notice that for management purposes the dunes have been divided into frontal and rear dunes.

Suggest reasons for this. Why do you think the line separating the two tapers?

4 Many sand dune localities have been forced to adopt stabilisation as their main management objective for their frontal dunes. Try to explain the reasons for this approach. Using an atlas, suggest a reason why an integrated three-fold approach (stabilisation; diversification and access; recreation and education) has emerged for the Oxwich site.

5 Why do you feel that mowing/grazing is important in the rear dune system?

6 Explain how these three broad management aims

are actually implemented with regard to the sand dune system.

7 The CCW are keen to examine the success of their management plan. Design a comprehensive programme of primary fieldwork that would allow you to collect data to evaluate their plan. You might like to produce an annotated sketch or map as part of your report and attempt to locate some of your fieldwork data collection techniques. Utilise your own landforms and/or ecosystems fieldwork or refer to one of the texts on geographical fieldwork methods, e.g. S. Warn or Lenon and Cleves.

Figure 1.12 Oxwich Bay National Nature Reserve

Figure 1.13 Briefing lecture to a group in the moist dune slack areas

Figure 1.14 Restricted access in the frontal dune system

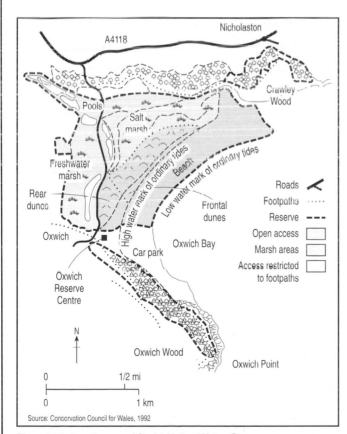

Figure 1.15 Location map of Oxwich National Nature Reserve

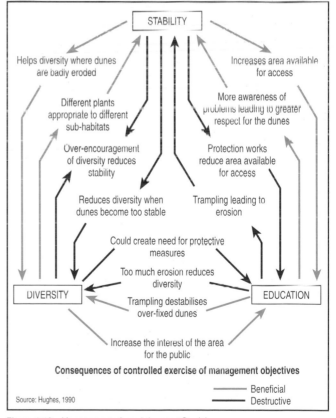

Figure 1.16 Management of sand dunes at Oxwich

How is the Coastline Managed in the USA?

In this section our enquiry has four main strands.

1 What are the causes of coastal conflicts in the USA?

2 In what way does the organisation of coastal management in the USA differ from that of the UK?

3 Having considered coastal management in general terms, we then move on to consider a key coastal management issue in detail, by focusing on the human response to the problem of coastal erosion of the Barrier Islands on the Atlantic seaboard.

4 Finally, to give this case study a context, we will explore the range of potential solutions sought elsewhere in the USA to

respond to this problem of erosion, and evaluate the benefits and impacts of these approaches.

Coastal conflicts and their causes in the USA

The coastline of the USA is managed using a different approach from the one we have been considering in the UK. Before we examine these contrasts we will briefly examine the potential coastal conflicts and causes of coastal erosion in the USA. This may help explain the differences in management strategies.

ANALYSIS

1 Study Figures 1.17 and 1.18. What are the main coastal conflicts? Compare and contrast these with the coastal conflicts you studied in the UK.

2 'Causes of coastal erosion in the USA' summarises the situation along the Atlantic seaboard. Are there any important differences in

the causes of erosion compared with areas suffering rapid coastal retreat in the UK?

The coastal zone is the interface between land, sea and the atmosphere and physically consists of a complex linear strip of land and the adjacent ocean space that are mutually interdependent. The zone contains many rich, diverse and unique habitats: some of these are very fragile, all of which are very biologically productive. The sea concentrates most of its energy at the coast, hence the land–water interface is very dynamic. This creates management problems for man due to our very intensive usage of the zone. The coastline is a zone of increasing multiplicity of demands for industry, commerce, residential development, mineral resource and fossil fuel extraction, transport and navigation, waste disposal, fishing, and the fastest growing and the largest sector, recreation. These activities have resulted in a loss of wildlife, decreasing open space for public use and general environmental degradation. More than half the US population resides in the coastal counties, and the population density along the Atlantic seaboard is ten times that of the non-coastal states. There are 189 coastal ports which move over 1.3 billion tons of cargo per year. Development pressure is three or four times greater in these coastal areas than elsewhere.

Massachusetts
Chatham, Cape Cod, Massachusetts. Early in 1987 winter storms broke through a barrier beach separating Chatham Harbour from the Atlantic. The internal and unprotected coastline was exposed to the full force of Atlantic storms. By 1 January 1988 20 m of erosion had occurred, and houses built on sand dunes 50 years ago are now threatened. Elsewhere on the east coast of Cape Cod the glacial tills and sands are being eroded at a rate of 1 m p.a. Massachusetts loses 26 hectares p.a. to erosion and rising sea level; 10 per cent of this is on Nantucket Island.

Cape Hatteras
An undeveloped barrier island and National Coastal Reserve Site on the North Carolina coast. The lighthouse, built 500 m from the sea in 1870, was only 30 m from the sea by 1930. Temporary measures have protected the site for 50 years but it is now endangered by the undermining of the promontory it now sits on. Engineers recommend the reconstruction of a new lighthouse 800 m inland.

Atlantic City
Like Miami Beach, Atlantic City pumps sand from the offshore zone to replenish recreational beaches. Other resorts along the coast, especially those on barrier islands, suffer severe erosional pressures, e.g. in the states of Virginia, Maryland, New Jersey and south to Florida.

Cape Canaveral
Although the cape itself is protected, the barrier islands to the north and south are threatened by sea-level changes and coastal erosion.

Florida
Florida is the most vulnerable state. Eighty of the 300 mobile barrier islands that occur in the 18 states making up the Atlantic Seaboard are in Florida. These islands cover 850,000 ha. The islands, zones of intense human development, are often very low-lying and exposed to Atlantic storms and wave energy Many lie in the paths of hurricanes.

Galveston, Texas
No coastal restrictions on development. A new beach front apartment block has been built at the western end of the seawall, where erosion is currently five metres per annum.

Coastal Louisiana
The US has 4,000,000 ha of wetlands which act as spawning, nursery and feeding grounds. Louisiana loses 40 ha of wetland a day, or 15,000 a year. Until 1900 sediment deposited by the Mississippi River added 200–500 ha of land a year to the state. Canalisation and deepening the channel for river navigation has increased its flow, and thus the river carries sediment out into the offshore zone, leaving no deposits to build up the land. As the old river sediments settle out, they subside. This process has been accelerated by the removal of coastal gas and oil deposits. New Orleans is now well below sea level. However, because the coastline here is marshy much of the coastal zone is undeveloped so the problem has attracted little attention.

The United States has over 95,000 miles of shoreline including the Great Lakes. The shoreline ranges from the rocky cliffs of Maine to the broad Louisiana wetlands to the rich Hawaiian coral reefs, the frozen coastal plain of Alaska and the steamy mangrove swamps of Florida.

Figure 1.17   USA coastal resources and pressures

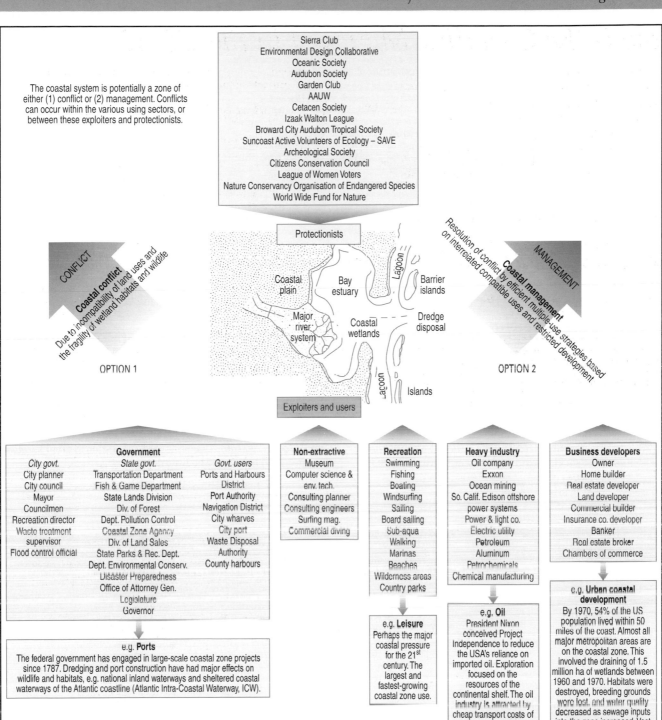

The coastal system is potentially a zone of either (1) conflict or (2) management. Conflicts can occur within the various using sectors, or between these exploiters and protectionists.

Sierra Club
Environmental Design Collaborative
Oceanic Society
Audubon Society
Garden Club
AAUW
Cetacen Society
Izaak Walton League
Broward City Audubon Tropical Society
Suncoast Active Volunteers of Ecology – SAVE
Archeological Society
Citizens Conservation Council
League of Women Voters
Nature Conservancy Organisation of Endangered Species
World Wide Fund for Nature

Protectionists

Coastal plain
Bay estuary
Lagoon
Barrier islands
Major river system
Coastal wetlands
Dredge disposal
Lagoon
Islands

CONFLICT
Coastal conflict
Due to incompatibility of land uses and the fragility of wetland habitats and wildlife

OPTION 1

MANAGEMENT
Coastal management
Resolution of conflict by efficient multiple-use strategies based on interrelated compatible uses and restricted development

OPTION 2

Exploiters and users

Government

City govt.	State govt.	Govt. users
City planner	Transportation Department	Ports and Harbours District
City council	Fish & Game Department	Port Authority
Mayor	State Lands Division	Navigation District
Councilmen	Div. of Forest	City wharves
Recreation director	Dept. Pollution Control	City port
Waste treatment supervisor	Coastal Zone Agency	Waste Disposal Authority
Flood control official	Div. of Land Sales	County harbours
	State Parks & Rec. Dept.	
	Dept. Environmental Conserv.	
	Disaster Preparedness	
	Office of Attorney Gen.	
	Legislature	
	Governor	

e.g. **Ports**
The federal government has engaged in large-scale coastal zone projects since 1787. Dredging and port construction have had major effects on wildlife and habitats, e.g. national inland waterways and sheltered coastal waterways of the Atlantic coastline (Atlantic Intra-Coastal Waterway, ICW).

Non-extractive
Museum
Computer science & env. tech.
Consulting planner
Consulting engineers
Surfing mag.
Commercial diving

Recreation
Swimming
Fishing
Boating
Windsurfing
Sailing
Board sailing
Sub-aqua
Walking
Marinas
Beaches
Wilderness areas
Country parks

e.g. **Leisure**
Perhaps the major coastal pressure for the 21st century. The largest and fastest-growing coastal zone use.

Heavy industry
Oil company
Exxon
Ocean mining
So. Calif. Edison offshore power systems
Power & light co.
Electric utility
Petroleum
Aluminum
Petrochemicals
Chemical manufacturing

e.g. **Oil**
President Nixon conceived Project Independence to reduce the USA's reliance on imported oil. Exploration focused on the resources of the continental shelf. The oil industry is attracted by cheap transport costs of water, and available coolant. Refineries and petro-chemical plants have a huge visual and ecological impact on wetland sites.
Environmental impacts of oil spills and blow-outs include habitat destruction and disruption of food chains and breeding cycles.

Business developers
Owner
Home builder
Real estate developer
Land developer
Commercial builder
Insurance co. developer
Banker
Real estate broker
Chambers of commerce

e.g. **Urban coastal development**
By 1970, 54% of the US population lived within 50 miles of the coast. Almost all major metropolitan areas are on the coastal zone. This involved the draining of 1.5 million ha of wetlands between 1960 and 1970. Habitats were destroyed, breeding grounds were lost, and water quality decreased as sewage inputs into the zone increased. Vast areas of ecological value and informal recreation were swallowed up by exclusive, monotonous and mainly private coastal developments. Recently developments have been controlled to minimise ecological damage and improve public access. Unsuitable and unstable environments are now avoided, e.g. wetlands and barrier islands.

Figure 1.18   Pressure points: human land use of the USA coastline

Causes of coastal erosion in the USA

1 *Global sea level changes*
   Global sea level has risen approximately 12 cm in the last 100 years. The increase in ocean volume is due to global temperature changes melting the polar ice-caps and causing thermal expansion of the surface waters of the oceans. The greenhouse effect may cause even more dramatic increases in the future.

2 *Subsidence of the coast*
   Much of this coastline is sinking relative to the ocean, so local sea levels are rising faster than global averages. UK coasts are far less vulnerable. Scotland is rising in slow rebound after the melting of the Pleistocene glaciers.

Southern England, which was never covered by ice, is maintaining the same level, or sinking very slowly at rates of 1 mm each year.

3 *Nature of the topography*
   Much of the coastline south of New Jersey consists of flat coastal plains, some with offshore or nearshore barrier islands. Miami is the lowest-lying city in the USA with very few parts 3 m above sea level. Many of the barrier islands from New York to the Mexican border are being driven onshore.

4 *Weather conditions*
   Coastal storms and hurricanes are not uncommon along this coastline. Wind driven waves can create storm surges, which, if combined with high tides, flood low-lying areas.

5 *Extensive human coastal development*
   It is estimated that by 1990 75% of all Americans will live within 100 km of a coast or the Great Lakes. Britain and Europe have a much lower coastal population. These urban centres are billion-dollar investments and many are located on the barrier islands. Miami Beach, Atlantic City and Longport on New Jersey and Galveston, Texas, are all built on barrier islands. These have not been allowed to retreat naturally and are now in exposed positions. Elsewhere, settlements are threatened by the accelerated erosion of their beaches, often related to the construction of coastal protection structures on shoreline communities updrift.

The organisation of coastal management in the USA

Coastal management could be defined as the prudent, sustainable utilisation of coastal environments and resources for maximum benefit with minimum environmental interference. Since the 1972 Coastal Zone Management Act the coastline of the USA has been managed centrally by the Federal Office of Coastal Zone Management (OCZM) (Figure 1.19). Currently it is managed by the Office of Ocean and Coastal Resource Management (OCRM). This national organisation provides support services and funds to individual states in order to allow them to implement the four main aims of the multi-focus programme:

1 To protect fragile coastlines and living marine resources, especially reefs, wetlands and estuarine sites.

2 To minimise life and property loss from coastal hazards, including shoreline erosion.

3 To create better conditions for the use of coastal resources for access and recreation, and to reduce conflicts among competing land and water uses.

4 To promote interdepartmental co-operation at all levels with minimal bureaucratic hindrance.

The evolution of the Coastal Zone Management Act

Stage 1 – Pre-management
Management of the coastline was diffuse and uncoordinated, based on single-purpose aims (e.g. profit). Public and private sector worked in isolation and in competition.

Private sector
1 Owns the vast majority of the coastline (98 %).
2 Owns a small percentage of bays, estuaries and coastal waters.
3 Aim is property development, and they are profit-motivated.
4 Development led to dredging, land drainage of wetlands, bulkheading, pollution, general water quality deterioration,

Public sector
1 Federal, state and local government have been involved since the early 1800s, especially in navigation projects. Increased pressures in the coastal zone ensured a more active approach after the Second World War.
2 By 1972 two major problems were identified: a) involvement was based on a single resource or a single issue: b) many government departments at various levels have become involved in coastal management, but without coordination.

There was therefore no means of tackling a complex issue on a multi-agency coordinated basis

Stage 2 – Evolution of integrated legislation
Gradual evolution of the coastal management concept supported by legislation.
The following movements can be identified:
1 increased demand for more consistent and coordinated government efforts;
2 an aroused environmental consciousness of the American public;
3 an increased demand for access for recreation;
4 the emergence of land use planning management;
5 increasing efforts to develop marine resources
These are responsible for the 1966 Clean Water Restoration Act, the 1968 Estuarine Protection Act and the 1971 National Shoreline Study.
These movements and acts were supplemented by numerous state-enacted Wetlands Acts which collectively formed the vital prerequisite for the 1972 Coastal Zone Management Act (CZMA).

Stage 5 – The future
Due to pressure on public funds the US Government is increasingly cutting back on OCZM staffing, resources and finances.

Stage 3 – The Act
On 27 October 1972 President Nixon enacted the CZMA. This was a national policy with federal funds to enable states to administer and develop systematic, coordinated and comprehensive coastal resource management programmes. The states were made responsible for their own coasts. Federal agencies were to ensure interstate cooperation, through the creation of the Office for Coastal Zone Management (OCZM). Their brief was to provide assistance and guidance, and to formulate and implement coastal zone management programmes. 'To preserve, protect, restore and enhance coastal resources and coastal development in such a way that natural systems and their interactions would be considered.'

Stage 4 – Mature management
Since 1972 increasingly inter-disciplinary tools have been developed to resolve coastal conflicts with land use planning controls.
1 Cost benefit analysis (CBA).
2 Environmental impact assessments and statements.
3 Technology assessments
Twenty-nine of the 35 eligible states participate in the Federal programme (see Fig 1.21).
The CZMA establishes a state-federal partnership for coastal zone management planning and regulation. The federal agency supports, approves and funds state programmes which emphasise dynamic, comprehensive, predictable and enforceable policies to guide coastal regulatory, planning and public investment programmes. Federal grants totalled US$33.4 million in 1988, a figure which has remained almost constant for nearly a decade. States match the grant dollar for dollar.

Figure 1.19 The evolution of the Coastal Zone Management Act

SYNTHESIS: ALTERNATIVE APPROACHES TO COASTAL MANAGEMENT

Study Figures 1.19, 1.20 and 1.21 and the extract from 'Solutions to Our Nation's Coastal Problems'.

1 By what legislation is the coast regulated?

2 How has this situation evolved? Produce a brief summary of the evolution of the 1972 Coastal Zone

Management Act. This has been reauthorised in 1976, 1980, 1986 and 1989/90.

3 Who is responsible for the legislation? How is it organised and how does it achieve its aims?

4 Compare the approaches to coastal management

in the UK and the USA. Do the differences in approach reflect varying problems and causal mechanisms? Debate the strengths and weaknesses of each approach. Tabulate your ideas. You may need to look back at your material on UK coastline management.

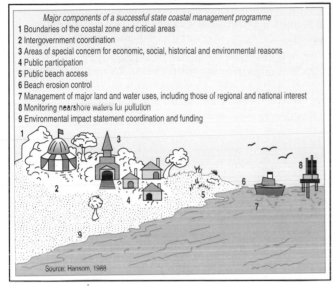

Major components of a successful state coastal management programme
1 Boundaries of the coastal zone and critical areas
2 Intergovernment coordination
3 Areas of special concern for economic, social, historical and environmental reasons
4 Public participation
5 Public beach access
6 Beach erosion control
7 Management of major land and water uses, including those of regional and national interest
8 Monitoring nearshore waters for pollution
9 Environmental impact statement coordination and funding

Source: Hansom, 1988

Figure 1.20   Major components of a successful state coastal management programme

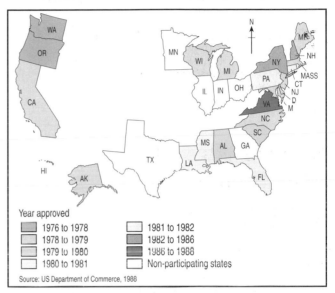

Year approved
- 1976 to 1978
- 1978 to 1979
- 1979 to 1980
- 1980 to 1981
- 1981 to 1982
- 1982 to 1986
- 1986 to 1988
- Non-participating states

Source: US Department of Commerce, 1988

Figure 1.21   Map of CZMA participating states

SOLUTIONS TO OUR NATION'S COASTAL PROBLEMS: SELECTED PROJECTS

This Bulletin documents a brief sample of successful projects carried out by the twenty-nine Federally approved state coastal management programs.

Hazards
Mechanisms such as building setbacks, construction standards, evacuation planning and development of early warning systems have all contributed to improved coastal protection from natural hazards.

In the projects reported in this section, $600 000 of CZM expenditure resulted in the following benefits:

* the largest peacetime evacuation in the United States, over 1.25 million people were successfully evacuated in west Florida in 1985 thereby avoiding significant casualties from hurricanes Elena and Kate.
* over $18 billion of property received increased protection from erosion in South Carolina, Maryland, New Jersey, and Pennsylvania; thirteen states established building setback and sand dune protection laws.

Natural resource protection and development
Coastal management programs have been actively involved

in protecting wildlife and fisheries habitats, regulating land use impacts on water quality and taking the lead in nationwide beach clean-ups.

Oil and gas, sand, fin and shell fish are all natural resources in the coastal zone. Coastal management programs have encouraged their development in an environmentally sensitive manner.

In the projects reported here, coastal programs have spent approximately $3 210 000 to provide benefits including:

* the most important spring habitat for over one million birds along the Atlantic Flyway has been protected by the New Jersey Coastal Program.
* 35 square miles of marshes are protected in South Carolina and development along the State's 2876 mile shoreline is now subject to pollution and storm water guidelines.
* a 1000-foot strip of land adjacent to the Chesapeake Bay in Maryland is now subject to critical areas review protecting an annual $56.5 million dockside value of fisheries.
* 24 coastal states were involved in the 1988 Beach Clean-Up covering 320 miles of beaches, involving 47 000 volunteers collecting 900 tons of trash.

Public access
With more than 50% of the population living within a short driving distance of the coast, increasing leisure time, and rapidly appreciating coastal properties, coastal management

programs have focused on providing more public access to the shore:

* coastal land valued at over $354 million was acquired for public access in the ten states and territories cited.
* 180 miles of access ways along the waterfront are open to the public in Michigan, California, Connecticut, Rhode Island, and New York.
* 238 access ways to the water have been designated in Rhode Island and California.

Urban waterfront redevelopment
Many urban waterfronts became deteriorated and abandoned in the mid-20th century. CZM grants to local governments to prepare waterfront land use plans have been catalysts for revitalizing waterfronts throughout the country for example:

* the Philadelphia Waterfront Comprehensive Plan has led to 18 miles of revitalized waterfront with $310 million in private investment completed and $1.7 billion more pledged for future investments.

Ports and marinas
Coastal programs have been active in encouraging the location of marinas in the coastal zone.

In five examples, $385 000 of CZM funds resulted in $75 million in public and private investment; 1500 new jobs; and $124 million in increased tourism and other economic inputs.

* $27 million cargo expansion in Maine.
* an $8 million marina constructed in Racine, Wisconsin.

Source: US Department of Commerce, 1988

CASE STUDY *Erosion of Developed Coastal Barriers*

In the previous section we discovered that coastal management is more than an attempt to tackle coastal erosion. However, it is now widely recognised that somewhere between 80% and 90% of all shorelines in the world are eroding. This makes coastal erosion the most widespread and often the most serious of all coastal management problems. This is especially true in the Atlantic states of the USA where the greatest challenge facing the OCZM, regional and local coastal managers is the very severe erosion of the coastal barrier islands. Currently they have three main strategies to resolve the conflicts, because legally they cannot ignore the problem. These strategies are:

1 To control the problem by coastal engineering defences, e.g. sea walls, bulkheads, revetments, groynes, jetties, breakwaters.

2 To alleviate the consequences of the problem.

3 To adjust to the problem, and live with the coastal processes.

All these options are costly, will have environmental impacts of varying degrees and depend upon clear and accurate understanding of the causal mechanisms.

Coastal barrier islands are the first line of defense for the low-lying US. They are separated from the mainland by low energy salt-water wetlands and marshes, lagoons and estuaries. The islands form from the interaction of wind, waves, tides which deposit and transport sediment. These natural systems are very dynamic, with constantly changing cycles of accretion, erosion and shoreward migration.

The barriers are very fragile, environmentally sensitive, and ecologically important, with many special populations.

It is the dynamic nature of the barrier island system that makes it stable. The islands offer little resistance to storm waves and effectively absorb and dissipate wave energy. As waves wash over and breach the dunes during storms, they carry sand and shell across the grasslands and marshes, and even into the estuaries. Storm overwash contributes new sediment to the islands, creating new dune growth, adding to the islands' elevation and extending the island laterally into the lagoon – i.e. overwash maintains the islands.

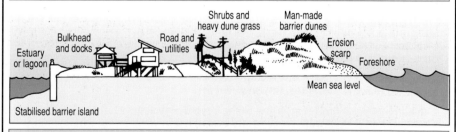

Artificially modified barriers often display a different morphology. The artificially stabilised dunes are higher and impenetrable, thus preventing overwash. The beaches are narrower and steeper: thus during storms there is a lot of scour, and the beach is further narrowed and steepened.

Barrier erosion and migration threaten the stability of developed areas. The main problem is that as the barrier retreats and migrates the political and legal boundaries remain fixed, leaving buildings and lives at risk. The response is to attempt to stabilise the area by groynes, seawalls, beach replenishment schemes and dune stabilisation. These are costly and temporary solutions which create further erosional problems.

Land use on the barriers is dominated by amenity housing, beach-orientated recreation and related services. Most lack industrial plants, commercial ports or agriculture. Cross-sections contrasting natural and stabilised barriers. (Note the narrow beach and high, steep dunes on the stabilised barrier.)

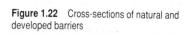

Figure 1.22   Cross-sections of natural and developed barriers

The dynamics of coastal barriers

Barrier beaches fringe the low-lying coastal plains of many oceanic shorelines. In the USA there is a nearly continuous, 2700-mile series of barrier borders stretching from Maine to Texas. This system consists of 400 distinct barrier beaches. Some are true islands; the rest are spits and tombolos.

Coastal barriers are not static but continually changing in response to environmental conditions. This state of dynamic equilibrium represents a balance between four elements:

1 Beach material in the form of sand.

2 Energy inputs from wave, wind, tidal and current actions, including hurricanes and storm surges.

3 Sea-level changes (the current rate is 25 cm per century).

4 The width and gradient of the beach.

Generally the shoreline is eroding, beaches are becoming narrower and steeper, and the whole system is migrating landward (see Figure 1.23). This process, however, is due to human intervention. Naturally, coastal barriers migrate very slowly. Beaches restore themselves from offshore bars, dune systems and erodable uplands.

Vegetation recolonises overwash areas and flourishes. But these processes cause dramatic spatial changes which have proved unacceptable in developed land-use systems. Fixed-site human exploitation and developments create the real problem.

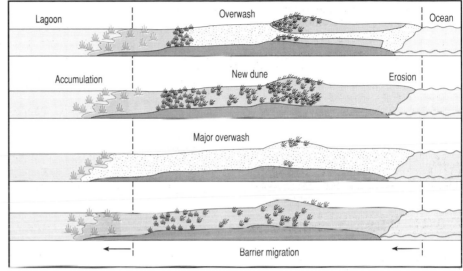

Figure 1.23 Landward migration of natural barrier islands due to the overwash process and long term sea level rise

SYNTHESIS: WHAT ARE BARRIER ISLANDS AND WHY ARE THEY IMPORTANT?

Study Figures 1.22 and 1.23.

1 What is a coastal barrier?

2 What controls the morphology of a coastal barrier? Produce an annotated diagram to highlight these controls.

3 Explain how the human occupation of the coastal barrier system creates environmental management problems.

4 Why are these areas potentially hazardous environments?

5 Using the cross-sections, suggest why they might be ecologically important.

6 How might they benefit zones of human occupation on the mainland? (You may need to consult an atlas, and study detailed maps of the Atlantic seaboard to help you.)

ANALYSIS: GRAPHS OF LAND USE CHANGES

Study Table 1.4 on land use changes, and produce two proportional graphs to highlight changing land use on the coastal barriers from 1945 to 1975. What important trends can be detected? Are the barriers becoming more developed? What are the implications of these figures ecologically, economically, and for environmental management?

Table 1.4 Land use change on Atlantic and Gulf coastal barriers

	1945–55 acres	%	1972–75 acres	%	Amount of change acres	%
Urban/built-up	90 410	5.5	228 679	13.6	+138 269	+153.0
Agricultural	14 746	0.9	10 160	0.6	−4586	−31.0
Rangeland	101 019	6.1	98 812	5.9	−2207	−2.0
Forest	168 161	10.2	152 224	9.1	−15 937	−10.0
Water bodies	101 992	6.2	101 250	6.0	−742	−0.7
Wetland	918 015	55.6	838 882	50.0	−79 133	−9.0
Barrier beach/dunes	256 357	15.5	249 241	14.8	−7116	−8.0
Total	1 650 700	100.0	1 679 248	100.0	+28 548	+2.0

Source: Platt, Pelczarski and Burbank (eds), 1987

Human land use of the coastal barriers – is this the real problem?

We have seen that the barrier islands are a very dynamic and potentially hazardous environment. We will now consider the human usage of the entire chain of coastal barriers, amounting to 1.6 million acres.

The urban/built-up category includes many new developments including hotels, motels, seasonal homes, restaurants, shopping centres and theatres. It includes the large and exceptional fully-fledged cities like Galveston, Miami Beach and Atlantic City, and the much more common, smaller and more isolated resort communities. They are very diverse in physical form, demography, political governance and economic functions. Many were very small communities that have grown very rapidly due to increases in personal income and leisure time which fuelled demand for residential units in coastal areas, e.g. Long Beach, North Carolina, whose population increased 1700% between 1960 and 1984.

Consequently, these areas suffer not only from natural risks but from other problems including inadequate water supply, visual blight, urban decay, liquid and solid waste disposal difficulties, lack of public open space, transport and parking problems. Growth development, to restore quality of life, *and* hazard management will be required for the future.

Figure 1.25 Daytona Beach

Figure 1.26 Access to Daytona Beach

Figure 1.27 Land use on the Barrier Islands

Figure 1.28 Landward side of the Barrier Islands

An overview of human responses to coastal erosion in the USA

In most coastal areas in the USA, population and economic investment have increased despite the increasing hazard potential due to shoreline recession, rising sea levels and the consequent increasing risk from storm surges and hurricanes. By 1970 it was estimated that 25% of the shoreline of the USA was suffering from severe erosion, at a real cost of $200 million per annum. Human land use intensification compounds the physical problems, by interfering with the natural stabilisation processes at work within the coastal barrier system. At the same time this increased human occupancy has also led to increased and more vociferous demands for public action to stabilise ocean front shorelines. The response to these demands has been to try to match appropriate solutions to local land use situations and environmental conditions.

Four broad coastal protection and management strategies have evolved.

1 Coastline protection engineering, involving both structural responses and beach replenishment.
2 Public preservation.
3 The National Flood Insurance Program.
4 The restraint of future development through national and local legislation, including strategic retreat options and land use zoning.

We will now look at these four options in detail.

GRAPHICAL TECHNIQUES AND DATA ANALYSIS

Comment on the degree of economic diversification in these communities, as reflected in the data contained in Figure 1.24 on primary economic activity. Do you think this is typical of most areas of the USA? What particular problems might these areas face?

Using the data from Table 1.5, produce a map with appropriate proportional symbols or shading to highlight the variable nature of ocean front development and built-up acreage on the coastal barriers along the Atlantic seaboard states. You will need to make a base map from an atlas.

Which states have the most developed and least developed barrier coastlines?

What factors might help explain this pattern?

In which states is there likely to be the most demand for engineering schemes for coastal protection? Give reasons for your selection.

Table 1.5 Developed land on coastal barriers by state, 1980

State	Area		Frontage	
	Acres built up	Barrier area built up (%)	Miles of ocean front developed	Ocean front developed (%)
Maine	1165	72	15.8	56
New Hampshire	780	72	8.1	100
Massachusetts	8128	22	47.7	22
Rhode Island	1226	35	11.2	30
Connecticut	576	42	8.8	41
New York	11 578	35	76.4	44
New Jersey	22 719	47	73.3	69
Delaware	2956	29	9.7	20
Maryland	1848	14	8.8	29
Virginia	1144	2	19.7	18
North Carolina	21 625	14	119.3	37
South Carolina	13 081	8	63.5	42
Georgia	8436	5	16.0	15
Florida	101 988	20	460.7	63
Alabama	5273	19	30.1	51
Mississippi	0	0	0	0
Louisiana	6746	18	14.9	10
Texas	19 410	5	64.2	18
Total	228 679	14%	1048.2	37%

Source: Platt, Pelczarski and Burbank (eds), 1987

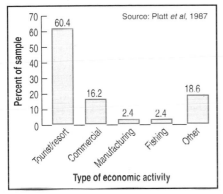

Figure 1.24 Primary economic activity of sample coastal barrier communities

CASE STUDY *Coastal Engineering: New Jersey's Structural Responses*

Traditionally, the coastline was fortified to cope with a storm event of an intensity likely to occur 'once in a hundred years', with major engineering structures. They are costly, have major environmental effects and do not tackle the problem, but attempt to control it. At best, they alleviate the problem; at worst, they transfer coastal erosion elsewhere (Table 1.6). They will be increasingly ineffective with rising land-to-sea levels and poor maintenance – in Texas and South Carolina, sea walls have recently failed. Yet sea walls are common from Sea Bright and Monmouth Beach, New Jersey, south to Miami and west to Galveston, Texas.

Between 1936 and 1975 over 75 coastal protection schemes were implemented by the US Army Corps of Engineers, costing over $100 million. These schemes took the form of jetties, sea walls and groyne fields. Expensive engineering solutions have been sought in those states with a highly developed coastline (Figure 1.29). The New Jersey shoreline has been altered from its natural state over the last 100 years, with urban development lining much of the ocean frontage. Coastal management in the state has three main aims:
management in the state has three main aims:

1 The construction of groynes, bulkheads and sea walls along heavily developed areas prone to beach erosion and storm flooding.
2 The retention of beaches in urban areas by beach nourishment schemes.
3 The retention of natural habitats in undeveloped areas.

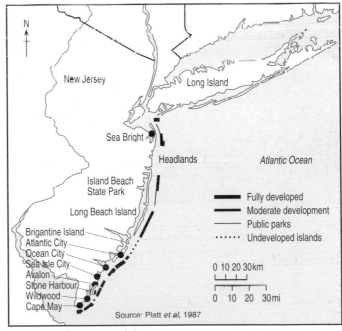

Figure 1.29 Development status of coastal barrier, New Jersey

ENQUIRY

1 Using the map (Figure 1.29) describe the nature of the New Jersey coastline.

2 Attempt to justify the three aims of their coastal management policy.

3 Summarise the environmental impact of these engineering schemes, highlighting both their direct and indirect effects (see Tables 1.6 and 1.7, and Figure 1.30 and read 'Environmental problems associated with engineering solutions').

Table 1.6   Human alterations to coastal barriers which affect configuration of landforms and alter sediment budgets

Human adjustment	Direct effects	Indirect effects
Building site modification (grading, paving)	Changes landform configuration. Eliminates sources of sediment. Changes rates of sediment transport across land surface	Creates disequilibrium landform configuration which can only be maintained through artificial means
Construction of buildings	Alters wind patterns. Obstruction to sediment flow. Truncates beach or dune zone	Focuses human use and human impacts. Leads to construction of support infrastructure and implementation of protection structures
Emplacement of shore protection structures	Armours shoreline. Alters sediment flows. Changes location of erosion/deposition and its severity	Leads to need for more structures
Beach nourishment	Changes sedimentation rates and severity of erosion	Masks nature of erosion problem. Leads to further development

Source: Platt, Pelczarski, Burbank (eds), 1987

Table 1.7   The impact of coastal engineering structures

Type of structure	Position	Form	Purpose	Potential problems
Sea wall	Parallel to the land–sea interface, i.e. shore normal	Static, massive, rigid, non-porous vertical or curved. Normally stone or concrete	To maintain the shoreline in an advanced position and to prevent further recession. Vertical walls deflect breaking waves. Curved walls reflect large waves	Erosion often continues at the ends of the schemes on adjacent shores. Can also be damaged by scour at the base or toe. Expensive
Revetment	Shore normal	Massive, rigid, porous. Armouring of beach/cliff foot with stone and/or timber	To protect against flooding from high tides and surges. Also allows waves to dissipate energy under normal, but not storm conditions	Often misused. Not effective for storm waves
Bulkhead	In more protected environments, e.g. marinas and navigation channels	Massive, rigid, non-porous. Normally stone or concrete or cheaper materials	A land-retaining structure on low energy coasts	Environmental and ecological impact
Groynes	Perpendicular to shoreline	Timber, stone, rubble, various sizes	To trap sand moving along the shoreline in order to protect a beach or retain artificially placed sand. Spacing varies from 1:1.5 length to 1:4 length	Terminal groyne syndrome. Erosion can be created downdrift of a groyne field in the sediment starved area
Jetties	Create a stable and constant entrance to rivers and tidal inlets by channelisation, dredging and training walls. Perpendicular to the shoreline	Concrete on a base of rubble or sand	Stabilise entrance and protection of vessels. Eliminate deposition by confining river or tidal current into a narrow and hydraulically efficient channel	Huge environmental impact. Disrupts longshore movement of sediment. Traps develop updrift and scouring downdrift
Breakwater	Offshore in deep water. Parallel or oblique to coast	Rough. Durable. Massive. Concrete or rubble or sandcore which is 80% by volume. Ideally veneer is reinforced concrete	Protect shoreline or harbour anchorage from wave attack, by breaking the waves offshore. Create a calm anchorage for shipping. Promote sedimentation in the wave shadow zone	High costs. Inadequate design to withstand direct wave action. Ecological disruption. High visual impact

Environmental problems associated with engineering solutions

1 Being static, engineering solutions conflict with the dynamic nature of the zone, especially sediment exchange processes.

2 Although the difficulties associated with engineering 'solutions' are well understood, solutions to overcome these problems are not easy to find.

3 They are not permanent, but finite solutions that often need careful maintenance – e.g. concrete suffers from shrinkage, debonding and weathering, especially from micro-fracturing and subsequent invasion from saline water. Deterioration can take from as little as a few weeks to 50 years.

The most widely used structural responses are sea walls and groynes. Both suffer from major specific problems. Sea walls can create difficulties in three places. *On the beach side of a sea wall*, the wall becomes undermined because wave reflection transports sediment seaward, resulting in a drop in beach level. At Porthcawl in South Wales, a sea wall built in 1906 caused the beach level to fall, resulting in the need for a new sea wall in 1934. The beach continues to fall and little beach sand now remains, and there is only a thin cobble veneer above rock outcrops. At Aberystwyth, the beach became narrow and lower following the construction of a promenade in 1866–67. So far, remedial action has included groyning in 1905–1949; beach filling in 1964, 1971 and 1980; armouring in 1952, 1954 and 1961; and even rebuilding and reinforcing the sea wall in 1938 and 1980.

On the landward side of a sea wall, ground water flow may be impeded unless the wall is adequately drained. This may lead to a build-up of pressure which causes the wall to burst or be undermined. The wall may also halt sediment exchange from the cliff to the beach, starving the beach of sediment.

At the ends of a sea wall, localised erosion by incident waves at the junction of the protected and unprotected section may produce a re-entrant which is progressively enlarged, eventually exposing the rear of the sea wall to wave action. Terminal scour of this type is very common where sea walls

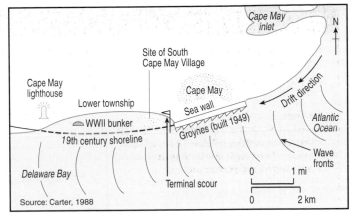

Figure 1.30   The shoreline to the west of Cape May City, New Jersey

have not been securely tied into the adjacent walls by flanking walls. At Cape May, New Jersey, shoreline erosion has averaged up to 20 m a year. Terminal scour has removed over 1 km of shoreline west of where the sea wall stops, destroyed the village of South Cape May, and exposed WWII gun emplacements formerly buried 400 m inland (Figure 1.30).

Groynes are very widely used wall-like structures inserted perpendicular to the beach to capture sediment drifting parallel to the shoreline. There are two basic types. *Anchor groynes* are designed to stabilise short lengths of shoreline by capturing a proportion of sediment drifting along the shore, or retaining a quantity of introduced fill. Once this material has been captured the design should allow bypassing either over or around the groyne, so as to maintain the longshore drift of material. *Terminal groynes* effectively stop longshore transport.

Many studies have shown that less than half of all groynes perform satisfactorily, and that some have led to serious problems of downdrift erosion and scour. This is due to the difficulty in predicting how a groyne will perform and to the fact that groyne development is more of an art than a science. Spacing and length are most critical, but also important are height, alignment, shape and design material. Their fundamental weakness is that they can behave as a hard static element in an essentially dynamic environment.

CASE STUDY *Beach Filling and Beach Nourishment on Miami Beach*

This technique was developed in the 1950s in the USA and is now a standard restorative method of nourishing a depleted beach by dumping sediment on or near the beach face. The method does not attempt to tackle the cause of the problem. Foreign material is imported and either dumped directly into an area or gradually fed in to nourish a beach over time. The approach often combines filling, nourishing and other measures, especially groynes. Advantages include a more natural appearance and a low environmental

impact if local fill material is used. The method is also economically attractive as there are no construction costs, or low material costs if local fill material is used.

This method is also used along the sand and shingle beaches of England's South Coast, where shingle recharge is accomplished by transporting material from downdrift accumulation zones known as sinks to updrift injection points. Bournemouth, for example, used china clay residue brought from Devon, 200 km away. Many of the world's most

famous beaches are composed largely of artificial sand – Copacabana in Rio de Janeiro and Miami Beach, Florida, are examples.

The effectiveness of this technique will depend on the suitability of the fill in terms of getting similiar or slightly coarser grain size and composition, and the rate of replenishment. Sediment is normally derived from ex-beach material found as inlet shoals or from lagoons, estuarine, fluvial or even industrial sources.

There are, however, two major

problems with this technique: the potentially rapid loss of fill, and the impact on the environment – both physical and ecological – in the source and depositional areas, especially by marine dredging.

Miami Beach is a classic example of a coastal site where several different coastal management techniques have been used to protect a developed and financially valuable coastline. In the past there has been no clear understanding of the causes of the problem, and consequently some protective measures actually artificially accelerated the problem (Figure 1.31).

Miami Beach is a city constructed on a narrow, 15 km barrier island. Extensive shoreline development started after the 1926 hurricane. Between 1920 and 1960 many individual properties constructed their own bulkheads and groynes to prevent erosion of their private beaches. The problem was compounded by the cutting of artificial inlets across the barrier for recreational boating. These cuts disrupted the southerly drift of sediment to Miami Beach. By 1965 the shoreline was a major environmental disaster. The recreation beach had been lost, the shoreface was being steepened, the nearshore reefs and backshore lagoons were being despoiled.

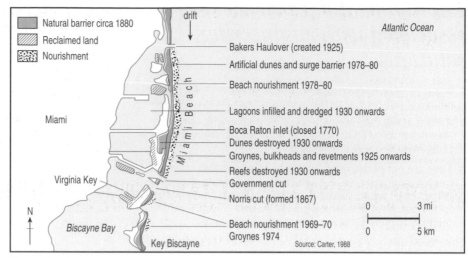

Figure 1.31   Shoreline protection measures at Miami Beach

Beach nourishment was seen as the solution, and Miami Beach is the largest such scheme yet undertaken. 17.7 x 10^6 m³ of sediment has been moved on to a badly eroded shore whose beach had dwindled to a width of 10–20 m. Now a 200 m wide beach has been created along an 18 km stretch of coastline by dredging sand from a shallow sand shelf 2.5 km offshore and pumping it onshore.

The new beach has been backed by a dune rampart to withstand hurricane force surges. The scheme was implemented between 1976 and 1982 at a cost of 67 million US dollars, a small outlay when compared with the estimated worth of the resort at 5000 million US dollars.

The scheme not only created a 200 m wide 'natural' coastal protection beach, but increased public access. This was desirable due to the high taxpayer subsidy of $67 million. The entire 18 km now has unimpeded access.

Public preservation

Nine barrier beaches and their associated ecosystems have been preserved through public acquisition and management. This includes 454 000 acres of wetlands. In addition, the US Fish and Wildlife Service administers 38 national wildlife refuges involving another 206 000 acres on barrier islands, and there are numerous smaller parcels managed by state and local governments and trusts. The Department of the Interior estimates that about 880 million acres (just over 50%) of barriers are protected (Figure 1.32).

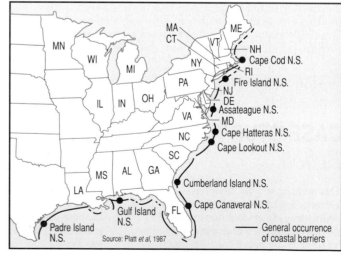

Figure 1.32   Map of national seashores of the USA

ENQUIRY: PUBLIC PRESERVATION AIMS AND OBJECTIVES

What are the aims of this form of coastal management?

With what land uses might these objectives conflict?

In what situation might this conflict be at its most acute?

The National Flood Insurance Program (NFIP)

This is a national flood insurance available to all existing and new structures that satisfy building standards, and that are not exempt by the 1982 Coastal Barrier Resources Act. It has been administered by a Federal agency since 1968.

Development pressure is three to four times greater in coastal areas than in the rest of the country. Peoples' desire to be near the coast has resulted in the development of areas vulnerable to coastal storms. The Federal Flood Insurance Program, which insures structures in flood-prone areas, represents the Federal government's second greatest liability, second only to Social Security. As of August 1987, there were 64 000 policies under the Flood Insurance Program in coastal high hazard areas or v-zones.

Out of 17 000 communities at risk from flooding in the whole up the USA, only 1395 are coastal. However, over 70% of all the policies in the USA are in these 1395 communities. In two of the 90 communities built totally on developed coastal barriers, 64 000 claims were settled between 1978 and 1981. This represented 54% of the total claims on the NFIP.

ENQUIRY: EVALUATION OF NFIP

What does this tell you about the scale of coastal development?

What factors will influence the success of such a programme as a hazard mitigation tool?

Legislative restraints on future development including strategic retreat

1982 Coastal Barrier Resources Act (CBRA)

Federal flood insurance and assistance with highways, sewers and beach protection were identified as incentives to further coastal development. Consequently, several bills were introduced to restrain further growth of undeveloped coastal barriers by removing federal subsidies to prohibit flood insurance on post-1981 constructed properties. In addition, there was to be no substantial improvement to coastal protection structures along 565 miles of designated 'undeveloped barriers' (24% of the ocean-facing shoreline of the coastline of the Atlantic and Gulf).

The act does not prohibit owners from building on undeveloped hazardous coastal barriers but does shift the cost of infrastructure and risk of loss from the federal treasury to the private sector and to state or local governments.

At present it is only a partial answer to the problems of barrier development, management and conservation. It does, however, create three major difficulties. It concentrates Federal benefits in the 'developed areas', reinforcing pressure for further development here. Secondly, expensive high density infill and redevelopment is more likely in other undeveloped areas, due to increased private insurance and construction costs, at the expense of single-family and moderate-cost housing projects. Thirdly, recent coastal developments suggest Federal aid may modify the type of development, but will not restrict development as city councils and private developers have few problems financing the urban infrastructure needed to support that development, e.g. Ocean City and Maryland.

Strategic retreat: coastal management by radical land use zoning

Recently a new strategy has emerged recognising the financial, social and environmental limitations of the very expensive coastal armouring programme.

Strategic retreat is a programme designed to limit future construction close to the ocean. It is based on the idea that as a species we should stop challenging natural coastal processes and start learning to live with them. It is very cost-effective and will certainly save many lives. It will preserve the natural coastline for wildlife and recreation and reduce the massive environmental impact caused by fortifications. The concept has evolved from studies made at the Skidaway Institute of Oceanography in Georgia. It is backed by the Federal Government through the National Flood Insurance Programme which insures coastal property. Previously they have paid out on properties when they fell into the water. A two-year pilot scheme in the late 1980s paid 40% of the insured value of the structure if it was removed and reconstructed inland at a minimum distance; 30 times the rate of annual shoreline erosion for small structures, and 60 times this rate for large structures.

Massachusetts and North Carolina are at the forefront of this approach, with legal restrictions on coastal development. Massachusetts has placed a total ban on any new coastal development, but will not abandon more traditional engineering options to protect Boston's CBD or the airport, both built on low-lying land facing the harbour. In North Carolina they implemented the '30 and 60 times rule' as early as 1979, and banned the construction of any new hard engineering structures, including groynes.

The greatest problem with strategic retreat lies in changing public attitudes. Often they prefer the 'security that a physical barrier provides'. The controversial border between retreat and fortification is very well illustrated by the Chatham coastal conflict in Massachusetts due to the Wetlands Protection Act. The act not only limits new development on coastal land, but bans the construction of sea walls or permanent protection structures on any scale to protect homes built on coastal dunes, or on coastal banks after 1978. Pre-1978 homes on banks can be protected. The situation is further complicated by the fact that some houses on the banks which can be protected do not need it, whereas many properties on the dunes require urgent protection! Furthermore, there is no clear distinction guiding home owners as to what their property is built on.

Consequently state officials and coastal geomorphologists are portrayed as hard-headed bureaucrats, and are being sued for blocking the construction of a sea wall by local residents. Many home owners living in threatened properties will now only consider permanent defensive structures, rejecting even consideration of all other means of coastal protection. The attitudes of both sides seem to be increasingly polarised.

VALUES ANALYSIS AND CLARIFICATION: STRATEGIC RETREAT

Relatively wide, high barriers are often more stable: here improved building, flood-proofing measures and shore protection can be effective. On low narrow barriers which experience severe wave impact, storm overwash and severe erosion, new approaches must be sought. This is especially true of tidal inlets in these areas. Gary Clayton at the Department of Environmental Quality Engineering, Boston, argues that although permanent evacuation is not generally feasible, the state authority should gradually acquire storm-damaged properties. It is the most efficient, economical and often the only way of protecting

future losses in high hazard zones. There are two potential problems: the high cost of coastal land prices and the demolition and clearance programme; and the lack of political support by both landowners and community officials not wishing to intrude and further restrict sensitive community affairs. Clayton argues that the acquired land could be used for other community objectives including recreation, increased coastal access or re-establishing a primary dune system as a natural resilient buffer for more landward properties and an ecological resource. Flood insurance premiums should then fall as the properties

in the maximum hazard zone are gradually acquired with consequent lower public costs to cover catastrophic storms.

1 Try to explain why a conflict has arisen over the coastal management issue at Chatham, Mass. What values do the various groups have? What are the future options? What do you think should be done in the area? Justify your decision.

2 Summarise the potential advantages and pitfalls of the retreat option.

SYNTHESIS

The coastline of the USA is very variable, and therefore many different coastal management strategies have evolved. Referring to the data in Table 1.8, justify the option you would use for the protection of each of the three types of shoreline (A, B and C). Using your knowledge of the North American coastline explain, with reference to a small stretch of coastline, how you might use cost-benefit analysis to select a coastal protection scheme (or schemes).

Table 1.8   A cost-benefit analysis of shoreline protection for three types of shoreline in Virginia, USA

Shoreline type	Strategy option	Durability (years)	Effectiveness (%)	Benefit/cost ratio
Underdeveloped A	Beach nourishment	10	15	0.105
	Revetments	25	50	0.182
	Walls	40	95	0.187
	Land acquisition/relocation	—	—	0.573
Partly developed B	Groynes	15	50	2.210
	Revetments	40	95	0.748
	Walls	40	95	0.397
	Land acquisition/relocation	—	—	0.187
Developed C	Revetments & limited walls	40	95	1.058
	Walls	40	95	0.528
	Land acquisition/relocation	—	—	0.372

Source: Carter/ULEAC, 1990

Review and cue

Coastal management: a global overview

1 There is no unified universal approach to coastal zone management.

2 There appear to be two main models, the American and the British options.

3 The American model places coastal issues in a single legislative and procedural system with a well-defined strategy run by a specifically created national agency which delegates authority at state level. Many people feel that this has not been entirely successful. Although the most comprehensive and historically the best-funded initiative, it has been fraught with difficulties in attaining its objectives, although substantial gains have been made.

4 Currently the *ad hoc* British approach has been to 'graft on' coastal problems to established administrative offices, thus allowing several 'interested' unco-ordinated agencies to become involved in each stretch of coast. Here coastal management is fragmentary and driven by events; this results in inter-agency conflict and less effective compromise solutions. Significant changes to both the approach and funding are expected.

5 Australia, Canada and Israel have compromised by setting up co-ordinating councils, but these often lack decision-making powers or suitable finances. They remain important as 'think tanks'.

6 All approaches share similar problems: inadequate finance, bureaucratic inflexibility, an absence of co-operation and consistency

between agencies and projects.

7 Internationally, with the exception of the Dutch, governments are reluctant to commit financial resources to programmes which are seen as peripheral to military security, economic and social well-being. Many governments see the private sector as a major funding source to overcome this problem – the National Trust in the UK operates on this basis, for example.

8 Developing nations have little time or resources for coastal zone management programmes, preferring to tackle problems as they arise. Management is directed at issues affecting human health and economic prosperity, e.g. water pollution or hazard mitigation from tropical cyclones.

Management of Drainage Basins and River Channels

Why is management needed?

We begin this section by focusing on human use and misuse of drainage basins and river channels, comparing and contrasting these with the problems we have already identified regarding coastal management.

In *The Business of Welsh Water* (Welsh Water, April 1989) the banner headline was 'Without water there is nothing'. They suggest that water is an essential commodity for life, community welfare and the economy of the area and nation. Recent human land use developments and the steady intensification in the use of Britain's water threaten to upset the natural processes at work within these natural systems and create management problems affecting both the quality and the quantity of water.

ANALYSIS: THE GLOBAL WATER BALANCE

Study Figure 1.33. What conclusions can you draw regarding the amount of freshwater directly available to the human race? Tabulate this data.

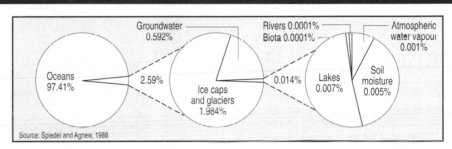

Figure 1.33   Distribution of the world's water

Source: Spiedel and Agnew, 1988

DIAGRAM ANALYSIS: WHY MANAGE 0.5%?

Why manage 0.5% of the world's water? What is the importance of the drainage basin? Less than 0.5% of freshwater is stored in drainage basins as rivers or in lakes, or as soil moisture, accessible ground water or in biotic components. Study Figure 1.34 and suggest why the drainage basin is an important human resource. Do you think that this model of drainage basin management can be regarded as typical?

1   Multiple-purpose reservoir.
2   Recreation; swimming, fishing, camping.
3   Hydroelectric station.
4   Municipal water supply
5   City and industrial waste treatment plant.
6   Pump to equalising reservoir for irrigation.
7   Diversion dam and lake.
8   High-level irrigation canal.
9   Levees for flood control.
10   Erosion control: stream dams and contour terracing.
11   Regulating basin for irrigation.
12   Wildlife refuge.
13   Low-level irrigation canal.
14   Gravity irrigation.
15   Contour ploughing.
16   Sprinkler irrigation.
17   Community water treatment plant.
18   Navigation: barge trains, locks, etc.
19   Re-regulating reservoir with locks.
20   Farm pond with pisciculture.

Source: T.V.A., 1975

Figure 1.34   Model for multipurpose river basin development

ENQUIRY: WHY MANAGE RIVERS TO CONTROL BOTH WATER QUALITY AND QUANTITY?

Effective environmental management must be based on a clear identification of the issues and conflicts to be resolved and a firm understanding of the active geomorphological processes at work within drainage basins and rivers. Study Figure 1.35 and identify six issues which highlight the need for effective drainage basin management.

Using Figures 1.34 and 1.35, compare and contrast the major conflicts and management techniques associated with coastal landform systems, on one hand, and drainage basins/river channels, on the other.

The Rivers of Shame

Every day seems to bring stories of new environmental scandals on Britain's waterways: toxic chemicals in the Wey, poison in the Balmoral lakes, farm slurry in an Oxfordshire reservoir. Some of it may have to do with the heightened interest in water created by the controversy over what is proving the most unpopular privatisation so far.

The Sunday Times Insight team has mounted a major investigation into the state of our waterways. More than 1,000 miles of clean river, five times the length of the M1, were officially downgraded between 1980 and 1987. Cases of pollution in inland waterways in England and Wales increased last year to a record 23,000, nearly double the 1982 figure. A tenth of Britain's rivers are now regarded by the Department of the Environment as class three (polluted) or four (biologically dead), due to pollution either from sewage, industrial effluent or farm waste.

Environmentalists have tended to believe that the situation will worsen once water is privatised. Maybe, but it need not be so if the government gets the new regulatory framework right. Indeed, privatisation, properly done, could see a dramatic turnround.

We should not fool ourselves, of course, into believing we can have clean rivers at no extra cost. Someone will have to pay for higher standards, and one way or another that someone is going to be the consumer. But in the long run, done well, with decent control and genuine commitment, it will be cheap at the price.

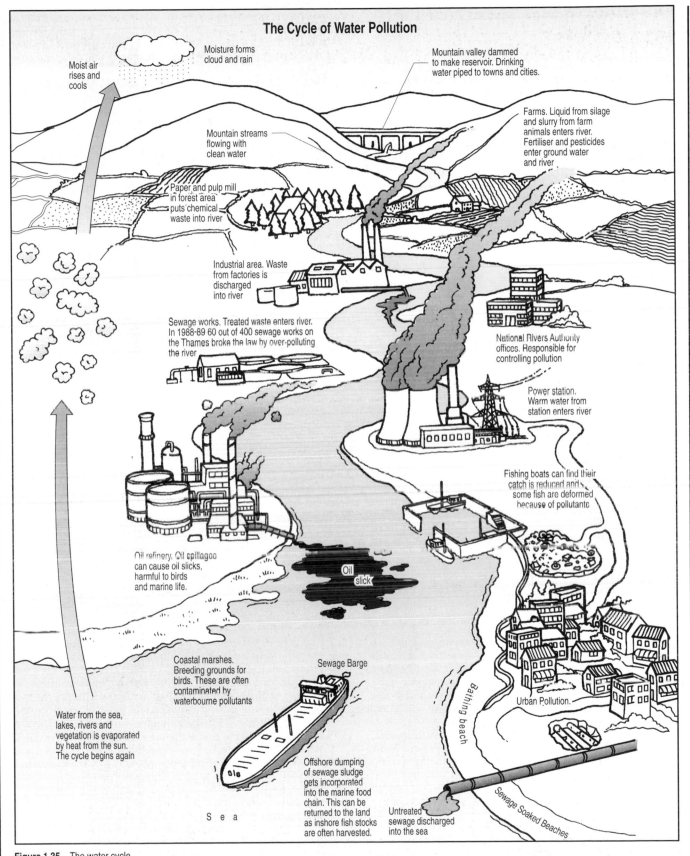

The Cycle of Water Pollution

Moist air rises and cools

Moisture forms cloud and rain

Mountain valley dammed to make reservoir. Drinking water piped to towns and cities.

Mountain streams flowing with clean water

Farms. Liquid from silage and slurry from farm animals enters river. Fertiliser and pesticides enter ground water and river

Paper and pulp mill in forest area puts chemical waste into river

Industrial area. Waste from factories is discharged into river

Sewage works. Treated waste enters river. In 1988-89 60 out of 400 sewage works on the Thames broke the law by over-polluting the river

National Rivers Authority offices. Responsible for controlling pollution

Power station. Warm water from station enters river

Fishing boats can find their catch is reduced and some fish are deformed because of pollutants

Oil refinery. Oil spillage can cause oil slicks, harmful to birds and marine life.

Oil slick

Water from the sea, lakes, rivers and vegetation is evaporated by heat from the sun. The cycle begins again

Coastal marshes. Breeding grounds for birds. These are often contaminated by waterbourne pollutants

Sewage Barge

Urban Pollution.

Bathing beach

Sea

Offshore dumping of sewage sludge gets incorporated into the marine food chain. This can be returned to the land as inshore fish stocks are often harvested.

Untreated sewage discharged into the sea

Sewage Soaked Beaches

Figure 1.35   The water cycle

How much water is carried by the world's rivers?

Any form of environmental management must be based on a firm understanding of the component processes. The *global hydrological cycle* or *system* examines water in a global context, and the exchanges and transfers from one stage of the cycle to another. These processes include evaporation, whereby moisture is transferred from the oceans to the atmosphere, and evapotranspiration, the process whereby plants absorb water through their roots, eventually evaporating it from their leaves. Precipitation includes drizzle, rain, snow, hail, dew and frost.

The global cycle can be regarded as a system, made up of a whole series of drainage basin hydrological cycles or sub-systems. A system is a set of organised objects or factors, in this case precipitation, evapotranspiration, surface runoff, and the relationships between them in the form of energy throughputs.

ENQUIRY: HUMAN DISRUPTION OF THE GLOBAL WATER BALANCE

Make a copy of Figure 1.36 and annotate it with the key points from the following extract.

Figure 1.36 The global watercycle

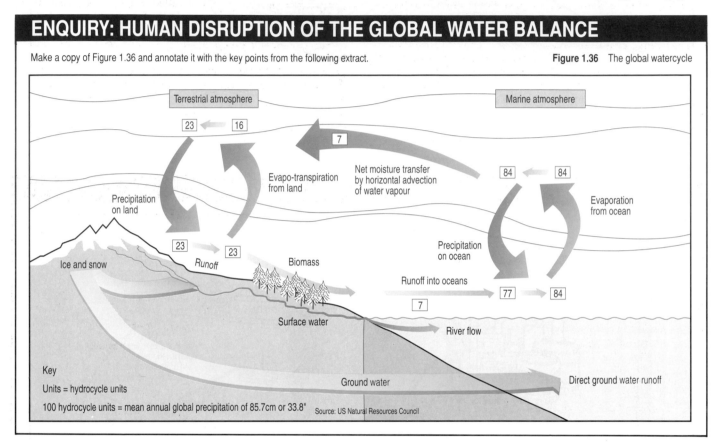

People, the water cycle and global warming

The water cycle connects many of today's environmental problems: deforestation, climatic change, desertification, soil erosion, water pollution. As human populations and economic activity have increased, the global water cycle has been modified from its natural state. Many of the flows and stores have been altered and it is not clear whether there will be major feedbacks.

1 Water is withdrawn from rivers and aquifers for domestic, industrial and agricultural purposes, e.g. irrigation, cooling water for industry, human consumption, reducing riverflow. The area under irrigation doubled between 1900 and 1950 to 90 million hectares. It is expected to triple between 1950 and 1990. Irrigation can cause waterlogging, salinisation and alkalinisation.

2 Reservoirs trap runoff, creating a rich local source of evaporation.

3 Asphalt and concrete in cities allows less water to soak into the ground, creating flood runoff.

4 Draining wetlands and cutting down forests modify evaporation and runoff regimes.

5 Although water is only a minor constituent of the atmosphere, and the atmosphere contains only one-thousandth of 1% of the global stock of water, the interactions between the atmosphere and water cycle are critical to sustain life and set the water cycle in motion. Human-induced disturbances of the water cycle have caused profound local, regional or even global climate changes. Human-induced climate change may cause alterations to the water cycle, e.g. global warming will affect every store and flow with incalculable consequences for humanity. We are currently unable to predict where the changes will occur, when, or their scale.

6 Evaporation and precipitation are expected to increase in a warmer world by up to 10%. This will create soil moisture changes which may have profound impacts on natural ecosystems and global cropping patterns.

7 In a warmer world runoff patterns will alter in both amount and timing. Water control structures based on the historical behaviour of the river's regime may now be inadequate.

8 Water stores such as polar ice caps and montane glaciers would retreat in a warmer world, transferring water to the oceans and raising sea levels.

How is water transferred from one part of its hydrological cycle to another?

The drainage basin is a catchment area of the Earth's surface bounded by a watershed that is drained by a stream. Individual streams and their catchment areas join together to form larger basins as the individual streams combine to form tributaries of the larger streams and rivers. The land surface of a region is covered by a nested hierarchy of drainage basins.

The drainage basin receives inputs of water as precipitation and distributes these from a number of vegetation, surface, soil and ground water stores via a series of transfer flows to become outputs as evapotranspiration, channel runoff or (see Figure 1.37) to form deep ground water.

The drainage basin system is part of a larger system, the global hydrological cycle. The drainage basin can be regarded as an 'open system' because it has an input of energy in the form of precipitation and a series of outputs as evapotranspiration and water returning to the sea. 'Closed systems' have no transfers of energy across their boundaries. Drainage basins, like many natural systems, attempt to maintain a balance between the factors or variables that operate within them. Thus if one factor changes, e.g. precipitation, other factors will alter to bring the system into balance. This state is known as *dynamic equilibrium*. If the alterations that take place when a variable changes attempt to damp down the change, this is called 'negative feedback'. If the alterations lead to an increasing rate of change this is called 'positive feedback'. Most natural systems have a degree of negative feedback, except where they have been modified by human interferences. Human interventions in rivers and drainage basin systems often have drastic and unexpected consequences resulting from accelerating change. We shall now investigate the components of the drainage basin hydrological cycle in detail, and explore some of the human interference associated with these process modifications and additional inputs.

BLOCK DIAGRAM CONSTRUCTION: THE DRAINAGE BASIN

1 Construct a basic block diagram to explain the term drainage basin.

2 a Make a simple copy of the drainage basin hydrological cycle diagram (Figure 1.37). Why is it an open system?

 b Attempt to highlight the three types of components that make up this system.
  Identify the stores, and shade these in red.
  Identify input(s) and shade them in blue.
  Use green to highlight outputs.
  Transfers or flows of water or energy should be shown in black.

 c Clearly and concisely define *all* the terms on your diagram. Refer to a standard geomorphology text, geographical dictionary, or the glossary to help you.

3 Now annotate your block diagram with this information.

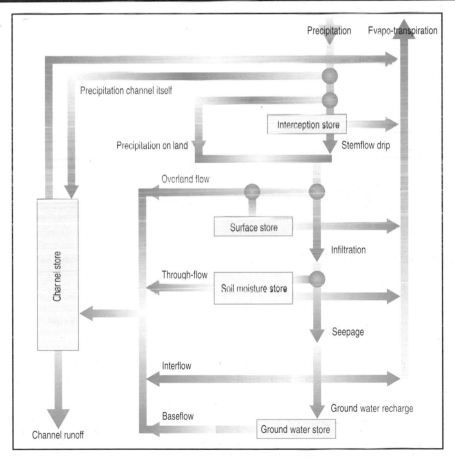

Figure 1.37 Components of the basin hydrological cycle

How does human activity modify the cycle?

ENQUIRY

Study Table 1.9. Produce an overlay of Figure 1.37 to highlight the varying degrees of human modification within the components of this cycle. Channel store and channel runoff are not included in your table. A detailed study of human modifications of river channel and process will be undertaken in the next section.

Table 1.9   Human impact on the non-channel components of the drainage basin hydrological cycle

Component	Nature of component store, input, output flow	Degree of human modification: none, slight, large, great	Detailed explanation
Precipitation	Input	Slight	Cloud seeding techniques. Initiate rain-making process by adding artificial hygroscopic nuclei of silver iodide, solid carbon dioxide, ammonium nitrate or, in clouds above 0°C, fine water droplets. Effective 10–30% increases can occur over small areas on a short time-scale. Urban and industrial pollution may have the same effect
Interception, stemflow and throughfall	Store. Flow. Flow	Large. Slight. Slight	Water stored on vegetation can be evaporated, pass through the plant layer as throughfall to become infiltrated or surface runoff. Interception will depend on the type, form and density of the vegetation cover. Today this often reflects the influence of human land-use patterns rather than climate and soils. 1 Cereal crops with vertical stems and leaves intercept less than a broad-leaved crop, e.g. potatoes. Cropland intercepts much less than a layered, natural ecosystem, e.g. a woodland. 2 Deforestation reduces interception in the short term
Evaporation and evapotranspiration	Outputs	Slight. Slight	1 Land use changes. Different types of vegetation have varying capacities for evapotranspiration. 2 Dams – reservoirs greatly increase local rates of evaporation, e.g. 33% of Lake Nasser in Egypt is lost in this way. 3 Urbanisation – the lack of vegetation drastically reduces evapotranspiration. Evaporation, however, may be increased due to the increased amount of surface storage on semi-permeable concrete surfaces. 4 Deforestation reduces evapotranspiration and evaporation
Surface storage and surface runoff	Store. Flow	Large. Large	1 Dams – increase surface storage as reservoirs. Losses to evapotranspiration and seepage can exceed 60% in the early years of a reservoir. This creates changes to local microclimates. 2 Urbanisation decreases surface storage. Built environments are made of impermeable or semi-permeable surfaces of concrete, tile, slate, brick, asphalt designed to speed up the drainage of water. Rapid runoff produces flash responses on hydrographs due to higher flood peaks and shorter timelags
Infiltration and soil moisture store	Flow. Store	Great. Slight	Migration of water into the soil can be altered by many land use changes and practices. 1 Urbanisation – infiltration rates are reduced on impermeable and compacted surfaces. 2 Deforestation decreases infiltration because tree roots channel water into the soil. 3 Trampling – human and animal feet compact the soil reducing infiltration. 4 Ploughing increases infiltration by breaking up the soil surface
Ground water, throughflow, percolation and baseflow	Store. Flow. Flow. Flow	Large. Slight. Slight. Large	On average 20% of water enters the ground water store via throughflow, if the rock is permeable. 1 Abstraction – water can be removed by pumping or under natural hydrostatic pressure at artesian wells. This poses few problems if the rate of abstraction is balanced by the rate of recharge in the aquifer. Over-extraction led to lowering of the water table with subsequent drying up of rivers and springs, and land subsidence in the London Basin in the 1950s. This has been halted by artificial recharge. In coastal areas of warmer regions salt-water incursions have contaminated supplies

ENQUIRY: URBANISATION AND THE HYDROLOGICAL CYCLE

Study Figure 1.38. What factors might help explain the differences between these two storm hydrographs?

1 State three major differences between the two graphs.

2 Complete the table opposite to help explain these differences.

3 Do all parts of the urban growth process have similiar hydrological impacts? Suggest four main differences between the construction phase and the mature urban fabric. How would you redesign some urban areas in the light of this knowledge? Use Table 1.10 to help you.

System	Type of change	Explanation of change
Component	+/−	
Precipitation		
Interception store		
Throughfall		
Stemflow		
Surface store		
Evaporation		
Evapo-transpiration		
Surface Runoff		
Infiltration		
Soil moisture store		
Throughflow		
Percolation		
Ground water store		
Baseflow		
Channel store		
Channel runoff		

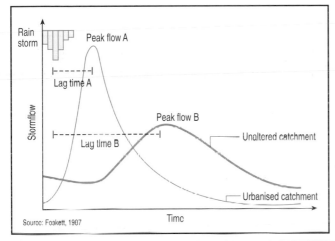

Figure 1.38 The effect of urbanisation on the shape of the storm hydrograph

Table 1.10 Stages of urban growth and their miscellaneous hydrological impacts

Stage	Impact
1 Transition from pre-urban to early-urban stage:	
a Removal of trees or vegetation	Decrease in transpiration and increase in storm flow
b Construction of scattered houses with limited sewerage and water facilities	
2 Transition from early-urban to middle-urban stage:	
a Bulldozing of land	Accelerated land erosion
b Mass construction of houses, etc.	Decreased infiltration
c Diversion of nearby streams for public supply	Decrease in runoff between points of diversion and disposal
d Untreated or inadequately treated sewerage into streams and wells	Pollution of streams and wells
3 Transition from middle-urban to late-urban stage:	
a Urbanisation of area completed by addition of more buildings	Reduced infiltration and lowered water table, higher flood peaks and lower low flows
b Larger quantities of untreated waste into local streams	Increased pollution
c Increase in population requiring establishment of new water supply and distribution systems	Increase in local stream-flow if supply is from outside basin
d Channels of streams restricted at least in part to artificial channels and tunnels	Higher stage for a given flow (therefore increased flood damage); changes in channel geometry and sediment load
e Waste-water reclamation and utilisation	Recharge to ground water aquifers; more efficient use of water resources
f Construction of sanitary drainage system and treatment plant for sewage	Removal of additional water from area
g Improvement of storm drainage system	
h Drilling of deeper, large-capacity industrial wells	Lowered water pressure, some subsidence, salt water encroachment
i Increased use of water for air conditioning	Overloading of sewers and other drainage facilities
j Drilling of recharge wells	

Source: Goudie, 1986

CASE STUDY *Processes in the River Channels of the Souteyran Valley*

The Souteyran Valley is on the southern side of Mount Lozere in the Cevennes area of the Massif Central. Water input comes from 1200 mm of annual precipitation resulting from Atlantic depressions. Some of this gets stored in the upland peat bogs which occur extensively in this granite-dominated landscape. Water stored in this source is slowly released throughout the year.

The valley contains many small streams which flow into the two main rivers, the Rieumalet and the Souteyran. These are tributaries of the River Tarn.

Water is a key resource in the area. It is vital for domestic consumption in the hamlets of Finiels and Prat and the small town of Le Pont de Montvert, as well as for agriculture and the Eagle's Nest Field Studies Centre.

PRELIMINARY RESEARCH ACTIVITY

In order to understand the data on the Souteyran Valley and draw the appropriate conclusions, you should first read about river channel processes in a standard geomorphological text, e.g, Clowes and Comfort or Hilton. This will give you a good general context into which to fit your case study.

DATA ANALYSIS

Using the base map (Figure 1.39), attempt a stream ordering exercise on the rivers in this valley. Is this a fully developed river system? It is often suggested that human impact is greatest on the highest order rivers. What factors could explain this?

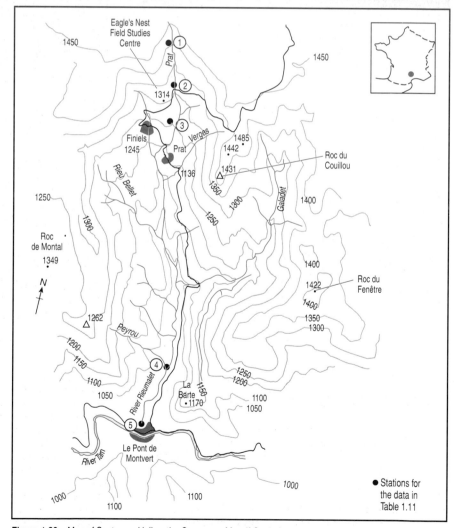

Figure 1.39   Map of Souteyran Valley, the Cevennes, Massif Central

ORAL PRESENTATIONS

What does the data in Table 1.11 tell you about the basic processes operating in the channels? Suggest three hypotheses to test and explain what you might expect to find in a typical channel. Working in small groups, test your hypotheses and report back on your findings. Comment on the limitations of the data. What improvements and further sources of data collection can you suggest?

Why might river channel processes not always conform to the model of a typical channel?

Table 1.11   Stream data from sites shown on Figure 1.39.

Units		Station number				
		1	2	3	4	5
m	Width of channel	1.9	4.0	2.9	9.4	6.1
m	Depth of channel	0.12	0.07	0.84	0.34	0.37
m	Wetted perimeter	2.1	4.4	3.3	11.1	6.6
m/s	Velocity:	0.029	0.42	0.33	0.1	0.027
m^2	Cross-sectional area	0.23	2.80	2.4	3.2	2.3
Degrees (°)	River bed gradient	11	3	3	7	3
cms	Bedload grain size (long axis)	27	16	32	10	23
	Soil pH	5.5	5.5	6.2	6	7
	Water quality					
°C	Temperature	5	6	8	8	9.5
	pH	8.3	7.7	7	5.5	8
ppM	Dissolved oxygen	5	15	26	25	18

Figure 1.40a   The upper section of the river valley

Figure 1.40b   The lower section of the river valley

How does human intervention modify river channel processes?

In this section we will examine two deliberate human modifications to the river at the channel scale. We will consider the impact of dam and reservoir construction after an analysis of channelisation.

Channelisation

Unlike dam construction, which involves modifying the channel at a specific location, channelisation involves modification along the river reach. Channels are straightened and dredged for navigation, gravel extraction, land drainage or channel regulation for flood control. The removal of meanders eliminates overbank floods associated with the swiftest currents on the outside banks of curves. The shortened course increases gradient and velocity and floodwaters erode and deepen the channel, increasing its flood capacity.

By 1950, six meanders on the Mississippi River had been cut off, reducing the length of the river by 270 km, representing a 12% loss of channel length. Unfortunately, because the channel slope is now steeper, the river is more unstable, and therefore more costly to manage.

The Jonglei Canal in Sudan, a 360 km channel, twice as long as Suez and carrying a quarter of the Nile, will now bypass the Southern Sudd papyrus swamps where more than half the White Nile's flow was lost to evapotranspiration every year.

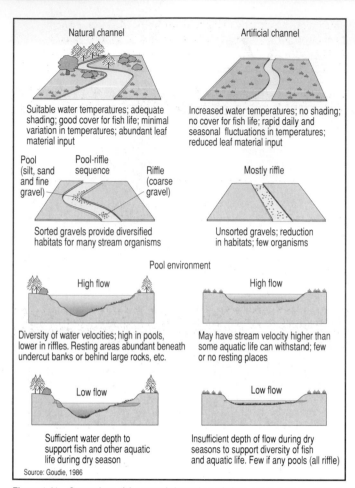

Natural channel

Suitable water temperatures; adequate shading; good cover for fish life; minimal variation in temperatures; abundant leaf material input

Pool (silt, sand and fine gravel) Pool-riffle sequence Riffle (coarse gravel)

Sorted gravels provide diversified habitats for many stream organisms

Pool environment

High flow

Diversity of water velocities; high in pools, lower in riffles. Resting areas abundant beneath undercut banks or behind large rocks, etc.

Low flow

Sufficient water depth to support fish and other aquatic life during dry season

Artificial channel

Increased water temperatures; no shading; no cover for fish life; rapid daily and seasonal fluctuations in temperatures; reduced leaf material input

Mostly riffle

Unsorted gravels; reduction in habitats; few organisms

High flow

May have stream velocity higher than some aquatic life can withstand; few or no resting places

Low flow

Insufficient depth of flow during dry seasons to support diversity of fish and aquatic life. Few if any pools (all riffle)

Source: Goudie, 1986

Figure 1.41 Comparison of the natural channel morphology and hydrology with that of a channelised stream, suggesting some possible ecological consequences

The scheme will provide an extra 4.75 billion m³ of water per year for Egypt and Sudan, but with major ecological impacts on the wetland area, and on the lifestyle of the local pastoral people. Prior to the scheme, no one even knew the exact size of the swamp, let alone made a detailed investigation into the potential consequences of the canal.

Channel straightening is the artificial equivalent of autogenic (natural) channel migration. Channel migration is a common feature in meandering rivers. Rates of migration vary, but changes of 10–15 m per year are not uncommon in large rivers. The rate of lateral migration depends upon the power of the river, the resistance of the banks and the curvature of the channel.

It is not only the flow of the river that can be modified, but also its form and course. River channel form can be modified in four main ways.

1 *Cross-section form*. The size and shape of the channel in cross profile, with width and mean depth being the key variables.

2 *Bed configuration*. The form of the bed of the river, e.g. ripples and dunes in sandy sediments, and pools and riffles in gravels.

3 *Channel pattern*. The view of the channel from above. This may be straight, meandering or, most commonly, braided.

4 *Channel slope*. The overall shape and gradient of the long profile of the river.

These components are not independent of one another, and are largely controlled by water discharge and sediment load. As these two parameters vary both spatially and over time, the river responds by adjusting the form of its channel. Natural rivers, therefore, are very sensitive and dynamic features often capable of rapid channel change. Two types of change are recognisable. *Autogenic* change is produced by natural processes within the river system under normal action, e.g. channel migration, meander cutoff. *Allogenic* change is the result of changes in external inputs produced by climatic change or human activity which change the inputs of water and/or sediments (e.g. very large floods of a magnitude that changes the form of the channel). These events are rare in humid areas, and more common in semi-arid areas, e.g. Arizona. In humid areas the small floods which occur almost every year are thought to control the size and shape of the channel. In the UK changes in climate over the last 10 000 years have altered the characteristic discharge and sediment load of rivers. Former discharges of some rivers may have been 50 times larger than present ones.

River channels are thus very varied, sensitive and dynamic features. The challenge in the next decade is to increase our understanding of processes within channels, and so be able to predict the direct consequences of human modification of the channel, or the indirect consequences of changes in land use in the catchment.

Dam construction

Many and various attempts have been made to modify either the quality or quantity of water in rivers, usually to improve the water resources of an area. This type of direct intervention is superimposed on the often accidental impact on various other parts of the drainage basin hydrological cycle due to such activities as urbanisation, pollution, and the removal of large quantities of water from ground water storage, especially in semi-arid areas.

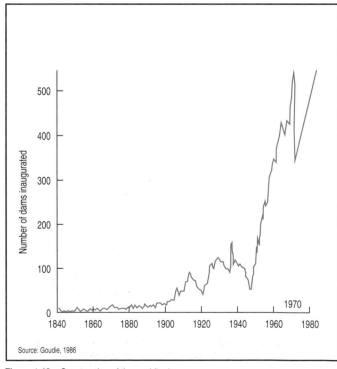

Source: Goudie, 1986

Figure 1.42 Construction of the world's dams

One of the most widespread of these deliberate modifications is the construction of dams and reservoirs. Since the construction of the first dams in Egypt over 5000 years ago, the adoption of the technique has spread rapidly. They were constructed to improve agriculture, provide power and prevent floods. The regulated river discharge provided a reliable source of stored water in a reservoir. Today, millions of people depend on dams for survival, welfare and employment.

ANALYSIS: DAM CONSTRUCTION RATES

Attempt to summarise the major trends in dam construction. What factors might help explain these trends?

Not only is dam construction on the increase, with as many as 600 new dams being built world-wide every year, but the size of these dams and reservoirs is increasing. In the 1930s the Hoover Dam (221 m high) at Boulder on the Colorado, and the Lake Mead reservoir it created (38 billion m³) was the largest project in the world. Today the dam is exceeded in height by at least 18 others, and in width by several including a 41 km barrage at Kiev. The reservoir appears small compared with Aswan's Lake Nasser, containing 157 billion m³. These large projects create dams which are capable of almost total regulation of the streams they impound. It is estimated that for the North American and African continents over 20% of total runoff is now controlled by dams.

INVESTIGATION: THE IMPACT OF DAMS

Make an A4-sized copy of this table. Attempt to organise and tabulate the information on the positive and negative impacts of dam and reservoir construction. Use Table 1.12, Figure 1.43, 'What is a good dam?' (page 44) and the summary of the case made against superdams by Goldsmith and Hildyard (page 45). Also consult the section on hydro-electric power in Chapter 3 ('The Energy Question') for further information on benefits and disadvantages associated with dam construction for hydro-electric power in Norway and Ghana.

Now highlight the differences between positive (+) and negative changes (−) using appropriate symbols. Distinguish the changes that will occur 'before the flood' (use a green dot) from those that will occur after the dam construction and subsequent flooding of the area to create a reservoir (use a blue dot).

Changes upstream of the dam	Changes downstream of the dam	
		Social impact The change to people's life styles and communities
		Economic impact Changes to financial patterns in an area
		Environmental impact Physical change to the landscape and ecology of the area

Table 1.12   Impacts of power developments on river systems

	Upstream	On-site	Downstream
Sedimentation		Accumulation	Loss and erosion
Nutrient status		Accumulation and entrophication	Loss
Flow modification		Shoreline fluctuation	Loss of flood flows
Resettlement	Immigration	Displacement	Immigration
Fisheries	Migratory limitation	Species modification	Population decline by nutrition
Transportation		Disruption	

Summary of major physical and human impacts of artificial lakes. Failure impacts are not incorporated. Widespread or debated impacts (seismic/climatic) are not incorporated.

Source: MacDonald, 1988

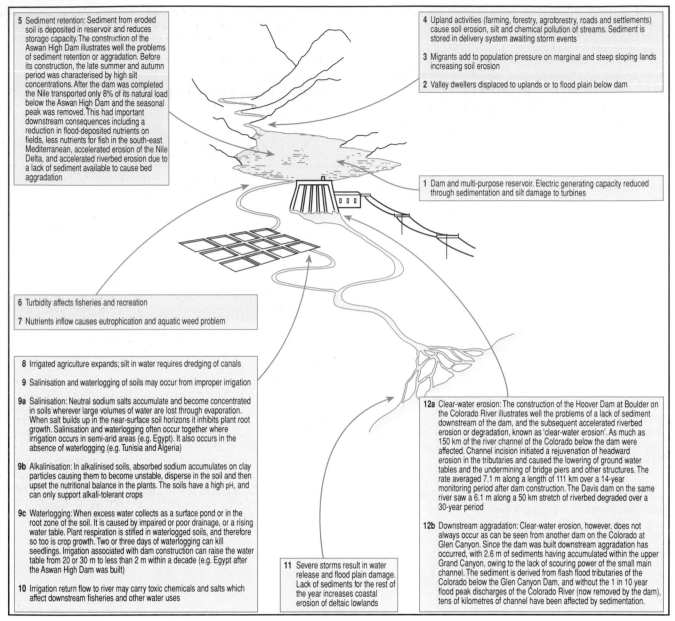

5 Sediment retention: Sediment from eroded soil is deposited in reservoir and reduces storage capacity. The construction of the Aswan High Dam illustrates well the problems of sediment retention or aggradation. Before its construction, the late summer and autumn period was characterised by high silt concentrations. After the dam was completed the Nile transported only 8% of its natural load below the Aswan High Dam and the seasonal peak was removed. This had important downstream consequences including a reduction in flood-deposited nutrients on fields, less nutrients for fish in the south-east Mediterranean, accelerated erosion of the Nile Delta, and accelerated riverbed erosion due to a lack of sediment available to cause bed aggradation

4 Upland activities (farming, forestry, agroforestry, roads and settlements) cause soil erosion, silt and chemical pollution of streams. Sediment is stored in delivery system awaiting storm events

3 Migrants add to population pressure on marginal and steep sloping lands increasing soil erosion

2 Valley dwellers displaced to uplands or to flood plain below dam

1 Dam and multi-purpose reservoir. Electric generating capacity reduced through sedimentation and silt damage to turbines

6 Turbidity affects fisheries and recreation

7 Nutrients inflow causes eutrophication and aquatic weed problem

8 Irrigated agriculture expands; silt in water requires dredging of canals

9 Salinisation and waterlogging of soils may occur from improper irrigation

9a Salinisation: Neutral sodium salts accumulate and become concentrated in soils wherever large volumes of water are lost through evaporation. When salt builds up in the near-surface soil horizons it inhibits plant root growth. Salinisation and waterlogging often occur together where irrigation occurs in semi-arid areas (e.g. Egypt). It also occurs in the absence of waterlogging (e.g. Tunisia and Algeria)

9b Alkalinisation: In alkalinised soils, absorbed sodium accumulates on clay particles causing them to become unstable, disperse in the soil and then upset the nutritional balance in the plants. The soils have a high pH, and can only support alkali-tolerant crops

9c Waterlogging: When excess water collects as a surface pond or in the root zone of the soil. It is caused by impaired or poor drainage, or a rising water table. Plant respiration is stifled in waterlogged soils, and therefore so too is crop growth. Two or three days of waterlogging can kill seedlings. Irrigation associated with dam construction can raise the water table from 20 or 30 m to less than 2 m within a decade (e.g. Egypt after the Aswan High Dam was built)

10 Irrigation return flow to river may carry toxic chemicals and salts which affect downstream fisheries and other water uses

12a Clear-water erosion: The construction of the Hoover Dam at Boulder on the Colorado River illustrates well the problems of a lack of sediment downstream of the dam, and the subsequent accelerated riverbed erosion or degradation, known as 'clear-water erosion'. As much as 150 km of the river channel of the Colorado below the dam were affected. Channel incision initiated a rejuvenation of headward erosion in the tributaries and caused the lowering of ground water tables and the undermining of bridge piers and other structures. The rate averaged 7.1 m along a length of 111 km over a 14-year monitoring period after dam construction. The Davis dam on the same river saw a 6.1 m along a 50 km stretch of riverbed degraded over a 30-year period

12b Downstream aggradation: Clear-water erosion, however, does not always occur as can be seen from another dam on the Colorado at Glen Canyon. Since the dam was built downstream aggradation has occurred, with 2.6 m of sediments having accumulated within the upper Grand Canyon, owing to the lack of scouring power of the small main channel. The sediment is derived from flash flood tributaries of the Colorado below the Glen Canyon Dam, and without the 1 in 10 year flood peak discharges of the Colorado River (now removed by the dam), tens of kilometres of channel have been affected by sedimentation.

11 Severe storms result in water release and flood plain damage. Lack of sediments for the rest of the year increases coastal erosion of deltaic lowlands

Figure 1.43   The physical and environmental impacts of dam and reservoir construction

What is a good dam?   A checklist

Here is an edited list of suggestions from *International Dams Newsletter*, 1986:

1 No dam should be built until an adequate assessment of its likely environmental effects has been undertaken *and* made available to the public.
2 Water-development projects should only be undertaken if they can be shown to benefit large sectors of the population instead of the urban elite.
3 Schemes should favour labour-intensive rather than capital-intensive economic activities.

4 They should produce food crops for feeding the local population rather than for export.
5 They should not compromise public health and safety.
6 They should not adversely affect national parks, heritage sites, areas of scientific and educational importance, tropical rainforests or areas inhabited by species threatened with extinction.
7 They must be viable for a minimum of 100 years. They should only be built where it can be guaranteed they will not silt up.
8 They should not be built if their associated irrigation schemes are likely to lead to the salinisation of agricultural land.

9 The funding should be based on sustainable long-term resource enhancement rather than short-term resource exploitation.
10 They should not involve displacing indigenous people from their homelands, and endangering their culture, unless compensation is provided and they are better off than before the project.
11 These must be no potential significant engineering or safety problems.
12 They should not be built where they are likely to inflict significant damage on estuarine or ocean fisheries.
13 They should not be built if they are likely to significantly harm the environment of a neighbouring country without its full consent.

The case against large-scale interference with river systems

Goldsmith and Hildyard argue that the case against superdams and irreversible manipulation of river systems on a global scale is so overwhelming that we proceed with funding these at our own peril. They stress three key points.

1 The developed world's approach to water development, as typified by America's Tennessee Valley Authority (TVA), is a sad mistake. TVA is often shown to the world as a model of how to make the economy of a valley flourish. In fact this is a myth. The Environmental Policy Institute's cost-benefit analysis for its first 50 years showed that the flood control and navigation objectives had yet to pay for themselves and that, furthermore, other areas of the south-eastern USA, which did not receive financial aid, did as well or even better than the TVA region.

   Studies from around the world illustrate how little of the extra food grown reaches those who need it most, and how irrigation schemes turn fertile areas into salt-encrusted deserts. Industries powered by hydro-electric power from the dams create pollution, millions of people are uprooted from their homes, social lives and cultures to make way for reservoirs, and their health is jeopardised by waterborne diseases.

2 The Third World seems intent on replicating the tragic social and environmental mistakes of the developing world by building short-lived, poorly designed superdam and reservoir projects, often funded directly or indirectly by the industrialised countries. For example, World Bank schemes designed to prevent starvation and flooding and promote development can, in fact, create social misery, ill-health, impoverishment and massive ecological destruction for communities.

3 For many Third World countries there are sustainable and appropriate alternatives based on ancient or traditional irrigation societies.

   Finally, they conclude that the real beneficiaries of large-scale dams are invariably large multinational companies, the urban elites of the Third World, and the politicians who commissioned the projects in the first place. Superdams are expensive veneers which condemn the vast majority of people to underdevelopment, offering little real hope of appropriate sustainable development.

Conclusions

Human intervention thus has a considerable and often detrimental effect on river channel processes.

1 Human impact on river channels and the drainage basin can be deliberate (e.g. flood alleviation schemes, dam construction) or inadvertent (e.g. land use change).

2 Human impact can modify water quality and water quantity.

3 Human impact on the drainage basin can alter all processes within the drainage basin hydrological cycle. This impact will vary between the components of the system.

4 Inadvertent changes are often more widespread and have long-term effects.

5 Deliberate modification occurs at the most accessible point, which is within the land phase of the cycle. Engineers and river managers seek to intervene at the most vulnerable and accessible point in the system, known as the leverage point, where maximum benefit can be obtained for minimum effort and cost. This is often the river or channel storage stage.

6 Irrigation, dam construction, urbanisation and deforestation have major impacts on the system.

How can we study the flows of water over time?

So far we have only explored the pathways of water through the drainage basin and tried to understand how we can have an impact on this system. We will now move on to consider how water input, storages and transfers combine to produce output from the basin; and to study this variation over time.

The water balance

The water balance is the relationship between basin input as precipitation and the corresponding basin output as changes in storage, evapotranspiration and runoff. This runoff or basin discharge is composed of several elements, including direct precipitation into channels, overland flow, and ground water flow. The mean discharge is usually measured at a time of year (e.g. the autumn) when there are normally minimal storage changes. It is recorded using a variety of techniques, including weirs and/or continuous recording devices. It is much more difficult to measure the evapotranspiration and storage change components of the water balance.

SYNTHESIS

'Although dams are constructed at a specific site on a river channel, the consequences of this modification can be seen not only in changes to channel processes upstream and downstream of the dam, but thoughout the entire drainage basin.'

Using an annotated diagram, with supporting channel cross-sections for the areas above and below the dam, discuss the validity of this statement. Ensure that you explain fully all the process modifications.

ENQUIRY: THE WATER BALANCE EQUATION

1 Write out a simple equation to express the water balance.

2 Why are some parts much more difficult to measure than others?

3 Study Table 1.13 of the water balances for four contrasting rivers in the mid-1960s.
   a Calculate the percentage lost anually to evapotranspiration and storage changes.
   b Briefly list the factors that might help explain these differences.
   c Consult an atlas and try to explain these variations.

Table 1.13   Water balances for the year October 1965 to September 1966

Station, location and area		Annual total (mm)
Haweswater Beck, Lake District	Rainfall	2679
(NY 515161) 34 km²	Runoff	2451
R. Wye, Rhyader, Mid-Wales	Rainfall	1819
(SN 969676) 167 km²	Runoff	1272
R. Adur, Sussex	Rainfall	892
(TQ 178197) 109 km²	Runoff	362
R. Glem, Suffolk	Rainfall	575
(TL 846672) 87 km²	Runoff	182

Source: Hilton, 1985

The river regime

Runoff in any drainage basin is subject to considerable variation depending on a complex series of interacting factors including climate, geology, soil type and relief. The actual channel runoff or stream flow pattern for a river for a 12-month period can be measured. This 'river regime' is plotted over the 12 months to create an annual hydrograph. Shorter periods can be studied and reflected as hydrographs, e.g. storm or flood hydrographs. The hydrographs are a way of summing up a river's 'performance', and they help predict stream flow changes which obviously exert crucial influences on the availability, reliability and quality of water supplies at different times of the year for towns, industry and agriculture.

A river's regime is generally determined by two aspects of climate: the monthly sequence of precipitation; and insolation or solar radiation, which controls evaporation and snow melt. Rivers of the tropics, excluding equatorial areas, generally have pronounced high- and low-flow seasons. Mid-latitude rivers have high flows, often with flooding, in winter or spring, and may even dry up in extreme summers due to increased evapotranspirational losses and low precipitation. In high latitudes and most mountainous regions stream flow reflects the pattern of snow and ice-melt (Figure 1.45).

The storm or flood hydrograph

This is a graph which attempts to plot the response of a river to a precipitation event. It is obtained by measuring discharge or channel runoff, and plots this over time.

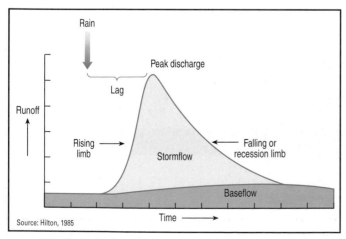

Source: Hilton, 1985

Figure 1.44   The flood hydrograph

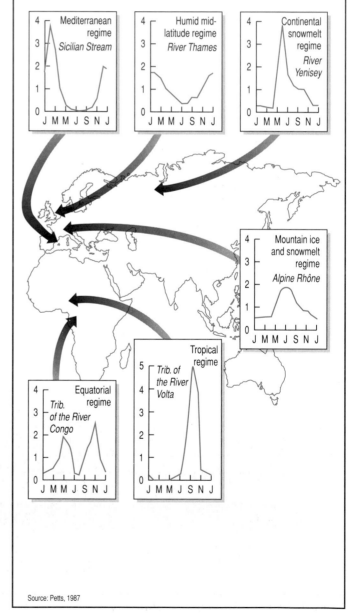

Source: Petts, 1987

Figure 1.45   Typical runoff regimes

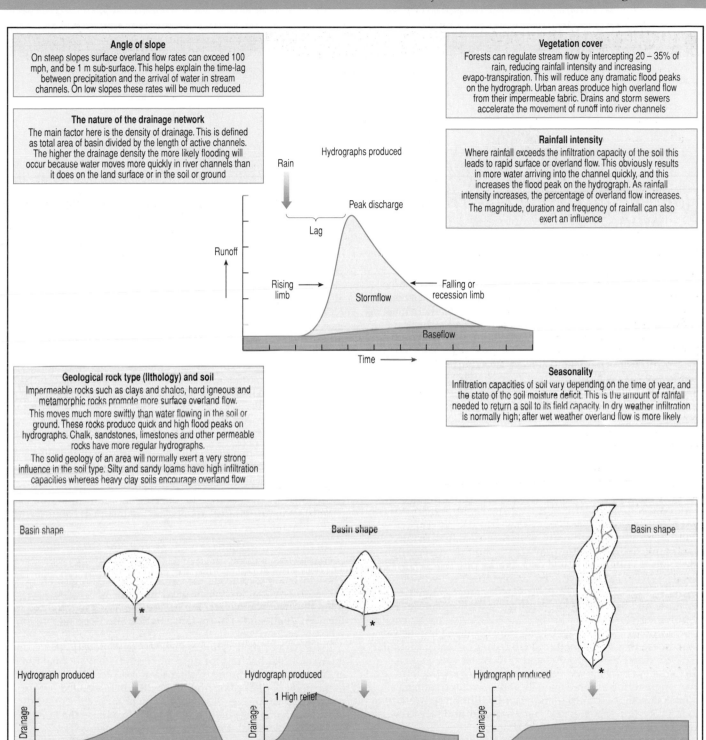

Angle of slope
On steep slopes surface overland flow rates can exceed 100 mph, and be 1 m sub-surface. This helps explain the time-lag between precipitation and the arrival of water in stream channels. On low slopes these rates will be much reduced

The nature of the drainage network
The main factor here is the density of drainage. This is defined as total area of basin divided by the length of active channels. The higher the drainage density the more likely flooding will occur because water moves more quickly in river channels than it does on the land surface or in the soil or ground

Vegetation cover
Forests can regulate stream flow by intercepting 20 – 35% of rain, reducing rainfall intensity and increasing evapo-transpiration. This will reduce any dramatic flood peaks on the hydrograph. Urban areas produce high overland flow from their impermeable fabric. Drains and storm sewers accelerate the movement of runoff into river channels

Rainfall intensity
Where rainfall exceeds the infiltration capacity of the soil this leads to rapid surface or overland flow. This obviously results in more water arriving into the channel quickly, and this increases the flood peak on the hydrograph. As rainfall intensity increases, the percentage of overland flow increases. The magnitude, duration and frequency of rainfall can also exert an influence

Hydrographs produced

Rain

Peak discharge

Lag

Runoff

Rising limb

Falling or recession limb

Stormflow

Baseflow

Time

Geological rock type (lithology) and soil
Impermeable rocks such as clays and shales, hard igneous and metamorphic rocks promote more surface overland flow.
This moves much more swiftly than water flowing in the soil or ground. These rocks produce quick and high flood peaks on hydrographs. Chalk, sandstones, limestones and other permeable rocks have more regular hydrographs.
The solid geology of an area will normally exert a very strong influence in the soil type. Silty and sandy loams have high infiltration capacities whereas heavy clay soils encourage overland flow

Seasonality
Infiltration capacities of soil vary depending on the time of year, and the state of the soil moisture deficit. This is the amount of rainfall needed to return a soil to its field capacity. In dry weather infiltration is normally high; after wet weather overland flow is more likely

Basin shape

Basin shape

Basin shape

Hydrograph produced

Hydrograph produced

1 High relief

Hydrograph produced

Drainage

Drainage

Drainage

Time

Time

Time

* Monitoring station

Hydrograph produced

2 Gentle slopes

Drainage

Time

Figure 1.46 Factors that affect the nature of the basin hydrograph

How should we manage rivers in the 1990s?

River management can be defined as 'the resolution of the conflicting demands upon a river whilst simultaneously attempting to conserve the essential features of that resource'. In the UK this means managing the quality and quantity of water. It must be fit for human consumption, and there must be sufficient to support abstraction for commercial, industrial and domestic uses at all times including minimum flow periods. Other tasks are the management of low flows, excess water and flood protection. These management objectives can create conflict and this is most apparent in areas of high and dense population and low rainfall – the urban areas of south-east England. The greatest conflicts arise during periods of maximum flow which create extensive flooding, and minimum flow which cause water shortages as seen in 1976 and 1989.

Management also involves the consideration of river landscapes. These are monitored to maintain the quality of the ecological resource and the physical environment for the various people who live and work within these areas, and those who use them for recreational and leisure pursuits.

The resolution of such conflicts can be very difficult. This can best be illustrated by considering the radically different views of the agricultural community, with their demands to lower the water table to drain and improve land, and the conservation and angling community who wish to conserve the variety of physical river characteristics by maintaining the hydraulic capacity of the channel and the frequency and magnitude of low flow, and by restricting the nitrate and phosphate levels within the rivers.

Many of the rivers of the UK are now managed but the key issue is: are they being managed effectively? In the past, under the 1963 Water Resources Act and 1973 Water Act, management by the river authorities largely took the form of river engineering at three main locations: water treatment plants (sewerage, sewage disposal and pollution control); river flood protection schemes and land drainage; and reservoir construction and water transfer schemes.

In the 1980s the consideration of the riverine environment began to emerge as a serious river management issue. In 1983 the NCC published *Nature Conservation and River Engineering*. The key theme of the publication was the need to integrate nature conservation (to prevent wildlife loss and habitat destruction) and river engineering. In the past straightened streams, culverted water courses, tree felling and the elimination of bankside vegetation, land drainage and flood alleviation have all had drastic environmental impacts. The NCC argued that this integration could be achieved without increased costs or loss of efficiency and recognised that the real problem was changing the attitudes of the river managers.

The second problem lay in pushing through legislation to save the winding rivers of the UK together with their multiple habitats and rich organic diversity. The 1973 Water Act stated that rivers should be managed with regard to preserving the natural beauty, flora and fauna of a river. The 1981 Wildlife and Countryside Act identified three principles for river management:

1 Parts of a river of outstanding nature conservation value should not be touched, except for minimal maintenance to sustain the wildlife interest of the area (SSSIs, for example).

2 Sections of a river of high nature conservation value should embrace nature conservation as the main aim in balance with other interests.

3 All river modifications should integrate the aims of the engineering work with environmental sensitivity.

The legislation recognised the value of these dynamic and enormously variable riverine environments, which depend upon the level of the water table. Additionally it highlighted the need to integrate nature conservation and flood alleviation schemes on *all* rivers.

Rivers can be seen as linear corridors or routeways of interconnected habitats for flora and fauna. Conventional river engineering would break this corridor and promote instability at the point of disruption and downstream. Integrated nature conservation and river engineering can minimise the quantity of water which flows on to the land and maximise the number of wildlife micro-habitats. This can only be achieved by ensuring close co-operation of all the interested professional bodies.

Progress toward environmentally sound river engineering

pre-1970
Hard engineering, e.g. concrete revetments; training structures; straightening, deepening and clearing of channels.

1970–80
Hiding local impact of hard engineering by improved architectural designs, planting trees, shrubs, etc.

1980–85
Reducing local impact by soft biotechnical engineering involving use of natural materials and fibres in place of steel and concrete.

1986–90
Mitigation of local impact by pre-investment studies:
1 Holistic review of the catchment drainage system.
2 Engineering environmental partnership to assess and refine the best practical environmental option at strategic and local levels.

Mitigation of adverse impact through post-investment review, e.g.
1 Restoration of low flows in rivers affected by abstraction.
2 Restoration of river habitats damaged by insensitive works.

Acceptance of environmental enhancement (beyond sensitive scheme design and mitigation of adverse impact) as legitimate activity for Water Authorities under the 1981 Wildlife and Countryside Act.

1990s?
Establishment of a sustainable dynamic equilibrium in river corridors by development of catchment management. The concept involves local authorities in:
1 Production of urban catchment management plans to marry into overall (rural and river system) Water Authority plan
2 Special (re-) designation of planned areas (floodplain, wet/dry storage areas, agricultural areas of set-aside used for induced storage).

Source: Gardiner, 1988

Integrating nature conservation and flood alleviation

Stage 1 *Co-operation in the feasibility stage*

A description of the existing situation is prepared with a justification for action and an analysis of the do-nothing option. At this stage the potential conflicts between traditional river engineering options and conservation interests must be resolved (i.e. compromise, not conflict).

Engineer
Aim   Minimise the extent and period of flooding.
Methods 1 Increase channel capacity and velocity by:
    a Excavation.
    b Removing obstacles to channel flow – islands, sandbars, lush growth.
    c Straightening.
    2 Raise banks or lower water table.
Control   Cost, including maintenance.

Conservationist
Aim   Maximise quality and quantity of habitats.
Method   Minimum interference.
Control   Cost.

Stage 2 *Option evaluation and design procedure*

The key environmental issues are defined and flood alleviation options are prepared. Engineering proposals are designed following detailed ecological and landscape impact analysis surveys. This original feasibility study can be modified to protect and enhance natural habitats, and is costed. Thus a preferred scheme emerges, and this too may be refined. Detailed environmental impact assessments (EIAs) are prepared for all sites that make up the Flood Alleviation Scheme (see 'The iterative refinement process'). At this stage local authority offices, statutory bodies, principal interest groups and the general public are consulted.

Stage 3 *Implementation*

A scheme is implemented using environmentally balanced river engineering techniques including:
1 Working from only one bank to reduce cost and ecological impact.
2 Minimum dredging.
3 Save meanders, islands, trees and reed beds.
4 Create berms, riffles, shoals, pools and ponds.
5 Do not create tight geometrical designs with fixed ratios.
6 Redesign riverside buildings and bank reinforcements, avoiding concrete and steel.
7 Manage and create new flood relief channels parallel to the main channel which would be permanently moist wetland environments.

CASE STUDY *The Colne: Environmentally Sensitive River Management*

Thames Water Authority has adopted and extended this approach in their management of the River Colne. Their philosophy is based on the idea of integrated catchment drainage. It recognises the fragility of river corridors and is concerned with managing the whole drainage area for its ecology and water quality/quantity, and not just flood protection at a few isolated sites.

The strategy involves using a multi-disciplinary team of specialist staff working on a management plan based on a clear understanding of the operative processes and the ecological resource base of the area.

The Colne is a river of contrasts. The Upper Colne has a problem of water shortage with some local flooding, whereas the Lower Colne floods almost annually. The Colne river management plan is based on an extensive hydrological, ecological and landscape survey which identified 62 flood-risk sites along the 75 km of the river. For these sites further detailed site visits allowed a number of alternative flood alleviation options to be drawn up for each site, based upon environmentally sound river engineering principles. For each site a best practical environmental option could then be identified and a hydraulic masterplan for the whole catchment could be constructed using a mathematical model.

The iterative refinement process for the Colne River plan

Level 1 *The catchment*
Data collection at regional level which highlighted key issues and sites.

Level 2 *The local scale*
Field surveys of ecological and landscape value and identification of engineering options. Identification of best practical environmental option. A design strategy could:
1 Preserve the floodplain if there was no economic disadvantage.
2 Remove bottlenecks for flood flow, i.e. straightening.
3 Divert or transfer flows to other channels or lakes.
4 Contain the flow using embankments or walls.
5 Increase channel capacity by widening.
6 As a last resort, dredging to increase channel capacity.

Level 3 *The site scale*
Modify proposals based on further detailed site visits and surveys and aerial surveys.

Lower Colne study area

The project began in April 1983. Several stages of data collection, mathematical modelling, evaluation and consultation took place throughout the next four years, leading to a preferred option for the catchment being identified in July 1987. The basic aim of the project is to produce an environmentally sound flood alleviation scheme to protect against a 1:100 year event.

General introduction. The Lower Colne Valley, a tributary of the Thames, runs from Rickmansworth in the north to the confluence of the Colne with the Thames at Staines. The geology of the area is mainly chalk with some clay in the south-east. The area is at risk from widespread flooding: a major flood in March 1947 is estimated to have a return period of 1:50 years and lesser but more frequent floods occurred in 1974, 1978 and 1979. Since the 1947 flood there have been extensive urban and infrastructure developments which have increased the flood risk potential.

The areas most at risk include Rickmansworth, the Poyle industrial estate, Stanwell Upper Mill area and parts of Staines. Stanwell suffers from poor drainage and is susceptible to regular flooding at a nuisance level.

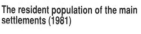

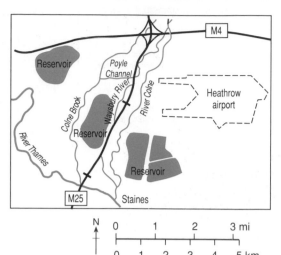

The resident population of the main settlements (1981)

Rickmansworth	30,000
Denham	7,000
Iver (inc. Colnbrook)	11,100
Harefield	6,650
Uxbridge	11,000
Cowley	9,000
West Drayton	6,500
Harmondsworth	9,000
Stanwell	13,000
Staines	20,000
Horton	850
Wraysbury	3,300

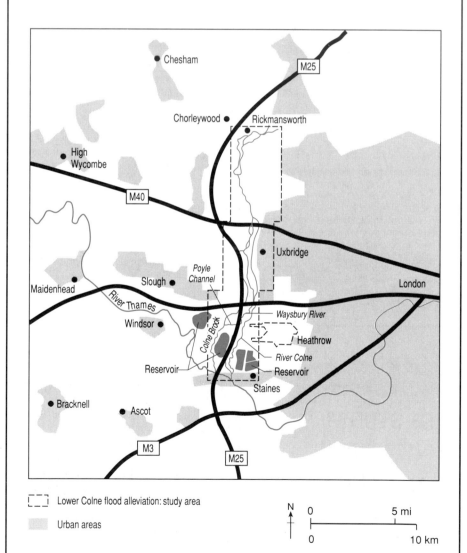

Figure 1.47 Lower Colne Valley

Land use of the Colne Valley

The area covers nine local authorities, and is largely covered by green belt planning policy. Although there are pockets of derelict land and areas of unfortunate development, the Colne Valley is both an environmentally sensitive and important area, with the rivers as the prime focus. The area supports a variety of land uses including housing, industry, mineral extraction, agriculture, water storage, recreation and urban fringe activities. Despite its green belt status various developments are mooted for the area – Terminal 5 Heathrow, a new sewage works, the widening of the M25, development pressures from out-of-town retailing, and sand and gravel workings. The area is of archaeological and historical interest and it has a wide range of habitats for plants, invertebrates, fish and birds. Eleven environmental disciplines were considered in assessing the impact of the scheme: agriculture, amenity, angling, aquatic biology, archaeology, fisheries, landscape, planning, recreation, water quality and wildlife.

Table 1.14 Impact of the Colne River Scheme on local land use

Land use	Impact of the scheme
Agriculture	Land taken at only one location
Angling	Temporary disruption in construction phase. Long-term improved access
Amenity and recreation	No disturbance to public amenities. Five gardens lost to local residents. Construction noise
Biology and fisheries	No long-term damage. Some short-term impact linked to regrading of channels in fish-spawning sites
Archaeology	No listed structures affected
Landscape	Very few long-term impacts with good design and landscaping
Wildlife	No SSSIs or non-recreatable habitats will be affected. Opportunities exist to create new habitats, such as marginal wetlands
Navigation	No current or proposed future routes affected
Planning	No planning policy objectives are compromised, and the scheme will have little adverse impact on the character and resources of the valley

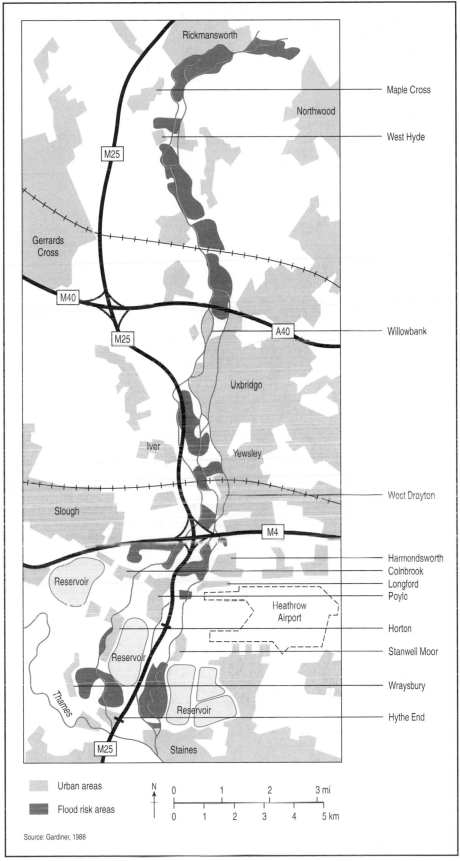

Figure 1.48 Map of flood risk areas

Existing river system

The river system is shown in Figure 1.48 and comprises a complex network of some 75 km of river channel, flanked by and interlinked in places with flooded gravel pits and the Grand Union Canal.

Over most of the length of the study area there are two or three rivers running in parallel, connected by numerous overflows and by major and minor channels including the Grand Union Canal. Historical human intervention in this area, not only through the construction of numerous mill complexes with bypass and flow control structures, but also through the excavation of diversion channels, has strongly influenced the valley by introducing an artificial element. The gravel pits mentioned above are another very important hydraulic element, contributing both storage and flow capacity to the system.

River management problems

Cost-effective flood control options must take many factors into account.

1 There are many areas of environmental concern in the valley, affecting both the ecology and the landscape.

2 There is great potential for environmental improvement both to the rivers and lakes and also to areas of derelict land.

3 The short- and long-term effects on agriculture, amenity (recreation and leisure), angling and fisheries, water quality, and the river regime during low or summer flow.

4 Certain areas are privately owned or accessible only through private land. This can create both operational and maintenance difficulties. This is especially true of the numerous existing mills which constitute substantial bottlenecks to the flow due to regular blocking. It is hoped to improve or replace many of these mills with structures that are less susceptible to blocking and easier to maintain – weirs and flumes, or a standard sluice.

5 There has been a significant reduction in the available storage capacities of gravel pits due to recent backfilling.

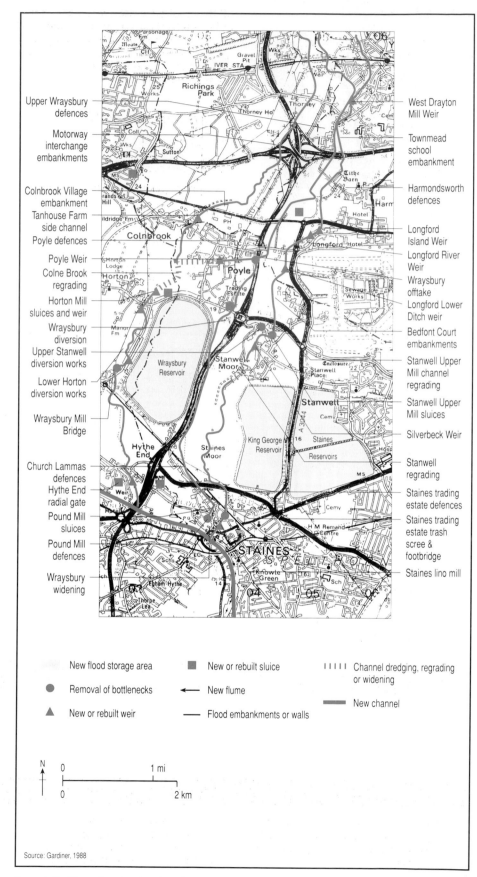

Source: Gardiner, 1988

Figure 1.49   The preferred engineering scheme

The scheme

The resulting flood alleviation scheme had the following broad aims:

1 To preserve existing flood plain storage where there were no economic disbenefits, allowing unbuilt areas (agricultural land, parkland, amenity areas) to flood to shallow depths – Staines Moor, for example.

2 To remove or alleviate significant bottlenecks associated with the old mill complexes which hold water in ponds or completely block the flow with vegetation and debris during floods. Bottlenecks such as Silverbeck Mill and Stanwell Upper Mill on the Colne would be fitted with improved slices or weirs.

3 To use strategic transfers of flow between channels or rivers to make maximum use of existing storage and channel conveyance capacity. One example is the Wraysbury River Works, including a diversion works around the south-east side of the Poyle industrial estate where the Wraysbury River has a constricted cross-section.

4 To use, as a last resort, river works such as flood embankments, flood walls and channel re-profiling. Environmentally sensitive materials such as compacted earth embankments would be preferred, and wherever possible marginal wetlands for wildlife would be created – not only preserving, but extending ecological diversity. The emphasis would be on small-scale schemes designed to be environmentally sympathetic, and dredging would be limited.

5 To provide individual protection to isolated properties.

All the required works were small-scale and less reliant on maintenance and manual operation; at each site, several options were usually assessed to achieve a given goal in order to minimise environmental impact.

Key environmental issues

The scheme should aim to:

1 Retain the existing riverine character of the valley by avoiding damage to non-recreatable habitats; limiting tree loss; blending new structures with their surroundings; ensuring there is no further reduction in current low-flow conditions; and preventing long-term disruption to riverside access.

2 Retain the wet gravel pits for their fishing, recreation and wildlife value.

3 Avoid SSSIs or other recognised sites of ecological or landscape significance.

4 Avoid disruption to local residents and businesses, including agriculture.

5 Seek out opportunities for environmental enhancement.

Economies of the scheme

The costs of the 1:100 year flood alleviation scheme total £7.859 million (excluding operation and maintenance). Total benefits are estimated at £17.799 million. These were measured using the MAFF 'flood damage assessment'. Benefit/cost ratio = 2.26 for 1:100 year flood.

Table 1.15 Flood damage assessment

Type of benefit	Examples
Tangible direct damage due to contact with floodwater measured in financial terms	Damage to residential, agricultural, retail, office, public sector and commercial properties
Tangible indirect damage due to social and economic disruption measured in financial terms	Traffic disruption, productivity losses, disruption of services (post, etc.), transport, sewage, costs of emergency services and extra heating to dry buildings and contents
Intangible damages to which it is not feasible or desirable to assign monetary values	Community anxiety, loss of life

ENQUIRY: ENVIRONMENTALLY SENSITIVE RIVER MANAGEMENT

1 Attempt to explain in as much detail as possible why there are increased flood risks in the areas. Include an annotated storm hydrograph as part of your answer.

2 How does the total scheme differ from a conventional flood alleviation project? Focus on the differences in both the general aims and the specifics at the channel modification scale.

We will look at the area south of the M25 to Staines Moor, and study a specific part of the scheme in detail (see Figure 1.49).

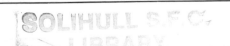

DECISION-MAKING EXERCISE

You are a team leader working for Thames Water on the Lower Colne flood alleviation scheme. Your team is responsible for the generation of four options for dealing with the flood risk at Stanwell, one of 62 sites that will form part of the flood alleviation scheme.

Your specific task is to recommend a preferred option and justify your decision. Your evaluation should include an analysis of the likely effectiveness of the scheme, a brief cost-benefit analysis and a statement of the likely environmental impact of your

proposal. You should include an annotated map as part of your submission.

Utilise the resources generated by recent site visits by your team, including maps (Figure 1.50) and written analysis of the likely impact (Table 1.16).

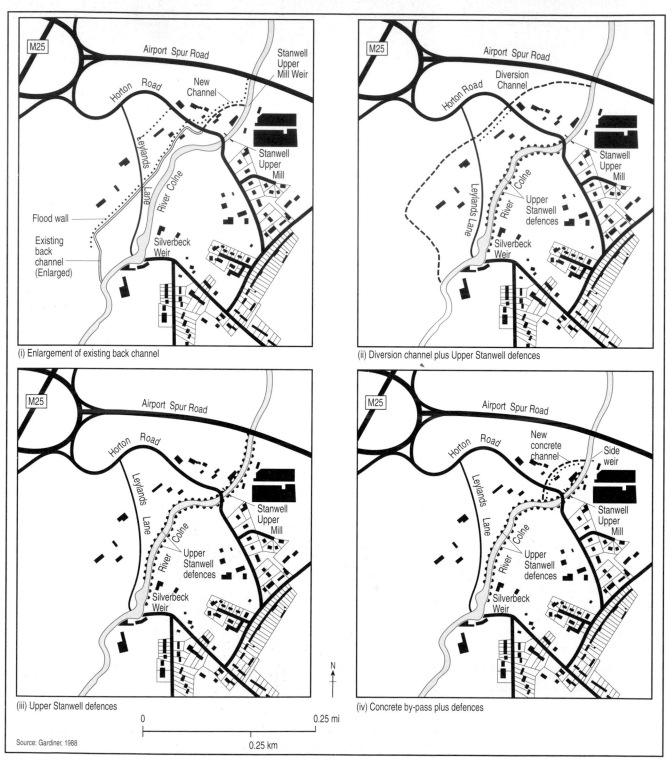

(i) Enlargement of existing back channel

(ii) Diversion channel plus Upper Stanwell defences

(iii) Upper Stanwell defences

(iv) Concrete by-pass plus defences

Source: Gardiner, 1988

Figure 1.50 Options for Stanwell Moor and Silverbeck areas

Figure 1.51 Silverbeck Weir

Figure 1.52 The river south of the airport spur road

Figure 1.53 The river below Silverbeck Weir

Table 1.16 Evaluation of options: Stanwell and Silverbeck

Engineering options	Key environmental impacts	Prime reason(s) for rejection
1 A new side weir on the right bank of the Colne upstream of Stanwell Upper Mill (Stanwell Upper Mill Weir) discharging into a new flood channel joining the existing back channel just upstream of the static caravan park	Amenity: disruption to static caravan park	Rejected on engineering grounds: only half of the built-up area would have been protected from flooding
2 A 25 m side weir on the right bank of the Colne discharging into a diversion channel. As this channel is narrow, defences (Upper Stanwell Defences) are required on both sides of the Colne downstream of Stanwell Upper Mill, and on the east side of the flood diversion channel between Horton Road and Leylands Lane	Amenity: disruption to 3 private houses which at present have direct access to the water's edge. Landscape: almost certain loss of mature trees on both banks of the Colne. Recreation: disruption and potential permanent relocation of public footpath following right bank of river upstream of Silverbeck Weir	Rejected on environmental grounds: because of the difficulty of providing flood defences in confined spaces along banks of Colne
3 No diversion channel, but flood defences 2.3 m high (Upper Stanwell Defences) on both sides of the Colne, upstream and downstream of Stanwell Upper Mill	Amenity, landscape and recreation: impacts as for 2 but impact very much more severe with greatly increased height of defences	Rejected on environmental and engineering grounds with height of defences making the existing river banks unsafe
4 A concrete-lined channel from a side weir on the right bank of the Colne constructed to by-pass Stanwell Upper Mill and rejoin the Colne downstream of the Mill. Plus flood defences as for 2	Amenity, landscape and recreation: impacts as for 2. Plus channel would have cut through a private garden	Rejected on environmental grounds

Source: Gardiner, 1988

Protection of Stanwell Moor and Silverbeck areas – the preferred option

The Stanwell and Silverbeck areas flood fairly regularly because, like many other parts of the Colne Valley, the rivers are perched above the flood plain and bottlenecks (Stanwell Upper Mill and Silverbeck Mill) cause flood flows to overtop the river banks. Therefore, the final option for this area, selected for inclusion in the preferred scheme (Figure 1.49), consists of a wide flood diversion channel (Upper Stanwell Diversion) leading from upstream of Stanwell Upper Mill, skirting the western side of the built-up area, rejoining the Colne downstream of Silverbeck Weir. This proposal does not involve any embankments along the Colne, and therefore does not carry the environmental problems of some of the earlier options.

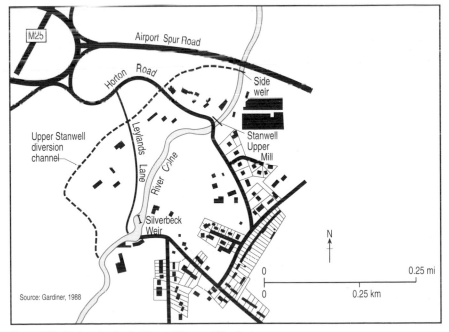

Source: Gardiner, 1988

Figure 1.54 Preferred option for Stanwell Moor and Silverbeck areas

Conclusion: How are Coastal Systems and Drainage Basins Interlinked?

CASE STUDY *Sinking and Shrinking in the Mississippi Delta*

The Mississippi delta is one of the world's oldest and largest deltaic environments. Until 1900 the delta was growing, since then it has been sinking and shrinking. Now 100 km² of wetlands are lost every year in the delta region, as the shoreline retreats by up to 25 m per year. This is of national importance as 40% of all USA wetlands occur in Louisiana.

The growth of the delta depends upon a delicate balance between six variables:

1 The amount and type of sediment brought into the region by the river (in the Mississippi much of the material is mud, composed of clay minerals which readily compact).

2 The growth of plant material.

3 The relative land–sea levels (subsidence of sediments combined with global sea level changes make the sea rise between 1.2 and 2.4 mm per year).

4 The geology of the area.

5 Wave and tidal forces where the river meets the sea.

6 Changes to the fluvial characteristics of the river due to human intervention (this includes building embankments or levees to control spring floods and the straightening and deepening of channels for easier navigation).

There is some evidence to suggest that the current shrinkage of the delta is part of a long-term natural cycle of delta growth and decay related to a predicted shift in the path of the Mississippi as it passes New Orleans. Some geomorphologists, however, think the increase in the scale of human intervention is responsible for the shrinkage. They argue that native Americans accepted the natural changes in the river, but that European settlers have tried to control the Mississippi and it is this intervention that is responsible for the shrinkage (see Table 1.17).

In the 1980s the Louisiana Wetlands Authority was created to resolve the conflicts associated with the shrinkage of the delta. A budget of 20 million US dollars was allocated for coastal restoration. Regulations were enacted to reduce the digging of new canals. Three controlled diversions of river flow to marsh areas subject to salt-water incursion were implemented. Highest priority was to preserve shorelines that abut on wetlands, such as the area around the Texas border. The use of sea walls for these areas was totally rejected.

The Conservationists' Coalition to Restore Coastal Louisiana has been very critical of the Wetland Authority and their coastal management strategy. They demand more positive and active methods. To improve funding, they suggest setting up a trust with finances coming from all users of the coastal resource, both corporate and individual. This would include oil and gas companies, chemical companies, fishermen and recreationists. Pressing for the stricter regulation of the digging of canals, they call for a total ban on new canals and back-filling of abandoned canals. Finally, they advocate strict regulation of the activities of the petroleum industry.

Table 1.17 Human impact on the Mississippi River

Type of human intervention	Purpose of intervention	Date(s) of intervention	Impact of intervention
Levees	To prevent flooding. Flood control is essential to maintain the economy of this poor state	Began in 1699. By 1738, 68 km around New Orleans. By 1990, 3200 km	Speeds up the flow of the river so that most of the massive sediment load is carried beyond the 'delta region' offshore out on to the conti ental shelf
Removal of bankside vegetation	To aid steamboat navigation	19th century	Removal of plants and shrubs speeds up the flow of the river and reduces blockages which may cause flooding
Dredging	To aid navigation	Began in 1879 with the setting up of the Mississippi River Commission	Speeds up river flow
Digging of canals	Access routes for local fishermen and the oil and gas industry. Oil and gas income is vital to the state's economy	None before 1900. Now 16,000 km occupying 2.4% of the delta	Wetland loss. They also act as easy routes for salt-water penetration of wetlands
Channel straightening and dyke construction	To aid navigation and prevent flooding	1879 onwards. Today 1750 km of artificial channel exist	Speeds up river flow
Improved land-use management in the drainage basin	Soil conservation methods to prevent soil erosion	Since 1950	Reduces sediment load of the river

ENQUIRY: EROSION PROBLEMS OF DELTA REGIONS

1 Fully explain how changes in the character of the Mississippi River have created coastal conflicts.

2 Why do you think the Louisiana Wetland Authority has rejected the use of sea walls to preserve its coastline in the delta region?

3 Study the extract from the *New Scientist* (see below) and the annotated map of the problems of the Nile Delta (Figure 1.56). Summarise the causes of the erosion problems of the Ganges, Mississippi and Nile Delta.

4 What might the impact of rising sea levels be on these areas? Read the short article 'The rising seas' to help you.

THE DELICATE BALANCE THAT BUILDS A DELTA

Figure 1.55
Big Muddy: the Mississippi has built a bird's foot delta

DELTAS result from erosion. Rain washes soil and rock fragments into a stream, which carries it to a river, which washes it toward the sea. Deposits at the river mouth are known as the delta. The name comes from the Greek letter Δ.

How far the debris travels depends on how heavy it is, and how fast the water flows. The lighter the grains of sand, silt and mud, and the stronger the current, the farther the river can carry it. Particles settle as the water slows. Deltas form as the river water spreads out and slows down where it flows into the sea.

Smaller particles, such as sand and silt, settle as the river slows down while it travels over plains. These sediments build plains lying close to sea level, such as those in Bangladesh and Louisiana.

Sediment settles in a river's channel and eventually blocks it. This forces the river to seek a new path. When the river overflows its banks, silt and mud spread over the surrounding flood plains. The flooding brings fertile silt to the plains, building up rich farming land, for example, in the Nile delta in Egypt.

Sediments are not deposited evenly. For example, the Mississippi tends to deposit extra material where it floods most frequently. This builds up 'natural levees' along the edges of the river, higher and drier than the surrounding land. Confined between these natural embankments, the river level rises as silt settles, and can become higher than the surrounding land. This is common in the Mississippi delta.

The present Mississippi delta, with its classic 'bird's foot' shape at the south-eastern tip of Louisiana, is river-dominated. The river has carried more sediments than tides and current can carry away, so the delta has grown out to sea.

Where waves are powerful, such as at the mouths of the Nile and Senegal Rivers, the coast is smoothly curved.

'Nearly all coastal deltaic plains have suffered extensive land loss within the past several centuries,' according to Coleman. Although human activities are part of the problem, all deltas suffer from natural subsidence, as their massive sediment deposits compress underlying layers.

The degree of compaction depends partly on the type of sediment; the Niger and the Danube, like the Mississippi, carry plenty of fine-grained muds and clays, which contain a lot of water when they settle out. Their deltas suffer higher subsidence than those built of sand.

The human component of the problem differs among deltas; dams capture silt before it can reach the deltas of the Nile and the Ganges, while the dredged channels of the Mississippi route its sediment load out into deep water in the Gulf of Mexico.

Source: *New Scientist*, 14 April 1990

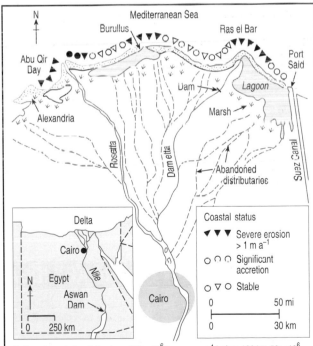

Sediment supply has fallen from 120×10^6 tonnes year^{-1} before 1964 to 50×10^6 tonnes year^{-1}, leading to progressive shoreline changes including erosion, lagoon entrance instability and even local accretion (from dispersing erosion products). A number of shore protection measures have been implemented, but several have been rapidly outflanked by erosion. Neilsen (1973) reports erosion rates approaching 30 m year^{-1} measured over 50 years

Source: Carter, 1988

Figure 1.56   Erosion problems around the Nile Delta

The effects of dams on coastal sediment supply

The construction of a dam across a river reduces the movement of both bed- and suspended-load down channel of the dam. The completion of the Aswan High Dam in 1964 has reduced the main eastern distributary, the Damietta, to the extent that it is now almost dry. The western distributary, the Rosetta, also supports a much reduced flow.

THE RISING SEAS

One aspect of the impending global warming from the greenhouse effect has already moved from the realm of computer models to the realm of engineering conferences. The U.S. Army Corps of Engineers and others are working on plans to protect coastal areas from a sea level rise. If average temperatures rise 1.5°–4.5°C by 2030, the global sea level is expected to rise 20–140 centimeters over the following several decades. This rise would be caused by the expansion of sea water as it is warmed, and by the melting of glaciers and ice caps.

Such a rise in sea level would have noticeable effects on shorelines around the world. In the past 100 years, the sea level has risen only 10–15 centimeters.

The major effects of a rising sea level include: the narrowing or destruction of recreational sandy beaches; loss of mangrove and wetland areas; and destruction or costly fortification of shoreline property. Higher water levels increase storm damage and salinity in ground water as saltwater intrudes on the freshwater table.

Several studies discuss how specific areas would be affected by a sea level rise.

■ Bangladesh would lose 12–28 per cent of its area, which houses 9–27 per cent of its population. Floods could penetrate further inland, leaving the nation vulnerable to the type of storm that killed 300,000 people in the early 1970s.

■ Maldives, a nation of 1,190 small islands that rises barely 2 meters above sea level in the Indian Ocean, would be entirely submerged by a 2-meter sea level rise and severely damaged by storm surges with a 1-meter rise .

■ In Asia, brackish-water fishponds constructed along coastal areas would be submerged, and rice paddies farther inland might be converted to fish ponds.

■ In Charleston, South Carolina, sea walls would probably have to be constructed around the historic downtown area, and residential areas on nearby marshy islands might have to be abandoned.

■ The world-famous beaches of Copacabana and Ipanema in Brazil would disappear unless they are constantly replenished at public expense.

■ Along the coast of Brazil and elsewhere, mangrove areas would disappear as the sea level lapped against developed land further inland.

In 1987, research moved from predicting the effects of sea level rise to evaluating engineering and management responses. The Dutch are planning to strengthen their dikes. The U.S. Army Corps of Engineers is considering how to integrate rising sea levels into its plans for waterway development, and the U.S. National Academy of Sciences published a report on engineering responses to changes in sea level. The state of Maine has proposed regulations putting property owners on notice that if their lands are flooded, they will be expected to move inland.

Source: WRI/UNEP, 1988–89

Review and cue

This chapter has attempted to answer the following key questions on coastal systems and drainage basins:

1 What are landform systems?

2 What natural processes are active within these systems?

3 What human processes and influences occur within these systems?

4 How do physical and human processes interact?

5 What landscapes and landforms result from these processes?

6 How and why do humans affect landform systems and with what consequences?

7 How can we better manage landform systems (at all scales) in the future?

ACTIVITY: REVIEW OF THE KEY IDEAS

For each of the above questions write a concise but general explanation. Look though your case study material and suggest which studies are most appropriate to illustrate each of your generalisations.

ACTIVITY: GROUP DEBATE

Environmental issues now enjoy a high profile in the media, but just how important do you think landform management issues are? To focus your thinking consider the following motion: 'The UK should have a central government agency responsible for all aspects of coastal and drainage basin planning and management'.

After your debate, produce a brief written summary assessing the relative merits of this approach and evaluating the factors that might influence its chances of success. Consider the alternatives and assess the priorities.

2
Ecosystems and Human Activity

How Ecosystems Work

People are gradually becoming more aware of the environment that they live in and the problems that can be caused by misusing natural resources. 'Green issues', once the domain of minority political parties, are now becoming central to the policies of the major political parties. You have only to listen to the news or read a daily newspaper to become familiar with ideas and terms that were until recently used only in universities or by environmentalists!

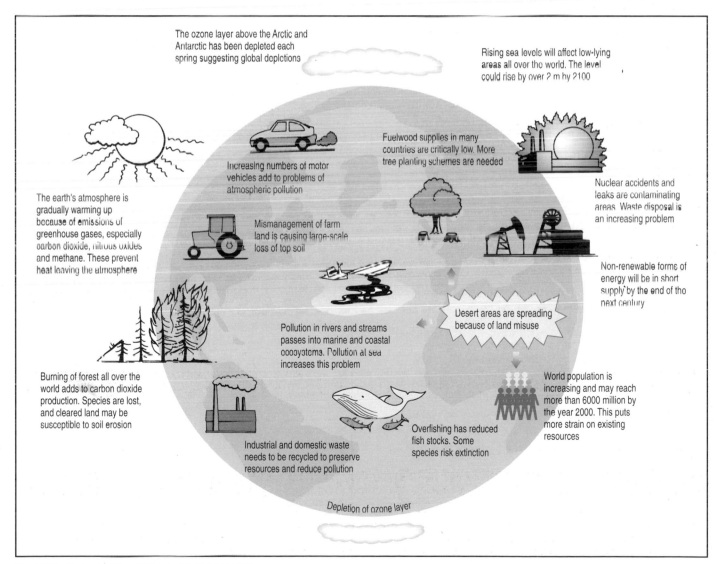

The ozone layer above the Arctic and Antarctic has been depleted each spring suggesting global depletions

Rising sea levels will affect low-lying areas all over the world. The level could rise by over 2 m by 2100

Fuelwood supplies in many countries are critically low. More tree planting schemes are needed

Increasing numbers of motor vehicles add to problems of atmospheric pollution

Nuclear accidents and leaks are contaminating areas. Waste disposal is an increasing problem

The earth's atmosphere is gradually warming up because of emissions of greenhouse gases, especially carbon dioxide, nitrous oxides and methane. These prevent heat leaving the atmosphere

Mismanagement of farm land is causing large-scale loss of top soil

Non-renewable forms of energy will be in short supply by the end of the next century

Desert areas are spreading because of land misuse

Pollution in rivers and streams passes into marine and coastal ecosystems. Pollution at sea increases this problem

Burning of forest all over the world adds to carbon dioxide production. Species are lost, and cleared land may be susceptible to soil erosion

World population is increasing and may reach more than 6000 million by the year 2000. This puts more strain on existing resources

Overfishing has reduced fish stocks. Some species risk extinction

Industrial and domestic waste needs to be recycled to preserve resources and reduce pollution

Depletion of ozone layer

Figure 2.1 Environmental problems causing global concern

ENQUIRY: ENVIRONMENTAL ISSUES

Look carefully at Figure 2.1.

1 You should be able to match each of the news headlines with one of the environmental problems illustrated below in Figure 2.1.
   'How long before we reach 6000 million?'
   'Chemical company faces fine'
   'Brazil razes rainforest'
   'Greenhouse hots up in a hurry'
   'Soviet reactor in big bang'
   'Ban on North sea trawlers'
   'Where *is* your local bottle bank?'
   'Pollution – seal death suspect'
   'Is your aerosol ozone-friendly?'
   'What future for wind energy?'
   'Kenya tries new tree-planting scheme'
   'Chancellor announces lead-free petrol to be cheaper'
   'Docklands – walk to work in wellies'

2 Concern about the state of the environment has gained popular support only since the 1960s. Why do you think that people are now more concerned about the environment? Consider these factors as you answer this question: population increase; changes in the type and scale of industry; the role of the media; pressure groups such as Greenpeace and Friends of the Earth; political response to public pressure; human capacity to change the natural environment.

3 Awareness of environmental problems varies greatly and depends on many factors such as television viewing habits or whether people read a daily newspaper. To assess the environmental awareness of people that you know, design a questionnaire to test one of the following hypotheses:
   a Younger age groups are more aware of environmental problems.

   b People's occupations affect their level of awareness.

   When you have collected all of your information, choose a suitable method to present your data, either graphically or statistically. As well as summarising your conclusions it is important to consider your experimental technique. Are there any improvements that you could now make?

4 As a group, carry out a 'media watch' on television, radio, newspapers and magazines over a period of time. Log the amount of time/space (in column inches) given to particular environmental issues. What factors appear to affect the amount of coverage?

Where do ecosystems fit in?

So far we have considered a variety of global problems, but for a better understanding of their causes – and, indeed, solutions – we need to look more closely at *ecosystems*. What are they? How do they function? How do people change them?

The word ecosystem is an abbreviation of the term 'ecological system'. Ecology is the study of the relationships between organisms and their environment. The word stems from the Greek root *oikos* meaning 'home'. Thus an ecosystem is a set of plants and animals, together with all the parts of their non-living environment. When we study an ecosystem, however, we study it as a *system*. A system is a set of organised rather than haphazardly arranged parts. You should be able to think of some familiar systems, for example a hi-fi sound system, a telephone system, or even your own digestive system! Each of these is made up of interdependent, interacting parts or components. In the same way, the component parts of an ecosystem interact in an organised fashion. Human beings just happen to be one of the interacting parts!

Figure 2.3 indicates the main components of *terrestrial* ecosystems (those on land). It is obviously a very simplified model of reality but it allows us to look at the way the components are interlinked. The arrows on the diagram indicate these links. Some of the components shown are *abiotic* or non-living, others are *biotic*, the name given to those that have lived or are living. Perhaps you can suggest why, in this case, humans have been shown as a separate component.

The size of ecosystems and their boundaries

How big are ecosystems? This is a difficult question to answer, but it is easier if we think of an ecosystem as a distinct unit. The size can vary from a small pool or rotting log to a large forest or even an ocean. We may even talk about the global ecosystem, for example when we are considering the increase in greenhouse gases and their effects on the planet as a whole. In

Figure 2.2   An ecosystem made by humans (Union Canal, Edinburgh)

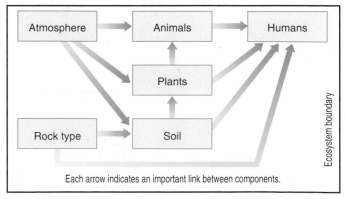

Each arrow indicates an important link between components.

Figure 2.3   The main components of terrestrial ecosystems

SYNTHESIS: UNDERSTANDING ECOSYSTEMS

1 Make your own full-page copy of Figure 2.3. Decide which of the component parts are abiotic and which biotic. Shade them to distinguish the two types. You will need to think carefully about soil and come up with a suitable solution.

2 Consider each of the links in turn (shown by the arrows). Label each of them to explain the link. For example, animals will be affected by the atmosphere because of the limits to particular species set by the temperature, and the amount and timing of precipitation. So you could write:

$$\text{Atmosphere} \xrightarrow[\text{Rainfall}]{\text{Temperature}} \text{Animals}$$

Between bedrock and soil you could write:

$$\text{Bedrock} \xrightarrow[\text{Acid/Alkali}]{\text{Nutrients}} \text{Soil}$$

This indicates the effect that bedrock has on the amount and type of nutrients in the soil and whether it is acid or alkali.

3 Finally, you may have noticed that some links appear to be missing, for the diagram shows arrows going in one direction only. People, for example, have a great effect both on plants and animals and on the atmosphere, as we saw in the introduction to this section. See if you can add further arrows, with labels, in order to make your diagram more accurate. You may find it easier to discuss this with the rest of your class.

some cases it is easy to see where the boundaries of an ecosystem are – the edge of a lake or forest, for example; but in others it may be more difficult. The boundary between an ecosystem in an estuary and one in the sea will not be clearly visible; indeed, it may move according to the state of the tide.

So far, we have assumed that the boundaries of ecosystems are fixed barriers, across which nothing passes – as indicated in the model in Figure 2.3. This is obviously not the case, however, as ecosystems are *open* systems. They have boundaries across which matter can pass. This can be seen in Figure 2.4, which shows in the form of an annotated diagram, a wide range of inputs and outputs, most of which are essential to the functioning of a typical pond ecosystem. The direct influence of human activity in this example has been shown in

two ways, but you may be able to think of others. It is also easy to see how human activity could indirectly alter a great many of the flows into and out of the system. Fertilising nearby fields, changing surface water flow or increasing industrial air pollution in the proximity of the pond could all change the components of the pond ecosystem or the way that it functions.

Notice that in this pond ecosystem the soil component has been replaced by sediments at the bottom of the pond. The plants are rooted in this only at the edge of the water where the light can penetrate down to the sediment. The depth of light penetration depends on the amount of dissolved and suspended matter in the water. In the deepest parts of the pond floating plants are the only ones that can survive. They take up all the nutrients they need directly from the water.

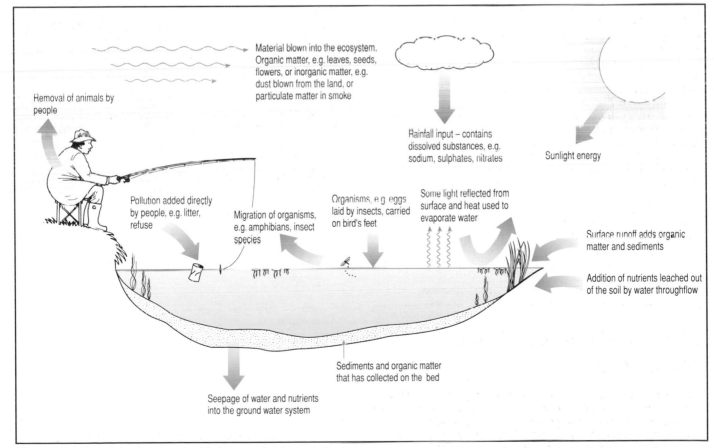

Figure 2.4 Some major flows into and out of a pond ecosystem

FIELD ENQUIRY: INTRODUCING AN ECOSYSTEM

Choose a small-scale ecosystem close to your school or close to where you live. It could be a small woodland nature reserve, a stream or a river. Even a canal or a single big oak tree would be suitable. Using the annotated diagram in Figure 2.4 as a guide, draw your own diagram to show the inputs and outputs for your ecosystem. It will be a great help if you can

actually visit your site to make measurements and observations. Look for signs of human interference and identify the types of plants and animals present. Some of the information you may need will not be obvious immediately. Work out where the prevailing wind is coming from and where the nearest industrial area is, so that you can tell if there is likely to be any

specific type of atmospheric pollution. Try to find out who uses the area and for what purpose; this may affect the way the ecosystem functions. Remember that you should aim to produce a simple diagram to show the main inputs and outputs of your ecosystem: do not make it too complicated.

Components and links in ecosystems

An ecosystem is made up of interlinking parts. In every ecosystem it is possible to identify some similar patterns. This is because of the important role that plants play. They are known as *producers* for they are the only organisms apart from a few types of bacteria that can use sunlight energy directly in order to produce their own food. They do this by the process of *photosynthesis*. This is a chemical process that takes place in the chlorophyll or green pigment found in plant leaves. The process can be shown as a written or chemical equation:

$$\text{Carbon dioxide} + \text{Water} \xrightarrow[\text{Light and Chlorophyll}]{\text{in the presence of}} \text{Glucose} + \text{Water}$$
$$6CO_2 + 6H_2O \longrightarrow C_6H_{12}O_6 + 6CO_2$$

The glucose that is produced by the plant is converted into other useful substances with the help of nutrients that the plant has absorbed from the soil or, in the case of an aquatic plant, directly from the water. These substances include proteins and more complicated types of carbohydrate such as cellulose. Photosynthesis, therefore, allows the plant to grow and increase its *biomass* (the weight of its living tissues). The plant is

then available for animals to eat, for they cannot make their own food. Animals are known as *consumers* or *heterotrophs* (hetero = other; troph = feeding). We can further divide animals into those that feed only on vegetation, the *herbivores*, and those that only eat other animals, the *carnivores*. Animals that feed off both animal matter and vegetation are called *omnivores*.

It is possible, therefore, to follow the path taken by the energy originally trapped from the sun. It passes along what is known as a *food web* or *food chain* like that of the heathland ecosystem shown in Figure 2.5. Each stage in the food chain is

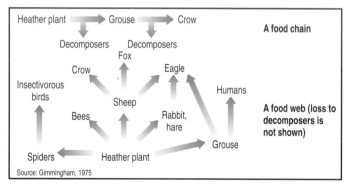

Figure 2.5   Feeding relationships in a heathland ecosystem

ANALYSIS: STRUCTURE AND FUNCTIONING OF ECOSYSTEMS

1 Which animals in the heathland ecosystem (Figure 2.5) are herbivores and which are carnivores?

2 Which trophic level is each of the following in: crow, spider, fox, bee, eagle, sheep?

3 Using the following groups of plants and animals devise your own examples of food chains:
   a *River ecosystem*: trout, light, phytoplankton (microscopic floating plants), decomposer organisms, people, midge larvae, nutrients.
   b *Woodland ecosystem*: hawk, oak tree, nutrients, ladybird, light, decomposer organisms, bluetit, aphids (e.g. greenfly).

4 a Use the information in Table 2.1 to draw your own food web for a rocky shore. Use a colour code to distinguish between autotrophs, herbivores, carnivores and omnivores.
   b Only those species present when the fieldwork took place (when the tide was out!) are included in your food web. What details may then be missing?

5 Suggest what knock-on effects the following might have on the food web you have just drawn.
   a To satisfy a sudden increase in demand for winkles, the local fishmonger starts to collect the

edible periwinkles from the fieldwork area.
   b In spring, suitable environmental conditions allow the numbers of phytoplankton and zooplankton to increase rapidly.

Table 2.1   Newbiggin-by-the-Sea, Northumberland. Rocky shore species

Species	Food source
Phytoplankton (plant plankton)	Autotrophic
Zooplankton (animal plankton)	Phytoplankton
Seaweeds	
Gutweed	
Red algae species	Autotrophic
Sea Lettuce	
Spiral Wrack	
Animals	
Barnacles	All types of plankton
Beadlet anemone	Zooplankton
Dogwhelks	Barnacles, edible and rough periwinkles and mussels
Limpets	Seaweeds and plankton
Mussels (various species)	All plankton
Shore crab	Detritus (small pieces of dead plants and animals broken up by wave action)
Periwinkles, edible and rough	Seaweeds

called a *trophic level*: the heather plants are in the first, the grouse in the second and so on. At each stage in the chain material is lost to *decomposer organisms*. This may take the form of plant and animal remains, or alternatively waste products such as urine and faeces. The decomposers, mainly bacteria and fungi, break this matter down into its constituent parts, making it available for reuse by plants.

Food chains and population pyramids

Food chains tend to be limited to four or five steps, or trophic levels. The reason for this is that energy is not passed from one trophic level to the next very efficiently. At each stage energy is 'lost' for a number of reasons.

Only a small part of the light energy that the plants receive is actually trapped by photosynthesis. The amount varies according to the plant species and the conditions they are growing in, but is usually between 0.01 and 5%. The remaining light remains un-fixed for many reasons: it is of the wrong wavelength; reflection from or passage through the leaf; losses take place during the chemical reactions of photosynthesis.

Further losses occur higher up the food chain. The herbivores may not eat all of the plant material available; some of it may be wasted during the feeding processes; some may be unpalatable. The herbivores also expend energy in finding the food and carrying out their other bodily functions. At each stage of the food chain, therefore, there is less energy available for next trophic level.

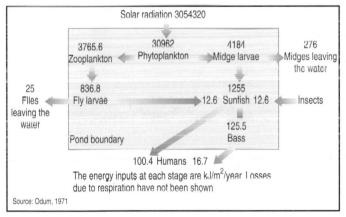

Figure 2.6   The main food chains in a fishpond in Georgia, USA, managed for recreational fishing

This pattern is evident when we examine an ecosystem in more detail. Figure 2.6 considers the energy flow through a pond that is managed to make it suitable for sport fishing: a simplified and slightly artificial situation. The management policy for this pond is to divert as much energy as possible into the highest trophic levels – the sunfish and bass. To do this, the managers interfere with the ecosystem by removing rooted aquatic plants, which would otherwise take over some of the pond and reduce the phytoplankton available for the bloodworms and zooplankton to eat.

In this case only about 1% of the available light energy is fixed in photosynthesis and losses at each stage of the chain mean that only 0.4% of this energy is taken in by the bass. This limits the numbers of bass that can be supported in this ecosystem.

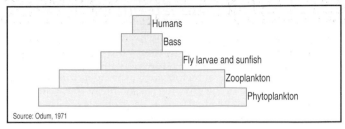

Figure 2.7   A pyramid of numbers for a fishpond in Georgia

We could draw a *pyramid of numbers* to indicate the numbers of each species we would expect to find at each stage in the food chain. It might look like the one shown in Figure 2.7, where the width of each bar represents the numbers of organisms at each level. The diagram is no longer a pyramid, though, when we use it to represent an ecosystem where there are a small number of large producers – a woodland ecosystem, for example. It is often better, therefore, to use biomass measurements to construct the pyramid. For the woodland ecosystem this would create a very different pattern (Figure 2.8b), especially if we were to include decomposer organisms. In a typical deciduous woodland the weight of decomposers, most of which are in the soil, can easily represent more than fifteen times the weight of the other animals! Figure 2.8b shows an example of a pyramid of biomass.

This method, too, has its disadvantages, for it does not take into account the time factor. An oak forest may take over a hundred years to reach maturity and create a large producer biomass, whereas phytoplankton growing in a pond, river or ocean may grow at a much faster rate but have a relatively small biomass at any one time. Their numbers and total biomass are constantly being reduced by the grazing activities of the zooplankton and larger filter feeding organisms. Pyramids of energy are sometimes used as an alternative for this reason. Figure 2.8c shows the pyramid of energy for the Georgia fishpond we looked at earlier (Figure 2.6).

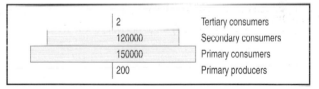

Figure 2.8a   A pyramid of numbers for a temperate oak forest, Whytham Woods, England

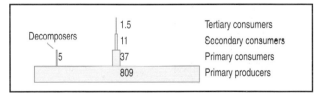

Figure 2.8b   A pyramid of biomass for a river in Florida (g/m^2)

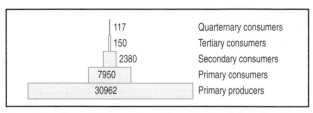

Figure 2.8c   A pyramid of energy for a fishpond in Georgia (kJ/m^2/year)

Productivity and global patterns

As we have seen, animals (including humans) are greatly dependent on plants for their means of survival. Variations in plant growth across the Earth's surface are therefore of great significance. The effects of factors such as temperature, rainfall, light and the length of the growing season mean that distinct vegetation zones can be identified at the global level. These zones, or *biomes*, are really groupings of similar ecosystems. Figure 2.9 shows these vegetation zones as they would naturally occur without any human interference. In many cases these have been greatly altered by human activity. In the northern hemisphere some of these biomes are visible as distinct bands; but in the southern hemisphere, where the land masses are much smaller and separated by large areas of water, the pattern is less regular.

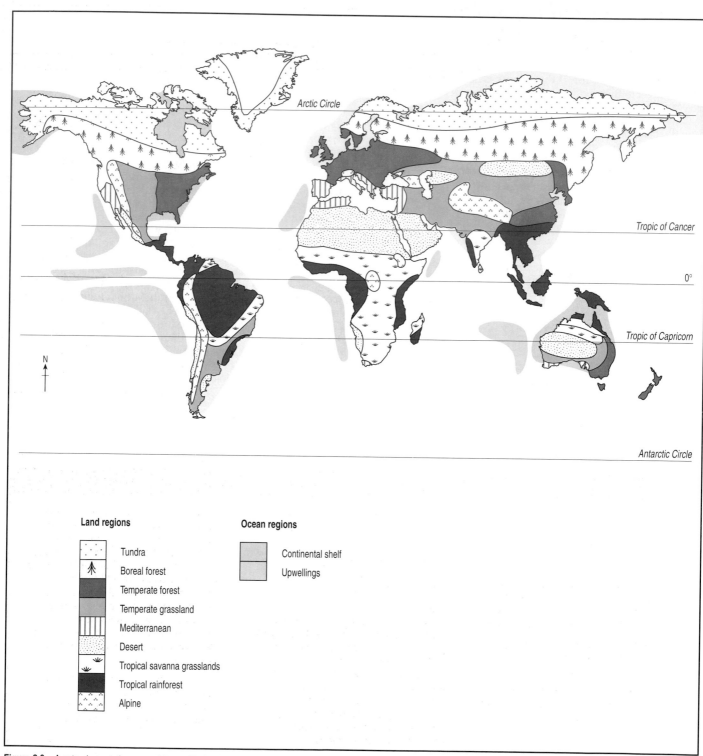

Land regions

- Tundra
- Boreal forest
- Temperate forest
- Temperate grassland
- Mediterranean
- Desert
- Tropical savanna grasslands
- Tropical rainforest
- Alpine

Ocean regions

- Continental shelf
- Upwellings

Figure 2.9   A natural vegetation map of the world showing the distribution of major vegetation regions

Primary productivity

In order to compare the functioning of each of these different ecosystem types we can examine the *primary productivity* of each of them. Productivity means the amount of energy that is fixed in organic matter. We refer to it as 'primary' production because plants are the first stage in the food chain. However, not all of the sun's energy trapped by the plant is available for animals to eat. The plant itself uses some of this energy in order to carry out its own chemical reactions. To do this it breaks down the glucose made by photosynthesis in the process of *respiration*:

$$\text{Glucose} + \text{Oxygen} \longrightarrow \text{Carbon dioxide} + \text{Water} + \text{Energy}$$

The reaction can also be written as a formula:

$$C_6H_{12}O_6 + 6O_2 \longrightarrow 6CO_2 + 6H_2O + \text{Energy}$$

The energy originally fixed by the plant is known as the *gross primary production* (GPP). After the plant has used some of this in respiration, the portion remaining is referred to as the *net primary production* (NPP).

$$\text{GPP} - \text{Respiration} = \text{NPP}$$

This is what can be measured as the growth of the plant. The amount is usually recorded in dry weight, that is, grams per square metre, per year ($g/m^2/yr$).

It is evident from the figures of average net primary productivity for different ecosystem types shown in Table 2.2 that production varies a great deal.

Table 2.2 Global patterns in primary productivity

Ecosystem type	NPP per unit area g/m²/yr (mean)	World NPP 10 tonnes/yr
Terrestrial ecosystems		
Tropical rainforest	2200	37.4
Tropical seasonal forest	1600	12.0
Temperate evergreen forest	1300	6.5
Temperate deciduous forest	1200	8.4
Boreal forest	800	9.6
Savanna	900	13.5
Temperate grassland	600	5.4
Tundra and alpine	140	1.1
Desert and semi-desert	90	1.6
Extreme desert rock, sand and ice	3	0.07
Swamp and marsh	2000	4.0
Lake and stream	250	0.5
Agricultural land		
Annual crops (temperate)	1300	–
Annual crops (tropical)	1350	Estimated –
Perennial crops (temperate)	1350	figures –
Perennial crops (tropical)	4000	–
Marine ecosystems		
Open ocean	125	41.5
Upwelling zones	500	0.2
Continental shelf	360	9.6
Algal beds and reefs	2500	1.6
Estuaries	1500	2.1

Source: Krebs, 1978

Limiting factors

As we have seen, vegetation productivity almost everywhere is limited by a range of factors. Some of the same limiting factors may directly affect the animal species living in the same environment, or may influence them indirectly through the vegetation. Figure 2.10 is a photograph taken in the French Alps at a height of 2360 m. The only types of vegetation able to grow here are a few coniferous trees, and alpine flowers on the scree slopes. Net primary productivity is very low. This could be due to one or more of the following factors. Among the *physical factors* are: temperature, water, light intensity and duration, nutrient availability, soil (pH, texture, drainage, depth), carbon dioxide, wind direction and speed, slope and aspect. Among the *biological factors* are: other organisms (grazing animals, disease-causing organisms, other plants sharing the same environment), the plant's own limitations, and the influence of humans.

PHOTOGRAPH INTERPRETATION: LIMITING FACTORS

1 Consider the landscape in Figure 2.10 and the possible list of limiting factors. Decide which ones are going to be of greatest importance, and which of least importance in this case.

2 For each of the limiting factors suggest how humans could overcome or reduce their effect in order to increase agricultural productivity. You do not need to confine your thoughts to alpine areas in order to answer this question.

Figure 2.10 Limiting factors prevent growth at 2360 m in the Col D'Izoard, Hautes Alpes, France

Natural Change in Ecosystems

Ecosystems develop and change naturally through time. As they do so, the characteristics and indeed species of the plants and animals present may alter too. This *succession* continues until the organisms present reach an equilibrium with the

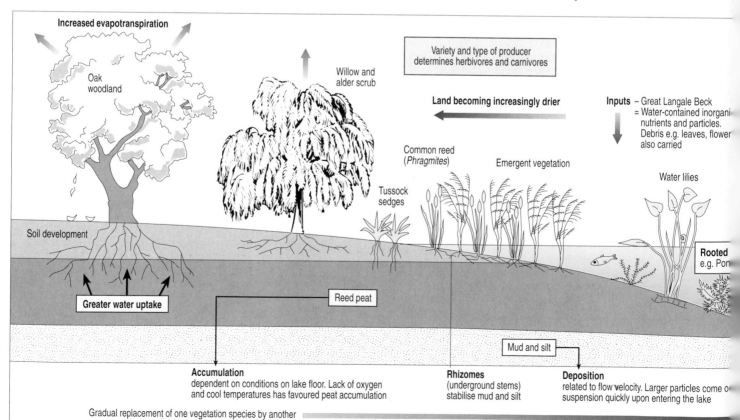

Figure 2.11 Elterwater – an example of a lake ecosystem showing change through time

environmental conditions around them. This is then referred to as the *climax community*. In this way a bare rock face that has been exposed, for example, by a rock fall along a valley side may initially be colonised by lichens:

Lichens help to weather the surface of the rock by producing acidic substances. The weathered surface can hold more water.

Mosses can now survive on the rock surface. Weathering continues and organic matter starts to build up. This provides a habitat for small organisms.

Grasses and ferns can become established once a reasonable depth of soil has developed. They themselves provide a supply of humus.

Shrubs and trees can ultimately colonise the area when the soil has become deep enough.

This progression is called *primary* succession because it has taken place on previously uncolonised ground and may take several hundred years to complete. A succession developing on exposed soil, produced for example by a landslide, would be a *secondary* succession. This would progress much more rapidly as the processes that produce the important soil layer have already taken place. Tree growth could occur after as little as 50 years. However, if the climatic conditions are not suitable the ecosystem may never reach the woodland stage. In tundra areas in the northern hemisphere, such a succession could stop at the moss stage with only a few grasses and small shrubs able to survive in the cold temperatures and strong winds. Similarly, human activity could just as easily alter the course of events. Figure 2.12 shows a similar succession taking place at the edge of a water body. In this case, the course of events could be altered by a variety of human activities, such as

changes in water supply, recreational activities, pollution, or the cutting of reeds for thatching – to name but a few.

Figure 2.12   Colonisation of fresh water at Wicken Fen, Norfolk

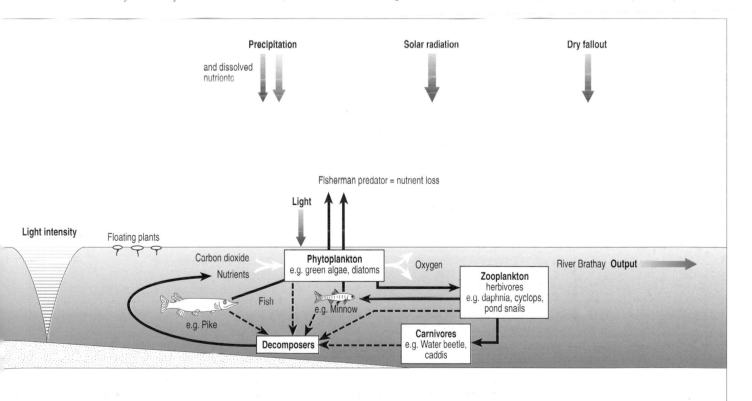

FIELD INVESTIGATION: SMALL-SCALE ENQUIRY INTO AN ECOSYSTEM

So far we have examined a large number of different ecosystem types and attempted to identify the major inputs, outputs and processes at work in each. In order to really understand how an ecosystem functions, however, actual observations and measurements in the field are essential – as well as more fun.

1 Choosing the site and making the preliminary visit

You will find it easiest to start with a terrestrial ecosystem rather than an aquatic one, as all the components are a lot more accessible. A suitable choice would be a small local woodland or plantation, or even a heath or sand dune system. It may be necessary to approach the landowner or the organisation that manages the site before you start your enquiry. Once you have done this, if possible, make a preliminary visit to your chosen site. This gives you the opportunity to assess the site and consider the types of measurements you wish to make. You should also have in mind, when you visit the site, the aim of your enquiry – for this will influence your approach. If a large-scale map of the area is not available, you may also wish to collect the information necessary to produce your own. Organisation is essential, so before your visit produce a 'check list' that you can refer to. This applies whether you are working individually or in small groups. If you are to study a woodland your list might look something like this:

Ecosystem enquiry: Fox Wood
Grid reference: 614484
Preliminary visit check list

1 Nature of site:

a Sloping or flat (measure angle of slopes with a clinometer).

b Aspect (which way slope faces can be measured with a compass).

c Altitude range (use Ordnance Survey map).

d Geology of bedrock (from a geology map).

e Soil type (can sometimes be obtained from a soil map).

f Soil characteristics (e.g. valley side, flood plain, hill top).

g Type of vegetation (e.g. deciduous woodland, heathland: record any variations within chosen site).

h Present land use (e.g. is it a semi-natural or a managed system?).

i What evidence is there of human activity (e.g. trampling, erosion, pollution)?

The *Practical Conservation Series* (Hodder and Stoughton) will give you many ideas on how to make an initial habitat assessment.

2 Sketch map of the site

Draw your own whilst you are there. Label important physical features of the site and any modified features such as roads, tracks, buildings and farmland (with details as to how it is being used at the time you visit). Unless you can obtain a large-scale base map, collect very precise mapping data so that you can produce your own more accurate map after your visit. Figure 2.14a shows an annotated sketch map of a mixed woodland about 1 km² in size. It is impossible to carry out a detailed survey of the whole wood, so decide on effective sampling techniques. You can sample randomly or at selected points, using quadrats (in the case of a woodland, 50 or 100 cm² are suitable sizes), or by line or belt transects.

Figure 2.13   Deciduous (oak) woodland in the English Lake District

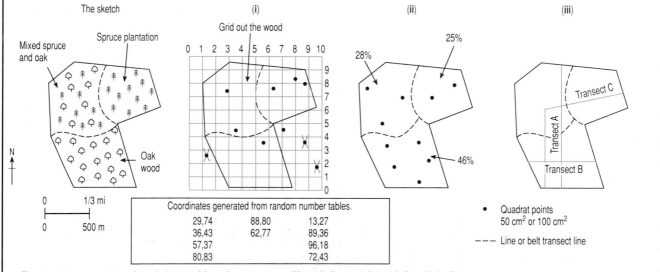

The sketch shows a typical small wooded area and the various ways you could sample the vegetation are indicated in i – iii.

(i) Shows random sampling — using random number tables to generate coordinates on the grid. The problem is that of the first ten coordinates only six of them fall in the woodland area and none in the southern area. The position would improve if 25 samples were taken, or by using the method outlined in (ii).

(ii) In this case the different woodland areas are sampled separately. The number of samples taken in each is related to the size of the woodland area. For example, five samples are taken in the oak wood which covers approximately half the area. The samples in each area could be taken randomly.

(iii) Shows the problem of siting transects. You must carry out an initial survey as only Transect C covers all three sections of the wood.

Figure 2.14a   Methods of sampling woodland vegetation

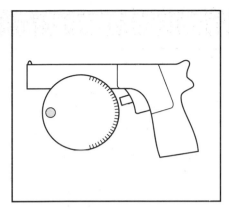

Figure 2.14b A Clinometer

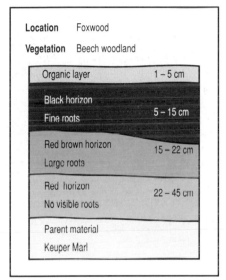

Location	Foxwood
Vegetation	Beech woodland

Organic layer	1 – 5 cm
Black horizon	
Fine roots	5 – 15 cm
Red brown horizon	
Large roots	15 – 22 cm
Red horizon	
No visible roots	22 – 45 cm
Parent material	
Keuper Marl	

Figure 2.14c An example of a soil profile

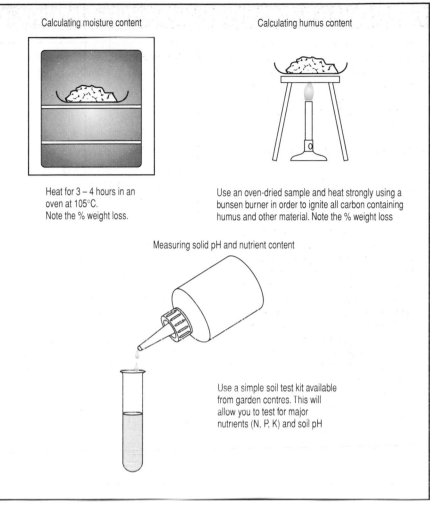

Calculating moisture content

Heat for 3 – 4 hours in an oven at 105°C.
Note the % weight loss.

Calculating humus content

Use an oven-dried sample and heat strongly using a bunsen burner in order to ignite all carbon containing humus and other material. Note the % weight loss

Measuring solid pH and nutrient content

Use a simple soil test kit available from garden centres. This will allow you to test for major nutrients (N, P, K) and soil pH

Figure 2.14d Calculating soil characteristics

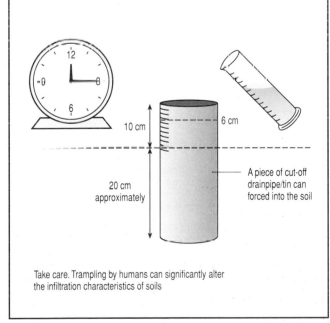

10 cm

6 cm

20 cm approximately

A piece of cut-off drainpipe/tin can forced into the soil

Take care. Trampling by humans can significantly alter the infiltration characteristics of soils

Figure 2.14e Measuring drainage characteristics

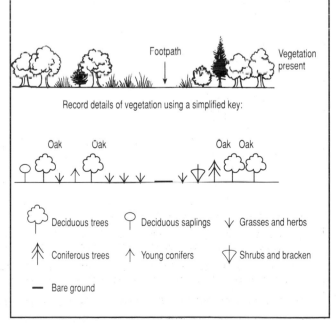

Footpath

Vegetation present

Record details of vegetation using a simplified key:

Oak   Oak   Oak Oak

🌳 Deciduous trees   🌱 Deciduous saplings   ↓ Grasses and herbs

🌲 Coniferous trees   ↑ Young conifers   ▽ Shrubs and bracken

— Bare ground

Figure 2.14f Vegetation study along a transect

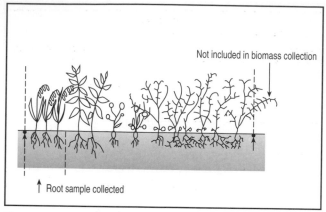

Figure 2.14g   Measuring the biomass of ground vegetation

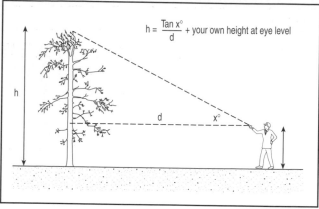

Figure 2.14h   Calculating the height of a tree

3   Making the field measurements

The hypothesis or study title you have chosen will decide what measurements you make. You might be concerned with either the ecological or the economic value of your ecosystem, or focus on a management issue such as the impact of tourism. Table 2.3a lists some of the first-hand (primary) data you might collect, and suggests some field methods.

Some possible hypotheses with a people environment focus include the following:

1   Trampling by humans has reduced tree and plant diversity and growth.

2   The variety and growth of shrubs, herbs and grasses is greater where trees have been thinned or planted less densely.

3   Coniferous plantations create an unsuitable microclimate for understorey plants.

The hypothesis that you choose to investigate will obviously be influenced by your own preferences and the type of ecosystem that you have access to. Not all of the information that you would ideally like to find out will be within the scope of a geographical enquiry at this level. As a result, you may have to concern yourself with the main ideas only. The notes in the following section and Figures 2.14b to 2.14h may give you some ideas. Most of all, make sure you know exactly what you are going to do during your next visit. It will be helpful to prepare some data collection sheets in advance. This will ensure you do not miss out any measurements and will also make the next section much easier. See page 309 for further references on ecological fieldwork.

4   Analysing and presenting your data

Your next step will be to carry out the necessary laboratory analysis of your samples to determine, for example, moisture or humus content. This needs to be completed (under supervision, for safety reasons) as soon as possible after your fieldwork, before the samples deteriorate. The precise methods of analysis will, depend on your original hypothesis. Make sure that the units you calculate are comparable. It is no use, for example, estimating undergrowth biomass in dry g/m² and root biomass in dry g/15 cm².

Table 2.3a   Elements of primary data collection

Biotic element	Number of flora species present	Point samples within quadrat
	% cover of species present including bare ground	Direct measurement of % cover within quadrats
	Spacing of vegetation (e.g. tree density)	Direct measurement in sample area
	Vegetation heights to see stratification	Transect profiles
	Biomass amounts	Sorting and weighing
	Size measurements e.g. height and girth of trees (age indications)	Girth measurements by tape, height by trigonometry
	Faunal species number and range	Use of beating nets, posters and traps
Abiotic elements	*Soil*	
	Moisture and humus content	Laboratory experiments
	°C	Thermometer in soil
	pH	pH meter, BDH kit
	Depth	Auger
	Texture	Sieving/mechanical analysis
	Infiltration rate	Funnel and water
	Profile description	Via cuttings
	Microclimate	
	Light	Photo-electric cells or light meter
	Relative humidity	Psychrometer/hygrometer
	Wind	Hand-held anemometer
	°C max/min	Thermometer
Evidence of human activity	Footpath erosion	Transects, soil compaction survey, cross-section measurement
	Litter deposition	Weight and type survey
	Trampling and other damage	Quadrats, twig damage
	Pollution	Ecometer in water, dust pollution, chemical inputs in precipitation
	Human usage	Activity maps, footpath usage
Additional secondary data	Changes over years (e.g. drainage)	Historic maps
	Annual precipitation total and monthly distribution, temperature variations throughout year	Climate statistics from meteorological office, e.g. at Bracknell

Present the information that you have collected in the form of an annotated diagram or graphs. Try to indicate relationships between components of the ecosystem. It might be a good idea to highlight the influence of humans by using a different colour. Figure 2.15 shows you how to present the results of a transect by means of kite diagrams. A computer programme such as Ecosoft will speed up both cartographic and statistical analysis. Useful statistical techniques include the development of indexes of diversity or commonality, the use of nearest neighbour techniques to look at distribution of species or the use of a version of χ^2 known as the Association Index to show how plant communities change – for example, across a sand dune transect. Books such as Kershaw or Slingsby and Cook give full details of these methods.

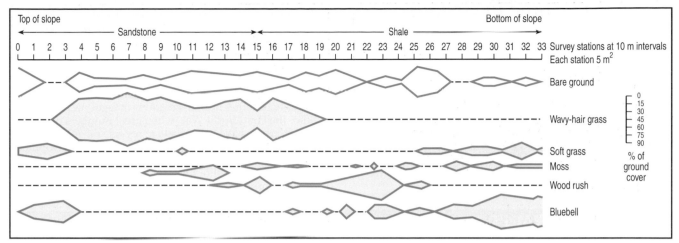

Figure 2.15 Kite diagram showing variations in vegetation cover

Enquiry: Woodland Ecosystem

Physical characteristics

The angle of slope can be measured using a clinometer or an Abney level. Use a compass to determine the aspect of the study area if there is a slope angle of more than five degress.

Soil characteristics

Your approach will depend on the type of information you wish to find out. A soil pit will allow you to gain most information about the depth of the soil and changes through the soil profile, otherwise use a soil auger. Dig your pit(s) approximately 50 cm square and down to bedrock, or a maximum of one metre. Take care to remove the soil clods carefully so that they can be replaced when you fill in your pit. Choose one of the walls of your pit where the different layers within the soil can be identified. You may need to re-cut parts where layers have become smeared together. Try to distinguish separate horizons (layers) and mark them. You may find it helpful to draw or take a photograph of the profile. Remember you will need to know the scale, and also the colour of each horizon. Take note of the different characteristics at each level in the soil and take samples in order to determine soil pH, nutrient content, humus content and water content. Try to make a sealed miniprofile to summarise these differences.

Observing drainage characteristics

If it has rained heavily shortly before your visit it might be possible to see evidence of waterlogging. However, the presence of indicator species such as rushes will give you a better long-term impression. Alternatively your own measurements can give you useful information, especially when you wish to compare sites.

Calculate rates of infiltration by measuring the amount of water draining into the soil at 30- or 60-second intervals for ten minutes. Do this by maintaining the water level at 6 cm and noting the amounts you need to add.

Biological characteristics

Vegetation types. It is unlikely, unless you are studying a coniferous plantation, that the vegetation growing at your study site will be of uniform composition. The best way to study variations in the vegetation characteristics and species is to use randomly spaced quadrats or a line transect. If you choose to use a transect, study the vegetation at 1 m intervals along a tape either on the ground where the tape touches (line transect); or in a 25 cm zone either side of the tape (belt transect). Record the species/characteristics of the vegetation using a key to help. This is also an ideal opportunity to note down animal species that you see (e.g. insects, birds) and if you wish to collect microclimate data (e.g. light intensity, wind speed or humidity).

Biomass measurements. In order to estimate the biomass of the ground vegetation it is necessary to harvest the vegetation from a number of randomly placed quadrats. (A size of 50 cm x 50 cm should be sufficient for most studies.) Cut the vegetation down to the soil level, but only include that which falls within the vertical constraints of the quadrat. (Do not cut back large shrubs, bushes or trees!) Also collect as many of the roots as possible from a measured part of the quadrat, e.g. 15 cm². You will find the easiest way to remove soil is to wash it off.

Use the cut vegetation to estimate biomass by drying it first in an oven at 105°C. Convert figures to dry g/m². An alternative method of calculating ground vegetation biomass is to estimate its contribution to the total biomass of the woodland. This is usually between 10% and 15% of the total woodland biomass. You can work this out if you estimate the biomass of the trees present.

Calculating the biomass of trees. It is usually impossible to determine the biomass of forest or woodland by harvesting sample areas. However, it is possible to estimate this figure, though it is based on the assumption that trees tend to be cone shaped. Using the following formula it is possible to estimate the amount of wood biomass:

$$\text{Volume of the trunk} = \frac{\pi r^2}{2}$$

where the height is measured by using simple trigonometry and the radius calculated:

$$r = \frac{\text{Girth measured at 1.3 m above ground}}{2\pi}$$

You will also need to take into account the amount of water present in wood of different types (see Table 2.3a). To calculate the dry weight of an oak tree you would therefore multiply your answer in m³ by 570. Similarly, to estimate the additional biomass added by branches and leaves multiply your answer by 1.5.

Table 2.3b

Conversion values for freshly felled forest timber (m³) to dry wood (kg)

Scots pine	420
Norway spruce	390
European larch	470
Douglas fir	420
Beech	560
Oak/Ash	570
Birch	510

Source: Jones, 1979

Vegetation change in Britain

Ecosystems tend to progress through the slow predictable stages that make up a succession until they reach an equilibrium with their environment. However, during this succession or once a stable end point has been reached, intervention by humans can precipitate changes far greater or faster than those that occur naturally. In many cases the entire functioning of the ecosystem is changed. Consider the landscape of Britain. As we have seen, Britain is part of the temperate deciduous biome. Figure 2.16 indicates the main woodland types that you would expect to find growing naturally. Notice, however, that in some areas deciduous trees make way for other vegetation types.

This pattern of vegetation has been altered radically. The deciduous woodland areas are not remnants of the naturally occurring vegetation. Pollen records indicate that the first grasses and cereals were present in Britain about 5000 years ago. This coincides with a reduction in the amount of forest cover which has continued since. There is some doubt whether any of the woodland areas in Britain are natural. Most are thought to be either human creations or semi-natural.

Since the First World War, when great numbers of trees were felled, attempts have been made to reverse the trend and replace trees. This has led in many cases to the development of large areas of coniferous plantations rather than broad-leaved forests (Table 2.4), although planning for the next decade places the emphasis on either mixed or deciduous forests.

ANALYSIS: BRITAIN'S CHANGING VEGETATION

1   Suggest why, in some areas of Britain, deciduous forests are not the natural climax vegetation. You will need to think carefully about limiting factors.

2   Table 2.4 indicates that woodland and forest cover in England and Wales seems to have increased since the Second World War. What has happened to the composition of the woodlands in this period?

3   Hedgerow losses have also contributed to the loss of deciduous trees in our landscape. Suggest why such long lengths of hedgerows have been removed, and why this process appeared to accelerate in the 1980s.

4   Why do you think that tree planting over the last sixty or so years has produced large areas of coniferous forests?

5   Table 2.4 suggests that in 1985 the national distribution of coniferous and broad-leaved forest was uneven. Using the figures given calculate the total amounts of private and Forestry Commission woodland growing in England, Scotland and Wales.

The land areas of these three countries are very different, however, and the data gives us no idea of what proportion of the land in each case is covered by each forest type. We can correct this by calculating the percentage land area of each forest type using the following figures:

Country	Land area (hectares)
Scotland	7 023 068
England	13 053 332
Wales	2 723 600

6   a   In which areas of Britain are most coniferous, and most broad-leaved forests found?
   b   In which parts of Britain do these forests use up the greatest land areas?
   c   What reasons can you suggest to explain your findings? It might help to look again at Figure 2.16, and also to consider land uses that could possibly compete with forestry.

7   Until recently private individuals seem to have invested more money than the Forestry Commission in establishing broad-leaved woodland. Why do you think this might be?

Table 2.4a   Composition of woodland in England and Wales (thousands of hectares)

	Broad-leaved woodland	Mixed woodland	Coniferous
1947	851	106	104
1969	712	149	329
1992	542	114	555

Table 2.4b   Hedgerows remaining in England and Wales (absolute length in m)

1947	309375
1969	273125
1980	253750
1985	241250

Table 2.4c   Annual rate of hedgerow loss in England and Wales (km)

1947–1969	1625
1970–1980	1812.5
1981–1985	2500

Table 2.4d   Productive woodland, March 1992

	Conifers	Broad-leaves (thousands of hectares)
Forestry Commission		
England	177	38
Wales	118	7
Scotland	508	6
Private woodlands		
England	207	401
Wales	53	56
Scotland	458	84

Source: Forestry Commission, 1992

Nutrient cycling and vegetation

All plants need a supply of nutrients in order to grow. The major nutrients are nitrogen, phosphorous and potassium. These form the basis of NPK fertiliser. Other nutrients are also needed, usually in smaller quantities. These include calcium, magnesium, copper and molybdenum, although there are many others. In a terrestrial ecosystem unaffected directly by human activity, nutrients are supplied from the breakdown of soil parent material, mainly by chemical weathering. Organic acids released by decomposing material in the soil may accelerate this process. The nutrients released are therefore dependent on the characteristics of this parent material. This is not the only source of nutrients, however, for there may be significant inputs of sulphate, sodium, magnesium, calcium

and chloride ions reaching the site in precipitation. Again, the inputs from this source will vary a great deal according to the location of the site in relation to urban and industrial areas, proximity to the sea, wind direction, etc. There may also be an input of nutrients from other sources. For example, migrating animals or birds may visit or move into the site and excrete nutrients that they ingested outside the ecosystem. Similarly, when these animals die, nutrients in their tissues could enter the ecosystem as the decomposer organisms break their tissues down.

There are also substantial losses from the undisturbed ecosystem. Water percolating through the soil can wash out nutrients and either redeposit them lower in the profile, or, more significantly, remove them completely so that they enter stream or ground water flow. This process is called *leaching*.

The degree of leaching depends on the amount of water percolating through the soil, along with other factors such as the characteristics of the soil itself. There may also be some loss of nutrients in any surface flow of water. Runoff is likely to be an especially important factor on sloping surfaces.

As a result of these inputs and outputs, the pool of nutrients in the soil may alter throughout the year. Vegetation can draw upon this pool to meet its needs. In a natural system the removal of nutrients from the soil by the vegetation does not constitute a loss from the ecosystem, for they will be replaced when the plant tissues die. The nutrients are merely being stored in the biomass of the vegetation, though in the case of a tree this may be for hundreds of years. Human intervention can quickly drain this store of nutrients if plants or animals are removed from the ecosystem, as when root crops are harvested, or areas deforested.

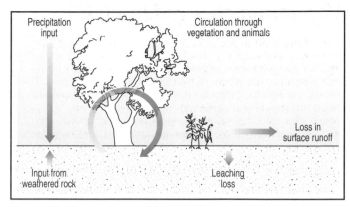

Figure 2.17 The general pattern of the nutrient flow of a terrestrial ecosystem

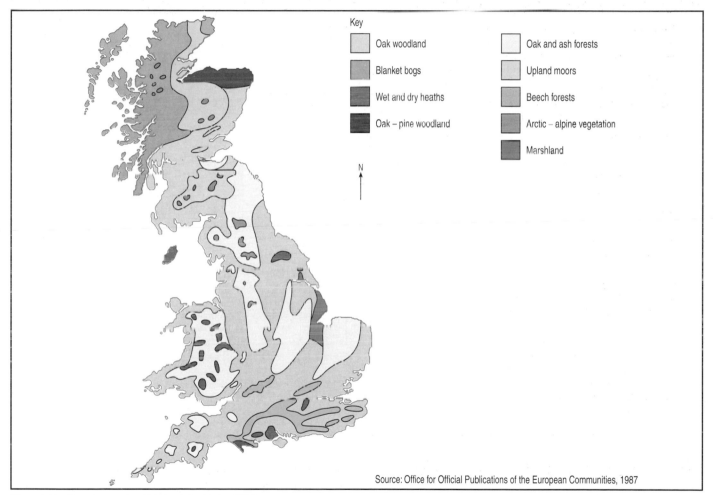

Key

Oak woodland

Blanket bogs

Wet and dry heaths

Oak – pine woodland

Oak and ash forests

Upland moors

Beech forests

Arctic – alpine vegetation

Marshland

N

Source: Office for Official Publications of the European Communities, 1987

Figure 2.16 Natural vegetation of England, Scotland and Wales

ENQUIRY: MAKING SENSE OF NUTRIENT FLOWS

1 a Make your own copy of Figure 2.17, which shows the major flows of nutrients into and out of an ecosystem you have investigated. Add extra arrows of your own in order to show other minor inputs and outputs of nutrients that occur naturally.

b Now add labelled arrows in a different colour to show how humans could affect the nutrient flows in and out of the system. It is important to consider the indirect influences that humans might have (e.g. pollutants in the rainfall) as well as the direct effects (e.g. removal of vegetation).

2 So far, we have only studied nutrient cycling in terrestrial ecosystems. See if you can draw a similar flow diagram to show the workings of an aquatic ecosystem such as a lake or river.

Nutrient stores and human influence

The flow diagrams we have studied are a useful way of indicating the movement of nutrients within ecosystems. They allow us to consider the main patterns and how human activity might influence those patterns. Moreover, if we can incorporate information about the sizes of the flows in each case, and indicate where in the ecosystem nutrients are stored, they are even more valuable.

Figure 2.18a is such a model for a temperate deciduous forest growing on a brown earth soil. Such a soil is usually free-draining, with a good nutrient content and abundant soil fauna (organisms). The diagram clearly shows the large stores of nutrients locked in the biomass. Some of these are returned annually to the soil when leaf fall occurs each autumn. This leaf litter appears to be broken down quite readily by the soil organisms, and so the nutrients are once again available for uptake by plants.

When coniferous trees are planted, however, the situation is quite different. As you will see from Figure 2.18b and Table 2.5 which shows calcium and potassium uptake by a variety of tree species, conifers tend not to make such heavy demands on the pool of soil nutrients. This is one reason why they are able to grow in upland areas of Britain where deciduous trees could not survive.

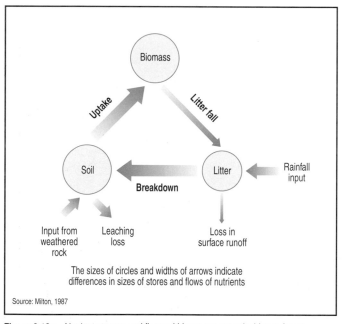

Figure 2.18a   Nutrient storage and flows within a temperate deciduous forest

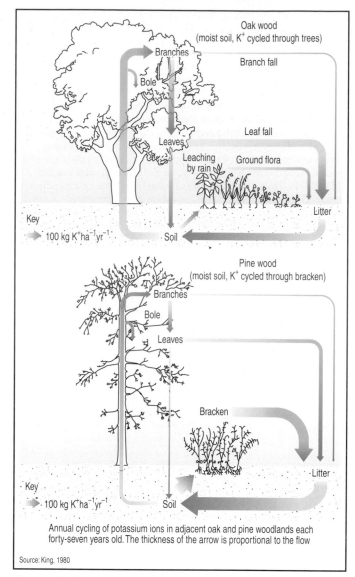

Annual cycling of potassium ions in adjacent oak and pine woodlands each forty-seven years old. The thickness of the arrow is proportional to the flow

Source: King, 1980

Figure 2.18b   The uptake of calcium and potassium by trees of different species

Table 2.5   Calcium cycling in different vegetation types (kg/ha)

Vegetation	Uptake	Retained	Released by litter fall
Spruce on podzol	56	8	48
Spruce on rich soil	51	6	45
Birch	107	53	54
Oakwood	102	16	86

Source: Trudgill, 1977

PREDICTION ENQUIRY: 'CONIFERISATION' – CLOTHING THE LANDSCAPE WITH CONIFERS

1 a Using the model in Figure 2.18a as a guide, draw your own diagram to show the nutrient flows into and within a coniferous plantation. As well as the difference in the nutrient demands of conifers you need to bear the following points in mind:

• The biomass will be quite similar to that found in deciduous forest.
• The needles from conifers are much tougher and contain fewer nutrients than deciduous leaves. As a result they decompose much more slowly.

• Assume in this instance that the inputs of nutrients from precipitation are similar although weathering of parent material (in this case, sandstone) provides less nutrients than shown in Figure 2.18a.

b How would felling of the conifers for timber production affect your model? Alter your diagram to show this.

2 In what ways would you have to change your nutrient flow diagram if you were considering a coniferous forest in northern Canada or Russia rather than Britain? In boreal forest areas winters are very cold, with little or no sunlight, and average temperatures may only rise above 6°C for three to five months of the year.

3 In Britain large swathes of conifers have been planted, usually for economic gain. As a result trees are usually planted close together in blocks of single species (stands). Apart from the changes in the pattern of nutrient flow, in what other ways would these forests differ from the temperate deciduous forests that originally covered much of Britain? You will need to consider associated flora (plants) and fauna (animals) as well as differences in microclimate and vegetation structure.

4 'It is essential that we increase the area of coniferous plantations especially in the upland regions of Britain, if we are to meet the demands for timber in the twenty-first century. The aesthetic appearance of the countryside must be of secondary importance.'

How far do you agree with this statement? Prepare your answer and then discuss it with other members of your class. Use Figure 2.19, which compares differing views about coniferisation to help you develop your answer into an essay.

Figure 2.19 Views of coniferisation

Managing a Natural Ecosystem in South-West Australia

We have already seen how drastically the natural vegetation of Britain has been altered, so much so that there is doubt whether any of it at all remains today. Similar changes are taking place all over the world, as natural ecosystems are replaced by those modified and manipulated by humans. When human interference threatens one ecosystem, 'knock-on' effects can also change undisturbed ecosystems nearby – as we shall see in this example of a natural forest area in Australia.

The Australian setting

The vegetation types growing in Australia vary a great deal because of the range of climatic conditions found over the continent (Figure 2.9). The ecosystem we are going to consider is found in south-west Australia where the climate is of the Mediterranean type (Figure 2.20). Winters are mild and moist, whereas the summers are hotter with abundant sunshine but little rain. 'Sclerophyllous' vegetation is ideally adapted to this

environment – a schlerophyll is a plant that generally has small tough leaves with thick waxy cuticles. These features prevent desiccation and, along with various other adaptations, allow the plants to survive the hot dry summers.

Human exploitation in this area has taken place where the summers are slightly cooler and the climate more moist. Two main forest types are found, the karri forests where *Eucalyptus diversicolor* is the dominant tree, and the jarrah forests where *Eucalyptus marginata* is found. In some areas both tree species are found growing together and also in association with a third eucalyptus referred to as marri (*Eucalyptus calophylla*). *Eucalyptus calophylla* is vital for the large quantities of honey that are gathered in this area as it supplies essential nectar.

This region of Australia, well known to tourists for its beautiful forests, is also an important source of timber for the sawmill industry and, since 1975, the woodchip export industry. As a result there has been considerable conflict between the Forests Department of the state of Western Australia and other bodies, as we shall see.

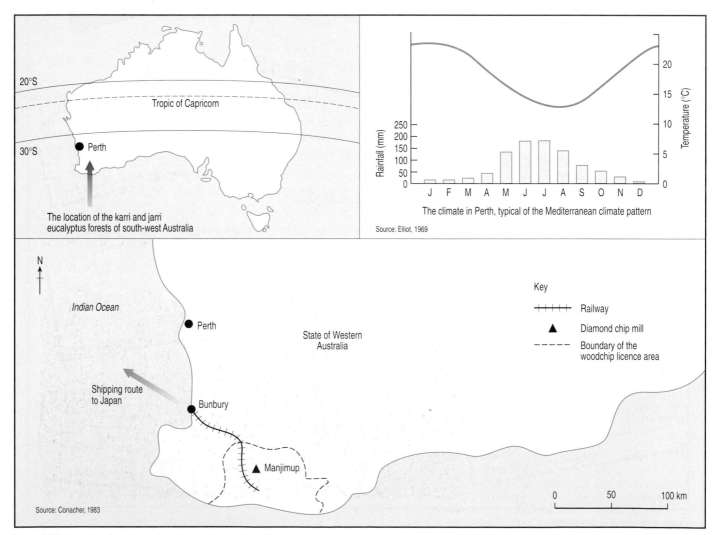

Figure 2.20   Location of eucalyptus forests in south-west Australia

CASE STUDY: *Exploitation of Bunbury Forest for the Woodchip and Sawmill Industries*

In 1973 the state government of Western Australia passed the Woodchip Agreement Act. This allowed felling of timber reserves in the state and their conversion to woodchip. The Federal government also granted export approval up to a maximum of 750 000 tonnes. A woodchip licence area was designated where felling could take place under the direction of the Forests Department. Marri and karri logs felled within the licence area are cut to produce these woodchips at the Diamond Chip Mill, south of Manjimup. They are then transported by rail to the port of Bunbury where they are exported to Japan (Figure 2.20).

Felling of the trees for woodchip is organised within each forestry administration unit or 'compartment'. These compartments are usually between 4000 and 6000 hectares. The clear-felled areas, or 'coupes', vary in size. The Forests Department recommends that in karri/marri forests, which are unique and have the greatest attraction for tourists, the cleared area is restricted to 200 hectares, whilst in the jarrah/marri forests the clearances are limited to 800 hectares. These recommendations are not part of the Act, however, and in some cases have been exceeded.

The Forests Department also suggests that in the karri/marri forests some trees are left standing as seed trees to allow regeneration to take place. The remaining trees are felled and the undergrowth flattened. In the summer, when the seeds have ripened in the karri seed trees, the area is burnt. The purpose of this burning is to remove any plants that may compete with the karri seeds. The heat also encourages the seeds to fall. They do this shortly after the fire, and the ash remaining on the forest floor also provides a suitable seed bed for germination. The seed trees are later removed for saw logs. In more than two-thirds of cases, though, this method has not been used; instead, coupes have been replanted in straight rows without natural regeneration. This changes the whole nature of the forest, even though naturally occurring species of trees are used.

As a result of the Woodchip Act the clear-felling rates of forests increased dramatically. Before 1975, 413.5 hectares of karri forest were being cleared each year, mainly for saw-wood. Once the Act was passed, however, this increased to 3116.7 hectares annually. The following article taken from a local newspaper in the south of the state highlights the depth of local feeling.

PROTEST IN BUNBURY OVER FOREST MAYHEM

Conservationists gathered at the docks in Bunbury today to register their protests against the continued deforestation that is taking place within the woodchip licence area, approximately 250 km south of Perth. The crowd consisted of more than a hundred people carrying placards and waving banners voicing their objections to the state Forests Department's destruction of the area. There was also a sizeable number of protesters in a flotilla of small boats and rubber dinghies in the river beside the large vessel, which towered above them. The demonstration was timed to coincide with the departure of one of the largest ships used to carry the woodchips to Japan. The police were called, though no arrests were made and with the help of two police launches the ship was able to sail with a delay of only two hours.

One of the organisers, Roger Stacey, expressed his views on the day's events. 'We have had a very well-supported demonstration here today. This indicates just how strongly people feel about the FD's total destruction of the forests around Manjimup.' He went on to explain why public objections to the scheme were growing. 'Forests in this region have already suffered because of exploitation of coal and bauxite. This use of beautiful and ecologically valuable forest is yet another threat to our landscape. Eighty-six per cent of the world's karri forest is found in this part of Australia, yet the Forest Department continue with their needless felling. Large areas of over 800 hectares are clear-felled, for there is no maximum limit laid down by the state government. Moreover, forest that has been felled does not regain its beauty for at least 50 years, if at all.

This area of Western Australia is the most heavily populated in the state; 85% of the state's population live here. As a result, the demand for recreational facilities is high. Beekeepers rely heavily on the marri trees for their honey production, whilst the forests also provide a haven for wildlife. More than 100 bird and 20 mammal species have been identified. All of these are now at risk.'

Figure 2.21   Jarrah forest with Karri

BIOLOGICAL REPORT

The Effects of Intensive Forestry Practice on Eucalyptus Forest in the Woodchip Licence Area

The use of the eucalyptus forests for a supply of woodchip timber is having disastrous consequences on the ecosystems in this area. Natural forest is being replaced by plantations where the ecology is totally different. In stands where clear-felling has taken place the number and diversity of animals is drastically reduced. Similarly, in adjacent un-cut forest some animal species remain at only 20% of their former level for many years. Soil organisms are equally affected. This is a direct result of the regeneration burn that takes place when an area has been felled. The litter layer in an undisturbed forest provides a habitat for a rich soil fauna, but burning converts this layer to ash. Moreover, the micro-organisms in the soil are reduced, and this seems to be allowing a rapid increase in the amounts of the fungus *Phytopthora cinnamomi* which causes the disease known as 'die-back'.

The ecological disruption to the forest has also allowed a population explosion in another pest, the jarrah leaf miner. This is a moth that in the larval form attacks eucalyptus trees, especially the jarrah variety, and causes dramatic defoliation. In uncut parts of the forest the pest's numbers are controlled by a number of species of parasitic wasp. In disturbed zones of the forest, loss of habitat vastly reduces these wasps in numbers, and the leaf miner population grows unchecked.

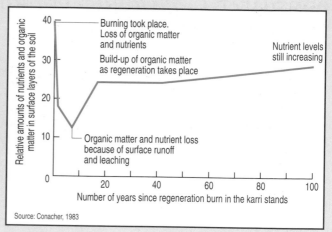

Source: Conacher, 1983

Figure 2.22   The effects of burning the eucalyptus forest on the organic matter content of the soil

Finally, the nutrient cycling of the forest is also disrupted by human activities. This means that successful regeneration of 'natural' forest is even less likely. The practice of burning felled areas causes a loss of nutrients in the smoke. This is compounded by the fact that bark which is not needed in the woodchip manufacturing process is not removed at the felling site, but only later at the mill, leading to an unnecessary extra loss of nutrients.

Source: Conacher, 1983

HYDROLOGICAL REPORT

Problems of Salinity in the Woodchip Licence Area
(Information from the report of an independent hydrologist)

Removal of an established tree cover has obvious consequences for the hydrological cycle. There is a sudden and dramatic reduction in the amount of water absorbed by the plants and the amount returned to the atmosphere by evapotranspiration. Instead there is more water in the soil and greater potential for the leaching of nutrients – a serious consideration if the forests are to be exploited successfully into the twenty-first century (though, at the present rate of clearance, there will be little karri forest remaining by 2022).

The problems that are of great concern at the present are outlined below. Some attempts have already being made to solve these, with limited success.

1 Erosion is increased by the removal of the canopy, which would otherwise reduce the raindrop impact on the soil. As a result rill erosion has developed on slopes of only 4 degrees. Obviously on steeper slopes the effect can be very serious. The Forests Department has made suggestions to assist erosion control. These include recommendations that access roads are carefully sited, that steep slopes remain un-cut, and that streams are bordered by a 100 m buffer zone of undisturbed forest. Unfortunately, in some areas felling has taken place adjacent to rivers and streams, and slopes of up to 33 degrees have been cleared. Debris from the forestry activities has also been dumped in streams.

2 Turbidity and sediment levels are raised in streams as a direct result of felling and the subsequent soil erosion that takes place. This is especially so when felling takes place on sloping ground during very wet weather. The problem subsides somewhat once regeneration is well developed, but in the meantime it affects fauna living in the rivers and also creates problems in the river systems further downstream.

3 Salinity becomes a problem in this area when vegetation is cleared either for agriculture or for timber production. The lateritic soils are rich in soluble salts such as sodium, magnesium and calcium. It has been found that up to 70% of these salts may be leached out of the soil under a karri forest within seven years of felling and burning. These salts find their way into ground water supplies and into rivers and streams. Indeed, near Manjimup some farmers have stopped growing potatoes because of the high salt content of their irrigation water. In many cases river water is unsuitable for human consumption as a result of agriculture or forestry. Some small catchments in the area have remained uncut, and have been dammed to provide a supply of fresh water. However, soon the demand for such water will outstrip the supply and so the conflict grows between timber production and water resources.

Source: Conacher, 1983

PLANNING ENQUIRY: HOW SHOULD THE FORESTS BE USED?

Now that you have studied all the information about human activity in the eucalyptus forests of south-west Australia you should be aware of the effects on the environment. It should also be evident that there is a conflict of interests between different land uses. The problem is made worse because many of these potential uses are incompatible.

1 Preparation for each individual

Identify the main threats to the forests in this area. Suggest what effects each of them is likely to have on the ecosystem. Some of your suggestions might have a very low environmental impact, others a much greater one.

Now list the arguments for and against exploitation of timber in this area. You may wish to consider timber production for woodchip and for saw-wood separately.

2 Role play

Hold your own environmental planning meeting to discuss the exploitation of the eucalyptus forests in this part of Australia. You will need to have representatives present from the following organisations if your group numbers permit: Forests Department, Diamond Chip Mill, conservation groups, local farmers, state employment office, state government, state water authority, tourism board, local residents, Bunbury port workers.

You should also appoint someone to chair the meeting. Make sure, before you start, that everyone has had time to analyse the information given so far, and carry out extra research if necessary.

3 Consider all the information that you have seen so far and gained from your preparation and role play. Imagine that you are an environmental planner, designing a management plan for this area. You will need to decide what level of human exploitation you are prepared to allow, ranging from none at all to uncontrolled use. Present your plan using the following structure as a guide:

a The context: what the region is like, climate characteristics, vegetation type, etc.

b Previous exploitation: how the land has been used in the past, and with what consequences.

c The management alternatives: possible ways of managing the area, and an assessment of each.

d The final choice: you need to present your proposal and give the reasons for your choice.

Global patterns of deforestation

It must be increasingly evident as you learn more about ecosystems that people have a powerful influence over the component parts. In the past we have often exploited ecosystems with little regard for the outcome. In recent years, with better technology, exploitation has become easier and resulted in more disastrous consequences. It has become clear that if we are to meet the ever-increasing global demand for resources we must exercise more restraint. Ecosystems should only be exploited in such a way that the basic characteristics remain unchanged. They may then prove to be sustainable and available in the future for us to use. Massive exploitation in the short term may irreversibly alter an an ecosystem so that it is of no ecological value or further economic use.

In some areas of the world ecosystems are currently being changed in just such a manner. Let us consider the forest resources of the world. Table 2.6 shows these resources in 1980. In 1980 world consumption of wood stood at 3159 m³. Of this total, broad-leaved trees (mostly hardwoods) accounted for 55% and conifers (softwoods) for 45%. The more developed countries consumed 42% of the total – using 35% (1106 million m³) for industrial purposes and 7% (221 million m³) for fuelwood. The less developed countries consumed 57%, using only 10% (316 million m³) for industrial purposes and a massive 47% (1485 million m³) for fuelwood.

The actual rates at which deforestation is occurring are difficult to judge and estimates vary widely in spite of successful mapping by remote sensing. In most regions of the world, deforestation greatly exceeds reforestation. The situation in tropical countries has been brought to our attention in recent years as the rates of felling have increased. The consequences are just being realised by the general public. The greenhouse effect has gained the attention of the media, for both felling and burning tropical forests adds carbon dioxide to the already increasing atmospheric pollution. Moreover, the rise in carbon dioxide levels is likely to affect the global climate patterns and global sea levels. Of more immediate concern to indigenous peoples living in these tropical areas, however, is the destruction of their farmland, lack of fuelwood and, ultimately, starvation. Although the destruction of the world's rainforests, especially in the Amazon, is the major media issue, destruction of temperate forests in Europe, the CIS and now in North America is also occurring very rapidly.

Table 2.6　The world's forest resources in 1980

Region	Forest area (millions of hectares)
Africa	744
Asia (excluding China)	298
China	137
Europe	159
North America	734
Oceania	299
South America	987
Soviet Union	929
World total	4287

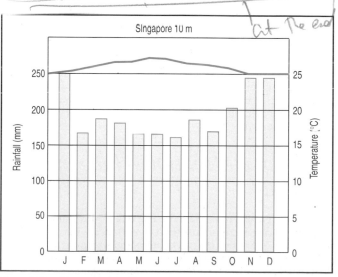

Figure 2.23a　Climate graph for Singapore

The key to the great diversity of plants and animals in the rainforests are the climatic conditions that have existed for many millions of years in these tropical areas. Figure 2.23a indicates the constantly high temperatures that are associated with the tropical rainforest environment. This, combined with the high annual rainfall total, creates ideal conditions for plant growth. The great range of species found there is supported by a forest structure more complicated than that in other biomes. The tallest trees (emergents) may exceed 45 m in height, whilst the very dense main canopy is usually about 30 m above the ground. This absorbs much of the sunlight and as a result the ground layer is very limited except where the light can penetrate at the edge of a clearing or a river. Figure 2.23b indicates these features. It is also interesting that some plants (e.g. epiphytes, lianas) gain access to the light received in the canopy by using other plants for support.

In the past, people have assumed that this rich vegetation is a sign of the fertile soils that lie under the forest, and this has led to rapid forest clearance for agriculture as well as timber. Table 2.7a gives an idea of the extent of this destruction. (*Closed forest* is dense forest with a continuous canopy, whilst *open forest* has a lower density of trees and therefore more ground vegetation.)

Table 2.7a   Deforestation and plantation in the tropics 1981–85 thousands of hectares per annum)

	Rates of deforestation			Rates of plantation	Plantation: deforestation ratio
	Closed forest	**Open forest**	**All**		
Tropical America	4339	1272	5611	535	1:10.5
Tropical Africa	1331	2345	3676	126	1:29
Tropical Asia	1826	190	2016	438	1:4.5
Total	7496	3807	11 303	1099	1:10

Source: OUP/WWF/Survival International, 1989

Table 2.7b   Reasons for clearance of closed tropical forest 1980–85

	Deforestation due to shifting cultivation (%)	**Deforestation due to other factors (%)**
Tropical America	35	65
Tropical Africa	77	23
Tropical Asia	49	51

Source: OUP/WWF/Survival International, 1989

It is apparent from these figures that in all regions of the world tropical forests are being cut down at a far greater rate than they are being replanted. Shifting cultivators were once blamed for this massive destruction, but it is becoming increasingly evident that in some areas other factors are of greater importance.

Shifting cultivation – how much of a threat?

Indigenous people have used the tropical rainforests successfully for many thousands of years. They have traditionally done this by gathering plant resources and hunting animals, or by subsistence farming within small forest clearances. These areas of forest are cleared using machetes, though large or useful trees (e.g. rubber) are usually left

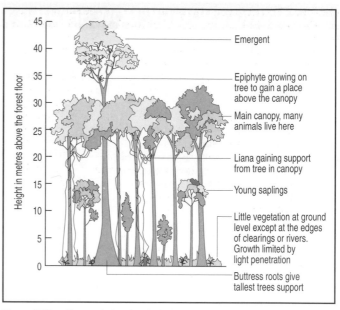

Figure 2.23b   Characteristics of tropical rainforest vegetation

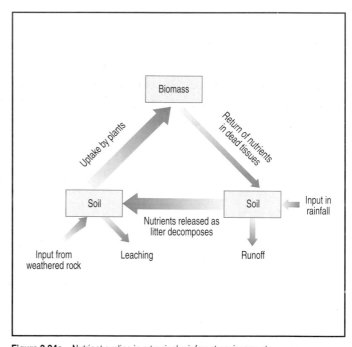

Figure 2.24a   Nutrient cycling in a tropical rainforest environment

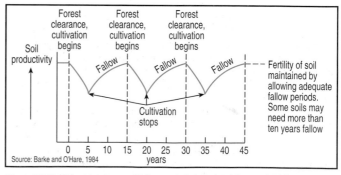

Figure 2.24b   The importance of fallow periods in maintaining productivity

standing. The cut vegetation is then burnt on the site and the ash allowed to fertilise the soil. The crops grown will vary from region to region depending on local preferences or rainfall patterns. In West Africa, for example, the crops often include maize, millet, sorghum and vegetables such as yams.

Even this small-scale method of rainforest exploitation alters the delicate balance of the natural nutrient cycle. As you can see from Figure 2.24a, when the forest is initially burnt a large store of nutrients will be released from the biomass. Some of these nutrients will be lost in the smoke, whilst those remaining in the ash will be more susceptible to loss by leaching or surface runoff. Each harvest also depletes the soil nutrient store and as a result the productivity of the crop and hence the yield will gradually reduce. After two to five years it is no longer worthwhile cultivating the plot so it is left fallow. Gradually, the area will become colonised by species from the surrounding forest and a secondary succession will develop, though it may take many decades before it remotely resembles the original ecosystem (Figure 2.24b). Population pressure increases the demands for fuelwood too (see page 106).

Such methods of shifting cultivation are a very successful way of utilising the forest resources when there are low population densities, for the fallow areas can be left to re-colonise for many years before they are farmed again. It is also (see page 219) one of the most energy-efficient agricultural systems in the world. If there is a natural population increase or migration of people into the forest, however, this fallow period may well be reduced. The system is then no longer a sustainable one.

Figure 2.25   Cassava in a rainforest clearing in Ecuador

ENQUIRY: THE IMPACT OF SHIFTING CULTIVATION

1   Consider the nutrient flow diagram in Figure 2.24a. How will shifting cultivation alter these flows? You will need to think about the initial burning that takes place as well as the removal of crops, and losses due to leaching. Make a copy of the diagram and annotate it to explain your modifications.

2   How are reduced fallow periods likely to change Figure 2.24b? Draw your own version to show this.

3   In Brazil there is a great concentration of population along the coast; you will be able to see this clearly if you look at a population density map of South America. This has led to overcrowding in many of the large cities, where the poor are often without a job or a proper home and live in squalid conditions in shanty towns (see page 150). In an attempt to alleviate the problem the government has tried to resettle some of these people and others from drought-stricken north-east Brazil within the rainforest, hundreds of kilometres from the coast. Similar programmes have also been set up in other countries such as Indonesia. Bearing in mind the information that you have obtained so far, assess how successful such policies are likely to be. Try to suggest both advantages and disadvantages.

4   Table 2.7b indicates that 77% of closed tropical forest in Africa is cleared by shifting cultivators. Suggest why this might be so high compared with other tropical forest areas.

Destruction on a larger scale

The traditional forms of rainforest exploitation were successful because of their small scale and the limited population numbers involved. People used the forest to support themselves. In recent years, however, rainforests all over the world have been felled at an ever-increasing rate, largely for economic gain. Unfortunately, many developing countries have found themselves with no other option when they are saddled with increasing levels of international debts. The `Rainforest Fact File' points out some of the consequences of this destruction.

Timber extraction is a major reason for the forest clearance that is going on. The main problems seem to be caused not by firewood collection, but by selective removal of hardwoods or, in some areas, by large-scale felling to meet the needs of industry. Tropical hardwoods such as mahogany, teak and lesser-known species such as afrormosia and intsia are very much sought after and can be sold for high prices to countries such as Japan, the USA and parts of Europe, though the market is quite conservative in the species it requires. However, the great species richness (diversity) of the forest makes felling such valuable trees very difficult. The logger has to be very selective and may remove only a few trees with the highest economic values per hectare. Unfortunately, the damage is not restricted to the trees that are removed. Research in Borneo has indicated that 30% of the forest area may be left as bare earth when the trees are removed by mechanical means. Loggers often pay scant attention to the trees that are brought down along with the tree that they are trying to fell, let alone those that are uprooted as they drag the timber out of the forest. The heavy machinery also compacts the soil and decreases the infiltration rates of the heavy rainfall. This in turn increases surface runoff and the risk of surface erosion. Moreover, as we have already seen, only a very small proportion of the trees that are felled are replaced by reforestation.

RAINFOREST FACT FILE

• Tropical rainforests play a critical role in regulating the climate and what is called the greenhouse effect. They act as the earth's lungs by producing vast quantities of oxygen and using up carbon dioxide during photosynthesis.

• Burning the forests sends at least two billion tonnes of carbon dioxide per year into the air. This increases global warming. The practice of burning fossil fuels currently adds around 5.6 billion tonnes to this per year.

• Forest cover is disappearing at a rate of more than 200,000 acres a year in Brazil, Colombia, Indonesia, Mexico, Thailand, Ivory Coast, Ecuador, Nigeria, Peru and Malaysia.

• Constant media reference to tropical rainforests suggests that all forests in the tropics are rainforests and consist of an extremely complex and fragile web of flora and fauna. This is not true. Not all moist tropical forests are evergreen, nor are all tropical forests moist.

• Commercial logging is directly responsible for only 20 per cent of the deforestation in tropical rainforests. But related activities, including road building and damage to other trees as logs are pulled clear, increase the toll.

• More critically, road construction in logging areas opens up huge tracts of forest to the landless poor who then move in to practise a version of the traditional method of cultivation that has been carried on for years. However these 'shifting cultivators' do not leave the forest soil long enough for it to recover its fertility before returning to clear the trees and farm again.

• Radical environmentalists say that commercial development of the forests is the root of the destruction. The World Bank says that lack of commercial development, by creating armies of landless poor, is to blame.

• Drier and more open tropical forest formations, together with the shrubland into which they merge (and which falls under the definition of forest) are even more acutely threatened and their shrinkage should give cause for concern.

• Since 1945 40 per cent of the world's rainforests have been destroyed. As a result, over 50 species of plants and animals become extinct every day.

• Rainforests cover only 6 per cent of the total land surface but contain at least 50 per cent of all species of life on earth.

Source: *Guardian*, 8 December 1989

In some regions, especially in Central and South America, large areas of forest have been clear-felled to provide agricultural land, particularly for cattle rearing. It is not usually economic to sell the timber and it is often burnt so that pasture can be established. Tax incentives often make it a very attractive proposition. The profits to be made in this way are small unless large areas of pasture are created, for the pasture is of poor quality and the stocking levels may be as low as one head of cattle per hectare. The loss of nutrients by leaching, and by removal in the cattle when they are taken away for slaughter, means that the pasture gradually deteriorates unless vast quantities of expensive fertiliser are applied. Since this reduces the final profit it is often a better proposition to clear more forest for grazing land, sometimes after only five or ten years.

Figure 2.26   Erosion caused by removal of forest cover, Amazon Basin, Brazil

Figure 2.27   Rainforest interior, Venezuela

Large areas in the Brazilian Amazon and Central American rainforests have been cleared in order to produce beef cattle for export to countries such as the United States, Japan and Europe. The beef often ends up in fast-food outlets to meet the ever-increasing demand; little wonder, then, that this has been referred to as the 'hamburgerisation' of the Amazon.

Chico Mendes and cattle ranching in western Brazil

Cattle ranching has a far-reaching impact not only on the forest ecosystem that is cleared but also on the human populations that rely on the forest for their livelihood and indeed their very existence. The case of Francisco 'Chico' Mendes came to the attention of the world media in 1988, though his fight began many years before in the state of Acre in western Brazil, when he successfully fought for the rights of the rubber-tappers of the region. In the late 1980s the state of Acre became less isolated with the extension of the roads leading from the coast in eastern Brazil, and the area became more attractive as a potential cattle-ranching area. The government policy of offering incentives for any agricultural project set up within the Amazon increased this appeal. Luckily, the campaign fought by the rubber-tappers and hunter-gatherers of the forest, and headed by Mendes, grabbed media attention at a time when concern about rainforest destruction was increasing world-wide. The idea of 'extractive reserves' was pioneered by Mendes, who understood the forest ecosystem and realised that reserves needed to be set up. Within these reserves the local population could hunt and gather food without destroying the ecosystem. This idea was fiercely opposed by the large rural landowners who wanted to reap the economic benefits by removing timber and raising cattle. As a result Chico Mendes was murdered in December 1988. His work has been continued by Antonio Macedo who received approval for the first extractive forest reserve from the Brazilian government in 1990.

The Jari Forest: a sustainable use for the rainforest?

Commercial exploitation of the tropical forests often changes the ecosystem irrevocably, reducing and sometimes destroying its economic and ecological value. The article below, however, reports one attempt to do otherwise.

LUDWIG'S FOREST BREAKTHROUGH

Daniel K. Ludwig, an American multi-millionnaire, bought 1.6 million hectares of forest adjacent to the Jari River in the late 1960s. One of his aims was to set up a forest company that would be able to supply the vast quantities of pulp needed for paper in the later decades of this century. In order to do this he built an enormous pulp factory and wood-burning power station. To overcome the problems of engineering such a plant in the Amazon he had the massive factory built in his own shipyard in Japan; it was then towed across the Indian and Atlantic Oceans and installed on a cleared area of land on the banks of the Jari.

Ludwig's strategy was based on a concept of sustainable development. He aimed to replace the naturally growing local tree species with faster-growing species imported from other tropical areas – for example, the gmelina tree from Asia, the Caribbean pine, and a tropical species of eucalyptus. To do this he cleared a large area of forest. Initially, large earth-moving equipment was used, but this tended to compact the soil and increase the problems of soil erosion. As a result, he resorted to traditional clearance methods, employing large armies of men to cut the trees down using axes and chain saws. Much of the forest was removed by burning. Unfortunately, the growth of the new plantations was not as successful as had been hoped, and some of the remaining rainforest areas were felled for pulp production. There were problems, too, with young saplings which were frequently smothered by fast-growing grass species. To combat this, herds of cattle were used to graze the newly planted areas in their first few years. This was successful, though fertiliser had eventually to be applied to counteract the losses of nutrients that occurred when the cattle were slaughtered.

Ludwig's dream needed much capital investment before returns were realised. Between 1967 and 1981 he invested over $900 million in the project, but eventually had to sell out to a Brazilian consortium of 27 companies. Now the future of the scheme is under some doubt, and the extended use of the area for cattle ranching rather than forestry is being considered.

Figure 2.28   Cattle ranching

CASE STUDY: *Hydro-electric Power and Mineral Extraction in the Amazon*

In order to exploit the massive wealth of resources in the unused parts of Brazil, the government is following a plan to establish both commercial agricultural areas and industrial centres. It is anticipated that disruption to the forest will then occur in a planned fashion in concentrated areas rather than haphazardly throughout the whole region. One such area is currently being established in northern Brazil around the newly built hydro-electric power station at Tucurui. The dam has been built across the Tocantins River approximately 300 km south of the city of Belém. It is the first large hydro-electric project to be built in the Legal Amazon (the administrative district of the Amazon), though many more large schemes have been planned. Construction of the dam took place between 1976 and 1984 and the finished reservoir covers an area in excess of 2000 km². The station provides about 4000 MW of electricity, though this is likely to be doubled with the installation of extra turbines. At the planning stage little attention seems to have been paid to the environmental impacts of the dam itself, let alone those of the associated industrial and agricultural developments.

The construction of the dam and the change in flow of the Tocantins River has had a number of serious consequences. Chemicals used to defoliate the forest vegetation before the area was flooded have contaminated the reservoir, and illnesses and deaths have been reported. These chemicals were used as a short cut instead of felling the trees. Further problems may be caused by the vegetation remaining in the water, for in some places tall trees stick up above the water level. Such vegetation may prove a hazard for fishermen, while the rotting vegetation may release nutrients into the water. By encouraging an increase in the populations of micro-organisms which remove oxygen, this may prevent other animals such as fish living there (a process called *eutrophication*).

Much plant and animal life was destroyed when the reservoir was created. The dam will also prevent the migration of fish up and down the river.

The creation of a large water body provides an ideal breeding ground for malaria-carrying mosquitoes and other insect species such as blackflies. This may increase the need to spray nearby homes with insecticides.

The dam will collect silt that would otherwise be transported by the river. The settlements downstream are used to the flooding that frequently takes place, and indeed depend on the floods to bring silt that fertilises and rebuilds the flood plain. Without this, farmers may need to rely more on chemical fertilisers and will have to turn to other areas such as uncleared forest for their farmland. There have been large forest clearances in the Tocantins drainage basin in the last few years, and this has undoubtedly increased surface runoff and erosion

rates. As a result the river carries large loads of silt which could quickly collect behind the dam. Fish production both in the reservoir and downstream are likely to be affected.

The agricultural and industrial activities associated with the power plant at Tucurui will also have a large impact on the local ecosystems. It is anticipated that once the planned developments have been set up (probably by the end of the century) there will be factories, farms, mines (many opencast), towns, roads and railways concentrated in the region around the dam. As an incentive the government will provide a cheap supply of electricity to mine the rich deposits of bauxite, copper and even gold. Already deposits of iron ore are being mined in the Serra dos Carajás hills and taken by a newly built railway to a deep water port at Itaqui, near São Luis. Tucurui electricity is used at every stage, to mine the ore, to power the railway and to process the ore at Itaqui. It also powers two aluminium plants at Barcarena and Vilo de Conde, near Belém. Other plans include a fertiliser factory and large agricultural enterprises, including cattle ranches and commercial plantations (Figure 2.29).

It is obvious that the environmental consequences of rainforest exploitation on such a massive scale are enormous, and this is just the start; for in addition there are at least five other major hydro-electric projects and numerous smaller ones planned for the Tocantins River alone!

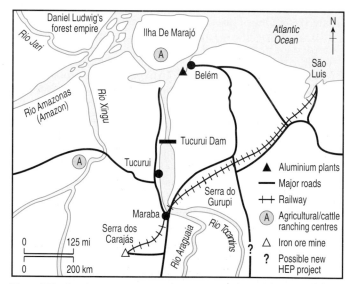

Figure 2.29   Developments in northern Brazil

ENQUIRY: COUNTING THE COSTS AT TUCURUI

1 Schemes like that associated with the Tucurui dam in Brazil allow the resources within the forest region to be utilised but the ecosystem may be totally changed as a result.

a Produce an annotated diagram or flow chart to summarise the effects of the Tucurui project. Think about the effects on the local people as well as the ecosystems.

b Could any of these changes have been prevented or reduced? Put any suggestions that you have on your diagram in a different colour.

c Do you think the concentration of agricultural and industrial land uses around schemes like the one at Tucurui are preferable to allowing much more piecemeal and widespread exploitation? Explain carefully the reasoning behind your argument.

GROUP ENQUIRY: SAVING THE RAINFOREST – IS THERE AN EASY SOLUTION?

1 Look at Figure 2.30 which shows the options. As a group evaluate the four options environmentally and economically.

2 Try to find out more about the work that is currently being done by governments and environmental groups alike in order to preserve the tropical forests. Did you know, for example, that some chain stores and many small individual shops in Britain refuse to use or sell products made from tropical timbers unless they have been grown in sustainable reserves? Useful sources include WWF literature, timber industry publications, Friends of the Earth campaign material and books such as J. Gradwell and R. Greenberg, *Saving the Tropical Forests* (Earthscan).

3 Prepare your answer to the following question in essay form (you must refer to named examples in your answer): How far do you agree that it is impossible to exploit the tropical rainforests of the world for economic gain without totally changing the functioning of the forest ecosystem?

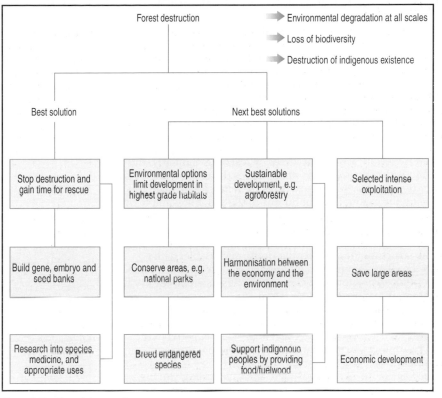

Figure 2.30   The rainforest options

Grasslands – Difficult to Manage?

Grassland ecosystems tend to be found in drier areas, often with seasonal rainfall, where the growth of trees is inhibited – although factors other than precipitation and temperature characteristics are also thought to be important. Obviously, the large grassland tracts found in the Amazon are there as a result of human modifications to the natural ecosystems. However, some of the grassland ecosystems that we would call 'natural' – the prairies of North America or the savanna of West Africa – may have been at least partly shaped by fires caused by humans many hundreds or thousands of years ago. Certainly, grazing animals have had a very important role in the long term. Let us look in a little more detail at the grassland ecosystems found in the Great Plains of the USA.

The natural vegetation of these areas was characterised by a range of different grass species such as Agropyron, Festuca and Buchloe. They were perennials dying back to leave just the extensive root system in winter and regrowing each spring. Some annual flowering plants and bulb species were found associated with these grasses. Grazing animals, such as buffalo, fire and the prevailing climatic conditions determined this ecosystem structure, for all these plant types can withstand occasional fires as well as the more predictable warm dry summers and cold winters of a continental climate like that found in the central states of the USA. In locations where the precipitation is slightly higher the grasses grow up to 2m in height, but in the driest areas, such as in Wyoming, a few

centimetres is all that is reached. The productivity of the vegetation varies correspondingly. The characteristics of this temperate grassland vegetation are shown in Figure 2.31a.

As with many ecosystem types, very little of the natural vegetation remains. Prior to the extension of the railroads few people lived on the Great Plains, where the warm dry summers combined with harsh winters created problems for farmers. But in the course of this century the Great Plains area has

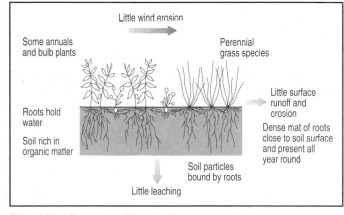

Figure 2.31a   The features of the natural temperate grassland ecosystem

increasingly been cultivated in order to meet the rising demand for food in a rapidly expanding population. Massive cereal production and cattle ranching on a grand scale are now typical of this part of America. This has not been without its consequences, for both of these agricultural land uses significantly alter the vegetation and the functioning of the whole ecosystem. Initially, the soil is quite fertile because of the gradual build-up of humus that has taken place over many years. Converting the vegetation to crops that will be harvested each year means that this organic matter is no longer replaced and gradually the levels reduce. In addition, in the undisturbed ecosystem the dense root mat that forms in the surface layers of the soil holds moisture after it has rained or snow has melted. This prevents rapid percolation of water through the soil which would increase the nutrient losses by leaching. Similarly, the mat binds the surface layers and reduces the erosion caused by water flowing across the surface, or by wind. Removal of this mat, and the gradual loss of humus in the soil, for example by planting annual crops such as wheat or maize, totally alters the characteristics of the soil. The humus that is important for maintaining the texture of the soil is lost, and instead of a good crumb structure the soil becomes loose and friable, with no matted root system to hold it together. The soil is much more susceptible to erosion, and chemical fertilisers are necessary to maintain its fertility (Figure 2.31b).

Ranching can produce equally disastrous results if stocking levels are too high, for overgrazing can kill or severely affect the grass species, so reducing levels of organic matter in the soil. Trampling by cattle can then speed up the process of erosion.

Such agricultural methods were used increasingly in the western states of the USA in the 1930s. The landscape, and indeed the way of life, were changed totally by the mismanagement that took place.

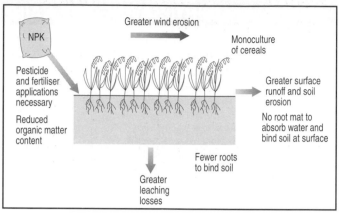

Figure 2.31b   The results of replacing perennial grasses with annual cereal crops

Figure 2.32   Bison on the prairie, South Dakota, USA

ENQUIRY: THE DUSTBOWL

1   Find out more about the great American 'dustbowl' that resulted from agricultural changes in western USA in the 1930s. The following guidelines should help you to organise your research:

- How the land was farmed.
- What problems were caused, e.g. environmental, social.
- The spatial extent of the damage (locate it on a map).
- The role of climate.
- Government action.
- Solutions to the problem and management for the future.

You could look at John Steinbeck's novel *The Grapes of Wrath* which vividly outlines the problems for farmers at this time.

2   Read the information given in this newspaper report which outlines some of the more modern threats to the Great Plains. Identify the possible threat to the predominantly grassland ecosystems in this state. From your earlier work on the dustbowl suggest what precautions should be taken to prevent the severe loss of soil, particularly by wind erosion like that in the 1930s.

WYOMING BEATS THE DUST – OR DOES IT?

Cattle, cereal farms and Wyoming have been synonymous for as long as folks can remember. But in the great expanse of sparsely populated countryside there is now another threat to add to that from oil and gas drilling and mineral production such as uranium – from the black gold itself, coal. The soaring oil prices in the 1970s increased the demand for coal so that by the early years of the 1980s more than 102 million tonnes were mined each year in Wyoming, compared with approximately 7 million tonnes at the beginning of the previous decade. The coal boom has been accompanied by a population boom as people from other states move in hoping to cash in on the increasing prosperity.

Most of the coal in Wyoming is extracted by opencast methods which disrupt huge areas of the land. The coal produced is used mainly by the power generating industry and is shipped to power stations in nearby states by new or improved railroads. The Green Lobby and farmers are concerned about the environmental damage that is being caused by these massive opencast sites. Mining activities on such a scale disrupt the hydrology of the adjacent farmland and may pollute rivers and streams. Ground water might also be reduced and farmers may have to drill even deeper in order to water their crops. The soils and climate of the area also make landscape renewal after the mines have closed more of a problem.

Desertification and the world's grassland margins

The problems that climate and landscape features pose are not confined to one part of the world. Cattle ranchers and arable farmers in many countries are experiencing equally severe difficulties. The farmers in the outback of Australia, for example, face desiccation of their grazing land, whilst huge areas of the continent of Africa face the prospect of encroaching deserts. It is thought that two-thirds of the world's countries are affected to some extent, though the problem was only brought to world attention by the catastrophic droughts of the Sahel region in the 1970s. The size of the problem is shown in Table 2.8a.

Table 2.8a The world-wide extent of desertification

	Crop-lands	Irrigated land	Forest and woodland
Sundano-Sahelian Africa	•	•	•
Southern Africa	•	•	•
North Africa	•	•	•
Western Asia	•	•	•
South Asia	•	•	•
Asian USSR	√	√	√
China, Mongolia	•	√	•
Australia	–	•	–
Mediterranean Europe	•	√	√
South America	•	•	•
Mexico	•	•	•
North America	√	√	√

• desertification accelerating   – static   √ improving

Source: UNEP, 1987

The arid and semi-arid grasslands that have been affected by this ever-increasing problem are very sensitive ecosystems.

Although they have high temperatures suitable for vegetation growth, effective precipitation is very low and tends to be erratic. The long periods of drought make cultivation very difficult and often keep the natural vegetation very sparse. Traditionally, people made use of the environment within these limitations, growing only drought-resistant crops in areas with regular rainfall and leaving long fallow periods. Where this was not possible because of the rainfall characteristics, animals were herded, often on a nomadic basis.

Recent pressures on these grassland ecosystems have had disastrous effects. As death rates fell and birth rates remained high, escalating populations in many less-developed countries led to an increased demand for food and the extension of agriculture into marginal lands not used previously. In many places fallow periods could not be as long because of the necessity to feed the growing population; as a result, yields fell and more land had to be cultivated.

At the same time, many countries in West Africa were increasing their cultivation of cash crops such as groundnuts. Niger, Senegal, Chad and Upper Volta, now Burkina Faso, exported the nuts to bring in foreign currency. Unfortunately, this often meant that land used for grazing animals was converted to continuous cultivation; fallow periods were eliminated or much reduced. As a result, increasing numbers of animals were moved into the very arid areas where rainfall was most erratic, though a run of fairly wet years kept the approaching problem at bay for some time. Eventually, though, overgrazed grass and scrubland combined with years of drought led to the great famines and widespread desertification of the 1970s. Similar problems have occurred since in many African countries such as Ethiopia, where unfortunately civil war has hampered the work of the relief agencies.

Our immediate response to the problems of desertification might be to suggest that water is provided to ease the situation. As we shall see, however, it is important to analyse the functioning of the whole ecosystem before one component as influential as water can be altered.

CASE STUDY: *The Water Produced a Desert – Ecosystem Changes in Northern Kenya*

If you look back at the map showing natural vegetation regions of the world (Figure 2.9) it will be evident that Kenya falls within Africa's enormous savanna belt. From your earlier research you should know that this vegetation region is characterised by large areas of grassland dotted occasionally with trees. This ecosystem is well adapted to survive the very seasonal climate pattern in which, although the temperatures show little variation, the monthly rainfall totals vary a great deal. Most of the rain falls during four or five months of the year, and the yearly total can be very variable. The grasses tend to die down during the dry season, whilst the trees depend on their capacity to

store their own supply of water or reach down to ground water supplies deep underground.

Such a climate pattern makes any form of arable farming very difficult and native people have for centuries been nomadic pastoralists instead, moving their animals (mainly camels) around in order to find fresh grazing land. The Rendille people in northern Kenya lived in this way. However, this life style was threatened by the well-intentioned deeds of a Italian missionary in the early 1970s. He saw the difficulties that the Rendille people had finding enough water for their animals and so raised money to provide the small village of Korr with many new wells and a deep

borehole. This meant that the village could meet the demands for water from a much larger number of people and their animals. This attracted many nomadic herders to the village, for they knew there would be a perennial supply of water. Many of them came to settle permanently in the rapidly growing village, bringing their families and their animals with them. The constant supply of water encouraged them to reduce their numbers of camels and instead keep sheep, goats and even some cattle. The people started to enjoy a much more settled way of life, and shops and simple services developed in the much larger village. Many of the traditional nomadic skills were slowly forgotten rather than being passed down to other members of the family.

The problem, though, was to find sufficient grazing land for the animals within range of Korr. For now there were many more animals and, unlike the camels that the Rendille originally kept, the sheep and goats needed to be brought back to the wells every couple of days. The pastures close to the town were therefore the most favoured and were overgrazed. Soil erosion increased because the binding effects of the grass roots were removed, especially by goats who will eat even the toughest shoots. Moreover the amount of fuelwood needed by the villagers of Korr increased and all the trees in the immediate area around the settlement were cleared. Drought exacerbated the situation and the result was a desert 60 km in diameter around Korr. Figure 2.33 summarises the factors leading to this ecosystem destruction.

Paradoxically, in this example the endeavour to provide a reliable water supply had in actual fact produced a man-made desert. The nomadic herders had previously been limited by water availability, and had moved around in order to find fresh water and grazing land. This, along with the relatively low numbers of animals, meant that no one grassland area became overgrazed. The solution to the man-made problem had to take this into account.

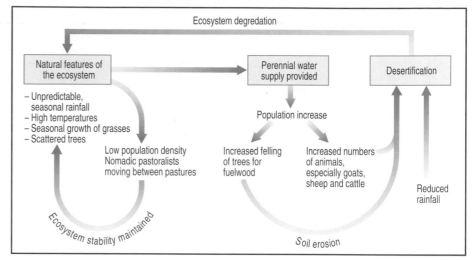

Figure 2.33   Factors leading to desertification in Korr

INVESTIGATION: WHAT IS THE SOLUTION TO THE RENDILLE DILEMMA?

1 Make a list of the main factors that led to the desertification problem around Korr. Use Figure 2.33 to help you.

2 In an attempt to improve the quality of life for people in the semi-arid lands of northern Kenya an IPAL (Integrated Project in Arid Lands) team was established. They worked alongside the staff of UNESCO (United Nations Educational, Scientific, and Cultural Organization). To achieve their aim they needed to reverse the damage that had already been done, as well as preventing further ecosystem destruction. Their plan of action included the following:

• Sinking new small wells throughout the area, not just in villages. The aim was to have one well for every 16 km² of grassland.
• Persuading the people to keep more camels and fewer sheep and goats.
• Encouraging traders to visit nomadic herders so that they could have some of the benefits of living in a village whilst still moving around.
• Setting up livestock associations to allow the spread of new ideas and help the Rendille get better prices for their animals.
• Reforesting cleared areas of woodland.

• Carrying out research to find out if, and how quickly, severely overgrazed land could recover.
a Work out how each of the points included in their plan is designed to improve the situation rather than make it worse. Can you think of any other ideas that you would include?
b Draw a diagram similar to the one in Figure 2.33 to show how the IPAL management plan will allow regeneration of the ecosystem and its future use by the nomadic pastoralists. Include in it any ideas of your own mentioned in your answer to **a**.

Desertification: easy solutions?

Kenya is just one of the countries in Africa that is currently taking steps to reduce the problems of desertification. The diagram in Figure 2.34 attempts to show a whole range of methods that can be used to arrest the problem and re-establish a *sustainable* ecosystem that can be used by people. Such changes, however, need a great deal of commitment from the nations concerned, over a long period of time. Once the first steps have been taken it is essential that the original mistakes are not made again. This takes considerable organisation and financial help, often in the form of international aid. Most of all, it is essential to have co-operation from the local inhabitants in those areas where schemes are implemented, otherwise they stand little chance of success.

Many successful schemes have been set up, including one in Senegal where coastal sand dunes were encroaching on the fertile and productive farming areas further inland. With international aid and help from the United Nations the dunes were stabilised and trees and windbreaks planted to contol wind erosion.

As Figure 2.34 indicates, trees are a very important line of defence in the battle against soil erosion and desertification, but once they are planted it is essential that they are managed correctly so that the young trees are not simply used by the local people as a supply of fuelwood or as a food source for their animals. This is where co-operation between the project organisers and the locals is essential and can be so beneficial. Small planting schemes that are run by the villagers themselves can often be successful. In the state of Gujarat in western India this has been shown to be the case. Here villagers have planted common grazing land with trees, protected and looked after them, and then together reaped the dividends. Social forestry schemes, as they are called in India, have not taken off to the same extent in African countries, but could point the way forward for the future. Already the people living in some villages and towns have established shelter belts of trees around the settlement. This reduces wind erosion and prevents desert encroachment, as well as providing a supply of fuelwood and animal fodder. Such belts of trees can be seen around Niamey (Niger) and Ouagadougou (Burkina Faso).

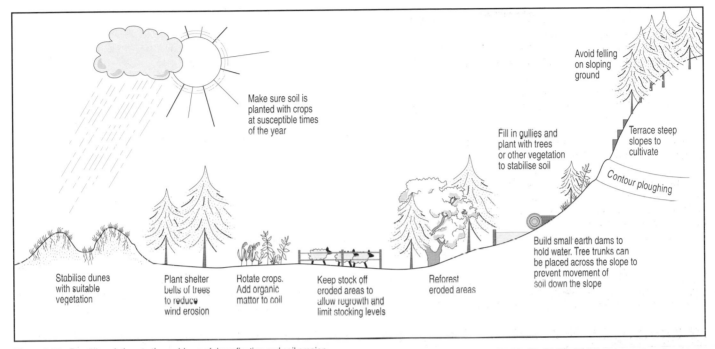

Figure 2.34 Possible solutions to the problems of deserfication and soil erosion

RESEARCH

We have looked in some detail at ecosystem degradation in the temperate grasslands of North America and the tropical savanna lands of Africa. Try to broaden your knowledge of this topic by researching examples of grassland management in other areas of the world. What factors have made grassland ecosystems so difficult to manage in many parts of the world? What common problems emerge? Useful sources include the Longman 16–19 series *Human Management of Savannah Areas in East Africa*, which will enable you to look at management issues in the tropical grasslands of East Africa, where these lands are used for game parks.

Managing Human Impacts

In this chapter we have often seen how humans greatly modify natural ecosystems in order to increase their productivity or exploit one particular part of the ecosystem. For example, hunting in general may have a major impact on the size and structure of a population of animals within a particular habitat, while hunting a particular animal species may modify a food web profoundly. Modern agricultural systems are a prime example of natural ecosystem modification, where plant or animal species are almost totally replaced by varieties more beneficial to people. The costs of maintaining such artificial systems can, however, be very high in both economic and environmental terms.

As Chapter 5 shows (page 203), highly intensive agricultural systems are almost invariably inefficient in the use of energy, demanding high inputs of fossil fuels. Moreover, if a high level of productivity is required, many environmental problems may result, such as those of accelerated soil erosion which you researched in the context of the 'dustbowl' (page 86), especially if the new ecosystem is mismanaged. 'Ludwig's Forest Breakthrough' (page 83) showed how *sustainable* development is actually very hard to achieve.

In ecosystems under human regulation the energy flow is modified considerably (page 219) in order to achieve the highest possible yield. The yield is defined as the rate at which an ecosystem produces useful products, such as hardwoods from the rainforest or meat and grain from a corn belt farm. To increase yields several steps can be taken. Limiting factors such as poor soil or water shortages can be minimised by the provision of nutrients from fertilisers or by irrigation; high quality adaptable seeds can overcome other deficiencies. The prevention of losses by predator consumption, pest attack or competition from weeds in a field can largely be achieved by deploying the great array of chemical weaponry available in the form of insecticides, fungicides and other types of pesticides.

As Chapter 5 also shows (page 203), modern farming methods (used from 1940 onwards in the developed countries and now spreading throughout the world) are largely concerned with increasing yields. In general, farmers use combinations of new farming methods, where the rewards make it economic to do so. These inputs of capital and technology remove many of the elements of chance, and in theory allow continuous use of land, often of more marginal capability.

Chapter 5 investigates how modern farming techniques changed the farming landscape. For example, in order to make mechanised cultivation more practical, most crops are now grown as monocultures in large hedgeless fields. The farmer fights continuously to avoid invasions of weeds, accelerated soil erosion after the harvest, pest infestations and soil exhaustion. In this chapter, however, our concern is to determine the impact of modern farming techniques on ecosystems, and to consider how this impact can be managed.

When we studied Britain's changing vegetation earlier in this chapter (page 72), it was very apparent that major changes had occurred, especially in the intensively farmed lowland areas. Figure 2.35, showing the percentage loss of high-quality, species-rich, semi-natural habitats, highlights the fact that a variety of habitats are involved and that many of these, such as moorland, are also found in upland areas.

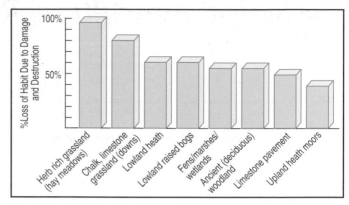

Figure 2.35   Habitat loss in the UK since 1945

Although the impact of modern farming techniques is seen as the major culprit, there are several other main causes, such as coniferisation (page 74) and urbanisation (page 146). As the Canford Heath enquiry showed (page 147), it is not only the habitat which is destroyed, but also very rare species can become extinct and certain significant species can become endangered unless areas of land are protected – by the creation of National Nature Reserves (NNRs), for example, or by designation as Sites of Special Scientific Interest (SSSIs).

STATISTICAL ENQUIRY: LOSING GROUND IN SHROPSHIRE

Losses in Shropshire's prime site resource are caused by:

- *Agriculture*. Includes drainage, ploughing, reseeding, chemical control of weeds and pests, fertilising and changes in grazing or stocking regimes.
- *Forestry*. Includes clear felling then change in land use, reafforestation and underplanting with exotic species, and afforestation of non-woodland habitat.
- *Development*. Includes building, road construction, engineering works, quarrying or reinstatement and rubbish tipping.

1 With reference to field investigations you have made, explain what criteria you would use to designate a 'prime site'.

2 What types of site are most under threat? Use statistical evidence (Table 2.8a and b) to justify your answer.

3 What are the main causes of habitat loss and destruction in Shropshire and what effects do they have on the habitat?

4 What can be done to reduce or halt habitat loss? You could tackle this enquiry by working in groups to produce wall displays showing the main causes of the problem and outlining some of your solutions.

Table 2.8b   Summary of the Shropshire prime site resource and losses in hectares by habitat

Habitat type	Original area	Original sites	Area lost	Area left	Sites left	Sites damaged or destroyed	Loss (%)
Woodland	6019.0	483	543.0	5476.0	436	95	9.0
Grassland	4552.9	466	922.7	3630.2	383	167	20.3
Tall herb	1259.1	69	74.3	1184.8	57	21	5.9
Heathland	2790.0	43	169.3	2620.7	39	14	6.1
Bog	313.3	46	11.1	302.2	43	5	3.5
Swamp and fen	207.4	99	5.9	201.5	95	9	2.8
Open water	1668.5	331	29.7	1638.8	303	35	1.8
Rock & quarry	169.4	82	10.1	159.3	75	7	5.9
Other	319.8	103	9.5	310.3	95	11	3.0
Totals	17 299.4	766	1775.6	15 523.8	538	228	10.3

Note that some sites contain more than one habitat.

Table 2.8c   Shropshine habitat – reasons for loss (areas of habitat lost, number of sites involved and percentage of loss of habitat due to the cause)

Habitat type	Agriculture			Forestry			Development		
	ha	sites	%	ha	sites	%	ha	sites	%
Woodland	114.9	38	21.2	299.3	31	55.1	128.8	26	23.7
Grassland	854.4	146	92.6	13.8	6	1.5	54.5	16	5.9
Tall herb	49.8	15	67.0	2.0	1	2.7	22.5	5	30.3
Heathland	82.8	10	48.9	42.0	1	24.8	44.5	3	26.3
Bog	9.2	2	82.9	1.0	1	9.0	0.9	2	8.1
Swamp and fen	4.8	7	81.4	0.0	0	0.0	1.1	2	18.6
Open water	12.7	24	42.8	6.7	3	22.6	10.3	8	34.7
Rock & quarry	3.9	4	38.6	0.0	0	0.0	6.2	3	61.4
Other	4.3	6	45.3	2.3	2	24.2	2.9	3	30.5
Totals	1136.8	252	64.0	367.1	34	20.7	71.7	35	15.3

Source: Shopshire Wildlife Trust

The Second Agricultural Revolution – A Blessing in Disguise

In Chapter 5 you will have an opportunity to evaluate the benefits and costs of fertilisers and agrochemicals, weighing the economic arguments against the adverse environmental impacts. Here we investigate some of the *ecological* management issues posed by modern farming methods.

Agrochemicals: how do they affect ecosystems?

The major effect has been to increase the resistance of the pests that the farmers wish to eradicate. If the farmer sprays the crop thoroughly this will indeed kill off most of the pest population – but the survivors, immune to the particular chemical used because of a slightly different genetic make-up, increase rapidly in numbers because of the large food supply available to them. The crop will need another application of pesticide at a greater strength. Development of resistance in pest species occurs even more rapidly in tropical areas where insects tend to reproduce more quickly. It is a continuous war in which the chemical industry tries to develop new types of pesticides to outwit the pests.

Another aspect to this dilemma is that as well as killing important pest species the farmer may be affecting, unintentionally, other animals which benefit the productivity of the land. Some systemic fungicides that work by entering the plant itself (benomyl, for example) were found to damage earthworms and reduce their populations in the soil. Other chemicals reduce the populations of important pollinating insects such as bumble bees, with obvious consequences. Moreover, animals that do not directly affect the crop may be keeping the populations of other potential pests low so that they are not economically damaging to the farmer. Remove these controlling animals and the pest problem becomes far worse. Further examples are discussed in Chapter 5, page 203.

The use of some agricultural chemicals has been reduced because of their harmful nature. In developed countries insecticides containing organochlorine compounds that were first made in the 1940s such as DDT, dieldrin and aldrin have in many cases been restricted or banned completely. The problem with these compounds is that they linger for a long time in the soil. This means that they are more likely to affect non-pest organisms. The way they behave when they have entered the food chain also caused great concern. Figure 2.36 indicates how the chemicals can become concentrated at higher levels of the food chain. This is because the organochlorine compounds tend to accumulate in fatty deposits when they are taken in by an animal, rather than being excreted. As a result the chemicals can be passed from prey to predator along the food chain. It was noticed in Britain that organisms at the top of food chains, such as the golden eagle and the peregrine falcon, were decreasing in numbers. This was because when food was short they relied on the fatty deposits in their bodies to survive. As the fat was used up, vast quantities of chemicals were released into their bodies. Their reproductive capacity was also affected, for they laid fewer eggs and those they did lay often had very thin shells, so that the young did not survive. The effects of the organochlorine pesticides was not confined to the vicinity in which they were used, for traces of them have been found in the flesh of penguins in Antarctica and in the bodies of Inuit.

Despite this ban, in some countries in less-developed areas of the world the same harmful pesticides are still being used. They are preferred because they are not quite as harmful in low doses to the workers that apply them as some of the more recently invented pesticides are. They are either imported from countries where the chemical has been banned for domestic use, or manufactured in the user state, often by a subsidiary of a major Western company.

The threat to human health from pesticides is, of course, of great concern. In the front line are the farm workers who apply the pesticides (page 241) though there are guidelines laid down regarding the methods of application and the safety equipment that should be worn. Complacency provides no protection though against contamination. In many less-developed countries, however, lack of equipment or knowledge of specific dangers are more likely to put the workers at risk; and, even with the best will in the world, it is difficult to survive for long periods in sweltering heat inside a thick and bulky protective suit! As a result, even though less-developed countries use only a small proportion of the world's pesticides, the people there suffer the large majority of deaths and severe poisonings.

As consumers, we often tend to take the safety of the food we eat for granted in this country, unless there is a major health scare. We have, for example, to rely on farmers to avoid spraying during the period before harvesting. The difficulty is that pesticide contamination cannot be detected unless specific scientific tests are carried out. There is also much debate about the levels of these chemicals we are prepared to accept in our food (see page 242). Are the 'safe levels' set by governments or organisations like the EEC or the FAO really safe? Since some of the agricultural chemicals that are used are only applied for cosmetic purposes in order to make our food look more appealing, perhaps we should reduce their use and be prepared to accept food which is less than perfect in appearance.

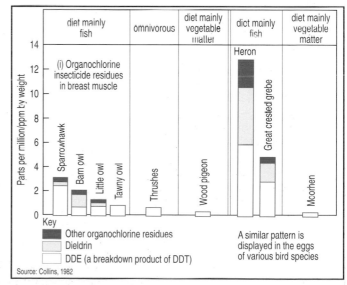

Figure 2.36 Organochlorine pesticides in the food chain

The fertiliser threat to ecosystems

The growth in use of artificial fertilisers accompanied that of other farm chemicals such as pesticides (page 240). Fertilisers usually contain the main plant nutrients nitrogen, potassium and phosphorous (NPK), often with other nutrients in smaller quantities.

Table 2.9   Annual growth rate of fertiliser consumption (%)

Economic classes and regions	1961–1989
World consumption	5.4
Developed countries	3.8
Europe	2.9
USSR	7.8
North America	3.0
Oceania	1.2
Other developed countries	1.4
Developing countries	10.8
Africa	7.8
Near East	10.2
Far East	11.3
Latin America	8.2
Other developing countries	9.2

Source: FAO, 1992

The problems arise when the fertilisers are washed or leached into water supplies, either above or below ground. As well as the threat to drinking water, there are major ecological implications. Nutrient enrichment of water in this way is referred to as eutrophication. It is caused by additional supplies of nitrates, usually from agricultural sources, and phosphates, the majority of which come from household detergents and sewage. These 'extra' nutrients encourage the growth of aquatic plants which may hamper water traffic in rivers and lakes. In addition, they cause a massive increase in the amounts of phytoplankton, especially in still water bodies such as lakes and ponds. These phytoplankton grow very quickly in response to the improved nutrient supply, but they have only a short life-span so they also die in large numbers, too. The dead organisms provide food for decomposers, mainly bacteria, and their numbers increase too. The bacteria use up the supplies of oxygen in the water, whilst some of them also produce harmful gases. Animals that require high levels of oxygen can no longer survive and water bodies that are severely affected may contain no fish but only a few invertebrates that are tolerant of low oxygen levels. The phytoplankton may also create difficulties where water supplies are withdrawn for human consumption, for they are difficult to remove and can taint the water.

Other types of organic pollution can have similar effects; for example, effluent discharged into rivers and streams from breweries or dairies can increase the food supply for the aquatic bacteria, and again deoxygenation can occur. This is a problem especially in slow-flowing rivers where there is little turbulence to re-introduce oxygen into the water. With adequate legislation and monitoring this type of pollution could be much reduced, whereas the leaching of fertilisers from agricultural land is much more difficult to contain.

ENQUIRY: EUTROPHICATION IN THE NORFOLK BROADS

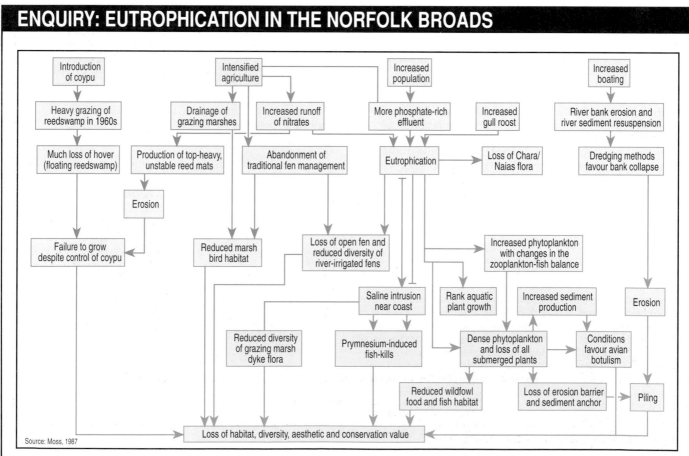

Source: Moss, 1987

Figure 2.37   Links between Broadland's problems

1 Explain how the enrichment caused by increased levels of nitrogen or phosphorous has affected the aquatic ecosystem of the Broads.

2 Make a summary flow diagram to explain how eutrophication occurs.

3 What solutions would you offer to the problem? The Broads Authority has stated that control and prevention strategies are likely to be easier than finding a cure. Some suggestions are listed below:

- Avoid leaving bare fields in the autumn and winter.
- Only put nitrogen fertiliser on crops that are growing quickly.

- Apply ferrous sulphate at sewage works to 'strip' phosphates and reduce nutrient levels entering waters.
- Use the correct amounts of fertiliser.
- Divert effluent away from the Broads out to sea in river channels.
- Use nitrogen-fixing plants such as clover as a fallow crop – this can then be ploughed in.
- Dredge the bases of the Broads (though this hinders navigation and is expensive).

a Explain how each of these suggestions could help to alleviate the nitrate problem.

b Can you think of any other suggestions? Explain how they would help. Refer to Figure 2.37.

4 a The northern and western parts of Britain tend to have lower levels of nitrate in the water supply compared with the south and east. Suggest why this might be.

b Find out what the EC's recommended limits are for the levels of nitrates in water. Does the water in your area fall within these limits?

c How does the nitrate content of bottled water that you find in supermarkets compare with your tap water? You may find the amount varies according to the source of the water.

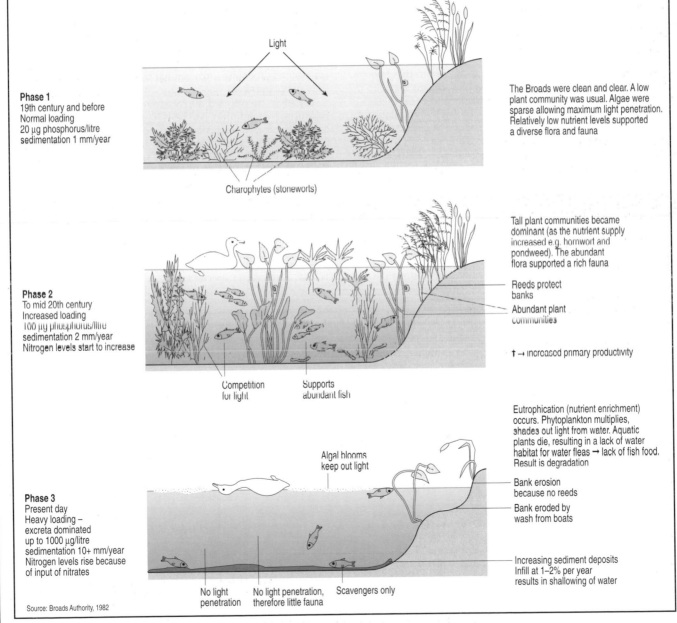

Phase 1
19th century and before
Normal loading
20 µg phosphorus/litre
sedimentation 1 mm/year

Charophytes (stoneworts)

The Broads were clean and clear. A low plant community was usual. Algae were sparse allowing maximum light penetration. Relatively low nutrient levels supported a diverse flora and fauna

Phase 2
To mid 20th century
Increased loading
100 µg phosphorus/litre
sedimentation 2 mm/year
Nitrogen levels start to increase

Competition for light

Supports abundant fish

Tall plant communities became dominant (as the nutrient supply increased e.g. hornwort and pondweed). The abundant flora supported a rich fauna

Reeds protect banks

Abundant plant communities

↑ → increased primary productivity

Phase 3
Present day
Heavy loading –
excreta dominated
up to 1000 µg/litre
sedimentation 10+ mm/year
Nitrogen levels rise because of input of nitrates

Algal blooms keep out light

No light penetration

No light penetration, therefore little fauna

Scavengers only

Eutrophication (nutrient enrichment) occurs. Phytoplankton multiplies, shades out light from water. Aquatic plants die, resulting in a lack of water habitat for water fleas → lack of fish food. Result is degradation

Bank erosion because no reeds

Bank eroded by wash from boats

Increasing sediment deposits Infill at 1–2% per year results in shallowing of water

Source: Broads Authority, 1982

Figure 2.38 Dramatic changes in the Broads resulting from enrichment

Alternatives to the agrochemicals?

A realistic alternative needs to be found so that we can reduce the escalating trend in fertiliser and pesticide use, and the pollution that is linked with them. As the rising price of crude oil forces up the cost of agrochemicals in the next century, this will make sound economic sense too.

A return to organic farming could point the way forward, reducing the need for chemicals and the current problem of overproduction in EEC countries. However, in some areas of the world pests and underproduction are the problems. Safe alternatives, therefore, need to be found to replace the pesticides in use today.

'Biological control' is one technique that warrants much further investigation and research. This relies on using the natural predators to reduce the numbers of pest organisms to a level that is not economically damaging to the crop, rather than removing them totally. In this way the predator species can continue to live in the field and regulate the pest population. Some pests have already been successfully controlled in this way: for example, scale insect on Californian citrus trees was controlled by a predatory beetle, and in Australia the spread of prickly pear cacti was stopped by the use of a moth that lays its eggs in the cactus leaves. When the larvae hatch out they damage the cactus and allow fungi or bacteria to enter the leaves and cause disease. In Britain, too, biological regulation of pests has been tried. It is possible to reduce the effects of some species of whitefly in greenhouses, for example, by using the eggs of one of its predators. The eggs can be sent to you through the post and under greenhouse conditions they hatch out and feed upon the whitefly.

The initial cost of the scientific research is high when developing a biological control project, though once a suitable controlling organism has been found the running costs can be quite low. Thorough checks must be made to ensure that all the effects of introducing what may be an additional species into an ecosystem have been studied. This is especially the case when it has been introduced from a different area, or even a different continent.

Other techniques, many of which were used before the widespread uptake of modern chemicals, could also reduce the problem. Some of these have always been part of the traditional methods of farmers in less-developed countries. Rotating crops, burning crop residues and having fallow periods can all help to reduce pest problems. Similarly, some farmers plant small areas of certain types of crop specifically because they are very attractive to insects. They can then destroy these crops or spray them in order to protect their important crops.

Resistant varieties of crop can also help the farmers to win the war against the pests. In order to breed new varieties we need to make sure, though, that we do not allow old varieties of crops to die out, for these may contain important genetic material that may be needed in the future. In the USA in 1970 they suffered the consequences of not maintaining the genetic variability (sometimes called *genetic diversity*) of the maize planted. Most of the maize grown was genetically identical and, unfortunately, identically susceptible to corn blight which devastated most of the crop. Old varieties then had to be found in order to breed new resistant ones. This is one very good reason why we need to preserve the tropical forests and other ecosystems, for who knows what important genetic material they may contain?

The ideas mentioned above are not intended for use in isolation. Instead, they can be integrated into what is often called Integrated Pest Management (IPM). As Figure 2.39 indicates, pesticides are not dismissed completely but used in much smaller quantities. Such an approach could well reduce the need for the massive use of agrochemicals and limit their harmful side-effects.

As the strain of achieving high yields leads to ecological stress, and growing evidence of overproduction in developed countries motivates cutbacks in subsidy support, new sustainable management practices are being developed – including grants to farmers to 'set aside' land and allow it to revert to a semi-natural state!

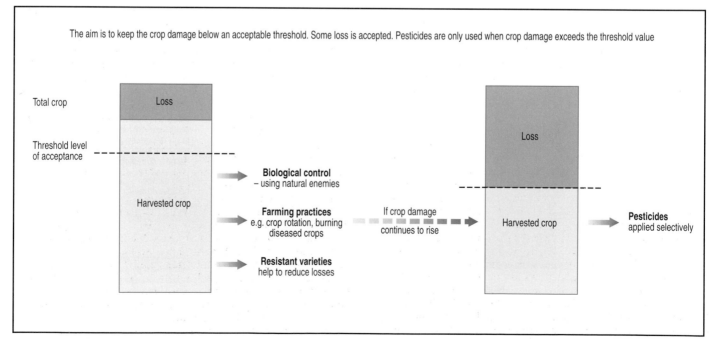

The aim is to keep the crop damage below an acceptable threshold. Some loss is accepted. Pesticides are only used when crop damage exceeds the threshold value

Total crop

Loss

Threshold level of acceptance

Harvested crop

Biological control – using natural enemies

Farming practices e.g. crop rotation, burning diseased crops

If crop damage continues to rise

Resistant varieties help to reduce losses

Loss

Harvested crop

Pesticides applied selectively

Figure 2.39   How integrated pest management works

The Future

The case studies in this chapter alone should have indicated to you the extent of the influence that humans have over ecosystems. The problems occur when they are mismanaged or exploited, either intentionally or unintentionally, without thought for the future consequences. Figure 2.40 shows that the characteristics of ecosystems influence human activity in the first instance. With careful management the ecosystem will remain relatively unchanged, and is therefore available for future use. However, without proper care the ecosystem can easily be changed. This will have a feedback effect and cause the people to change their activities, too.

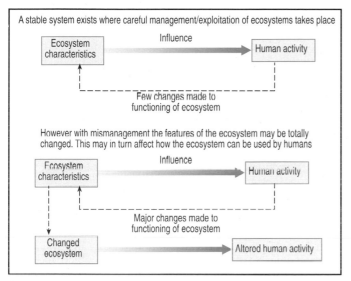

Figure 2.40   The influence of ecosystems on human activity

Mismanagement

Resource depletion applies as much to the animal components of an ecosystem as to the plant species, for many of our activities are dependent on wild animal populations. In the past, many animals have been domesticated and bred selectively to enhance those characteristics that we consider favourable. This has not prevented our attack on populations of wild animals, though. Hunting and the removal of their habitats and food sources have made many animal species extinct and the list of animals at risk increases every year. In some cases urgent international or government intervention has been necessary to prevent extinction. In 1946, for example, the International Whaling Commission was set up in an attempt to reduce the rate of depletion of the whale stocks, though it was not until they got better support from countries with whaling fleets that they were able to apply any great pressure. Many whale species including humpback, Sei and blue whales were in danger, though now only two countries – Russia and Japan – still have commercial whaling fleets. As a result, whale numbers may start to rise again.

More recently the world's attention has been drawn to the severe reduction in numbers of the African elephant. Recent estimates (1990) suggest that there may be only 600 000 animals left in the continent as a result of the valuable, often illegal trade in ivory. In response some countries, including Britain, have put a complete ban on imports of ivory in any form.

Closer to home are the problems caused by the harvesting of fish stocks in the North Sea and the Norwegian Sea. In the past this has led to disputes between countries fishing in these waters, for example between Iceland and Britain in the so-called 'Cod Wars' of the 1960s and 1970s. In the North Sea competition for fish stocks and the resulting overfishing have reduced both the catches and the size of fish caught. Stocks of herring and mackerel have been severely depleted, so much so that in some years fishing for these species has been prohibited or greatly restricted. Catches of other important fish such as cod, haddock, and plaice have also been affected. This has caused many EC countries to look for fishing grounds further afield, such as the North Atlantic Ocean off the coast of Newfoundland. This area is just outside Canada's exclusive economic zone (EEZ). Such an exclusion zone, usually extending 200 miles out to sea, allows a country to control economic activity along its coast. Where the EEZs of different countries overlap, as they do in the North Sea, the delimitation line is decided by mutual agreement. The Canadians have carefully monitored the catches within their zone and managed the fishing industry successfully to maintain sustainable catches of fish such as cod. Unfortunately, in recent years not only have the fishing activities of European countries in adjacent waters reduced the catches of cod, but they have also started to affect the catches within the Canadian exclusion zone because of the migratory characteristics of the fish.

The problems of overfishing and competition for marine resources have occurred the world over as ships and fishing techniques have improved, and the demand for food has increased. This in turn has put extra pressure on the stocks of fish available. In many areas fishing catches have fallen, and more intensive fishing to maintain volume has simply made the situation worse. Tuna nets, for example, have decimated dolphin stocks in the Pacific. Proper management of ocean resources is needed in the future if we wish to look to the sea for a sustainable supply of food.

Human activity is also affecting river and ocean ecosystems in other ways. On a smaller scale, thermal pollution in the form of warm water, perhaps from power stations, can disrupt river communities. In Southampton Water, for example, such discharges have encouraged the growth of Japanese seaweed which would not otherwise be able to survive! Usually, though, it is far more serious and far-reaching pollution events that hit the news headlines. Oil tankers have run aground, among them the *Torrey Canyon* (Lands End, 1967), *Amoco Cadiz* (Brittany, 1978) and the *Exxon Valdez* (Prince William Sound, Alaska, 1989). Whilst in 1991, environmentalist concern focused on the huge discharge of oil into the Persian Gulf during the Gulf War. These catastrophies can, if weather conditions and tides assist, wreak havoc with coastal ecosystems as well as those in the open sea.

Pollutants discharged into rivers will also ultimately reach the sea. This can have especially disastrous consequences where there is an enclosed sea like the Mediterranean or to a lesser extent the North Sea; for this prevents the efficient removal of pollutants and their subsequent dilution. Concern is rising about the levels of pollution in both of these sea areas as some of the beaches become notoriously polluted and holidaymakers are put off entering the sea by blooms of algae or other forms of visible pollution.

The pollutants that we are unable to see are at least as harmful, however. In 1986 a massive chemical accident in

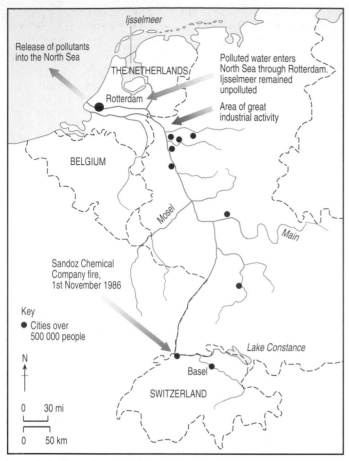

Figure 2.41   Route of pollution after November 1986 chemical accident at Basel

way into the river – from all sources – in a whole year. They were washed in by firefighters trying to put out the fire, for the company had failed to install adequate safeguards against such an event. The disastrous ecological results of pollution on such a massive scale led French people to name it 'Chernobasel'. The river ecosystems downstream of the plant were rendered lifeless for hundreds of kilometres. It will take years for them to recover and in some cases the river may have been irreversibly altered. Water supplies may also be threatened in the future if any of the chemicals have seeped through the river bed to reach essential ground water supplies.

This was just one event that added to the pollution of the North Sea; unfortunately, the dumping of wastes in Europe's rivers is an everyday and usually quite legal occurrence. The virus that led to the widespread death of seals in 1989 may have spread particularly fast because the animals were already weakened by the presence of pollutants in the water and in the food that they were eating. Some harmful pollutants pass into the food chain more readily than others, for those that are not very soluble in water tend to concentrate in a very thin layer at the surface. It is here that phytoplankton tend to concentrate, too, for they are dependent on light, whilst herbivores are attracted by the rich source of food.

Moreover, some of these chemicals behave in a similar way to the pesticide DDT that we looked at earlier. Polychlorinated biphenyls (PCBs) fall into this category. Developed through laboratory experiments, these substances are used to make industrial products such as plastics and insulation for electrical appliances; they are also used in some industrial processes. They can be transported in the air or in water and are very persistent, remaining stable for a long time. They are also known to cause cancer. Like DDT they are not very soluble in water and tend to accumulate in fatty tissue. Measurements taken in the North Sea show that although PCBs are present in the water at levels of far less than one part per million, their concentration in the bodies of marine organisms can be many thousands of times higher.

The problem of where to dispose of harmful chemicals and other waste products of our 'throw-away' society is becoming a very big headache. Recently some Western countries have looked elsewhere for a solution to their waste problem and turned to less-developed countries prepared to accept the hazardous waste in return for handsome rewards. In many

Switzerland greatly added to the large chemical input normally received by the North Sea from just one of the major rivers entering it, the Rhine. The Rhine passes through many heavily industrialised and urbanised areas on its way to the sea (Figure 2.41). When one of the warehouses of the Sandoz chemical company in Basel caught fire in November 1986, more chemical pollutants were added to the Rhine than usually found their

---

CARTOGRAPHIC EXERCISE: WHO DUMPS WHAT IN THE NORTH SEA?

Table 2.10   River pollution of the North Sea (1989 figures)

River	Mercury (tonnes per year)	Cadmium (tonnes per year)	Nitrogen (thousand tonnes per year)	Phosphorus (thousand tonnes per year)
Forth	0.1	2.0	1	–
Tyne	1.4	1.3	1	0.2
Tees	0.6	0.6	2	0.2
Humber	0.7	3.5	41	0.6
Thames	1.1	1.5	31	0.1
Scheldt	1.0	7.4	62	7.0
Rhine	3.9	13.8	420	37.0
Ems	0.4	0.7	22	0.7
Weser	1.1	2.9	87	3.8
Elbe	7.3	8.4	150	12.0

Prepare a map to show the nature and extent of river pollution flowing into the North Sea. It should be suitable for display (either as an overhead projector transparency or as a flipchart) for use at an international conference on North Sea pollution issues. You should aim to use imaginative cartographic techniques to provide maximum visual impact. Suggest why pollution in the North Sea is so difficult to control.

cases, there are no incineration plants to deal safely with the waste, which may be dumped without adequate investigation to ensure that the site is safe and ground water supplies are not at risk.

Other alternatives to dumping the waste on land include container storage on the sea bed (where it is hoped the toxic materials will remain) and recycling waste products. Though sometimes impossible or expensive, recycling may become increasingly attractive as our available resources become less abundant and the cost of production becomes higher.

As well as altering terrestrial and aquatic ecosystems, humans have also indirectly influenced their gaseous environment, the atmosphere. The effects were minimal until rapid industrialisation led to increased atmospheric pollution which now threatens both natural and managed ecosystems. In the latter part of this century we have seen the devastation caused by acid rain and terms like 'greenhouse effect' and 'ozone window' have become part of everyday conversation (see Chapter 3). Growing concerns like these provide us with a global management problem of immense proportions – and we are facing it with very little knowledge about the possible consequences of our actions. No one really knows how the global ecosystem will react to the increasing levels of CO_2 in

the atmosphere, though many possible scenarios have been suggested. Figure 2.42 suggests how the vegetation patterns of the Earth's surface may alter in response to global warming. It remains to be seen how good our predictions are, and how far we can reduce the problem over the coming decades.

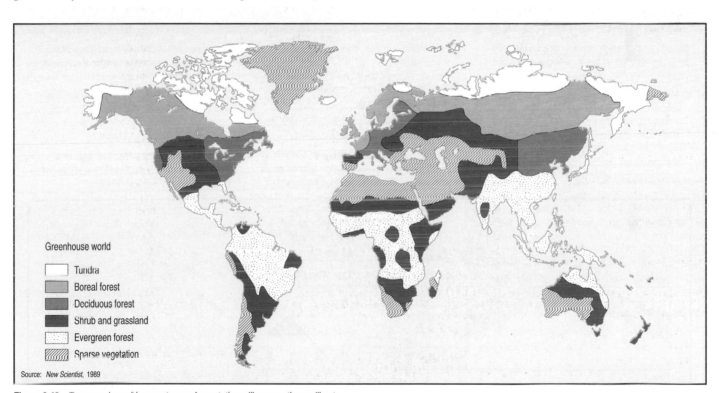

Greenhouse world

- Tundra
- Boreal forest
- Deciduous forest
- Shrub and grassland
- Evergreen forest
- Sparse vegetation

Source: *New Scientist*, 1989

Figure 2.42   Tomorrow's world: some types of vegetation will move, others will not

ACTIVITY: ASSESSING MANAGEMENT PROBLEMS AND LOOKING FOR SOLUTIONS

1   Using Figure 2.40 as a guide, draw a flow diagram to show how human manipulation has changed an ecosystem you have studied, with knock-on consequences for human activity. Add annotation to your diagram to explain what it shows.

2   What exactly is meant by the 'management of ecosystems'? Why are some more difficult to manage than others?

3   For one of the 'hotspots' shown in your flow diagram, identify the cause of the problem and prepare a policy which begins to address the issue.

3

The Use and Misuse of Natural Resources

The Energy Question

'The world is so full of a number of things,
I'm sure we should all be as happy as Kings.'

Robert Louis Stevenson entitled this short poem 'Happy

Thought', but since he wrote it in 1885 much change has occurred and our view of the world's resources – the 'number of things' – is less optimistic.

ENQUIRY: WHAT IS A RESOURCE?

Study Figure 3.1 which shows a people living within the same environment but, as time passes, using it in very different ways.

1 Make a list of the primary, secondary and tertiary resources being used in each time period.
Primary resources are raw materials extracted from nature (e.g. from forestry, fishing, mining etc.).
Secondary resources are the product of manufacturing which processes materials into further useful

commodities (e.g. nuts, bolts and steel plate used in engineering).
*Tertiary resource*s are the knowledge and the abilities of people (e.g. foreign engineers involved in development projects).

2 In a world context, attempt to date each of the time periods. Explain your answers.

3 Time periods 1–4 represent the evolution from a primitive agricultural economy to a technologically developed economy. Name areas where each of

these economies could be found today. How important is trade – or the transfer of resources – in each of these areas, and why?

4 Describe the economic, physical and social environment suggested in Time period 5. In what ways might people in Time period 4 be able to prevent Time period 5 becoming a reality?

5 Using your ideas and answers, explain what a resource is and why resources used in different situations and at different times vary.

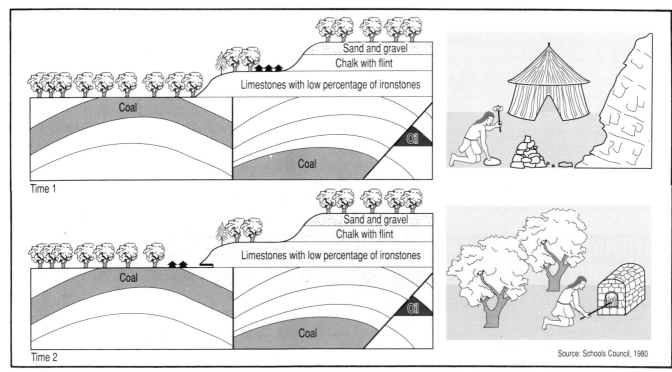

Source: Schools Council, 1980

Figure 3.1 People and their use of resources

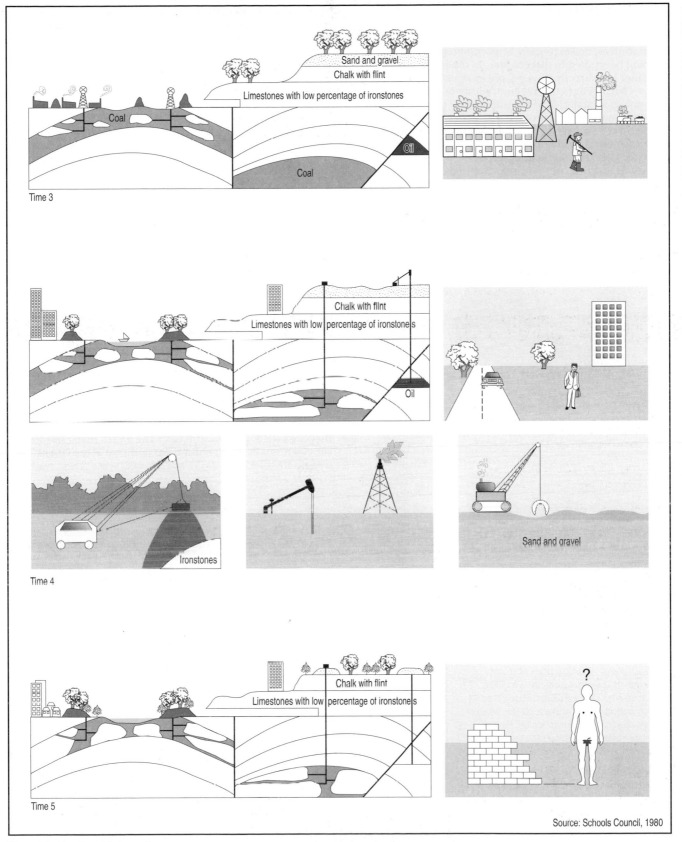

Figure 3.1 People and their use of resources

Source: Schools Council, 1980

Energy resources

In order to understand more about the use and misuse of natural resources, one extremely important resource sector, energy, will be studied in this chapter. In other chapters you will consider less directly how people have used a variety of resources – such as agricultural land, sandy beaches, forests and technological skills – and the impact that this use has had on the people and their environment.

Most natural resources are used as raw materials for some form of processing and manufacture. Iron ore, for example, is used to make steel for engineering products. However, the energy resources are a complex mix. Some (coal, oil, gas) are in demand as raw materials for the chemical industry and *also* as the fuel supply for domestic, commercial and industrial power

and transport. Often the fuel is used by the power-supply industry to generate electricity, a much cleaner, more transportable and more versatile form of energy. Competition exists between those who believe that the resource should be used as a limited raw material and those who wish to use it as a fuel supply even though alternatives could possibly be developed. Figure 3.2 shows world energy use by sector in 1990.

Energy itself is available as a *primary* resource such as coal, which can provide heat energy and some light energy when it is burnt, or as water which provides mechanical energy when it turns a water wheel. It is also available as a *secondary* resource in the form of electricity which has been made from a primary energy resource such as oil, uranium or wind. Energy supplies and other resources which cannot be replenished fast enough to keep pace with use will eventually run out. These are called *finite* or non-renewable. Those which can be replenished, or will become available again, are called non-finite or *renewable*.

Energy reserves

In the less-developed areas of the world, much energy still comes from human and animal effort and from fuelwood, peat and animal waste. However, during the twentieth century, the main sources of world energy have been the *fossil fuels* (coal, oil and natural gas) and, more recently, nuclear and hydro-electric power. Fossil fuels have been formed in the Earth's crust over many millions of years. Except where they naturally appear at the surface, a thorough understanding of the geology of the area is necessary before resources can be explored and exploited. When deposits have been found in sufficient quantities, and are geologically and geographically accessible, they are called 'proven reserves'. The world maps show the proven reserves of oil, natural gas and coal at the end of 1991 (Figures 3.3, 3.4, 3.5).

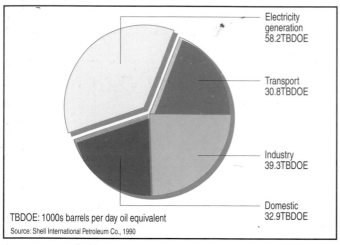

TBDOE: 1000s barrels per day oil equivalent

Source: Shell International Petroleum Co., 1990

Figure 3.2   World energy use by sector

ENQUIRY: CLASSIFYING ENERGY RESOURCES

1 Make a list of all the energy resources you can think of. Identify each of the resources as renewable or non-renewable. A further category lies somewhere between these two. *Sustainable* resources will renew themselves if they are not over-exploited. Can you think of an energy resource in this category?

2 For each energy resource suggest what uses, other than for energy purposes, there might be. Would the alternative use prevent it being used for energy production? For example, coal for industrial carbon could not also be burnt for fuel. However, water for hydroelectricity production could *afterwards* be used for irrigation.

3 Attempt to devise several different forms of classification for energy resources. Possibilities might be:
   a a classification based on natural systems (cycles of nature), e.g. air circulation, tides.
   b a classification based on mineral/animal/ vegetable/solar. In what circumstances might any of these classifications prove useful? What are their disadvantages?

4 It would be possible also to classify energy resources according to their occurrence. Using an atlas, classify each of your energy resources into

'widespread', 'localised' or 'unavailable'. You could apply it to one country, one continent, or the world.

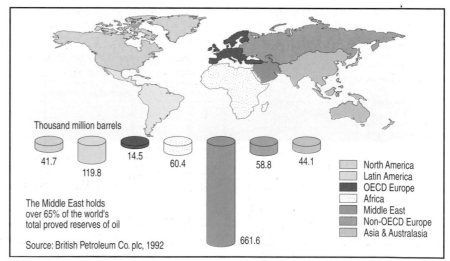

Figure 3.3   Proven reserves of oil, 1991

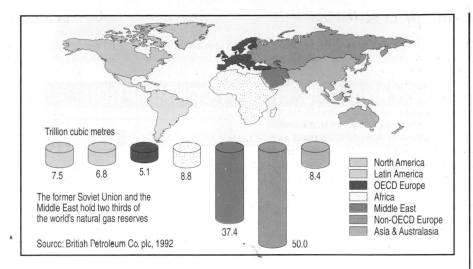

Figure 3.4   Proven reserves of natural gas, 1991

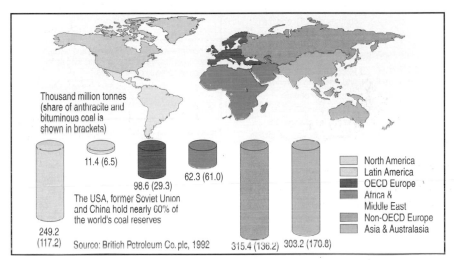

Figure 3.5   Proven reserves of coal, 1991

STATISTICAL AND CARTOGRAPHIC ANALYSIS: WHERE ARE THE RESERVES?

1   Describe what the maps show about the proven reserves of each fuel. What are the political and economic implications?

2   Comment on the suitability of the technique used.

3   Where do you think the greatest future increases in proven reserves for each fuel will be? Justify your answers. (Consider present knowledge of reserves, changes in technology, accessibility, availability of geological mapping surveys, etc.).

4   The tables below show the percentage increase in main fossil fuel reserves 1968–1988. Identify any statistics that do not fit your own prediction in **3**, and attempt to explain the anomaly.

Table 3.1   Increase in fossil fuel reserves, 1968–88 (%)

a   Oil and gas

	Oil	Gas
Latin America	20.5	8.5
Middle East	66.1	31.4
Socialist countries	4.6	42.8 (mostly former USSR)
Western Europe	3.3	4.2
Other	5.5	13.1

b   Coal

	Coal
Africa	21.8
China	47.6
USA	27.4
Others	3.2

Source: British Petroleum Company Plc, 1989

Coal remains the prime source of energy in Asia and Australasia, while Oil and Gas account for more than 60% of demand in all other regions

Source: British Petroleum Co. plc, 1992

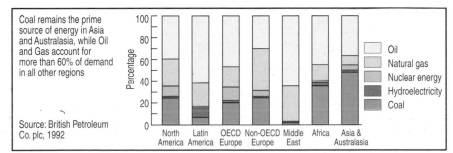

Figure 3.6   Regional consumption patterns, 1991

Energy consumption

All of the fossil fuels are finite and although new sources may be found, they are unlikely to keep pace with the increased demand for energy which is predicted as 75% between 1980 and 2000. Even at today's production (usage) rates the proven world reserves of some fossil fuels will run out in your lifetime, as shown in Figure 3.7.

GRAPH ANALYSIS: ENERGY CONSUMPTION

Study the graph of fossil fuel reserves/production ratio and the table showing classification of economies by fuel-mix in 1983 (Figure 3.7, Table 3.2).

1 a Use an outline political map of the world to show the pattern in Table 3.2.

  b Comment on the probable changes in fuel usage from 1991 to 2066 and 2066 to 2191 as suggested in Figure 3.7.

  c What changes do you expect to see in future in:
    (i) the cost of oil?
    (ii) trade in fossil fuels?
    (iii) energy use in the economically more-developed countries (OECD) and the economically less-developed countries

2 In the late 1960s people and governments became aware of the 'energy problem' (the fact that energy reserves were finite, and dwindling fast). From the graph (Figure 3.8), describe how energy consumption per capita has changed from 1966–91 and attempt to predict changes for 1991–2001. Explain the basis for your prediction.

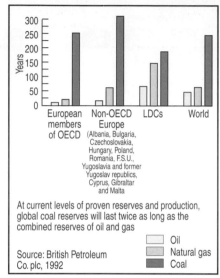

At current levels of proven reserves and production, global coal reserves will last twice as long as the combined reserves of oil and gas

Source: British Petroleum Co. plc, 1992

☐ Oil
☐ Natural gas
■ Coal

Figure 3.7   Fossil fuels, reserve to production, 1991

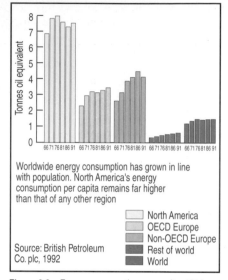

Worldwide energy consumption has grown in line with population. North America's energy consumption per capita remains far higher than that of any other region

Source: British Petroleum Co. plc, 1992

☐ North America
☐ OECD Europe
☐ Non-OECD Europe
■ Rest of world
■ World

Figure 3.8   Energy consumption per capita, 1991

Table 3.2   Classification of economies by fuel-mix 1983

		Liquid						Solid		Gas		
		Liquid solely dominant						Solid solely dominant		Gas solely dominant		Primary
Diversity	One-fuel	Portugal Ghana Sudan Iran Malaysia Syria Cuba Nether. Antilles Ecuador	Angola Ivory Coast Tunisia Iraq Philippines Thailand Domin. Rep. Panama Peru	Egypt Kenya Cyprus Israel Saudi Arabia Guam El Salvador Puerto Rico Surinam	Ethiopia Morocco Dem. Yemen Jordan Singapore Bahamas Guatemala US Virgin Uruguay	Gabon Senegal Indonesia Lebanon Sri Lanka Costa Rica Jamaica Bolivia		Poland North Korea	China S. Africa	Bahrain	Qatar	
		Liquid/solid		**Liquid/gas**		**Liquid/primary**		**Solid/liquid**		**Gas/liquid**		**Primary/liquid**
	Two-fuel	Denmark Greece Hong Kong Mozambique	Japan Spain S. Korea	Turkey Albania Chile	Italy Libya Mexico Kuwait	Algeria Nigeria Myanmar (Burma) Venezuela	Iceland Switzerland Zaire Argentina	Sweden Brazil	Luxembourg Bulgaria India Vietnam	Yugoslavia Czechoslovaskia Mongolia	Netherlands Bangladesh Pakistan	Trinidad Brunei Utd Arab Emirates	Norway
		Liquid/solid/primary	**Liquid/solid/gas**	**Liquid/gas/solid**	**Liquid/primary/solid**	**Solid/liquid/gas**		**Solid/liquid/primary**		**Gas/liquid/solid**		**Gas/solid/liquid**
	Three-fuel	Finland	Belgium Ireland	France Austria	Zambia Colombia USA	Australia		Zimbabwe UK		USSR		Hungary Romania
		Liquid/gas/solid/primary				**Liquid/gas/primary/solid**						
	Four-fuel	Canada Germany				New Zealand						
		Total liquid 80						Total solid 14		Total gas 11		Total primary 1

Source: Aitchinson and Heal, 1987

Energy alternatives

Electricity generation accounted for 34% of world energy use in 1986. Figure 3.9 shows the variety of methods of generating electricity and the amount of primary energy input required. It also shows the relative costs of developing new generating capacity and the cost of on-going production. The choice of fuel depends on local or national energy policies which are influenced by availability of resources, security of energy supplies, cost, and environmental considerations.

A further 25% of the world's energy is used for transport, almost all of it as oil for road transport. Over 20% of the world's energy is burnt in car engines and the less-developed countries are likely to increase this usage in the future as they become more industrialised and more personally mobile. In Canada and the USA there is roughly one car for every two people, in Brazil it is one to sixteen, in India one to 877 and in Bangladesh one to 3000. Alternative fuels (such as alcohol), improved fuel consumption and, eventually, electric vehicles may reduce this demand on oil.

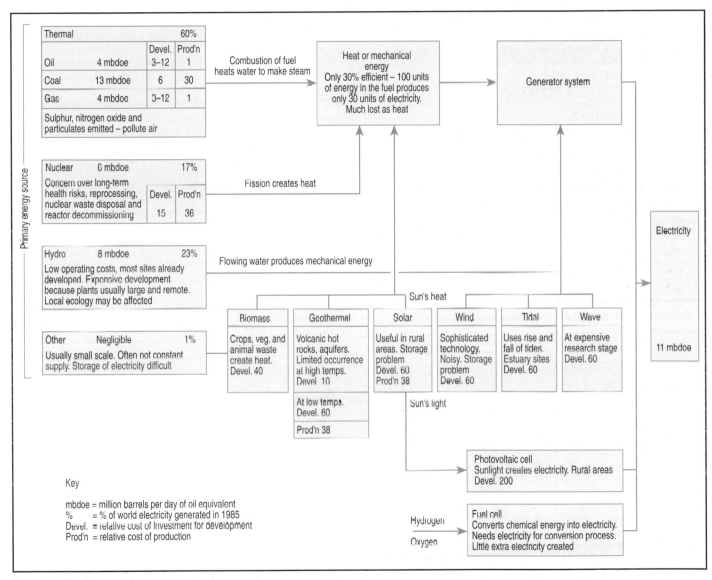

Figure 3.9 Electricity generation

ENQUIRY: ALTERNATIVES TO FOSSIL FUELS

1 Study Figure 3.9 and identify the factors which pose the greatest problem for the widespread long-term development or use of the various alternatives. Cost is often a problem. Who could and who do you think should make the necessary investment? Why?

2 Draw a poster to encourage a change from or a decreased use of a finite energy resource. Explain at whom the poster is aimed, the need for the change, and its likely impact.

Energy Issues – the Topics of World Concern

An ever-increasing demand for energy now affects the world on a global scale. Although different countries perceive the problems in various ways, the underlying issues are broadly similar.

The energy issue that caused greatest concern *in the 1960s and 1970s* was that the supplies of energy might be exhausted before alternatives had been adequately developed. International trade in the limited commodities became increasingly important and those countries with precious oil supplies acquired political strength and organised themselves to form a powerful body, OPEC. *In the 1970s* world attention was focused on the question of how the non-renewable resources should best be used.

- How should dwindling oil supplies be allocated?
- Should the rich nations be allowed to outbid the poor for limited commodities?
- Who should regulate production and demand?
- How should dependence on oil be reduced?

International decisions were needed on conservation issues.

In the 1980s the emphasis changed to focus on the environmental issues.

- Can we protect our seas and beaches from oil?
- What procedures should follow an accident at a nuclear power station?
- Are forests being killed by coal-fired power station emissions?
- Is the burning of fossil fuels warming the world?

International decisions are needed on pollution control.

The issues in the 1990s consider the energy alternatives and their feasibility world-wide.

- Who should finance the development of alternative resources?
- Should new energy technology be made available world-wide?
- Does the economically more-developed world (the North) have a responsibility towards the economically less-developed nations (the South) whose demands are set to escalate by the year 2000?

International co-operation is required for energy development which is efficient, yet environmentally less damaging. Sustainability or 'green growth' is the new watchword.

The issues for the year 2000 may include no assumptions of increased growth in demand but may be concerned entirely with the conservation and efficient use of supplies.

In this section some of the questions and answers concerned with conservation and pollution control will be considered and in the following section the resource options will be studied and assessed.

Making the most of it – conservation in the North

The economically more-developed world is still largely dependent upon depleting fossil fuel resources. Despite the demands for cleaner fuels, which add to the pressures for change, little progress has been made in most countries towards a 'greener' energy budget. What has changed in recent years is our awareness of the limited nature of these supplies and their tendency to pollute. As a result, world-wide efforts have been made to use them efficiently. Since the 1970s the Western nations have boosted their energy efficiency by 20%. In the colder North, newer homes require only 5 kilowatt hours to heat, whereas the older non-insulated home (with the same area) would have required 12 to 20 kilowatt hours. The fuel industries have done much to educate the public in energy-saving at home and at work. Further improvements would be possible if consumers selected those manufacturers' appliances – freezers, washing machines, dishwashers, tumbledriers, etc.— which used least electricity. Greater emphasis is also required on the need to reduce transport energy costs by encouraging more mass-transport systems and persuading short-distance travellers to use human energy. Energy can also be saved by cost-conscious industrialists and by recycling. Local enterprises are being set up and, internationally, organisations such as the European Commission are working towards greater co-ordination of effort.

GROUP DISCUSSION: SAVING IT

1 Read the article about recycling in Camden ('Valuing our . . .') and make a list of changes that you think could help save potential energy resources (fossil fuels and trees).

2 Draw diagrams to show the weekend activities of each member of the group. Remember what you did, where you went and what you ate last weekend. In what ways could you have been more energy efficient? (That's fuel energy, not human energy!)

3 Produce a group chart listing what changes are needed to encourage, or force, people to be more energy efficient. Consider costs, timetables, routes, laws, facts, time.

VALUING OUR HOUSEHOLD WASTE

Each year a family of four throws out a tonne of waste and contributes to the 23 million tonnes of British domestic waste which costs £720 million to get rid of. Its value if recycled would be £750 million. At regular intervals council workers sort through a tonne of household rubbish to find out exactly what we throw away: glass, plastic, cans, newspaper.

A comprehensive recycling centre has been developed at Camden, the London borough that recycles more domestic waste than most. However, even here, only 2.5 per cent is recycled. Of the 180,000 residents only a small number make up the 65,000 trips to the centre each year.

At the recycling centre in Jamestown Road, it is possible to dispose of paper, cardboard and metals cans. Almost 100% of glass is recyclable but nationally only 16% of glass is recycled, compared with 40% in Europe as a whole. Almost 85% of the weight of a dustbin load could be deposited in skips at the Camden centre and much of the rest of the rubbish would make good compost (from kitchen food waste). Some items such as packaging and small objects (ring pulls, bottle tops, paper bags and scraps of aluminium foil) are considered too tiny or dirty to bother with.

Foil-coated papers and waxed paper milk cartons cannot be recycled because they are combinations of materials and contamination is built into the design.

Of the 40 types of plastic in the consumer market only a few can, at present, be recycled. Some of the clear plastics used in food packaging will be able to be reclaimed in the future. Plastic bottles are a real problem because they cannot easily be squashed; they fill up the skips before reaching economically viable quantities. On average in Europe about 7 per cent by weight of plastics is recycled but this accounts for 20 per cent by volume.

A further difficulty is that it is still practically impossible even for trained staff to identify and separate the different types of plastic. Fizzy drinks bottles or washing-up bottles make two categories that are easily described and manufacturers are now beginning to identify the type of plastic and the containers themselves.

In the past certain items were more profitable for recycling than they are today. Returnable bottles became unpopular when it was realised that millions of pounds worth were being thrown away unclaimed. Newspaper collections used to be very lucrative money-earners because it was worth £40 per tonne. Now it is £3 a tonne because supply outstrips demand.

Some local authorities are encouraging individuals to separate their waste into different categories that are acceptable for recycling: metals, paper, food waste, glass and plastic. Each category is collected separately when the rubbish is picked up each week. Sheffield already has a scheme like this.

Once facilities are widely available for recycling the consumer must then look carefully at what is bought. Purchasing habits must change to reflect the new slogan: 'Don't choose what you can't re-use.'

The other crisis – conservation in the South

Managing energy in the economically less-developed areas of the South is much more complicated than in the Northern industrialised nations. Fossil fuels are usually too expensive for everyday use and electricity is often available only to the more affluent in the major cities. If there is any market at all for fuel it is on a local or regional scale. The fuels that are important here are dung, wood, biomass and charcoal.

At least two billion people rely on fuelwood to cook. They do not heat their homes or light their rooms and yet 70% of them are unable to find the supplies they need and are forced to fell forests to survive. They require about 3 kg (a few sticks) a day but their large population numbers and dwindling forested areas mean that a potentially sustainable resource is plundered. For many families it now costs as much to heat the food as the food itself costs. Fuelwood collection can take 100 to 300 days of work each year, the equivalent of a quarter of an urban family's income. Uncooked food tastes unpleasant and also contains parasites which harm the stomach, affecting the health of many families. Others turn to alternative fuels such as dung. Unfortunately, this then deprives the fields of fertiliser and grain yields are reduced. In Africa and Asia, 400 million tonnes of dung are burned annually, at the expense of a potential 20 million tonnes of grain which could have fed millions of people (Figure 3.10).

Cooking on an open fire is a very inefficient use of energy. Much of the heat escapes to the surrounding air and does not heat the food in the cooking pot. Consider how much longer it takes to heat food over a campfire than on the kitchen cooker. 'Three stone' fires are common in parts of the Third World. They are easy to set up and they cost nothing. However, sparks and smoke from the fires make them dangerous to the health of the cook's family. Consequently, with the help of Western agencies, appropriate fuel-efficient stoves have been designed to meet the needs of various communities.

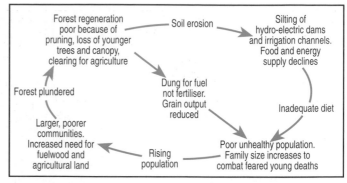

Figure 3.10   The fuelwood crisis

CASE STUDY *An Energy-Saving Stove in Sri Lanka*

The Intermediate Technology Group, based in Rugby, England, have been working with the Ceylon Electricity Board in Sri Lanka to develop and promote a stove in the region (Figure 3.11). In rural areas the new stove is spreading fast. At present, however, the main contributors to the problem of deforestation in Sri Lanka are the urban population, who buy their fuelwood commercially. At present there is an ample supply of wood from trees felled at hydro-electric dam sites and in restocked rubber plantations. Within two to three years, however, these sources will run out and the pressure on Sri Lanka's dwindling forests will be

immense as demand for fuelwood escalates. A new portable version of the stove, based on the rural experience, has been developed for the urban market. It is manufactured locally and vigorously marketed through commercial outlets: 100 000 stoves are now produced annually and sales are rising. Woodfuel demand is falling and the new industry provides employment for men and women in the villages. For the cooks, the new stove means a fuel saving, so that either less time is lost collecting wood or less money is spent buying it. The time can be spent on other tasks or on paid employment to provide a better income for the family. The enclosed firebox

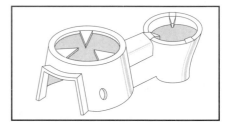

Figure 3.11   Portable Sri Lankan stove

keeps the kitchen cleaner, improving hygiene and home safety. The stoves are demonstrated by local health workers who also arrange for the purchase of the stoves, help to install them, and provide instruction on using them.

ENQUIRY: FUELWOOD

1 Using the data in Table 3.3 devise an appropriate method to show on a world map where the fuelwood crisis is greatest. For example, you may wish to use located bar graphs or proportional circles, or you may prefer to calculate an 'availability factor' and map your results.

2 Study the other fuel-saving devices shown in Figure 3.12. Design a series of posters suitable for use by the local health visitor in rural areas in economically less-developed countries to promote one of the devices.

3 Produce a leaflet, suitable for use by a charity promoting intermediate technology, which explains why devices such as those shown in Figure 3.12 have local, national and international benefits, and which urges support for their development.

Table 3.3   Required and available amounts of fuelwood

	Population dependent on fuelwood supplies (millions)	Amount required (millions m³)	Amount available
West Latin America (arid, densely populated)	16	14	5
East Latin America (abundant forest resources)	38	45.6	380
Africa (savannah)	131.4	197	118
Africa (high forest)	36.5	62	73
Far East Asia (mountain areas – Himalayas)	29	52	9
Far East Asia (plains)	297	208	74

Source: Myers, 1985

Open fire 1
- Inefficient fuel useage
- Smokey and dirty

		Stove 1	Stove 2	Stove 3	Stove 4
Cost:	No cost	✓			
	Low cost		✓	✓	
	High cost				✓
Use:	No training needed	✓	✓	✓	
	Training needed				✓
	Trained operator needed				
Construction:	Self built	✓			
	Artesian-built		✓	✓	
	Factory-built				✓
Power source:	Diesel/electricity				
	Animal/manual			✓	
	Renewable	✓	✓	✓	✓
Purpose:	Labour-saving		✓	✓	
	Income-generating				✓
	Domestic	✓		✓	✓
Maintainance:	Simple	✓			
	Training needed		✓	✓	
	Specialist needed				

Community cooker 3
- For use in schools, hospitals
- 42-litre capacity metal pot fits inside stove
- Chimney removes smoke from wood or biomass fire
- Cheaply made by local artisan
- Materials range from clay, brick to cast iron to match purchaser's budget

Source: Sandhu and Sandler, 1986

Pottery liner stove 2
- Cheaply made in two pieces by local potters
- Installed in kitchen with protective mud layer
- Easily repaired by owner, fire easily relit
- Two cooking holes but one enclosed wood-burning firebox
- In rural Sri Lanka, save 30–50% fuelwood

Green charcoal cooker 4
- Use partially decayed organic matter such as grass, made into cheap, uniform compact briquettes which last longer and burn cleaner
- For household, commercial and industrial heating and cooking
- Ash used as fertiliser or scourer for cleaning
- Saves wood; little smoke (if charcoal thoroughly dry)

Figure 3.12 Intermediate technology – details of open fire, community cooker, pottery liner stove and green charcoal cooker

Managing the Environment

As energy sources are harnessed to provide power they have an impact on the environment. Buildings and structures, waste products or mining activity all modify the environment, and the transport of fuels or power will have a further impact. Careful siting, landscaping and screening may lessen the effects but at an additional cost to the developer. Where strict planning controls are enforced, the impact may be considered an acceptable result of exploitation — but decisions should always be made as to which alternative is most acceptable to producer, consumer and the environment. Energy exploitation is regarded by many people as diametrically opposed to environmental conservation. It is therefore a very controversial issue.

Table 3.4 Comparative environmental impact

Energy source	Resource type	Possible environmental impact
Coal	Non-renewable	Extraction, waste spoil, dust, subsidence, CO_2
Oil	Non-renewable	Extraction, oil pollution, subsidence, CO_2
Gas	Non-renewable	Extraction, subsidence, CO_2
Nuclear	Sustainable	Ore extraction, radioactive waste, fallout, explosion
Wood	Sustainable	Afforestation/deforestation
Dung	Sustainable	Reduced addition to soil as fertiliser
Geothermal	Renewable	Extraction plant
Wind	Renewable	Wind 'farm' sites – visual
Hydro	Renewable	Dams, flooding, water flow
Solar	Renewable	Building appearance
Tidal	Renewable	Barrages – ecological, navigational

GROUP ACTIVITY: CREATING AN ENVIRONMENTAL IMPACT SCALE

1 For each energy source shown in Table 3.4, evaluate the environmental impact. You will need to think about a scale of severity (for example, 0–5, or 1–10) and also about the types of environmental impact (for example, air and water pollution, visual disamenity, land-use impacts, waste issues, health risks, potential world-scale disasters). You should also remember that the environmental impact depends on the scenario – deep-mined coal versus opencast extraction, or nuclear fission versus nuclear fusion. You then need to agree as a group (because scales like this rely on individual perceptions) on an average and composite weighting.

2 Each choose one energy source and suggest ways in which the environmental impact might be minimised.

Pollution control

Several energy resources pollute the atmosphere, the oceans or the land during their exploitation. The unequal distribution and use of these energy resources means that pollution is worse in some areas of the world than others. However, because of movements of air masses, winds and ocean currents, the pollution of the air and sea, though occurring in one area, may have an impact world-wide. The water and air pollution resulting from the 1991 Gulf War had an impact on many countries adjacent to the Gulf, and scientists continue to speculate that it may have a wider long-term impact – on world climate patterns, for example. There is no doubt that global solutions have to be found.

CASE STUDY *Oil on Troubled Waters: Sea and River Pollution*

Figure 3.13 shows the origin of oil found in the sea, while Figure 3.14 shows the oil industry's assessment of the processes following a spill. The environmental organisation Gaia estimates that 6 million tonnes of oil enter the ocean each year. The largest contribution comes from the consumers of oil (industry and the public) as land runoff, mostly from the cities. A large proportion, however, is deliberately deposited into the sea by tanker operations, while tanker accidents contribute a further 12%.

When empty a tanker has to take on water for ballast. Until recently the same tanks were used alternately for the oil cargo and for ballast water. When this water was jettisoned into the sea, some oil went with it. International conventions have now reduced the amount of oil which can be washed into the sea legally, and all new ships have to be fitted with separate ballast and cargo tanks. The amount of oil released has thus been reduced considerably.

The following newspaper extracts give examples of tanker accidents which all occurred in the space of a year. None of these incidents are as well known as those involving the *Torrey Canyon* or *Exxon Valdez*, but their environmental effects were immediately devastating at a local level and had the potential to cause widespread pollution with the aid of strong ocean currents.

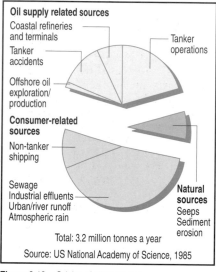

Figure 3.13 Origins of oil in the sea

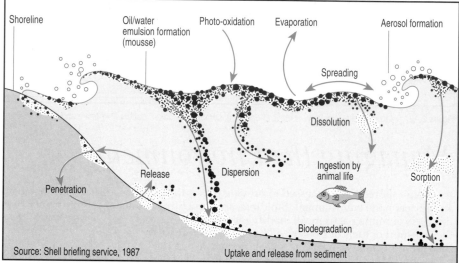

Figure 3.14 Processes following a spill

WILDLIFE AT RISK AS OIL POURS FROM CRASH SHIP

Martin Charlesworth

A CLEAN-UP battle to save thousands of birds, seals and fish began yesterday after a tanker collision caused a six-mile-long oil slick off the east coast.

Planes were spraying detergent to disperse the 500 tonnes of light crude spilled off the Humber.

Labour's environment spokesman Tony Blair called for a Government inquiry into Britain's third major oil leak in the past three weeks.

This latest spillage is more than three times bigger than the pipe leak on the Mersey last month.

A week ago guillemots coated in oil were washed up along the shores of Northumberland and Tyne and Wear.

Conservationists fear the new disaster could disturb the annual migration of cod and sole.

Friends of the Earth spokesman Steve Terry said it was vital to clear the slick as quickly as possible.

'The Wash is a very important area for birds, seals and other wildlife,' he said. 'Any threat to them would be terrible.'

Stricken

The spillage occurred after the Phillips Oklahoma and the Fiona collided just before 5 a.m. in a misty drizzle at the mouth of the Humber.

Oil poured from a 20 ft gash in the hull of the Oklahoma.

A major air and sea rescue operation was mounted when fire broke out on the ships and spread to the slick.

An RAF Nimrod, three helicopters, a Royal Navy minesweeper and a Humber lifeboat raced to the scene, helping most of the stricken ship's Filipino crew to escape.

The Fiona's 30 crew members stayed on board while five fire-fighting tugs rushed to help and 20 Humberside firemen were airlifted to the vessels.

It took them three hours to control the fire on the Phillips Oklahoma.

Tugs and planes immediately began spraying detergent on the slick which drifted towards Lincolnshire, only 20 miles from the resorts of Cleethorpes and Mablethorpe.

Source: *Daily Express*, 18 September 1989

ROGUE SHIP BLAMED FOR OIL DISASTER

Ian Birrell and Tom Revill

ROBIN LESLIE spent yesterday in a boat off the Dorset coast, scouring the waves for dying birds. Some he pulled out of the sea were already beyond rescue, poisoned by the thick brown sludge weighing down their wings.

The RSPCA inspector is at the forefront of the struggle to cope with Britain's worst case of oil pollution at sea since 1985. 'It's a desperate task. I'm doing what I can but there are so many helpless birds. I can't save them all,' he said.

Nearly 2,000 birds were found dead or dying along Britain's south coast last week. The final death toll is likely to be three times as high.

Government chemists are preparing to analyse samples of oil washed on to the coastline. Most experts suspect it is from a ship washing out its bilges at sea.

The slick was first spotted off east Sussex.

But it was not until the end of last week that the scale of the pollution became clear, with hundreds of birds found dying on a 300-mile stretch of coast from Essex to Cornwall.

Captains defy regulations laid down by the International Maritime Organisation, a UN body, if they jettison oil. But Dr John Wonham, marine pollution expert with the IMO, said unscrupulous owners might be tempted to get rid of oily waste at sea to avoid port charges which can be thousands of pounds.

Oil pollution off most British beaches has been declining this decade and the government has won praise from conservationists for its efforts to further this trend. But many environmental groups are concerned that offenders escape with derisory fines.

In 1987 there were 10 convictions for illegal discharges. The fines totalled £11,850 and the Royal Society for the Protection of Birds is among those seeking heavier penalties. Kevin Standring, conservation planning officer said: 'When these ships are caught in the act we want the book thrown at them.'

Source: *Sunday Times*, 8 January 1989

RACE TO AVERT HUGE NORTH SEA OIL SPILLAGE

NORTH SEA nations were on alert for a major oil spillage last night as American experts raced to reinforce a sea-bed valve holding back a blow-out on an exploratory well in the Norwegian Ecofisk field.

A safety valve understood to be capable of withstanding pressures of 15,000 pounds per square inch is thought to be the only thing preventing an eruption of thousands of tons of oil and gas which are pushing upwards at 10,000 psi.

If the valve failed there would be 'dire environmental consequences'.

Mr Lars Bjelke, a Saga Oil spokesman, said: 'The situation is critical.' Vessels equipped to deal with oil slicks were standing by.

An American oil specialist, Mr Ansgar Hansen said he was 'relatively optimistic' that the valve would hold.

Source: *Daily Telegraph*, 24 January 1989

VALUES ENQUIRY: POLLUTION AT SEA

1 Comment on the way the newspapers reported the oil pollution incidents. (As well as the articles above and left, consider the montage of photographs in Figure 3.15.)

2 What are the major causes and effects of oil spillage incidents?

3 Who is to blame for the oil spills?

4 Can anything be done about the problem?

Figure 3.15 After an oil spill

ANALYSIS: WHO SHOULD GET COMPENSATION, AND FOR WHAT?

After the Mersey spill, Shell UK agreed to pay the costs incurred. Using the list of organisations involved, make out a list for Shell of what these charges will be for. In some cases you may want to ask them for a contribution for ongoing problems, or as a token charge for suffering or lack of amenity. You may wish to give advice to prevent future accidents and to aid other clean-up operations. The organisations involved are listed below.

- National Rivers Authority (pollution watchdog body).
- Department of Energy – Pipeline Inspectorate.

- Royal Society for the Protection of Birds.
- Royal Society for the Prevention of Cruelty to Animals.
- Oil Spill Service Centre, Southampton (this body was set up by the oil industry and is to be advised of any spill within an hour of the occurrence, with regular reports thereafter. Experts are sent to the site immediately if the minimum spill level is exceeded. Payment is made by the offender to the centre to cover any costs it incurs in reacting to the spill).

- Department of Transport, Marine Pollution Control Unit, Coventry (the Unit takes responsibility in any area affected by a water-based oil spill. The offender must pay the Unit for costs incurred).
- Volunteers – local residents, walkers, bird watchers, sailing clubs, naturalists.
- Martin Mere Wildfowl Trust (9 miles from Southport).
- Local district councils – Liverpool, Wirral, Sefton, Warrington, Halton, Ellesmere Port and Neston.
- Cheshire Fire Department.
- Merseyside Fire Department.

SHELL TO PAY A HIGH PRICE FOR MERSEY SLICK

HUNDREDS of firemen, council workers and volunteers worked along the banks of the river Mersey yesterday to help clear the spillage of 150 tons of crude oil from a fractured pipeline at the weekend.

Shell estimated the cost of the clean-up at hundreds of thousands of pounds. The company could face a claim from Wirral council, which has spent £30,000 since 1986 laying 100,000 tons of sand to improve tourism at New Brighton.

The worst affected shorelines were from Widnes on the north bank and Runcorn on the south downriver to Warrington. At least 1,000 birds – most of them black-headed gulls – have been affected by the slick. Many have died.

Merseyside and Cheshire fire brigades co-ordinated the clean-up using 900 gallons of detergent, high-powered water jets and manual labour.

The fractured section of pipeline was raised at low tide yesterday by Shell technicians. Detailed tests will be carried out, but metal fatigue or

corrosion could be to blame, said a Shell spokesman.

The pipeline, set in the rock of the river bed, was last checked 16 months ago by the Government Pipeline Inspectorate, which usually requires a check every two years. 'We may have to look at shortening the time of the inspection,' said the spokesman. The pipe laid 30 years ago, is not considered particularly old.

Twenty-four species of birds have been affected, including mallard, shelduck, ringed plover, redshank and common sandpiper. Many were taken to the RSPCA at Southport and the country park ranger centre at Thurstaston on the Wirral, where cleaning operations have been set up.

Mr Andrew Best, Merseyside's chief fire officer, said that some oil might be left to break down naturally.

'We will do more damage to the vegetation and to the types of soil by having people treading about in large numbers,' he said.

Mr John Armitage a regional officer of the RSPB, said: ' We have oil going on to the feeding and roosting areas and birds yet to arrive will feel the

effects because of the shortage of foods.

'I would hope things won't get worse but with the oil slick covering up to 30 miles of shoreline on both sides of the river, that is unlikely.'

The number of birds initially affected was not as high as had been expected.

But conservationists were concerned yesterday about the effect of the spillage on the salt banks, mud flats, and other estuarial areas used by winter migratory birds.

The worst affected areas for birds were Dungeon Banks on the north shore and Eastham mud flats, near the Shell oil storage tanks at Tranmere from where a 12-inch pipe carries the crude oil to the Shell refinery at Stanlow 12 miles away.

The emergency services were yesterday holding talks with the Nature Conservancy Council, the Royal Society for the Protection of Birds, and other agencies on the best way to clean salt marshes that are difficult to reach.

Source: *Guardian*, 22 August 1989

Evaluating the effects of marine pollution

All the newspaper articles have concentrated on major environmental impacts of oil pollution incidents. The volume of oil spilled is only one measure of potential damage. Other factors include the ingredients of the oil, the salinity and depth of the water, local water temperature (cold water inhibits evaporation and bacteria breakdown),

the time of year, the strength of waves and currents, the relative purity of the environment (which determines the ecology), the types of life that the oil reaches and the speed and effectiveness of the clean-up operation.

In the Mersey incident, for example, Cheshire's Chief Fire Officer said that, 'There was a general lack of information – on some of the effects of the more commonly transported oils, about the river itself and how the oil would behave. Many of the resources available

to tackle the slick were not known about initially.'

The Mersey seems to have been incredibly lucky. There was a very high tide straight after the leak, which washed the oil high on the banks where it was very visible, above the normal feeding areas of the birds. If it had been lighter North Sea oil, it would have spread everywhere, and if the wind had not been favourable the oil would have swamped major feeding grounds.

ENQUIRY: EFFECTS OF THE MERSEY OIL SPILL

Using the comments of Cheshire's Chief Fire Officer and information from page 110, identify the factors which made the spill less disastrous than it might have been. What factors could have exacerbated the effects?

TWO VIEWS OF A DISASTER

Richard North

One, rather gloomy, [view] was written for the United States Department of Justice as part of the legal proceedings which wrap American accidents in litigation practically as hazardous as oil tankers. It pointed to high – and disputed – losses to various populations, and especially of murres (which we call guillemots). The report suggested that perhaps 300,000 of the 1,400,000 murres in the Gulf of Alaska died. It suggested that only studies this year would reveal the population losses, if any, among wild salmon that were larvae at the time of the spill.

Certainly many of them were damaged. Some whales are missing. Sea otters died miserably and even now show lower survival rates in areas that were oiled. Sea lions and harbour seals were in decline before the spill, confounding attempts to assess the damage, though the seals appear to be suffering more in the spill's aftermath. Much of the report's unease flows from insisting that the present position is hard to assess, and that answers must await further research.

A very different sense emerges from Robert Clark, emeritus professor of zoology at Newcastle University and editor of the Marine Pollution Bulletin. He is one of many scientists paid by Exxon to research the impact of the spill from its ship, and one of the authors cited in Exxon's own upbeat report on the damage. Returning from a trip to the disaster area a fortnight ago, he said. 'The place is absolutely marvellous You wouldn't know it had happened. The winter storms have polished most of the beaches. You have to look for signs of oil.'

People talk of the damage to the murres as severe, but Clark's observation of the colonies was that 'zillions of birds fly off when you approach'. He reports oiled beaches as now being 'very healthy-looking'. The area's beauty was not long blighted by the spill, and aesthetics matter. So does being seen to do something: the American National Oceanic and Atmospheric Administration has just reported that much of the $2 billion clean-up in Alaska delayed nature's own recovery.

This story of recovery after supposed disasters is repeated any time you talk to people who follow them closely. Dr Roger Mitchell, senior marine specialist with the Joint Nature Conservation Committee (JNCC), the successor to the chief scientist's team at the disbanded Nature Conservancy Council, says: 'I went to the Roscoff coastline of Brittany in the days after the Amoco Cadiz spill. It was pretty horrific at the time, and the poor French squaddies were being sick as they cleaned it up. But the next year, it was a very different picture.'

Mitchell describes a process of a return to near normality, both aesthetically and in conservation terms, which saw rapid progress after the spill in 1978, with the last of the noticeable damage restored in three years or so. A skilled biologist could detect impacts from spills like this many years afterwards: but these amount to slightly skewed species distribution, and are very different from aesthetic or ecological blight. Much of the ugliness a slick can bring can be cleaned with a bit of effort.

None of the scientists I spoke to last week are complacent, but all were anxious to get away from talk of ecological disaster, and on to a subtler sense of loss. Slicks join many other human activities and accidents that erode the value and beauty of our shorelines.

For Dr Andrew Price, a tropical coast expert, it is the way tar pavements join litter, debris and land reclamation in producing whole coasts that are ugly and less useful for wildlife.

Exxon Valdez, the Gulf, Torrey Canyon, Amoco Cadiz, and now probably the Haven, join the ranks of incidents that have mattered less than at first thought. Their proper lesson is that every scrap of variety lost, every creature and plant that dies, is part of an accumulation of damage that does not by a long chalk spell ecological collapse, but which erodes the amount of beauty in the world.

Source: Extracts from an article in *Sunday Times*, 12 April 1991

ESSAY: EVALUATING THE EVIDENCE

1 Working in groups, collect as much evidence as you can in support of the two opposing views expressed above on major oil pollution incidents. Your college or school will almost certainly have newspaper cuttings and videos of major events, which are also documented in many textbooks.

2 When you have collected the evidence you need, write an essay in which you evaluate the causes and effects of marine oil pollution under the title, 'Ecological disaster or avoidable and partially reparable setback'?

It's all in the atmosphere
The greenhouse effect

In recent years there has been growing concern about the impact of increased energy consumption on the atmosphere. The atmosphere is a layer of gases which the forms of life on Earth breathe to live. It is composed of nitrogen (78%), oxygen (21%), argon (0.93%), carbon dioxide (0.03%) and smaller amounts of neon, helium, krypton, xenon, ozone and radon. It is also a blanket layer which absorbs the short-wave solar radiation as it reaches the Earth, scatters it back into space, or deflects it to the surface. The Earth's surface is heated by the Sun but then radiates back heat in longer wavelengths (infra-red radiation). This infra-red heat is prevented from escaping back through the Earth's atmosphere by certain gases in the atmosphere. These gases in the atmosphere let through the short-wave solar radiation but trap the long-wave terrestrial radiation and bounce it back to the Earth's surface, keeping it warmer (by 35°C) than if they were not there – thus making the Earth a habitable place.

Levels of these gases in the atmosphere are rapidly increasing and it appears that the Earth's temperature is, as a result, also rising steadily. This warming process is known as the greenhouse effect and the gases that produce it are termed the greenhouse gases. Those which occur naturally are water vapour, carbon dioxide, methane and nitrous oxide; the industrial gases are the chlorofluorocarbons (CFCs). Activities which add greenhouse gases to the atmosphere are shown in Figures 3.16 and 3.17. As can be seen from Table 3.5, the levels have risen greatly since pre-industrial times (the 1880s) and the global average temperature is thought to have risen by 0.3–0.6°C. Climatologists are still uncertain exactly how the global climatic system works, but many scientists, campaigning organisations and government leaders have agreed that some precautionary action should be taken now.

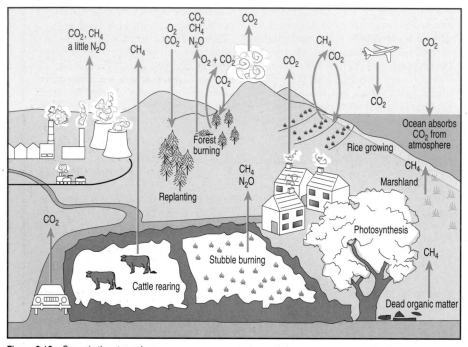

Figure 3.16   Gases in the atmosphere

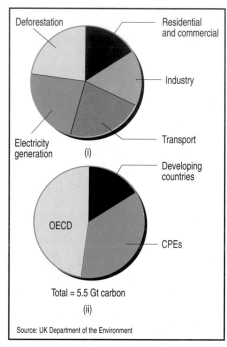

Source: UK Department of the Environment

Figure 3.17   Unnatural carbon dioxide emissions (i) (ii)

VALUES ENQUIRY: WHOSE POLLUTION IS IT?

In a group of four or five, study the resources in Figure 3.18. Each student should choose to represent a different group of people whose attitude and possible role is outlined in these extracts. Prepare an explanation of the activities which you believe that your group can undertake in the next five years and explain the contribution that this will make towards global warming. Present your reports to each other. The other students should then lobby for further steps which they see as necessary and a group discussion should attempt to reach a viable and valuable solution. All but one of these resources were taken from items in British national newspapers. Possible groups are:

1   Representative of the economically more-developed nations – wealthy, highly mechanised industrial and domestic economy, energy supplies taken for granted by population, individually mobile.

2   Car manufactures' representative – competitive industry, anxious to keep prices low, potential market in developing world, speed and fuel availability important.

3   Member of the British public – increasing standard of living expected, unwilling to pay 'too much' for goods, 'not in my back yard' attitude.

4   Aid organisation for economically less-developed world power station projects – closely dependent on industry and governments in developed world for financing, pressure from developing world for prestigious schemes.

5   Representative of the Chinese government – large population, many in poorly developed areas, limited national income, industrial development priority (consumer boom expected, demand for refrigerators, cars, etc.).

Table 3.5 The principal greenhouse gases

Gas		CO$_2$	CH$_4$	CFC–11	CFC-12	N$_2$O
Concentration	Pre-industrial	280 ppmv*	0.79 ppmv	0	0	280 ppbv
	Present	353 ppmv	1.72 ppmv	280 pptv*	484 pptv	310 ppbv
Lifetime in atmosphere	Years	(50–200)	10	65	130	150
Global warming potential relative to CO$_2$†	20 years	1	63	4500	7100	270
	100 years	1	21	3500	7300	290
	500 years	1	9	1500	4500	190
Contribution to total radiactive effect 1980–1990	(%)	55	15	24 (all CFCs)		6

Source: UN Statistical Yearbook, 1985–86

* ppmv: parts per million by volume   ppbv: parts per billion by volume
  pptv: parts per trillion (million million) by volume
†The warming effect of an emission of 1 kg of each gas relative to CO$_2$ based on the present-day atmosphere

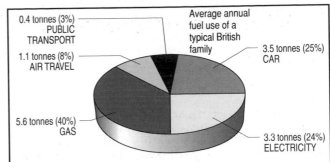

Average annual fuel use of a typical British family

0.4 tonnes (3%) PUBLIC TRANSPORT
1.1 tonnes (8%) AIR TRAVEL
3.5 tonnes (25%) CAR
5.6 tonnes (40%) GAS
3.3 tonnes (24%) ELECTRICITY

Individual action

REDUCING ENERGY CONSUMPTION IN YOUR HOME
The burning of fossil fuels (coal, oil and gas) to produce electricity and heat contributes to the green house effect through a build up of carbon dioxide.
- Insulate your attics and walls and draft-strip your doors and windows.
- Fit thermostats to your hot water tank, to each radiator and in each room and install zone valves to divide your home into separate heating areas.
- Buy the most energy efficient electrical appliances – from your fridge or washing machine to your kettle.
- Use recycling facilities – such as bottlebanks – for your used paper, glass and cans. If these are not available, urge your local authority to provide them. And very importantly, buy recycled products, as there is considerably less used in the production process.

REDUCING ENERGY CONSUMPTION OUTSIDE YOUR HOME
Your car's engine burns petrol and in the process produces carbon dioxide and other gases which contribute to the Greenhouse Effect.
- Next time you buy a new car, consider one fitted with a catalytic converter which reduces the polluting exhaust gases which contribute to the greenhouse effect. Wherever possible walk, cycle or use public transport.

REDUCING THE DESTRUCTION OF THE WORLD'S TROPICAL RAINFORESTS
Tropical rainforests play a vital role in maintaining the climate balance. Yet an area the size of 40 football pitches is destroyed each minute. It is estimated that logging accounts for up to 50% of all losses.
- Don't buy products made from tropical hardwoods, unless you can be certain that they are from sustainable managed sources. Urge suppliers of tropical hardwood products to do the same.

LOBBYING
More funds must be provided by the government for research into the Greenhouse Effect, in addition to the concerted action at government level.
- Write to your MP, and join lobbying organisations such as WWF, which are campaigning on this issue.

One nation's waste of energy

CHINA possesses one fifth of the world's population and one third of the world's coal. Not surprisingly, it is the world's leading producer and consumer of coal and accounts for one tenth of fossil fuel emissions of carbon dioxide worldwide, or more than France and West Germany combined. Carbon dioxide contributes about half of the greenhouse effect.

The country derives almost three-quarters of its commercial energy from coal. This is three times more than the average for industrialised countries. But because of its 1.1 billion people, China's per-capita energy consumption is only one third the world average, and less than seven per cent of that of the United States. So China plans to double its use of coal during the period 1985–2000, and almost double it again by 2020.

As a result of its inefficient use of energy, China has one the highest rates of carbon emissions per unit of economic output in the world. It uses over twice as much energy per unit of economic output as the United States. However, it is trying to do something about the problem, improving its energy efficiency by an annual average of 3.4 per cent during the 1980s.

But with an infusion of energy-efficent and energy-saving technology from more advanced nations, this rate could readily be raised by another two per cent per year. For instance, small scale hydropower dams could supply electricity equivalent to 25 standardised power plants by the year 2000. In addition, China needs to reform its energy pricing. Coal is priced at only one quarter the international level. Folk wisdom has it that "one ton of coal could not even buy one ton of sand". To the extent that that helps China's economy, fine. But if additional efforts are required primarily to safeguard the world's climate at a cost to China's economic growth, the Chinese will understandably raise an eyebrow while their per-capita income remains only about $650 per year, or five per cent that in Britain.

At the same time, China might consider that its own climate will suffer severely in a greenhouse-affected world. It is highly likely that China's interior will dry out as a result of higher temperatures and lower rainfall – with all that means for a country that has trouble enough already in feeding itself. More predictable, and probably no less problematical, is that rising sea levels will inflict widespread flooding along China's coastline, with the inundations and their knock-on effects expected to displace a full 50 million people, possibly many more.

It is China's sheer numbers that compound the impact of its energy practices, meaning that small increases in per-capita energy use multiply into an enormous impact overall.

A view from space

Before they blasted off on September 29 last year on the first space shuttle mission since the Challenger disaster, the crew of the spacecraft Discovery received the routine induction in 'earth observation'. One request by Houston was to look for columns of smoke rising from the Amazon, for it was the height of the burning season.

No one prepared them for the scale of what they saw. The photographs brought back by commander Frederick Hauck and his crew, taken by a hand-held Hasselblad camera from the shuttle's windows, show the colossal extent of the 1988's record rain forest burning, described by one Brazilian conservationist as nothing short of a 'biological holocaust'.

Discovery's pictures show a vast smoke pall from forests being burned by settlers on just one day of Brazil's burning season, from August to October. If superimposed upon Europe, it would stretch from London to Moscow.

Manufacturer's action

Mr Derek Barron, Ford of Britain chairman and chief executive, said "We are bringing forward our plans to offer catalysts in Britain in view of the rapid increase in availability of unleaded petrol, which is the only fuel which can be used in these cars".

Ford says it has committed 800 engineers and £50 million to exhaust emission research all over Europe.

Ford, like other leading companies, has been reluctant to offer catalyst-equipped cars as there would be a price penalty which would put its best-selling range at a disadvantage to competitors.

The converter – which can cut emissions of noxious gases from the exhaust by as much as 90 per cent – will be compulsory on all models by 1993 to comply with stringent European Parliament regulations.

But if things go on as they are

A report studied several areas to predict how the greenhouse effect would probably affect them or the world by the year 2030 compared with the pre-industrial era. (The experts warn that their predictions could vary from 70 to 150 per cent).

1: Central North America: Temperatures up 2 to 4°C in winter and 2 to 3°C in summer. Rain/snow to rise by up to 15 per cent in winter but decrease by 5 to 10 per cent in summer. Soil moisture decreased in summer by 15 to 20 percent.

2: Southern Europe: Temperatures up 2°C in winter and 2 to 3°C in summer. Some extra rain in winter by 5 to 15 per cent, and summer soil moisture by 15 to 25 per cent.

3: Sahara region: Temperatures up 1 to 3°C. Average rainfall up but some small drop in soil moisture in summer. Areas of increase and decrease in both, within the region.

4: Australia: Temperatures up 1 to 2°C in summer and 2°C in winter. Summer rain up by around 10 per cent. The region averages hide large variations within it.

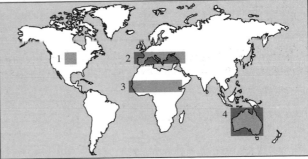

Figure 3.18 Greenhouse gases

Acid rain

in own words

Carbon dioxide is not the only pollutant resulting from the burning of fossil fuels. Heavily industrialised areas pump 90 million tonnes of sulphur dioxide into the air each year. The chief sources of these emissions are electricity generating plants, industrial boilers and large smelters. The sulphur dioxide may cause damage near the industrial site when it is dry and settles on surfaces. It corrodes metals and stonework and has an effect on tree and crop growth as well as human health. When oxides of sulphur and of nitrogen are released from tall chimneys and carried by prevailing winds, they mix with moisture in the air and form weak solutions of sulphuric and nitric acids. When this moisture is then deposited as rain, snow, fog or mist it may be several thousand miles from its source. It is known as 'acid rain'. Acid rain percolates into the ground, changing the soil chemistry and interfering with the ability of plants and trees to absorb the nutrients they need. It also releases toxic heavy metals, which are held in compounds in the soil and water, and are poisonous for both plants and fish. In areas with limestone rocks or rich soil the acidity is neutralised when it reacts with the soil; where there are already very acidic soils (moorlands and pine forests) the threat will be greatest.

ENQUIRY: ACID DROPS

1 Using the description in the text above, draw an annotated flow diagram of the causes and effects of acid rain.

2 Read the article about acid rain in Mexico. What damage is being caused to the Maya Ruins? Which two Mexican businesses are in conflict here? Why do the Mexicans find it difficult to decide on the appropriate steps to take?

3 Study the chart below ('Possible action against acid rain'). Select those procedures which would be appropriate for Mexico and explain what you think are the appropriate steps to take.

ACID RAIN FROM THE MEXICO OILFIELDS DAMAGING TREASURES

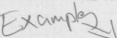
Examples

Norman Hammond

Acid rain from Mexico's oilfields is destroying the architecture and art of the ancient Maya civilization …

Nitrogen and sulphur oxides, resulting from the burning of petroleum by-products at the Gulf Coast refineries of Pemex, the Mexican state monopoly, are borne inland eastwards to the Maya ruins in the jungles of Tabasco and Chiapas and the forests of the Yucatan Peninsula to the north. Turned to acid by atmospheric water, the chemicals settle on the limestone buildings and corrode their surfaces.

The cracks thus created also allow water seepage, and foster the growth of plants and microorganisms that cause further mechanical and chemical erosion …

At the site of Palenque, a major tourist attraction on the edge of the Gulf Coast plain, only 75 miles from the nearest oilfield, walls that were bright with red or blue paint less than twenty years ago are now almost white, and inscriptions and stucco sculptures are severely eroded.

Acid deposit, a black crust that removes the surface from the limestone architecture, is visible on the Great Ball Court of Chichen Itza, a major site in Yucatan, and has been documented at Uxmal near Merida, and as far east as the Caribbean coastal city of Tulum, which until recently had rare Postclassic murals in superb condition. At Tulum some of the damage … comes from the exhausts of numerous tour buses, which keep their engines running for hours in order to sustain air-conditioning.

The collision between petroleum production and tourism, two of Mexico's biggest dollar earners, is likely to be politically difficult. Mr Charles Gallenkamp, organiser of a recent museum display of Maya artefacts that toured museums in the United States, said: 'Mexicans are very sensitive about their archaeological patrimony, but this brings you up against very powerful commercial interests.'

Source: *The Times*, 2 August 1989

Possible action against acid rain

International and bilateral agreements
1979
31 members of Economic Commission for Europe sign the Convention on Long Range Transboundary Air Pollution. Agree to collaborate and make effective reductions in emissions.
1983
Central Electricity Board and National Coal Board (now British Coal) provide £5 million for joint 5-year research project.

Individual countries
• It is technically possible to remove most of the sulphur dioxide from the gases produced when fossil fuels are burnt. Desulphurisation equipment can be installed, and the resulting by-product can be sold.
• The sulphur content of oil can be reduced by fuel desulphurisation processes at the oil refinery.
• Coal can be crushed and washed to halve the sulphur content (fluidisation).
• It is likely that governments will have to follow the lead of Sweden and Germany in imposing controls, because their power industries will not readily pay the increased cost.
• Countries can change the energy mix, moving away from fossil fuels.

• They can also encourage conservation and efficiency measures to ensure that less fuel is burnt off.

Local action
• Lime can be added to lakes and water supplies, a measure now taken by Sweden and the United Kingdom.
• Special varieties of fish and crops can be developed.
• Buildings can be coated with anti-corrosive film.
• Legislation on car exhausts and use of vehicles in conserved areas can be effective.
• As yet, no successful treatment for coniferous forest areas has been developed.

Is sustainable development the answer?

The pollution of the seas and of the atmosphere are matters of international concern. In 1972 a group called the Club of Rome drew up a report, *The Limits to Growth*, to illustrate their view of world growth and resource use. As can be seen (Figure 3.19) they believed that as certain key resources (such as oil) began to run out and as pollution rose to unacceptable levels, so the ever-increasing population would be faced with rapidly decreasing amounts of food per capita and then a decline in industrial output, the source of their wealth. Large numbers of people would die as the environment turned toxic or hostile, or was unable to support them. These ideas, although challenged, did much to influence public opinion about population control, pollution and resource conservation.

Towards the end of the 1980s an alternative view was propounded (Figure 3.20). Professor David Pearce, an economist, set out his ideas on sustainable development. He believed that the well-being, or standard of living, of the present generation should not increase at the expense of future generations. People should see the environment as the nation's or the world's asset. There is a stock of available environmental capital (wealth). If we simply spend this wealth without investing for the future then we will run out of resources. However, if we were to use some of this environmental capital to research and develop new resources for the future, we could build machines that substitute for the environmental resource (e.g. solar panels instead of oil; trains and railways instead of cars). It is important, then, that we value the environmental assets correctly. We must not extract oil at the short-term price it costs for the well, the workforce and the transport. We must pay for research and development to provide an alternative energy source for the next generation. We must not dispose of sulphur dioxide into the air at the short-term cost of a high chimney. Future generations will pay the price in hospital bills for polluted air. Instead, we must pay the price today to maintain the environmental equilibrium by affording equipment or new resources that help to maintain the balance.

Some forms of environmental asset, such as bio-diversity or the ozone layer, are not readily substituted by other forms of environmental capital. For these resources there should be an acceptable minimum standard: an agreed lowest level for both amount and quality.

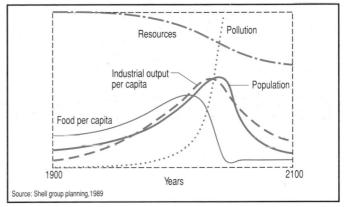

Figure 3.19   Economic growth and environmental collapse

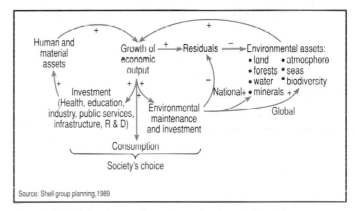

Figure 3.20   Linkages between the environment and economic growth

---

EXERCISE: LINKAGES – THE ENVIRONMENT AND ECONOMIC GROWTH

Study Figure 3.20. Fit the following captions under the appropriate headings:

Evening classes held
Mechanisation of cloth manufacture
Law limiting sulphur emissions
Increased electrification in rural area
Factory for cloth manufacture

More graduates with business management capabilities
Street lighting
Trees planted to reduce carbon dioxide content of air
Newly literate population seeks employment
Sulphur dioxide released into atmosphere
Grants available for higher education

Power-generating material extracted (e.g. coal)
Energy conservation measures advertised
Carbon dioxide emitted
Research into tidal energy production
Refrigeration of vaccines
Breeding of endangered species in captivity

The beginnings of sustainable development

Already in Britain we see the implications of this attitude. We now pay more tax per litre of leaded petrol than we do for unleaded. We will pay more for a car with a catalytic converter but the law will prevent us from buying any other. If we buy 'environmentally friendly' recycled goods which have taken less energy to produce then we can expect to pay a little more because, at present, they cost more to make.

Instead of considering a nation's wealth in terms of gross national product (GNP) it is necessary to combine economic development with environmental impact. Germany plans to publish official statistics on an environmentally adjusted GNP and Japan already does this unofficially. In Britain it would be possible to combine environmental trends and economic statistics and to measure sustainable income. If we are to accept this responsibility to the next generation then it is necessary to consider the options. In the next section we will look at the possible future energy choices, which might release the stranglehold of fossil fuels.

Present Sustainable Energy Options

Conservation and pollution control will enable the world's resources to last longer and the balance in natural systems to be maintained, but if sustainable energy production is the answer for the twenty-first century then we must consider the options.

The developing world will continue to require greater amounts of energy as its industries develop and its standard of living improves, and so the present sources of energy will quickly become insufficient. Prices of fossil fuels will rise and countries may restrict the export of their fuel resources. It is therefore necessary that the world seeks new forms of power production. Countries such as Japan or Ecuador, which rely very heavily on oil, may see the need to diversify; it is just as important that the coal-rich nations address the world problem of dwindling fossil fuel reserves. World reserves of coal may well extend into the twenty-first century, but doubts exist concerning the economic viability of deep mining, and the environmental implications of opencast mining. Full details of a coal mining controversy are found in *Hawkhurst Moor* (Naish and Warn, 1993).

Already two sources of sustainable power are available worldwide: hydro-electricity and nuclear power. Hydro-power contributes 23% of the world's electricity; nuclear power accounts for 16%. In certain places alternative energies have been developed but they are by no means widespread and doubts are at present expressed concerning their ability to provide large-scale supplies at low cost.

1 Hydro-Electric Power (HEP)

Hydro-electric power has been identified as one of the 'saviours' of a world threatened by dwindling resources and environmental pollution. Here we consider the problems and issues associated with its use and development in different regional and national contexts. What is the maximum contribution HEP could make to the world's energy supplies? And is HEP truly such a saviour? It may be a sustainable resource, but is it as clean in environmental terms as its supporters suggest? We shall examine the evidence provided by three HEP case studies: Norway, an economically more-developed country almost entirely dependent on HEP; Ghana, an economically less-developed country which opted for an early HEP mega-scheme; and Nepal, an economically less-developed country where HEP is being developed in rural areas through micro/mini hydro-stations.

ENQUIRY: HOW DOES HEP WORK?

1 You will recall the hydrological cycle, discussed in Chapter 1. Explain how water and the power of the Sun can provide the appropriate conditions for HEP generation (see Figure 3.21). What conditions are necessary and why can HEP be considered a renewable resource?

2 Consider Figure 3.21 and Table 3.6, and use an atlas showing physical features and precipitation to explain what conditions make hydro-power possible in the main producing countries of the world. Which area would you expect to use a smaller amount of water and a large head, and which would use a large amount of water and a smaller head?

Table 3.6   Countries with the largest hydro-power production in 1986

Country	Production (hydro) (terawatthours)	Installed capacity (hydro) (megawatts)
Canada	310.7	56 800
USA	294.6	84 152
USSR	215.7	62 141
Brazil	182.6	37 702
China	100.0	27 000
Norway	95.9	23 418
Japan	86.6	35 150
France	60.9	22 800
Sweden	60.7	15 813
India	53.8	15 965

Source: The United Nations

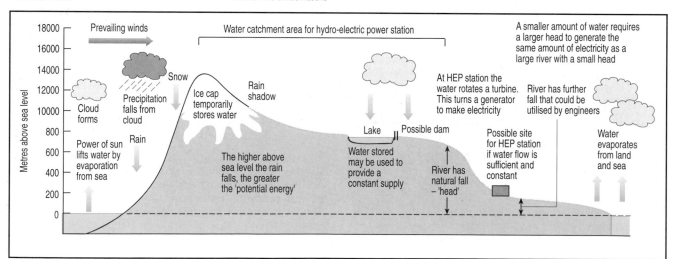

Figure 3.21   The hydrological cycle and hydro-power production

CASE STUDY *Hydro-Electricity: Norway's Major Power Source*

In Norway, high precipitation (on average 1415 mm per annum), high heads of water and many glacial lakes make hydro-power a viable source of energy. However, the storage of electricity in batteries is expensive, so electricity must be generated exactly when it is needed. Almost 100% of electricity requirement comes from hydro-power stations and only 260 households do not receive their electricity from this source. Approximately 31% is supplied by the State Power System, 51% is produced by municipal and county utilities and about 18% is generated privately, mostly by industrial companies. The Norwegian Power Pool arranges exchanges of surplus electricity between the power companies.

From the beginning of the twentieth century the production of cheap hydro-electricity has encouraged the development and profitability of power-intensive industries such as manufacture of fertilisers, plastics, iron and steel, ferro-alloys, aluminium and magnesium. These industries are major employers, with many of the factories located in outlying districts. They provide the industrial base for Norway and have encouraged the development of expertise in electro-chemistry, electrometallurgy and electrotechnics. This has resulted in world-wide orders for machinery, expert technical advice and aid, and has encouraged further processing activities in Norway itself.

ENQUIRY: THE IMPACTS OF HEP IN NORWAY

The sketch shown in Figure 3.22 is taken from the front cover of *Water Power in Norway*, an information booklet prepared by the Norwegian Water Resources and Electricity Board. Annotate the sketch to show the impact of HEP in Norway. Identify the advantages and disadvantages and suggest any possible needs for alternative forms of energy.

Figure 3.22 Water power in Norway

STATISTICAL AND CARTOGRAPHIC ANALYSIS: NORWEGIAN HEP

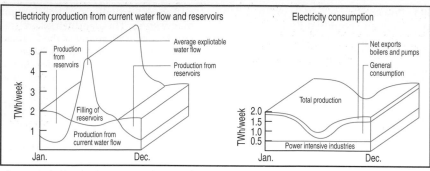

Figure 3.23   Electricity consumption in Norway

Refer to Figures 3.23, 3.24 and Tables 3.7 and 3.8.

1 Describe the distribution of hydro-power stations and hydro-power potential in Norway. On a map use proportional circles to show the total potential in each county. Subdivide the circles to show the relative development of this potential.

2 Some potential hydro-power sites are described as permanently protected, i.e. the natural water flow will not be modified to provide power. Why do you think protection is necessary?

3 Describe and explain why production varies throughout the year. Use an atlas to find temperature and rainfall conditions.

4 Describe how this production is used. What other forms of energy are also used in Norway? Apart from oil which is needed by ships in foreign trade, why else must oil still be a large energy source in Norway?

Figure 3.24   Counties of Norway

Table 3.7   Hydro power potential as of 12.31.92 (Mean annual production in GWh)

County	Operational	Approved for development	Remaining*	Protected	Total
Østfold	4232	0	16	20	4268
Akershus	900	0	0	74	974
Oslo	20	0	0	0	20
Hedmark	2276	16	1327	2397	6016
Oppland	5513	18	5429	1782	12743
Buskerud	8850	0	1553	833	11235
Vestfold	16	32	166	0	214
Telemark	11800	176	1433	418	13827
Aust-Agder	3971	288	1808	124	6192
Vest-Agder	8223	0	1256	731	10210
Rogaland	9454	18	3851	229	13552
Hordaland	13740	144	3600	5201	22686
Sogn og Fjordane	11561	124	6533	2445	20663
Møre og Romsdal	5409	0	3688	1560	10658
Sør-Trøndelag	4038	7	1148	1218	6411
Nord-Trøndelag	2389	401	2161	940	5892
Nordland	13356	1678	6472	1593	23099
Troms	2436	0	719	1839	4994
Finnmark	1373	10	620	842	2845
Total Norway	109457	2913	41779	22246	176395

* Including the following: Under licencing, under planning and remaining
Source: NVE Norwegian Water Resources and Energy Administration, 1993

Table 3.8   The largest power stations in Norway as of 12.31.92

Power station	County	Max. capacity (MW)	Mean annual production (GWh/year)
Kvilldal	Rogaland	1240	2913
Sima	Hordaland	1120	2812
Tonstad	Vest-Agder	960	3666
Aurland I	Sogn og Fjordane	675	1956
Saurdal*	Rogaland	640	846
Rana	Nordland	500	1890
Tokke	Telemark	430	2142
Evanger	Hordaland	330	1229
Brokke	Aust-Agder	330	1417
Svartisen	Nordland	310	1200
Nedre Vinstra	Oppland	308	1212
Skjomen	Nordland	300	1085
Vinje	Telemark	300	961
Kobbelv	Nordland	300	652
Aura	Møre og Romsdal	290	1605
Jostedal	Sogn og Fjordane	288	867

*Pumping power plant
Source: NVE Norwegian Water Resources and Energy Administration, 1993

VALUES ENQUIRY: HEP – BENEFIT OR INCONVENIENCE?

'Until the first half of the 1960s there was practically complete political agreement on water power development. Since that time, there has been a great deal of public controversy concerning the environmental effects of continuing development of hydro-electric power. This point of view has become increasingly more important compared to the public good further development of water power may have' (Source: Norwegian Parliamentary report No. 54, 1979–80 – The Energy White Paper).

From the quotations given in Figure 3.25 identify the interested party from the list and find any statements that conflict with the opinion stated. What compromise could be suggested? You may need to add ideas of your own. Construct and complete a table like this:

Statement	Interested party	Conflicting statement	Possible solution
5	D	15	Regulate water levels below hydro sites; 'permanent protection' for some conserved sites

1. The natural river provides an excellent transport route for logs from forestry and for ships and boats.

2. Logs and ice used to jam the river courses and cause flooding and erosion of farm land, forests, industry, roads and settlements.

3. Timber floating spoilt the appearance of rivers. Now forest roads are built and have opened up new areas for second homes and recreation.

4. Some power stations have to finance log slides to enable continued use of the river past the station.

5. Fishing and hunting are national pastimes. When the river is depleted of water, so that it can be held back for power supply, then the fisheries suffer.

6. Roads are built when power stations are developed. These open up previously impassable terrain.

7. Power stations now have to provide the money to stock the water courses with fish, construct weirs to regulate water levels, build fish ladders at power plants and clean up fishing sites. These are positive developments.

8. Sufficient natural gas to last 100 years has been found in the Norwegian sector of the North Sea. A gas-powered electricity plant should be built. We could sell gas to Denmark and Sweden (as well as the UK as at present) and sell gas-powered electricity to Finland.

9. Cheap HEP has enabled our industry to exist.

10. Warm water from the power station is used to develop fish hatcheries within some power stations.

11. HEP is made more expensive and less competitive by all the environmental constraints placed upon it.

12. Not all the roads are kept when construction finishes. Sometimes the landscape is completely restored at an expense to the power station.

13. The waterfalls provide beauty spots for Norwegian and international tourists, and must not be modified.

14. We need rivers in their natural state for scientific research and education.

15. Water is needed from the rivers for water supply as well as power supply. Irrigation is increasingly important for agriculture.

16. The large lakes change the local climate and cause problems for animal and plant life.

17. The water is polluted by the power stations. It may be warmed. This causes changes in animal and plant life.

18. When the water is held back in the lake, it alters the amount of fresh water entering the fiord. This affects salinity and temperature in the surface layers and can increase the risk of ice formation in winter.

19. We want some areas to remain inaccessible – both to preserve wildlife and to provide a challenge for outdoor pursuits.

20. A greater minimum flow of water is sometimes necessary in summer to retain the beauty of our natural waterfalls.

21. The new roads open up exciting areas for ordinary people, providing more land for recreation, fishing, hunting and holiday homes.

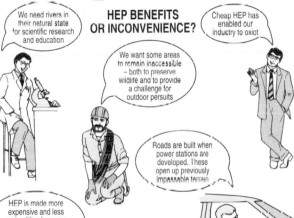

HEP BENEFITS OR INCONVENIENCE?

The natural river provides an excellent transport route for logs from forestry and for ships and boats

We need rivers in their natural state for scientific research and education

Cheap HEP has enabled our industry to exist

We want some areas to remain inaccessible – both to preserve wildlife and to provide a challenge for outdoor pursuits

Roads are built when power stations are developed. These open up previously impassable terrain

HEP is made more expensive and less competitive because of all the environmental constraints placed upon it

Fishing and hunting are national pastimes. When the river is depleted of water, so that it can be held back for power supply, then the fisheries suffer

Interested parties
A Power production
B Log driving
C Navigation
D Fishing
E Water supply
F Irrigation
G Sewerage waste outlets
H Recreation
I Agriculture – climatic effects
J Conservationists
K Industrialists
L Local settlements
M Road users

Figure 3.25   Hydro-electric power – benefits or inconvenience?

ENQUIRY: THE ULLA FØRRE SCHEME

Study the annotated map of this scheme, the most extensive water power project in Northern Europe (Figure 3.26).

1 Describe the scheme.

2 Suggest what problems might occur during its planning, construction and daily maintenance. Consider the various issues raised in the previous section and the effect of Norway's climatic conditions.

3 Explain the likely impact of the scheme on the environment – physical, visual, social and economic.

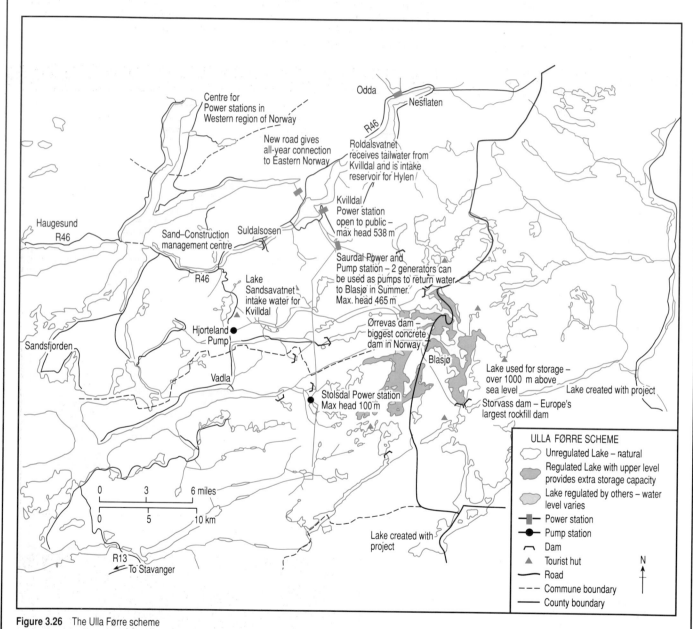

Centre for Power stations in Western region of Norway

New road gives all-year connection to Eastern Norway

Odda

Nesflaten

R46

Roldalsvatnet receives tailwater from Kvilldal and is intake reservoir for Hylen

Haugesund R46

Sand–Construction management centre

Suldalsosen

Kvilldal Power station open to public – max head 538 m

R46

Lake Sandsavatnet intake water for Kvilldal

Saurdal Power and Pump station – 2 generators can be used as pumps to return water to Blasjø in Summer. Max. head 465 m

Hjorteland Pump

Ørrevass dam – biggest concrete dam in Norway

Blasjø

Sandsfjorden

Vadla

Stolsdal Power station Max head 100 m

Lake used for storage – over 1000 m above sea level

Lake created with project

Storvass dam – Europe's largest rockfill dam

0	3	6 miles
0	5	10 km

R13 To Stavanger

Lake created with project

ULLA FØRRE SCHEME

- Unregulated Lake – natural
- Regulated Lake with upper level provides extra storage capacity
- Lake regulated by others – water level varies
- Power station
- Pump station
- Dam
- Tourist hut
- Road
- Commune boundary
- County boundary

N

Figure 3.26   The Ulla Førre scheme

ROLE-PLAY EXERCISE: THE SUITABILITY OF HEP

In a small group, prepare a talk or submit a paper to explain to a developing nation with similar environmental conditions to Norway why they should, or should not, concentrate on HEP development to provide their nation with much of the power they require. You should mention any problems which might have to be overcome and any possible alternatives. Appoint a technical representative, an environmental adviser and a regional development manager concerned with spin-off effects in the region.

CASE STUDY *Hydro-Electric Power in Ghana*

In contrast to the many hydro-power schemes of various sizes which have been developed in Norway, in the 1960s, Ghana built one large dam and generating station at Akosombo in the hope of providing electricity for the establishment of modern industry in Ghana towards the end of the twentieth century. The project was one of the earliest multipurpose mega-schemes and served as a model for many subsequent schemes.

Between 1961 and 1966 what was then the biggest artificial lake in the world was created when the River Volta was dammed as it passed through a gap in the Akwapim hills in Southern Ghana. The lake was to provide the water and pressure necessary to generate hydro-electricity for an aluminium smelter in the new port of Tema, and to provide the power for the development of industry in Ghana.

COST BENEFIT ANALYSIS: THE GREATEST LAKE?

Read the extracts on pages 122–23 and study Figures 3.27, 3.28 and 3.29. You may also wish to refer to pages 42–44 in Chapter 1 for further information.

1 Using the following headings, make a list of the changes that occurred when the dam was built and the likely long-term effects of the whole scheme:
   a *Impact on the environment* – e.g. flora, fauna, land-use, climate, river-flow and water usage.
   b *Impact on the economy* – e.g. finance, industrial development, agriculture and food changes, transport, exports and employment.
   c *Impact on the people* – e.g. homes, jobs, culture, health and availability of electricity.

2 Indicate whether you think these changes were an advantage, disadvantage, or both.

3 Make a copy of the chart below and complete it to summarise the main issues.

Costs	Who pays/loses?	Benefits	Who gains?

4 Who would be likely to influence the decision to construct the Akosombo Dam?

5 In what ways do you think these costs and benefits reflect their value judgements?

6 Write a letter to the World Bank outlining the views and values of a resettled tribal chief.

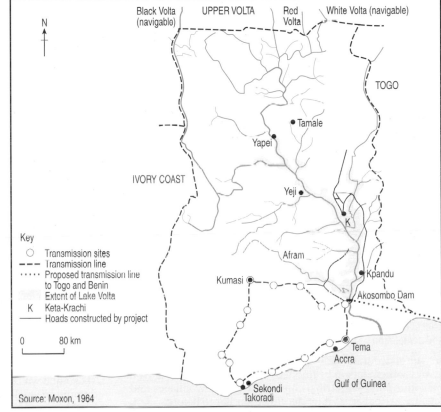

Figure 3.27 The impact of the Volta River Project on Ghana and the surrounding countries

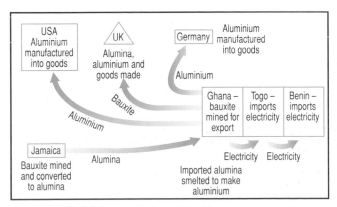

Figure 3.28 Trade in bauxite, alumina and aluminium

Figure 3.29 The Akosombo dam

AKOSOMBO

The series of blueprints projects, orders and counterorders that preceded the construction of the Akosombo high dam is a long story. It has been aptly written up in James Moxon's book, *Volta, Man's greatest lake*. In fact, not until 1915 did an English geologist, A. E. Kitson, discover the potentialities of the Volta river between Ajena and Kpong for the building of a hydro-electric power plant. But Europe was then at war and time and capital were lacking for carrying out such an operation.

Down through the years the project was sporadically revived, modified and shelved. The official spokesmen were replaced by other official spokesmen, the sites both of the dam and of the aluminium foundry designed to use the power generated and to amortize the investment were ceaselessly changed on paper. Everything would either have been definitively pigeonholed or allowed to drag on endlessly without the determination of Kwame Nkrumah who viewed the dam as a major factor in the modernisation of the Ghana of the future.

Work at length got under way at Akosombo and in January 1966, the dam and power plant were inaugurated by the head of the State, while the foundry was finally built in the new town of Tema on the east coast.

The world's biggest man-made lake

The dam water eventually formed a lake 400 kilometers long extending from north to south. It is deep enough for boats carrying freight, passengers and cars to sail its full length.

Travellers with or without cars will doubtless enjoy using this means of conveyance: it enables them to visit Keta-Krachi, an erstwhile major caravan route crossroads and to return the same evening to Akosombo. Another boat makes a three-day trip including stopovers at Kpandu, Keta-Krachi, and Yeji, to Yapei, the port of the northern capital of Tamale.

At the outset of the dam construction work, a town was built at Akosombo to accommodate the workers. From the great metal bridge across the river at the entrance to the gorges that run downstream from the city to Kpong, the road sporadically follows the river. Beyond Akwamu it climbs to the top of a hill whence there is a view over the oldest quarter of Akosombo, built for the dam workers. After traversing this quarter and following the contours of another hill, the road winds up the latter's northern slope to the buildings of the Volta River Authority and to the Akosombo hotel, whose terrace looks out over the dam, the lake, and its wooded islands.

Behind one of the promontories that protrude like headlands into this magnificent expanse of water lies the port, invisible from the nearby town. There travellers will find boats that provide [a] shuttle service northward and on Sundays, there are lake cruises lasting a few hours, including shipboard lunches cooked by the hotel's chef.

For the time being, these cruises are designed only to enable visitors to explore the many islands near the shores, or simply to indulge in a bit of fishing. In all likelihood, there will eventually be a pleasure-craft port, which is all that Akosombo lacks to become a popular vacation resort.

Source: Tourist leaflet from Ghanaian Embassy

Journalist's notes at a press conference as the Akosombo Dam project neared completion

Dam completed. Lake filling. Trees, wildlife, hills, agricultural land and settlements to be flooded. 80 000 people moving from small community with tribal chief to form 52 new villages and townships. Tribal areas intended to be similar to before.

6000–7000 acres of forest cleared to provide every relocated family with new single-room house of sandcrete blocks with aluminium roof – add more rooms themselves so eventually take form of traditional single-storey house round open courtyard. Each family originally allocated 12 acres of land. Now guaranteed 4 acres and can be paid if they help to clear this area. Virgin forest has proved difficult to clear and other activities have taken priority.

Co-operative farms established – share new technology (tractor) and learn new methods. Can move on from traditional subsistence farming and make a greater contribution to expanding economy. Irrigated farming of rice and sugar cane possible.

All-weather roads built in order to construct new townships – some very remote. Costly to maintain. 500 miles of road built – many places still not served.

Chance to start a new life – rural Ghana to modernise and progress in 20th century.

Some facts and figures

The use of the electricity
From the outset, the development of the power station at Akosombo was to enable electricity to be sent to a newly built aluminium smelter at Tema. The smelter was paid for by North American companies and banks and £31 million of the £42 million needed was given as a loan. It was agreed that half of the electricity would go to the VALCO smelter for the first thirty years and there were plans to send electricity to Accra, Takoradi, Kumasi and the mining area so that the diesel-operated stations that had provided the power could close. 3000 Ghanaians were employed by the American company for the building of the smelter and 1000 Ghanaians worked there on completion. It was hoped that they would become the core of a technically well-qualified labour force.

International links
Kaiser Construction from USA.
Impregilo from Italy – dam builders.
Rodio from Italy – grouting of dam.
Flumes tested in France.
Canadian team to train power workers.
UK finance – £ 5 million.
USA finance – £62 million.
World Bank finance – £92 million.

MAN'S GREATEST LAKE

'The whir of machines, the shuffling, stamping feet of plastic-helmeted human beings and the constant thunderous dynamite explosions, all conspired to make one long earsplitting din that drove away crocodiles, monkeys, rodents and reptiles in an unprecedented stampede.'

Ten per cent of those resettled were Tongus. They were river fishermen before the lake was built.

'Now Lake Volta is already fringed with Tongu resettlements up and down its length: in a very real sense the Tongus are the people of the lake. At first, however many aspects took them by surprise. As they found to their cost, a squall of quite alarming proportions can quickly blow up, with waves comparable to a rough sea, and in such conditions their flat-bottomed river canoes are little safer than a cockle shell. More than a few fishermen have already perished in such storms ... It is true that the lakeside people have never had such regular supplies of fresh and smoked fish, which being so plentiful is much cheaper than it used to be.'

'Whilst the lake will probably help to mitigate the river-blindness problem over a wide area it will have exactly the opposite effect on other serious diseases such as bilharzia and hookworm ... It is partly for these reasons that the new townships have been sited well away from the lake with their own pure bore-hole water supplies and septic tank latrine blocks, but old habits sometimes die hard. Malaria too must increase to some extent as the 4,500 mile lake perimeter inevitably provides new breeding grounds for mosquito larvae.'

Source: Moxon, 1964

CASE STUDY *Electricity in Nepal*

The previous case study of the massive HEP project on the Volta River provided an opportunity to understand the enormous physical, social and economic impact which such a large-scale development can have on an area. Furthermore, because of the high costs involved, the electricity was used in the major urban areas and to encourage the development of energy-intensive industries in Ghana. The rural areas would appear to have gained little from this development, although they perhaps suffered the greatest effects.

In some rural areas of the world, in both economically more-developed and economically less-developed countries, small-scale hydro-electric power schemes have been built. In the People's Republic of China 80 000 mini-hydro plants have been installed since the 1960s. There are about 600 installations in Nepal.

Nepal nestles on the edge of the Tibetan plateau in the Himalayas. It rises from the Ganges valley to the heights of Mount Everest and along its northern border the peaks are snow-capped. It is an exceptionally poor country with limited natural resources and a population of only 18 million. Most of its people (91.7%) still live in rural areas and agriculture accounts for 58% of the gross domestic product. Electricity production in 1986 amounted to 427 million kWh.

GROUP DECISION-MAKING EXERCISE: MICRO-HYDRO FOR KHAIRENI?

Khaireni is a small village in central Nepal near Annapurna. It is two days' walk from the nearest road and so it is difficult to import anything and it would be far too expensive to connect the village to the national grid. The villagers have the opportunity of establishing a local micro-hydro scheme. Your group is to take on the role of advisers and villagers, and to decide whether the project should be undertaken.

Within your group appoint 3 representatives: a *planner*, an *engineer* and a *financial and legal expert*. The rest of the group are villagers and can take on a variety of roles: *women*, whose job it is daily to grind corn, hull rice, thresh corn, spin wool, weave and collect water and fuelwood; *men*, who look after and work with the animals; a *blacksmith*, who works on a metal spinning lathe powered by his wife; *farmers* who will lose some of their land when the settling tanks, penstocks and power house are built; *teenagers* who have not acquired the basic literacy skills and are therefore denied opportunities of self-improvement and consequent better jobs.

The three representatives have recently been on a training course run by a British-based non-governmental organisation called Intermediate Technology. The villagers have now asked them to undertake a feasibility study to assess the value of a scheme in Khaireni.

The villagers have submitted their appraisal of the possible uses (see chart on page 124). The representatives have studied the site and each has produced notes to enable recommendations to be made (see reports on pages 124–25).

1 Each representative should read through the notes and give a short talk outlining his/her opinion on the future development. All information relevant to the decision must be given but the representative may bias his/her remarks.

2 The villagers should decide whether they believe that the installation will benefit their village and justify the costs with particular reference to their individual roles.

3 At the end of the presentations and discussion the whole group should vote on whether they think that the micro-hydro scheme should be implemented.

Villagers' view: uses of micro-hydro

Corn grinding
Each family requires 2–3 hours grinding per meal, 2 meals per day. Mill grinds three days' corn in 15 minutes. Usually 12 to 20 families in village.

Oil-seed pressing
Mustard seed pressed to make cooking oil. Processed oil is worth more than unprocessed seeds. Farmer increases income. Mechanical press extracts up to 50% more than hand press.

Rice-huller
At present women push see-saw up and down to smash husks from rice grains. Machine could do this.

Generator
Will produce electricity, to be used for:
Lighting
Learn to read (only 20% literacy rate in Nepal, less in village). Evening work on traditional crafts possible – marketable handicrafts for expanding tourist trade and for export.

Fridges
For clinic, to store vaccines.
Power loom weaving
Cottage industry. Some villagers have the necessary skills.
Low-wattage storage cookers
Save fuelwood and collecting time.
Water and space heating
For community centre.

Planning Report
For planning of end uses, see 'Villagers' view'.

Surveys
Topographical
Suitable hillside providing 'head' and area for tanks.

Hydrological
Rainfall and snowmelt cause fluctuations in fall during year. However, there is an adequate minimum flow at all times in this channel.

Socio-economic
Inefficient hand methods are slow and wasteful. Much of this work is done by the women who are very enthusiastic about the scheme. It should allow them more time to tend the crops and gather fuelwood. Possible development of handicrafts. Evening education classes (reading/writing) should be possible and also a new small-scale weaving industry. Men are a little wary of the cost.

System design
Mechanical power needed for milling, oil-pressing and rice-hulling.
Generator possible – lighting in homes; fridge for community hall. Some low-wattage cookers. Power-looms.
Use ballast (excess electricity produced) for water heating at village community.
Good load factor (actual use of electricity generated) of 40% (50% is maximum to be expected on a scheme like this).

Engineer's Report

Installation
Site plan – see annotated diagram, Figure 3.30.

Materials
Wood, stones, concrete, plastic pipe available locally.

Turbines and hardware
13 Nepali companies make suitable turbines and recently one firm has begun to make electronic load controllers (to regulate the flow of electricity). Intermediate Technology has agreed to help with the electrical aspects of the installation. No transformer should be needed as electricity supply will remain local. With the use of an electronic load controller, simpler and more reliable turbines can be used. Also lighter and cheaper penstocks.

Civil construction work
No dam, only a small weir is required.
Locals will provide the labour for all the construction work.

Operation
Maintenance
This will be minimised but 2 operators will be needed: 4 to 5 likely candidates in village. Intermediate Technology has a training centre available for use. A base engineer is available for major overhaul or a breakdown emergency. He serves a large area but is multi-disciplined so can cope with electrical, mechanical or civil repair work without senior assistance.

Costs
The scheme should generate sufficient income from charges to cover the annual maintenance and running costs. Local labour rates are low.

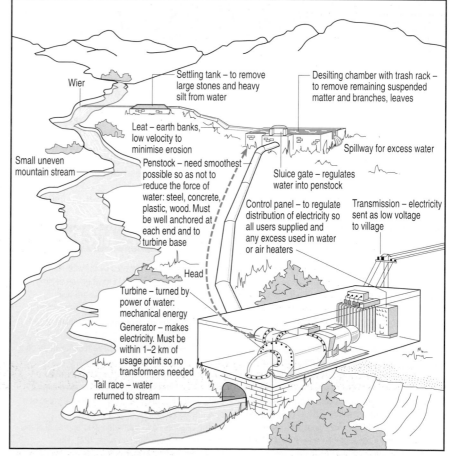

Figure 3.30   A micro-hydro installation

Financial and legal report

Alternatives

Electricity from grid
Length of transmission line – 20 km.
Unit cost per km of transmission line –
£8000–£10 000.
Also need to pay for maintenance of transmission
line each year – approximately £1000 per km.
Charge per unit from grid – 5p–10p per kWh.
Not usually very reliably supplied to rural areas
(often cut off).

Diesel set
Low initial cost.
High maintenance costs.
High fuel costs – 15p per kWh.
Short life of machinery.
Fuel supply problems, especially in remote area.
Fuel costs account for 75% of total diesel
generating costs.

Battery supply for lighting
Costs £300 per kWh.

Kerosene for lighting only
Transport costs high.
Supply difficult in remote area.

Micro-hydro and electronic load control
Little maintenance required – cheaper electricity if
less manpower needed. Is not an employment
scheme!
At least 20-year life for machinery.
Unit cost is 3.6p–7p per kWh.
Must have high load factor (high usage of
electricity) – about 40–50%. About 10% will be for
domestic needs (lighting – usually 200 watts per
household – and eventually cooking) but about 40%
for processing.
Initial cost is £1000–£2000 per kW. Can be
reduced if local labour and materials are used. This
would seem possible in the future. Very reliable and
a technology we could control.

Electricity production
Nepal government have recently lifted restrictions
on private production of electricity.

Water use
Possible conflict with irrigation and water supply. In
area where water will be extracted there is no
conflict over use.

Tariff
Charges for water power and electricity to include
running costs, maintenance costs and depreciation,
estimating a 20-year life span for the machinery.
Major users – corn grinder, oil crusher – will collect
in kind from their customers.
Electricity charges should be paid for by increased
earnings from more field work and evening crafts.

Sources of finance
From village community.
From Agricultural Development Bank which gives
cheap or interest-free loans.
From Intermediate Technology, Myson House,
Railway Terrace, Rugby CV21 3HT, UK.
Income should then come from increased oil sales
and additional crops harvested and the sale of
handicrafts from evening work.

The future of hydro-electric power

In an information brief prepared for the Royal Dutch/Shell
Group, the following description of HEP appeared in the
section entitled 'other renewable energy sources'.

Hydropower is used to generate 25% of the world's electricity and 3% of the world's total energy requirement (1990). Large hydropower stations of up to 7000 megawatts (MW) are generally built in remote areas with little or no local demand. The long overhead power lines required are expensive and have significant transmission losses. Considerable investments are required, due to their size and remoteness, and with lead times up to 10–15 years these power schemes tend to be difficult to plan and develop. Large hydropower stations are relatively clean but their environmental impact can be considerable and sometimes detrimental. A service life of some 50 years is common, with low operating cost the main attraction. Many of the prime sites in economically more-developed countries have been utilised, although there is still considerable development potential in Africa, Asia and South America. Many of the planned schemes are financed by World Bank or EC funding and are extremely controversial hydrologically or ecologically. The drive for utilisation of local resources and energy efficiency has prompted interest in smaller (1–5 MW) and micro (smaller than 1 MW) stations. Over the past few years the trend has been to design standard small hydro machines. These are easy to transport and install in remote areas, where reliability and ease of operation are essential.

By 1985 a total hydropower capacity of 300 gigawatts (GW) had been installed. Considerable resources are still available for further development of both small and large hydropower schemes and, as a result, their contribution towards energy supplies for electricity generation may be expected to rise in the future.

Source: Shell Briefing Service, 1987

SUMMARY EVALUATION EXERCISE

Read the article above.

1 At present what contribution does hydropower make to the world's electricity production? How is this expected to change in the future?

2 From the work you have done in this section, explain where, why and how you think these changes should and will occur.

3 Do you see HEP as a 'saviour' of the world? Write an essay looking at this issue. You will find numerous articles on major HEP schemes such as Aswan in Egypt, Volta in Ghana or Three Gorges in China, as well as details from textbooks on countries such as Norway, Sweden or Switzerland where HEP is a major source of energy.

2 Nuclear Power – the Infinite Power or just an energy gap filler?

Nuclear electricity is made from uranium, which is found in a number of locations throughout the world. Only small amounts of the fuel are required. One tonne of uranium can produce as much energy as 20 000 tons of coal. As uranium has no other uses at present, the world supplies should, if used in fast-breeder reactors, last for at least 1000 years. After use, uranium can also be reprocessed and 96% can be recovered as a new uranium fuel and a further 1% as plutonium. Nuclear energy provides about a fifth of the world's primary energy consumption. The twenty-five countries with the highest nuclear shares of electricity generation are shown in Figure 3.31.

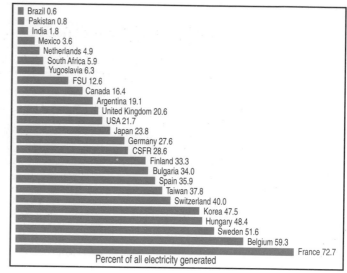

Brazil 0.6
Pakistan 0.8
India 1.8
Mexico 3.6
Netherlands 4.9
South Africa 5.9
Yugoslavia 6.3
FSU 12.6
Canada 16.4
Argentina 19.1
United Kingdom 20.6
USA 21.7
Japan 23.8
Germany 27.6
CSFR 28.6
Finland 33.3
Bulgaria 34.0
Spain 35.9
Taiwan 37.8
Switzerland 40.0
Korea 47.5
Hungary 48.4
Sweden 51.6
Belgium 59.3
France 72.7

Percent of all electricity generated

Figure 3.31 The twenty-five countries with the highest share of nuclear generation in 1991

FIFTY NUCLEAR POWER STATIONS 'NEEDED EVERY YEAR BY 2000'

Tom Wilkie

THE world's nuclear industries could be building more than 50 nuclear power stations a year by 2000, each of them as large as the Sizewell reactor in Suffolk, the director-general of the International Atomic Agency said yesterday.

Global warming and the Gulf crisis will bring about a renaissance in the fortunes of nuclear power, Dr Hans Blix, head of the Vienna-based UN agency told an international conference in Lyons. More than 2,000 scientists and engineers are attending the conference, ENC 90, to discuss issues ranging from nuclear safety to the contribution that nuclear power can make to global energy supplies in the 21st century. The conference is the latest in a series organised once every four years by the European Nuclear Society and by the European nuclear industry's trade body, Foratom.

Dr Blix told the conference that 'the challenge to reduce carbon dioxide emissions will probably be very hard to meet even with an expanded use of nuclear power. I don't think the world can afford to do without nuclear power'.

Dr Blix said that Britain – where 70 per cent of the electricity is generated in coal-fired generators – releases 10 times as much carbon dioxide into the atmosphere per unit of electricity consumed, as France, where 70 per cent of the electricity is generated by nuclear power stations. He said that although Chernobyl 'will never be forgotten, it will gradually be viewed as an exceptional event' provided an international culture of nuclear safety was maintained.

But criticism of the Soviet Union's nuclear engineering emerged as a theme of the conference. A series of speakers from Western Europe's nuclear industry took it in turns to heap blame on the Russians for Chernobyl and for causing the public relations difficulties that the West was experiencing.

Jean-Claude Leny, the chairman of Framatome, builders of France's nuclear power stations, said all the reactors built in the Soviet Union and Eastern Europe needed urgent safety improvements. The Chernobyl design was a nightmare, he said. Western industrial nations should help the Soviet Union to improve the safety of existing reactors and design a new generation of pressurised-water reactors to prevent another catastrophe. The new independence of the countries of Eastern Europe 'may be the best chance for the near-term revival of the world's nuclear power market', he said. The opportunity of selling nuclear reactors, parts and services to Eastern Europe was 'not to be missed'.

The deputy head of the biggest German electricity company, PreussenElektra AG, Dr Hans-Ulrich Fabian, said Chernobyl was the result of 'irresponsible management of nuclear energy'. He warned that although primary energy demand in Western Europe had risen only 1.6 per cent over the past decade, the demand for electricity had risen by approximately a third as people switched to electricity from other sources of power. 'Always less and less electricity per application, but always more and more applications with electricity,' Dr Fabian said. The switch to electricity would increase the need for nuclear power.

But the conference's confidence in a nuclear future came the day after a referendum in Switzerland, which decided that there should be a decade-long moratorium on building new nuclear power plants. The conference also heard that Sweden is still committed to phasing out all existing nuclear power stations by 2010; there has not been a new order for a nuclear reactor in the United States for 17 years, and in the UK there is a four-year moratorium on the construction of new reactors after Sizewell.

Source: *Independent*, 25 September 1990

THE SHADOW CAST ON SACRED WATERS

Pride of Indian technology or monster on the Ganges? Vijay Singh reports on the troubled construction of a nuclear power station at Narora

'The Ganges waters have incredible magical properties, to the rich and to the poor...to both with the same sacred hand...the water can cure all' – thus spoke Ram Bhai, my boatman. Suddenly as we rounded a sharp bend I could see the funnel-like architecture of an enormous structure. 'That is a monster', says Ram, 'which could deprive the Ganges of her magical properties. It could bring death to the world...how can it help me?'

As we anchored the boat I asked Krishna Swaroop, an engineer, what the huge structure was. 'It's not a monster like your illiterate fool of a boatman said, it's the flagship of Indian technology, the pride of our nation, the Narora Atomic Power Project. Do you realise India is not like the other wretched Third World countries? We are now going to be a superpower. We manufacture our own computers, we'll have our own nuclear energy and soon our own atomic bomb.' The Narora plant is about 100 km from Delhi, and only 50 km from a zone of severe earthquakes.

Dr Dhirendra Sharma, the organiser of the Anti-Narora campaign, claims that the plant is modelled on the Chernobyl style. He says that there is a severe shortage of heavy water, which causes the three existing plants to run at high cost, far more expensively than hydro-electric plants. As he said, 'not even the telephones work around here. So what hope for NAPP (Narora Atomic Power Project)?'

Gupta Singh, a progressive local farmer owning 150 hectares of land, disagrees. 'The plant is safe, absolutely safe. We need cheap and efficient power in this area, the green revolution belt of India.'

Source: 16–19 Geography, Paper 2, 1990 (University of London Exam and Assessment Council)

VALUES ENQUIRY: NUCLEAR NEEDS

The two articles above and left show something of the variety of opinions held throughout the world on the potential of nuclear power. In the second article the attitudes of four people towards the development of a nuclear power station at Narora near Delhi are outlined.

1 What factors will affect the perceived need for nuclear power?

2 Devise a diagram to show the potential conflict of values generated by the development of nuclear power.

CASE STUDY *The Nuclear Option in Japan: the Main Issues*

Nuclear reactors now generate over 25% of Japan's electricity and the country ranks fourth in world nuclear energy production, after the United States, France and the FSU. Hydro-electricity contributes 12% and there is a small amount of geothermal energy. The rest comes from imported fossil fuels and in 1986 Japan imported fuels which accounted for 80% of its total energy demand. In the developed world only Italy has a similar deficit in energy trade.

Since the Chernobyl accident of 1986 (Figure 3.33) the Japanese people, whose history makes them especially sensitive to the impact of nuclear explosions, have become increasingly opposed to nuclear power. A demonstration held in Tokyo on the first anniversary of the disaster was supported by 2500 people. Despite an extensive public relations campaign, mounted by the nuclear industry and the government, and about 14 000 meetings between the nuclear industry and local groups, by 1988 20 000 people attended a demonstration organised by about 150 local groups. The nation's usually apolitical youth found a cause for protest and the Toshiba-EMI company, a leading contractor in nuclear power, refused to release a record with anti-nuclear lyrics because they said that some of the songs were 'not appropriate'.

Protests are most vocal at the proposed sites of the new nuclear installations. In 1989 around 10 000 people formed a human chain around the site for a plant handling nuclear waste at the northern end of the main island, Honshu. They say that the site's geological conditions are uncertain and there is also a risk from aircraft crashes from the nearby USA airforce base. Local pressure has already caused the Japan Nuclear Fuel Industry Company to make radical changes in the design for the storage of low-level waste. Instead of being placed on a rock base, the waste will now be stored in pits within the rock and covered by 2 m of clay as well as the original 4 m of soil. Tunnels will also be built so that workers, rather than instruments, can make regular inspections for damage and leaking water. The issue remained so important that at the local elections a moderate opponent unseated the mayor who supported the development.

A steady stream of breakdowns and other incidents has kept nuclear issues in the news. The Japanese nuclear industry is rightly proud of its safety record and 'downtime' is around the lowest in the world because there is good engineering and a motivated and stable workforce. The Atomic Energy Commission in Japan also claims that the industry has achieved record low levels of employee exposure to radiation. To counter the opposition the government has increased its budget for public relations more than tenfold and aimed one campaign at housewives who, they claim, are being misled by extremists. They stress that radiation is a natural phenomenon and that the alternative to nuclear power is burning polluting fossil fuels. For the first 'Nuclear Power Day' in October 1989, railway stations and schools displayed posters showing a happy couple expressing their gratitude to nuclear power.

Protests have also influenced the way the government announces its nuclear plans. Safety records are stressed before outlining the plans for the future. A new system has also been introduced for classifying incidents at nuclear plants so that the reports will appear less alarming to ordinary people. Ministers are also worried that a high profile nuclear programme will stir up even more opposition and so they have delayed the plans to increase the capacity from 29 GW to 53 GW by the year 2000. Further problems are caused by the need to decommission the older power stations, perhaps as early as 1996. It is estimated that the first, at Tokai, north-east of Tokyo, will cost £130 million. The power companies will have to raise this money themselves and British estimates for similar jobs are more than double this figure.

More immediately, there is the problem of the disposal of wastes. At the moment the power stations store their own low-level waste on site but soon the vast new complex at Rokkasho will start to handle this waste and a new plant, probably on Hokkaido Island, will deal with high-level waste. The location of the deep storage sites is likely to be controversial.

The government is also committed to closing Japan's fuel cycle. At present it relies on foreign countries to enrich the uranium before it can be used and also to reprocess the spent fuel rods. In order to do this, further installations must be completed at Rokkasho. A new reactor is due to be completed to demonstrate fast-breeder reactors and to enable the Japanese to become almost self-sufficient in uranium. The fast-breeder reactors run on uranium enriched with plutonium and in the process produce more plutonium. One further hurdle needs to be overcome before this stage can be achieved. Plutonium which has been sent to Britain and France to be reprocessed must be returned to Japan. Japan actually owns the fuel and has to pay to store it in the foreign countries. The fuel is required for the fast-breeder programme and Japan will not be able to reprocess enough of its own for at least 10 years. The fuel is a mixture of oxides of uranium and plutonium and as such is much less useful to terrorists than hijacked pure plutonium would be. Spent fuels have travelled from Japan to Sellafield in Britain since 1969 and the contract is worth £2.5 billion to British Nuclear Fuels. However, the return of the reprocessed plutonium is much more difficult. Originally the Japanese wanted to fly non-stop flights over the North Pole but the American government prohibited this because they refused to set technical specifications for containers which would survive a plane crash. They also insisted that any shipments by sea should have an armed escort, but Japan has been an unarmed nation since 1945

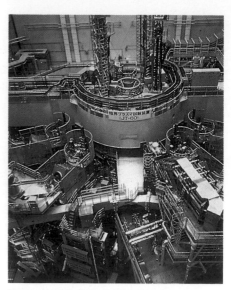

Figure 3.32   Nuclear industry in Japan

and has armed forces only for self-defence. In order to overcome the problem Tokyo gave the responsibility to the Maritime Safety Agency, a coastguard force. However, there is the need to build a suitable escort ship that could circumnavigate the world non-stop. Money has been set aside for this.

Japan does have another option – geothermal energy. By tapping the vast reserves of superheated water and steam that lie beneath the seismically active archipelago, the country could provide a fifth of its energy needs. The technology has been available but the problems are political. The opposition comes from the owners of Japan's 2189 commercial spa baths known as *onsen*. They are used by the Japanese as a place to relax and socialise. The owners fear that if water is removed for geothermal power there will be insufficient heat for their baths. Where owners have co-operated with the geothermal companies there have been no problems.

ENQUIRY: SHOULD BRITAIN PRODUCE MORE NUCLEAR ELECTRICITY?

Since 1954 the United Kingdom has produced nuclear power. There are now 17 locations where nuclear reactors are sited or proposed and nuclear power contributes 20% of our electricity. However, in 1989 the government imposed a four-year moratorium on the building of new reactors. There are opposing views in Britain as to whether nuclear power should be developed for the twenty-first century. The

material below presents the opposing positions taken by two organisations and a number of related facts and views. Consider the evidence and then tackle the essay title 'Should Britain produce more nuclear electricity?'.

In 1989 it was assumed that the substantial amounts of nuclear electricity would be generated for the forseeable future as base load provision.

However, privatisation of electricity has raised cost issues (research and development, waste and decommissioning) to be added to environmental concerns. The dash for gas-fired power stations in the early nineties has not only challenged the role of coal-fired power stations but also thrown further uncertainty as to the role of nuclear power beyond the year 2000.

The Greenpeace view

Inefficient process – much of available energy lost.
Dangerous process – radiation from fuel and waste.
Uneconomic.
Large waste problem.
Leaks occur.
Discharges are radioactive.
Accidents are possible.
Risk of atomic war – produces plutonium (used in nuclear weapons).
Industry has little insurance against third party claims.
Contingency plans if accident occurs are inadequate.
Public permanently anxious about accidents.
Instead:
Increase energy efficiency from other fuels.
Conserve energy use.
Use alternative sources.

UK Atomic Energy Authority view

'Fast' reactors are efficient – possible commercial use in 2020.
Small amount of uranium needed – future of reserves assured.
Renewable energy sources do not provide constant energy – biomass crops fail, rivers dry up, solar power deficient in winter or at night when heating needed.
Price of nuclear energy will not increase like exhaustible fossil fuels (little required of plentiful fuel). Lower energy costs for industry and households as result.
Heat from generating nuclear electricity could be used for manufacturing and home heating.
Reduces amount of carbon dioxide and sulphur dioxide released into the atmosphere.
Safety and waste problems can be managed so that risks to public are at least as low as those of other industries.
Provides diversity of power sources.
Provides employment in nuclear industry and may lead to exports.
Reduces risk of accidents, disease and pollution from coal mining.
Saves fossil fuels for other uses.
Higher energy costs will mean less money for other things (both nation's balance of payments and household budget). If nuclear energy keeps costs down there is more money for education, health care, roads, investment in science and technology, aid to developing world.
Renewables are unlikely to contribute more than a quarter of total supplies in the long term because of cost, availability and technical reasons.

THE SAFETY MAN
Andrew Marshall

THE Day Operations Manager at Sellafield's Magnox Reprocessing Plant Peter Maher starts each day by passing through changing rooms into the so-called 'active area' – a potentially radioactive zone – and pins a special badge to his overalls which monitors the radiation dosage in his body.

After many years at Sellafield these everyday procedures cause him no alarm. But a recent report from independent scientists has confirmed that there is a statistical link between workers at the Sellafield nuclear plant and leukaemia in their children. The study conclusions are based on small numbers, and the Government is cautious in its interpretations of the results, but they are keen to see further research.

As well as dealing with the basic staffing tasks of industrial relations, on-site safety and sickness absences, Maher also has a role in the continual design changes at Sellafield, such as fitting better radiation shields and installing modern equipment. 'I sometimes initiate a modification and have the authority to issue a work permit after assessing how the engineers intend to do the job.'

Maher's duties also involve investigating technical hiccups in the plant's operation. 'These aren't nuclear accidents but small, infrequent events,' he says. 'But even these must be treated seriously and investigated to prevent a recurrence.'

The 700-acre Sellafield site saw more than 150,000 visitors last year, which means that Maher's plant has tours almost every day – an extra hassle, which most plant managers do not face.

'The only way to convince people who are firmly antinuclear is to let them look at what we do – we have to make allowances for them. But it doesn't affect the standard to which I do my job.'

Source: *Daily Telegraph*, 19 April 1990

NEW GENERATION REACTORS

THE NUCLEAR industry in the US is down but not out. At least, not if the Advanced Light Water Reactor (ALWR) Program comes to anything. John Taylor a scientist from the Electric Power Research Institute in California, described the industry's attempts to design reactors that are safer, simpler and cheaper than existing models. The idea is also to produce standardised designs that do not become bogged down in the licensing process.

Taylor and his colleagues also run the programme to clean up the reactor at Three Mile Island that was wrecked in an accident in 1979. Taylor blamed many of today's problems on the competition between designers and reactor makers in the early days of nuclear power. This, he said, 'resulted in rapidly increased sizes, reduced engineering margins, and greater system complexity.'

As a consequence, he said, 'the biggest problems we face in operating our nuclear plants are ones based on human performance.'

The ALWR programme has produced initial designs for reactors with cooling systems that will continue to operate no matter what happens in an accident. There are two types of design. The proposed 'passive' plants would work under natural circulation even during normal operation: the 'evolutionary' designs would use pumps during normal operation but natural circulation would remove heat in the event of an accident.

Source: *New Scientist*, 24 February 1990

A NUCLEAR NEIGHBOUR

• A SECRET report admits that French nuclear power stations are so unsafe that Britain risks contamination. The report – released after being leaked to a French Green member of the European Parliament – says there have been two disturbing incidents in the last 12 months at Gravelines nuclear complex, 30 miles from Kent.

Its author, Pierre Tanguy, chief inspector of nuclear safety in France, attacks official French estimates that an accident the size of the 1957 Windscale fire or the 1969 near-disaster at Three Mile Island, Pennsylvania, is only likely to happen once in every 100,000 years.

He says the prediction is 'stained with a considerable margin of uncertainty' and that the chances of an accident occurring in a French reactor in the next 20 years amounted to several per cent.

The narrow escapes at Gravelines, where there are six reactors each twice the size of the largest in Britain, occurred when operators failed to replace the proper bolts in safety valves and when a control rod got stuck.

Source: *Sunday Times*, 18 March 1990

Sources of radioactivity: the percentage view

51% Radon and thoron are radioactive gases present in the air. They are given off from rocks and soil, including building materials, and so are concentrated inside buildings.

14% Direct radiation from traces of uranium and related elements in the rocks and soil.

12% Radiation from our own bodies and from the food and drink we eat.

12% Mainly from X-rays.

10% Radiation from outer space.

0.4% Fallout from nuclear weapons testing and the Chernobyl accident .

0.4% Travel by air. Burning of coal (like other rocks, coal has traces of uranium, etc.).

0.2% Radiation dose to workers from medical and industrial uses.

0.1% Routine discharges from the entire nuclear industry.

BRITISH ALTERNATIVES

DAVID ELLIOT

THE SUN provides the energy for plant life and drives the weather system, creating winds, which in turn creates waves. And the gravitational pull of the moon and sun combine to produce tides. These natural 'renewable' energy flows are vast – considerably more than we could ever need. And they will last forever. The problem is to find ways to tap them, economically and acceptably.

Britain actually has amongst the world's best wind, wave and tidal resources.

Several prototype wind turbines have already been installed and more are planned. In the longer term, wind power has the potential to supply up to 20% of UK electricity, from land-based sites, at competitive costs. But that would involve siting dozens of 'wind farms' each with hundreds of wind turbines in arrays in windy areas.

Some people find wind turbines positively attractive, but there obviously could be amenity loss and visual intrusion problems. Fortunately, however, it seems likely that there are enough remote sites to be able to provide a fair degree of choice concerning location, at least up to a 10% contribution.

But we could also deploy wind farms in shallow water offshore, where the visual impact (over the horizon) is negligible and wind speeds are higher – thus offsetting the cost of delivering power back to the land. Assuming it was fully developed, the ultimate UK offshore wind potential is put at around 50% of current electricity requirements.

Deep sea wavepower has a similarly minimal impact and large ultimate potential. Although the initial pioneering UK programme was wound up in 1982 on the basis of some disputed costings, a new UK review is currently underway.

Source: Advertisement for the British Gas Environmental Debate, 1990

Sizing up the alternatives

To generate the same amount of electricity as a modern nuclear power station produces we would need:

Solar
150 km^2 of solar panels.

Wind
300 wind turbines (each 60 m in diameter) covering an area about the size of Birmingham.

Tidal
A tidal barrier across the Severn Estuary, about 10 miles long.

Wave
100 km of wave energy converters.

Hydro
A hydro station about 10 times the size of the largest station in Britain (130 MW).

Nuclear power: global prospects

Although the construction of some 2000 reactors (in addition to over 500 operating at present) is technologically feasible, strong social and political opposition is certain. The Brundtland Report stipulated certain safety controls, such as early notification procedures in case of nuclear accident or excessive radioactive emissions, training in early response to an emergency, regulations for the transport of radioactive material and specifications for waste disposal procedures. At present the problems of waste disposal and the operation of reprocessing facilities for spent fuel are the most contentious issues. As nuclear reactors are developed in a variety of economically less-developed countries such as Iran, Pakistan, Cuba and South Korea, there is inevitable concern over the proliferation of nuclear weapons and over explosions. Cost, too, will have a significant impact. At present there are very high construction costs and delays caused by public opposition often double the cost. Running costs, too, have to be considered in relation to those of other sources of electricity. Nuclear power may have a significant role in a sustainable future; nevertheless, it will need to be administered carefully. Its wide acceptance will depend on international regulation of safety standards, design features, waste storage and other controversial aspects.

3 Alternative Energy: Power of the Future?

Increasingly scientists are searching for renewable energy sources. Whether the energy is renewed by the Sun, the Moon, the interior of the Earth or the people that live in the region is a matter of the level of technological development and the availability of technical skills. 'Sizing up the alternatives' (page

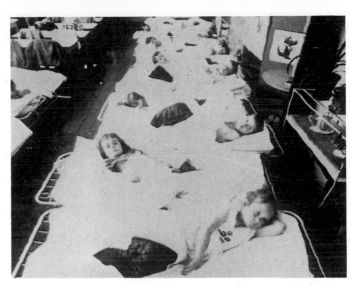

Figure 3.33 Collective farm children suffering intestinal problems from radiation exposure in a hospital at Syekoyo, near Chernobyl, site of the world's worst nuclear disaster

130) suggested comparative costs for the development of alternative energy sources (see also Figure 3.34).

Some of these sources are now capable of economic production. The extract 'British alternatives' (from an advertisement placed in the quality newspapers by British Gas as part of their campaign for environmental awareness) gives a very encouraging analysis of the future of renewable energy in Britain. Table 3.9 suggests systems that would be suitable for the less technologically developed areas of the world where both money and local availability of technical skills limit other developments which will be sustainable in the near future.

Table 3.9 Alternative energy options for economically less-developed countries

System	Needs	Suitable for	Benefits / Problems
Small-scale hydro	Water flow	Electricity for: rural industry domestic use schools hospitals	Local supply – no grid needed
Windmills	Windy location	Pumping water to: irrigate land supply livestock	Cheaper than diesel or bullock power. High installation cost. Technical service skills needed
Biogas	Dung, human excreta, crop residues	Methane produced: heats stoves lights lamps runs machinery produces electricity	Collection of sewage improves hygiene as well
Fuelwood plantation	Local areas to be replanted with fast-growing trees	Urban fuelwood needs	Expensive to set up. Needs local co-operation to avoid poaching of trees or abandonment of plantation
Village woodlots	Trees planted by villagers for own use. Self-help/village managed	Village fuelwood needs	Small scale, local
Liquid fuel	Surplus local product which can be fermented to produce fuel	Transport	25% of Brazilian cars run on pure ethanol from sugarcane (alcool project). The rest run on a 20% ethanol blend. Cassava and maize are converted into ethanol. Fast-growing water weeds and algae produce methane

ENQUIRY: ALTERNATIVE ENERGY RESOURCES

1 Summarise Dr David Elliot's views (see 'British alternatives') on the future of renewable energy in Britain.

2 Read the articles on pages 132–33 on small-scale schemes (using processed rubbish and ocean temperature gradients) and large tidal schemes for several British estuaries. Make a chart to show possible advantages and disadvantages of large and small schemes.

3 Using the article on 'Free power from beneath the waves', write a report similar to Dr David Elliot's to outline the potential for renewable energy in the economically less-developed world.

FREE POWER FROM BENEATH THE WAVES

Nick Nuttall

BRITISH marine engineers are working with the Taiwanese government and industry to harvest electricity from the sea using a novel method known as ocean thermal energy conversion (Otec).

The five-megawatt project, which would provide power for about 5,000 homes, could lead to the wide-scale commercial development of a form of renewable energy claimed to be one of the world's most environmentally benign.

Unlike tidal and wave power, Otec systems work 24 hours a day, exploiting the temperature difference between the warm surface seas and the deep, cold, polar waters found in tropical and sub-tropical regions at 1,000-metre depths.

Many of the countries in these regions are reliant on fuel imports. Recent estimates from the United States calculate that 60,000 megawatts of the world's electricity could be generated from the oceans' temperature gradients by the year 2010.

Otec systems, apart from generating electricity, bring up nutrient-rich cold waters from the deep that could be discharged into tanks, sited next to power stations, for raising fish and shellfish, and high-value marine plants such as seaweed for food and medical purposes.

In addition, areas of the world with coastal borders that are short of drinking and irrigation water, such as the Caribbean island of St Lucia, can use part of an Otec plant's electricity production to desalinate sea water. Calculations indicate that, with oil at $28 to $30 a barrel, the economic equation begins swinging in favour of Otec stations. At $40 a barrel the attractiveness soars because virtually all the capital costs will be paid off after eight-and-a-half years.

The main hurdle, however, which supporters of such systems need to overcome is the traditional scepticism of financiers towards new technologies.

Source: *The Times*, 18 October 1990

TIDAL POWER PUSHES FORWARD

Nick Nuttall

A TIDAL power barrage may be built in the North-West for almost a tenth of the cost of the proposed 8,500-megawatt Severn barrage and take a quarter of the time to build. The energy department is expected this week to announce funding for studies into a 47MW project at Fleetwood, Lancashire, across the River Wyre.

Initial investigations into small tidal-power schemes, carried out for the department's energy technology support unit at Harwell in Oxfordshire have examined more than 120 possible locations along Britain's coastline.

The North Western Electricity Board (Norweb) has also been studying the potential in its region for renewables, including wind power, landfill gas, small-scale hydro and tidal-power schemes.

Both investigations have concluded that the Wyre estuary, which runs into Morecambe Bay, potentially has the geographical and tidal features capable of making a barrage cost-effective. The new study will be into the technical, economic and environmental acceptability of a 13 turbine, 530 metre construction at the mouth of the Wyre.

Other aspects of the study, now deemed crucial to a tidal-power project's funding, are the regional-development implications, including leisure opportunities and the possibility of the barrage's use as a river crossing.

Fleetwood's position as the main deep-water fishing port on the west coast and an important port for ferries to the Isle of Man could be harmed by an insensitively sited barrage.

The decision to investigate the Wyre highlights the slow but steady push to exploit Britain's coastline to generate clean, cheap electricity from the tides. Findings from a pre-feasibility study of the Humber will probably be used to seek the backing needed to present the idea of a barrage across the Humber to the European Commission as a regional development scheme. In July, the Mersey Barrage Company, which wants to build across the Mersey, said it hoped a private bill would be put before Parliament in autumn next year, enabling it to start construction. Environmental and technical studies into the effect of a huge barrage across the Severn estuary are also continuing. A report is expected this autumn and some experts hope that construction could start at the end of the decade.

Source: *The Times*, 2 August 1990

POWER OUT OF TRASH

Roger Highfield

EVERY 3 lb of household waste contains the equivalent heat energy of 1lb of coal. Increasingly, this lost energy is being put to work with the help of bacteria that abound in rubbish tips – or landfill sites, as industry prefers to call them. The bacteria turn degradable waste into gas that can be burnt.

Britain discards some 80 million tonnes of mixed household, commercial and industrial wastes each year. Of the 500 or so rubbish sites that are thought to be suitable for energy production, we are currently using 20 or so. Another 20 sites are at the planning proposal stage. The largest individual project generates 3.5 megawatts but, within five years, this could grow to as much as 30 megawatts.

The Government has found that by imposing controls on the management of waste to protect the environment it can also encourage the operators of the landfill sites to extract energy.

But how do you unlock the energy stored in rubbish? In the past, waste has simply been burnt off. Incineration equipment is expensive, can release pollutants, is technically tricky and a much simpler way to destroy it is to let bacteria do the job.

Conditions in landfills are rarely ideal and it is unusual for more than 25 per cent of the degradable fraction of waste to decompose during the first 15 years. Efficiency depends on a cocktail of factors and it is best to customise the site for bio-gas production, or even build 'digestion tanks' rather than adapt an existing site.

In 1986 the Department of Energy estimated that Britain's landfills could generate the equivalent of 1.3 million tonnes of coal, of which at least one million tonnes are worth exploiting commercially.

Source: *Daily Telegraph*, 30 October 1989

BARRAGE ON SEVERN 'WILL HELP REDUCE POLLUTION'

A TIDAL BARRAGE generating electricity on the River Severn could provide 100 years of environmentally-friendly energy, according to a study published by its backers yesterday.

The report said the barrage could displace 7 per cent of the electricity demand of England and Wales now supplied by coal-fired power stations, reducing pollution and helping to curb the greenhouse effect.

The study, which cost £4.4m, was carried out jointly by the Department of Energy, the Central Electricity Generating Board and the Severn Tidal Power Group. They say the project would create thousands of jobs for the region.

But the development's effect on the immediate environment is causing a major dilemma.

The proposed site for the barrage – between Lavernock in South Glamorgan and Brean Down in Somerset – would affect some important mudflats and designated Sites of Special Scientific Interest. The Royal Society for the Protection of Birds is particulary concerned about the loss of important habitats. Conservation groups fear they would be trading off the advantage of reduced pollution for the disadvantage of damage to the region's wildlife

Yesterday's report claimed the project would create 'no insuperable ecological problems.' But it said that 'a great deal more work will be necessary before a full environmental assessment may be made.'

Simon Roberts, energy campaigner for Friends of the Earth, said the scheme came some way down the list of environmentally-sensitive energy projects.

'The Severn Tidal Barrage risks being a very expensive international environmental disaster,' he said. 'It would be money and an internationally important natural habitat wasted.'

The cost of building the 10-mile barrage is estimated at £828m at 1988 prices, excluding the cost of roads, with a further £850m for off-barrage transmission and grid reinforcement. More exact costs could not be worked out until after privatisation of the electricity supply industry, the study said.

The barrage would include two power stations, containing 216 turbine generators. It would carry a dual carriageway linking motorways on both shores and providing a second crossing of the estuary 25 miles from the Severn Bridge.

Building work could take up to seven years, with the creation of 35,000 jobs during the third year. Half of those jobs would be filled locally, the study said.

The report concluded: 'If renewable energy sources are to be utilised to increase diversification of electricity generation and reduce pollution, the Severn Barrage remains the largest single project which could make a significant contribution on a reasonable timescale.'

Source: *Independent*, 24 October 1989

CASE STUDY *Renewable energy for Norweb*

Norweb (North West Electricity Board) serves the counties of north-west England such as Lancashire and Cumbria. In assessing the feasibility of renewable energy sources three aspects of the scheme were considered: the availability of an exploitable resource, technical feasibility and economic viability. The findings are shown in Table 3.10. The potential for electricity generation was also assessed, and its likely cost (Table 3.11 and Figure 3.34). To be commercially viable electricity must cost no more than 5 pence per kWh and evaluation of present development potential assumes that costs are less than 3 pence per kWh. It is probable that the cost of renewable energy will decrease in future as the technology becomes cheaper when it is produced on a larger scale. The cost of fossil-fuel energy, on the other hand, is likely to increase with stricter pollution controls and fluctuations in oil prices, to which gas prices are linked. The cost of producing energy from waste is greatly reduced because it is possible to offset the previous cost of waste disposal. In some cases, this disposal cost actually exceeds the cost of the generation plant.

Table 3.10   Summary of the assessment of the renewables options

Renewable energy resource		Presently feasible	Resource available	Economically viable
Biofuels	Forestry	■	■	■
	Landfill gas	■	■	■
	General ind. waste	■	■	■
	Special ind. waste	■	■	■ *
	Municipal waste	■	■	■
Geothermal	Hot dry rocks	○	■	○
	Aquifers	■	○	○
Water	Small-scale hydro	■	■	■
	Tidal	■	■	■
	Wave inshore	○	○	○
	Wave offshore	○	■	○
Wind	Onshore +	■	■	■

■ Positive   * Resource not quantified in the present study   + Offshore wind energy not considered in the present study
○ Negative

Source: 'Overview report', *Prospects for renewable energy in the NORWEB area* (ETSU and NORWEB), 1989

Table 3.11   Potential of the renewable energy technologies in the Norweb area

Renewable energy resource	Potential capacity (MW)	Potential generation (GWh/year)
Forestry	100	700
Landfill gas	40	300
General industrial waste	270	2150
Special industrial waste	8	60
Municipal waste	270	1900
Geothermal hot dry rocks	560	4500
Small-scale hydro	9	55
Tidal	1000	1850
Wind	1600	3500
Totals	3850	15 000

Source: 'Overview report', *Prospects for renewable energy in the NORWEB area* (ETSU and NORWEB), 1989

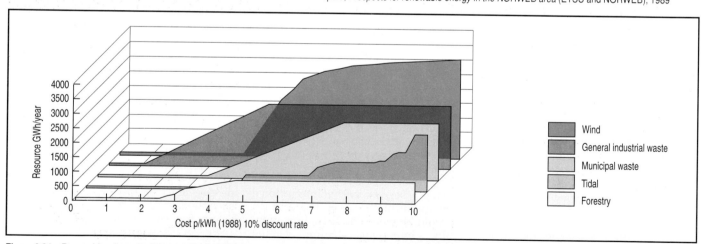

Figure 3.34   Renewable energy resources cost curves, Norweb area. The 10% discount rate refers to the need to pay off development costs in the first 10 years

ASSESSMENT EXERCISE: ENERGY PLAN FOR THE NORWEB REGION

Assess the future of alternative energy in the region in terms of availability, feasibility and viability. Decide which renewable energy resources you would develop as a priority for the region and justify your choice.

Energy Planning for Individual Countries

At all levels in society, decisions are taken about energy policy. Individuals choose between different forms of space heating or transport, for example, and also decide how intensively they will use these. Companies decide which fuel sources are most economical to exploit and can negotiate prices to some extent. In planned economies the government has a more significant role in energy development than in market-led economies. In the economically less-developed world the pressure to develop an energy resource may come from foreign companies or international banks.

Thus many different considerations influence energy policy. An idealised view of the decision-making process is shown in Figure 3.35. The process applies at individual, company, national and even global levels.

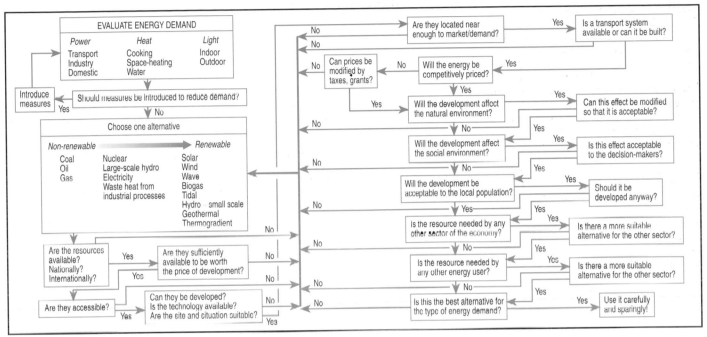

Figure 3.35   The decision-making process for planning an energy policy

GRAPHIC ANALYSIS: COMPARATIVE ENERGY USE

The charts in Figure 3.36 show energy production and consumption for two different countries: the United States and India.

1 Briefly analyse the differences between the charts.

2 Identify key factors which may account for those differences. You should look again at Figure 3.35 which outlines some of the environmental, economic and political considerations which influence decisions on energy planning.

3 Suggest how the budgets may have changed since 1980.

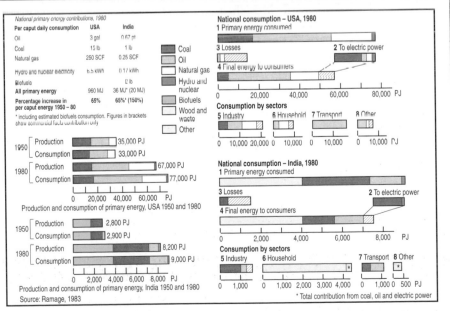

Figure 3.36   Contrasting energy budgets

CASE STUDY *Power Engineering in the former Soviet Union*

Stretching across eleven time zones, from the Arctic Ocean to the Black Sea and the Sea of Japan, lies the former Soviet Union (FSU). In the north conditions are sub-polar and in the south they are hot desert. The population of 283.1 million is unevenly distributed across the area and socio-economic conditions vary considerably. The FSU was established in 1917 and further lands were added later. The economy was largely agrarian and the country exported agricultural produce and raw minerals. In 1990 the FSU was second only to the USA total industrial output and produced more industrial goods than the whole world produced in 1950. With increased industrialisation has come a higher standard of mechanisation in many homes, in transport and in industry. This has been reflected by an increased demand for energy. The FSU is now first in the world for fuel output and second in the world for electricity output.

The FSU is fortunate in being able to rely on its own energy resources. It accounts for almost a quarter of all oil and coal and a third of all natural gas produced in the world. Its potential hydro-electric resources are greater than those of any other country. Recent political changes and increased moves towards independence have highlighted the unequal distribution of resources between the various republics.

CARTOGRAPHIC AND STATISTICAL ENQUIRY: SOVIET ENERGY

1 Make a copy of the outline base map provided (Figure 3.37) and draw on the main climatic zones of the FSU. Annotate your map to indicate temperature conditions and the need for heating or air-conditioning. Draw another map to show the main towns, the trans-Siberian railway and the general pattern of population distribution. This information should be available from an atlas.

2 Much of the FSU fuel is used to produce electricity for domestic use and for industry. Is it true that the increases in electricity production are matched by the increases in industrial output? Compare the two sets of statistics in Table 3.13. You must first calculate the percentage increase in electricity production for each state. Then apply an appropriate correlation technique to discover whether the two sets of variables are linked. What other factors do you think will influence the increase in electricity production in a planned economy?

3 Where do you think most energy will be required in the FSU? Justify your answer with reference to the maps you have just constructed.

4 Study the maps of energy supply in Figures 3.38, 3.39 and 3.40. Which forms of energy are near to the areas of demand and which will need transporting? Describe the patterns of refined petroleum transport shown in Figure 3.41. Compare it visually with the pattern of electricity distribution. Attempt to explain these patterns.

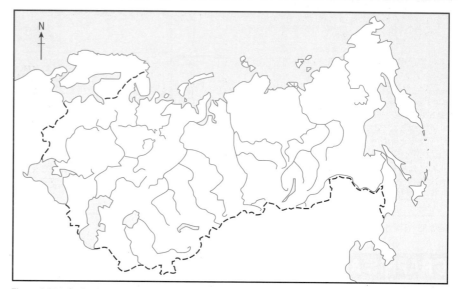

Figure 3.37   Outline base map of the former Soviet Union

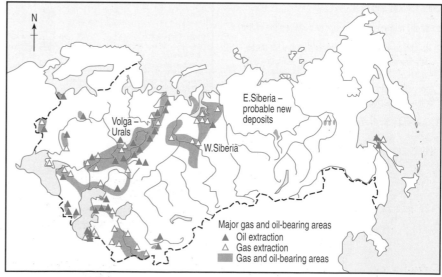

Figure 3.38   Gas and oilfields of the FSU

Problems of energy use

The FSU faces energy issues similar to those in the UK and throughout the world. The cost and the value of different fuels varies and the FSU must make the best use of its resources. Coal which is cheap to mine should not be used wastefully: when it is exhausted, the newer supplies will be much more expensive to extract and process. Oil and gas are required as raw materials in the chemical industry and should not be burnt carelessly in vehicle engines, heating equipment and power stations. For each type of demand (heat, power, light) the best alternative should be sought. For example, by introducing 'summer time' (putting the clock back), using natural daylight and the Sun's warmth, 3500 million kW of electricity are saved each year at no extra capital cost.

Four main problem areas exist: (1) *accessibility* of newer reserves; (2) the present *overdependence* on more expensive and less abundant sources; (3) the need for *consumer awareness and environmental protections;* and (4) the *uneven distribution* of resources between republics, exacerbated by weakening political links as increasing numbers of republics gain independence.

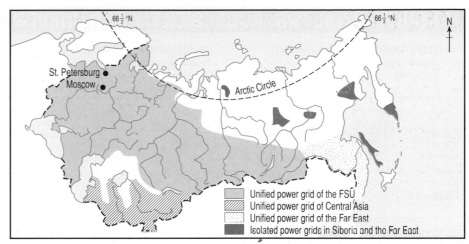

Figure 3.39   Power distribution in the FSU

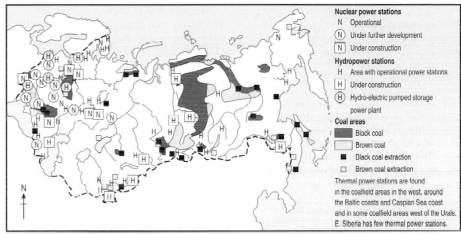

Figure 3.40   Coalfields and nuclear and hydro-power stations of the FSU

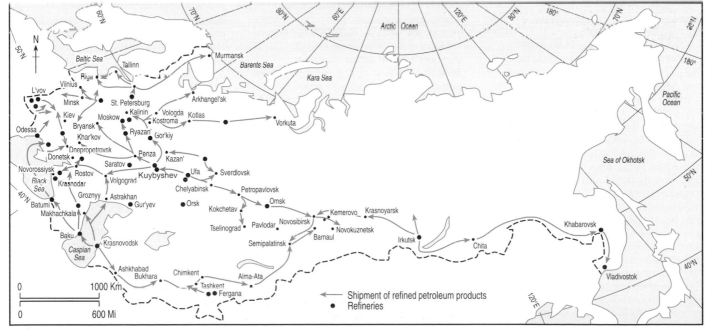

Figure 3.41   Actual refined product flows in the 1970s

TABULAR ANALYSIS: ACCESSIBILITY AND UNEVEN DISTRIBUTION

1 Use the maps from the previous exercise to complete the following table summarising accessibility.

2 Identify the areas where deposits are at present inaccessible and suggest what developments will be required before the resources will be exploited.

3 Consider the impact that the break-up of the Soviet Union may have on the various energy policies of the Republics, for example, those with currently unexploited reserves.

Fuel or power	Locations and present development	Climatic conditions	Workforce available	Use	Demand (market)	Transport available
Oil						
Gas						
Coal						
Hydro						
Nuclear						

Overdependence: Oil and gas account for 75% of fuel usage but only 10% of the FSU's reserves. More deposits may be found but they will certainly be costly to develop. If alternatives are to be used they must be developed now because it takes five to ten years to plan and build a power station. Until recently the FSU did not have to overcome political dissent when proposals were made but public involvement is increasing. There are present plans to provide a wider and more flexible electricity supply and to incorporate the potential reserves of oil and gas. Consequently six major pipelines have been built to transport gas from the Urengoi deposit to the central and western regions. It is also planned to develop the Yamburg, Karachaganak and Astrakhan deposits and to start work in the Yamal Peninsula. Oil and gas are to be developed from deep-seated deposits in the Caspian lowlands.

Hydro-electric power is 80–83% cheaper than thermal or nuclear power. Stations are being built in the central and north-west regions, where consumption load is very variable, and beyond the Urals with the object of developing industry in the area.

The vast reserves of coal east of the Urals are becoming increasingly important as the reserves in the west become exhausted and more expensive to mine. The Ekibastuz coalfield produces 25% of the country's opencast coal but it has a high ash content and so it is sensible to process it on site and transmit electricity over the long distances to the market in the west. Five large thermal power stations are therefore being built. At Kansk-Achinsk the brown coal deposits will be processed to obtain high calorific solid and liquid fuels and raw chemicals. Power stations are also being built there

to supply the European part of the FSU.

Nuclear power is planned to provide electricity in remote areas far from other fuel sources. The cost of transport of the fuel required by nuclear power stations is insignificant in comparison with the costs of transporting coal or even oil. In densely populated areas nuclear plants will be built simply to generate heat for people's homes in a community of 200 000. As they will operate under reduced loads they should have an increased safety level. Since the nuclear power station accident at Chernobyl in 1986 the Soviet strategy on nuclear power engineering has not changed but it is said that the construction of new projects has been slowed so that the technology, equipment and construction work can be thoroughly checked. There has been increasing public concern and several demonstrations over nuclear power developments. Western influence over decisions is increasingly likely.

Many of the new projects will combine several forms of power generation: thermal, nuclear, hydro and pumped storage. This will enable a much more efficient use of energy as the main stations can work constantly at capacity and use their surplus to pump the water back into the storage reservoirs to generate extra electricity at the peaks in the morning and the evening.

Consumer awareness and *environmental protection*: The government of the FSU recognises the problem of global warming and is therefore seeking alternative energy sources which will not add to the overall heat budget. A number of alternatives are available and are being actively developed. They are shown in diagrammatic form in Figure 3.42. There is also the need to encourage industry and individuals to use their energy more efficiently and effectively.

The appropriate source of heat energy should be used so that in most cases electricity can be saved for more restricted users. Until recently industry did not worry about how it used energy and any additional cost of the product was passed on to the consumer. The government is now considering pricing policies and tax incentives as well as educational programmes such as 'Switch off lights when leaving room'.

The energy programme

Since 1928 the FSU has had a centrally planned socialist economy. Plans are drawn up for five-year periods and cover all aspects of the economy, from the locating of new settlements to the commissioning of a new factory. Power production facilities have featured in all plans. The government of the FSU believes that there must be long-term planning in order to foresee, evaluate and co-ordinate future requirements and concentrate resources in the key areas. They have drawn up a twenty-year plan for power engineering to cover all processes involved in the transformation of energy, from the development of energy resources to energy consumption. They have three main objectives:

- To streamline the power industry.
- To promote energy-saving technologies especially in the power-intensive industries and transport.
- To replace costly and scarce fuels with cheaper, more generally available ones.

As a result there are new policies for the 1990s. Increased production of natural gas will allow a reduction in oil consumption, and coal and nuclear power stations will be developed for the future. The short- and long-term changes are shown in Figure 3.43.

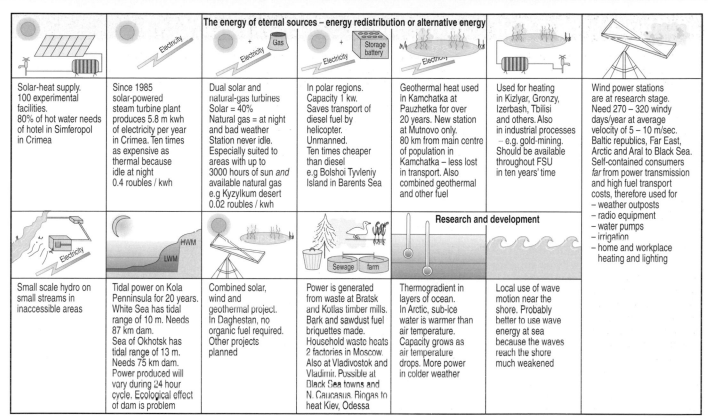

Figure 3.42   The energy of eternal sources – energy redistribution or alternative energy

Demand 1979 Energy consumption		Supply		
Oil 38% Gas 27% Coal 30%	Nuclear 1% Hydro 4%	Now	Short term	Long term
Demand doubled 1980 – 90				
Heat	Agricultural Industrial Domestic	Oil – no growth in output (twice as expensive as gas) Gas – growth in output (expensive because of pipeline costs) Electricity – (to use alternative fuels) Geothermal – increasing Waste heat – one-third of all thermal power stations provide heat locally	Better technology – more extracted from deposits Stable output Power grid serves 220 million people Local small scale Local small scale	Solar Biogas (from sewage and manure) (1990 output of biogas = 320,000 tons of equivalent fuel) Household waste — increasing Timber waste — increasing
Transport fuel	Cars Trains Aircraft	Oil	Lignite – processed to provide pollutant free petrol, fuel oil	Electricity?
Chemicals for industry		Oil Gas Coal Lignite (brown coal) – processed to chemical raw materials		
Power stations		Oil — Thermal 76.4% Gas — Hydro 13.5% Out-dated thermal (coal) — Nuclear 10.1% Some nuclear Hydro electric 80 – 83% cheaper than thermal or nuclear Tidal	New efficient coalfield Nuclear Hydro – large-scale pumped storage – small scale – increasing in remote areas Use of water outflow from agricultural and industrial processing	Nuclear? Coal Hydro Geothermal Solar Wind Tidal
Export		Oil Gas Coal	Receiving countries help pay for pipeline	World's largest exporter

Figure 3.43   Energy policy in the 1990s

PLANNING THE FORMER SOVIET UNION'S ENERGY POLICY

In small groups, devise an integrated energy programme for the FSU for five years. You will need to submit proposals for establishing or expanding local communities, for linking these communities to appropriate communications and for transporting the resulting energy to the market. You will also have to

establish schemes to enhance environmental awareness and energy conservation. Base your decision on the likely demand as shown in Figure 3.43. Use the maps (Figure 3.38–3.41) and the table you completed to assess where production could be increased. Consider the problems of climate,

workforce, and transport of the product. Incorporate any policies necessary to overcome the problem of increased independence between republics and growing trade with non-Communist countries. Explain how each of your developments will contribute to the national energy requirements for each demand sector.

The international impact of the energy industry

As a result of its vast wealth of energy resources the FSU exports much of its oil, gas and coal. The countries of Eastern Europe rely heavily on supplies from the FSU but so do many other nations (Table 3.12). There is also a trade in machinery for the energy industries in other countries. Soviet mining equipment is used in Argentina, Hungary, China, Spain, Poland, Turkey, Germany, Czechoslovakia, Yugoslavia and Japan. Turbines for hydro-power have been sold in Romania, Brazil and Canada.

The exchange of scientific information and the co-operation of nuclear physicists across the world has led to the more rapid development of many high-technology projects and may possibly now lead to greater co-operation world-wide to overcome the environmental problems of the twentieth century.

Table 3.12 FSU oil exports[1] to OECD countries 1980–83 (thousand tonnes)

	1983[2]	Oil imports from FSU as a % of total oil imports
Finland	4540	87.0
Iceland	118	74.2
Switzerland	1411	21.6
Netherlands	7276	19.2
Austria	713	18.0
Belgium	2247	12.9
Greece	987	12.1
Sweden	1314	11.8
West Germany	4751	8.7
Denmark	442	7.8
France	3505	7.7
Norway	143	7.5
UK	1407	7.1
Portugal	198	6.6
Italy	3048	6.6
Spain	885	4.9
Ireland	64	3.0
Turkey	44	0.6
Japan	265	0.3
USA	1	neg.
Totals	33 359	5.4[3]

1 Includes crude oil and refined products. 3 Average FSU oil import dependency for all OECD countries.
2 Figures for January–June 1983.
Source: *Petroleum Economist*, 50 (7), July 1983 and 51 (2), February 1984

Table 3.13 Electricity generation in the FSU (thousand million kWhours)

	1980	1987	% growth	% growth in industrial output 1980–86
Russia Fed.	805	1047		21.05
Ukraine	236	282		28.57
Byelorussia	34.1	37.8		37.93
Uzbekistan	33.9	54.8		37.50
Kazakhstan	61.5	88.5		25.00
Georgia	14.7	14.5		37.50
Azerbaijan	15.0	22.9		41.67
Lithuania	11.7	22.8		32.76
Moldavia	15.6	17.4		35.29
Latvia	4.7	5.9		22.22
Kirghizia	9.2	9.4		32.43
Tadjikistan	13.6	15.9		33.33
Armenia	13.5	15.2		42.22
Turkmenia	6.7	13.3		16.67
Estonia	18.9	17.9		20.83
FSU Total	1294	1665		23.80

ANALYSIS

On a world map, for the relevant countries, show the percentage of oil which comes from the FSU (Table 3.12) and then identify those countries which have

made links with the FSU energy industries. Choose an appropriate technique (e.g. choropleth mapping or proportional symbols) and comment

on the distribution shown.

CASE STUDY *Ecuador's Energy and the Environment*

Situated astride the Equator on the west coast of South America is the small country of Ecuador. It is only 275 341 km² in area and consists of three mainland regions and the Galapagos Islands in the Pacific Ocean. The low-lying coastal belt (La Costa), the central Andean mountain range (La Sierra) and the interior tropical rainforest area (El Oriente) contrast greatly in their climates, vegetation and animal life, populations, cultures, customs and economic bases. The annotated map (Figure 3.44) shows some of these characteristics.

The Ecuadorian economy, however, is one of the fastest growing in South America, with an average annual GDP increase of 5.2% from 1964 to 1979. This is largely the effect of the country's developing oil industry. However Ecuador is still dependent on cash crops from the agricultural sector: bananas, cacao, coffee, citrus and tropical fruits, tobacco, grains, vegetables and sugar cane. Although oil is now the main export (57%), Ecuador is still the fourth largest producer of bananas and the sixth largest producer of cacao in the world.

The population of Ecuador reached about 9 million in 1982 and continues to rise at about 3% each year. One third are pure Indians who are found mostly in La Sierra and in small numbers in El Oriente. Urbanisation is rapid and already more than 44% live in urban areas. Unfortunately, industrialisation and development have been unable to keep pace. Ecuador faces problems typical of countries in the South: inadequate housing, poor services, lack of employment, extremes of wealth and poverty and dependence on foreign investment and loans.

Oil – the key to the future?

Oil was eventually discovered in La Oriente in 1967 by a Texaco-Gulf consortium and a significant volume of production was achieved by the end of 1971. The state oil company, CEPE (Corporacion Estatal Petrolera Ecuatoriana), holds a majority share in the consortium but exploration and exploitation remain in the hands of foreign investors with imported technology and an immigrant skilled workforce. Since the border war in 1941 Peru has claimed much of the previously Ecuadorian Oriente where precious metals, oil and coffee were produced.

In 1965 the Oriente was described in the passage below from a standard geographical text. In contrast, an extract from a tourist guide in 1990 shows the changes.

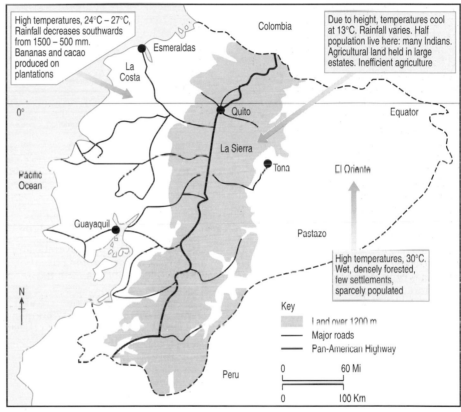

Figure 3.44   Map of Ecuador

'The Oriente is a region of humid heat, of tropical jungle, few settlements and very little commercial production. Much of the area is scarcely known: parts, in fact, have probably not been explored by white men. The first serious attempt to open up the Oriente was made in 1948, when petroleum prospecting was undertaken and several camps established. However, at the time the hope that rich oil deposits might or would occur in the Oriente proved illusory.

So the Oriente continues to remain as it has always been, a thinly peopled area contributing little to the national economy. The few inhabitants of the region, perhaps totalling 30 000–50 000, consist almost exclusively of tribes of pure-blooded Indians, such as Jivaros, Auca and Colorados, who live outside government control. Living in small, scattered, isolated groups, the Indians have had little contact with white people and deliberately shun any attempt to make contact. Some of the Jivaros were employed by the oil company and thereby introduced, if in a casual manner, to western civilisation. Frequently, however, when the Indians have come into contact with the white man they have caught, and been decimated by, his diseases. The Jivaros have a reputation as head-hunters, but this unsavoury practice is being abandoned ... The Lowland Indians dwell in rude palm-thatched huts grouped usually near rivers and live by hunting and fishing and a little primitive shifting agriculture. Theirs is essentially a self-sufficient existence.'

Source: Robinson, 1966

'Sliding across silver moonlit waters that mirror the silhouetted surrounding trees, the longboat engine fades. The guide has spotted a cayman, the Amazonian alligator; mesmerized, its eyes blaze under the flashlight. It raises its back and tail above the water, threatening the intruders, stares cold defiance, and suddenly vanishes with a lightning thrash.

This is the Ecuadorian Oriente, the upper Amazon basin east of the Andes – nowadays known as the province of the future. It is a place of endless virgin rainforest cut by fast-flowing rivers and inhabited by jaguars, ocelots, anacondas, monkeys, tapirs, fish-eating bats, piranhas and over 450 species of bird... Development has affected the lifestyles of all the tribes, and many traditions have died... Some... retain their Stone Age culture... They hunt with spears, blow-pipes and poison darts, keep harpie eagles as both pets and watch-dogs, and still make fire by rubbing two sticks together. Several missionaries, including the Bishop of Coca, have recently been killed for trying to encroach upon their precious culture.

The face of the region has changed dramatically since [the oil discovery of 1967], with towns constructed overnight to provide services for the booming industry, which quickly became Ecuador's main money-spinner. The influx of people has sent the wildlife deeper into the forests.

The canopy is thickest at a height of 100 feet, beneath which grows, in damp dimness, an astonishing assortment of ferns and wild lemon trees with tiny edible ants living inside its stems. A boardwalk across swamps passes a giant kapok tree... its branches are cluttered with bromeliads, strangler vines and bella dona, from which atropine is extracted.'

Source: Rachowiecki, 1990

Table 3.14　Production and consumption of energy in Ecuador (thousand metric tons of coal equivalent)

	Fuelwood	Liquid	Gas	Electricity			Fuelwood	Liquid	Gas	Electricity
Production						*Consumption*				
1975	1337	11 677	51	79		1975	1337	2687	51	79
1980	1849	14 894	51	109		1980	1849	5518	51	111
1985	1959	20 447	129	458		1985	1959	5415	129	459
1986	2079	20 919	144	530		1986	2079	5650	144	531

Oil and the economy in Ecuador

The discovery, development and export of oil has brought real change to the Ecuadorian economy. Ecuador is now the second largest producer of oil in South America, after Venezuela. Oil revenues have enabled Ecuador to borrow money to fund development. Taxes from oil pay for increased military activity, but also for modernisation of the economy by improving infrastructure, increasing industrialisation, introducing agrarian reform and improving agricultural productivity. Foreign investment has increased. Recent investments include:

- A large HEP plant at Pisayambo and many smaller ones, aiming to provide electricity to 45% of the population.
- Improved communications – road network increased from 10 750 km in 1958 to 18 000 km in 1977.
- Capital investment for industry, especially steel, shipbuilding and petrochemicals. Oil refinery built near Esmeraldas with capacity for 50 000 barrels per day.
- Aid to fishing industry for the production of prawns, flatfish, tinned tuna fish and sardines.
- Government has usually represented the interests of the landowning, commercial, industrial and professional élite, and so has supported technical modernisation of agriculture and industry and has encouraged home and foreign investment in capital goods.

Manufacturing contribution to economy

1950 – 65	5.3 %
1965 – 73	7.1 %
1973 – 78	11.9 %

Two-thirds of manufacturing production is food processing – sugar refining, flour milling, brewing, soft drinks and cocoa manufacture, meat and fish canning. Textiles and pharmaceuticals are also made. More trade is required and the internal market is still too small because too many are too poor. An increase in agricultural productivity is needed and the level of income for the rural population must be raised.

Table 3.15　Ecuador's trade in oil, thousands of barrels

	1960	1973	1977	1978	1980	1981
Imports	1566	5813	5175	178	—	—
Exports	—	71 126	50 453	42 000	39 636	46 449

The social and physical environment in La Oriente

'The bus ride from Coca to Lago Agrio gives an interesting look at how the discovery of oil has changed the Oriente. Fifteen years ago, this was all virgin jungle and communications were limited to mission airstrips and river travel. Today there are roads and buses, and there are always signs of the oil industry – the pipeline, oil wells or trucks.

A short way north of Coca you have to wait for an ancient car ferry to take the bus across the Rio Coca... The bus heads east and passes the belching wells of the Sacha oil works. It continues through the small oil town of La Joya de las Sachas... The road is narrow but in good condition and paved in places. It follows the oil pipeline most of the way and there are several stretches with fine scenery and vistas of the jungle. You'll frequently see tropical birds; one of the most common is the all-black *ani* with a long drooping tail and extremely thick bill. The bus passes occasional small communities and reaches the Rio Aguarico. Here another ferry takes the bus across the river. The town of Lago Agrio is a few kilometres beyond.

Lago Agrio is one of the fastest-growing towns in Ecuador (Figure 3.45). Since the discovery of oil it has changed from literally virgin jungle to the most important of Ecuador's oil towns. It now has a population of over 8000. A road has been built from Quito and there are daily flights. There are new road links with Colombia and a modern hotel has been opened. Lago Agrio became the capital of its canton in 1979; the streets are beginning to be paved and a new town plaza has been laid out on the north-western edge of town ... Lago Agrio is lobbying to have the province of Napo divided into two, with the southern half keeping the present capital of Tena and the northern half having Lago Agrio as its new capital.

Source: Rachowiecki, 1990

Population growth in La Oriente		
1950	46 500	
1962	75 000	
1974	168 000	(2.6% of national population)

Prosperity, development – with what cost?

Resources of minerals, agricultural land, forest products and people remain unexploited and undeveloped in La Oriente. The government and foreign companies know that wealth exists and could be used to aid the development of the rest of Ecuador. However, not everyone wants change. Conservationists are anxious that the last remaining areas of rainforest and the small number of tribespeople living in the area should not be destroyed. The problem is: can these two views be reconciled and realised?

Recently British Gas and its subsidiaries were challenged about their impact on the environment in the 500 000-acre concession in the remote Pastaza region near the Peruvian border. Initial exploratory work was undertaken in 1989 and in 1990 Morley Read, a British biologist working in Ecuador, reported to Friends of the Earth that there were still severe environmental problems in the forest. He claimed that workers test-drilling for oil have driven away game animals, spent their spare time killing fish with dynamite and polluted the rivers. The tribespeople also accused the workers of bringing new diseases into their villages. They have complained that the central area of the village was used as a base for supplies and that a seismic trail – a track along which explosives are detonated to determine the structure of the underlying strata – was cut across their airstrip and part of their crops. Bob Hawker, head of safety and environment for British Gas, led a team of experts into the forest to investigate the complaints and said they have been disproved by a lengthy environmental assessment conducted to conform to Ecuadorian law. 'In all our operations we pay serious attention to safeguarding the environment and minimising the effects on the local habitat and population.'

David Bellamy, the conservationist and chairman of advisers to the TSB Environmental Investor Fund, said, 'Several oil companies have got out of the area of the Amazon because they found they couldn't work there in an environmentally friendly way.'

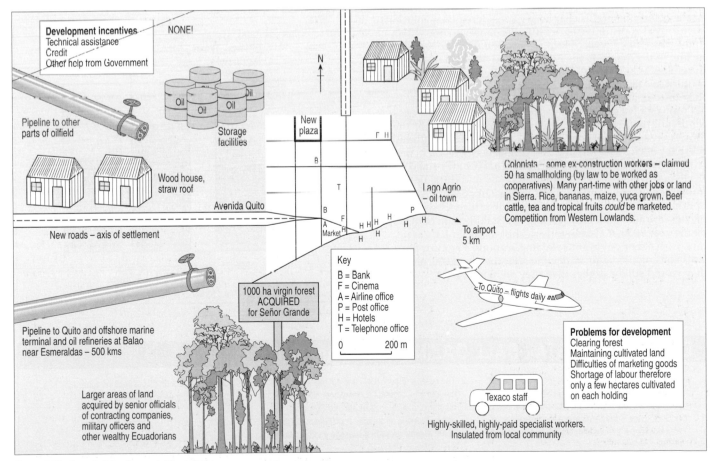

Figure 3.45 Impact of development at Lago Agrio

ENQUIRY: IS OIL THE KEY TO ECUADOR'S FUTURE?

Using the extracts, the statistics and the diagrams, produce a report for the Ecuadorian government to advise them about exploitation in the Amazon rainforest. You should:

1 Describe the physical and social environment as it is at present in La Oriente. Include the views of the tribal leaders, the young Indians and the conservationists.

2 Explain the likely changes which would occur if full-scale exploitation begins in Pastaza. Assume that the oil from Pastaza would be piped to Lago Agrio.

A road would be built to service the pipeline. Why did some oil companies find that they could not work there in an environmentally friendly way?

3 Make a list of recommendations for 'safeguarding the environment and minimising the effects on the local habitat and population'.

4 'In the interests of all Ecuadorians and the world population, development of oil in La Oriente should be allowed to proceed.' Discuss this statement. A classroom debate would be appropriate. Analyse who wins the debate and why.

Remember that the government is responsible for development throughout Ecuador and that it tends to represent the wealthier citizens. Oil is the major export and foreign currency earner and has enabled much investment for the future. The conservationists are mostly foreigners and the Indians are self-sufficient tribespeople who have been isolated from twentieth-century developments.

We have now examined the considerations influencing energy planning in two contrasting countries. You may have the resources to look at a third country. The United Kingdom is an obvious choice, though Brazil, Japan, China and most EC countries are well documented. You need to gain accurate statistical information on energy production and consumption from the *Geographical Digest* or *BP World Statistics,* and then look at the impacts the energy policies have had on development.

Back to the Future

At the beginning of this chapter we considered the evolution of an area with a primitive agricultural economy to one with a highly developed level of technology, and then looked to the future. In the diagram, the future looked bleak. Having studied the energy issues that face the world at the end of the twentieth century, we are probably in a better position to consider what the future really holds in store.

From a global standpoint we are faced by two major options for the future (Figure 3.46). The first can be described as the 'business as usual' option. Basically, this involves continuing present policies as if nothing had changed. There are many temptations to do this from the individual country standpoint, as change in energy development is costly and difficult to implement. The second option is the sustainable option. This option assumes radical improvements in efficiency as a result of conservation strategies, leading to a stabilisation of demand by the year 2000. It also assumes a shift in the global energy mix, with major environmental implications. For example, CO_2 emissions would begin to decline after the year 2000, although they would still be higher than they were in 1988.

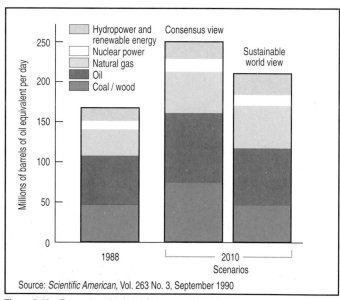

Source: *Scientific American*, Vol. 263 No. 3, September 1990

Figure 3.46   Two options for the global energy mix in 2010

ENQUIRY: CRYSTAL BALL GAZING – 2010 AND 2050

1 In the light of all your research in the course of this chapter, write an essay in which you analyse the potential impacts of the two options summarised in 'Back to the Future'. What are the prospects, in your opinion, of the sustainable option operating by 2010?

2 The collage (Figure 3.47) has put together a number of photographs, headlines, articles and diagrams in order to illustrate one view of the future. Working as a class, each select one aspect of the energy question as we see it today. Write an updated article on this aspect for publication in a daily newspaper on 27 January 2050.

Switch on a ray of sunshine

Photovoltaic cells, as used for years in watches and calculators, are now producing electricity for Californians. Inexpensive, low-purity silica provides pollution-free power. The US Government has agreed to finance and supervise the building of five large plants in Haiti, Chad, Senegal, Bolivia and New Guinea. It is expected that the less-developed countries will provide a vast market for solar kits powerful enough to run televisions and some lights if used in conjunction with batteries.

LIO – Final substitute found after years of research to provide chemicals to replace dwindling oil reserves

Peterborough Museum has made a collection of chimney pots to show youngsters what roof tops used to be like. Instead of today's windmills and solar panels on the roof, in the 1950s homes were always built with chimneys to vent the coal fires

Germany again reviews nuclear policy. Since 1991, when the Germans agreed to defer plans for the further development of nuclear power in the re-unified country, pressure has increased from energy-intensive industries and the anti-green lobby, who believe that the country is paying too much for non-polluting measures at power-stations.

The saga of Chernobyl

This week the final tonnes of cement have been mixed at Chernobyl to complete the tenth shell or sarcophagus around the massive radio-active fuel cell which has caused so much destruction since 1986. The previous shell had been built in 2041 and had therefore lasted longer than any of its predecessors but, by 2048, cracks had reappeared as the entire structure once again sank into the earth. Unlike the Phoenix which rose from the ashes, the great structures at Chernobyl are repeatedly swallowed up. Despite the use of modern pliable material it has been impossible to prevent further cracking and radiation is again leaking out. It is hoped that research into new construction techniques, and recent advances in space technology, might this time provide the answer.

Wild flowers bloom. The 60 species of wild flowers planted at Sizewell in 1993, after being stored at low temperatures since 1984, are again in bloom in the now peaceful setting of the Suffolk coast. Despite years of protest at the closure of the nuclear plant in 2002, the

50 years ago

EVENING NEWS FC PUT 'GREEN' TAX ON COAL – ELECTRICITY COSTS SOAR

'and they say it'll reduce CO_2 emissions'

OTEC plants provide food, water, and power for mineral exploitation at sea

The Ocean Thermal Energy Conversion plants which have been developed in Hawaii and Taiwan are now well-established to provide power for small communities at on-shore and off-shore sites. Recently a platform has been placed in the Pacific Ocean to allow the mining and processing of low-grade ores at sea. Large factory ships, powered by electricity generated from the heat of the oceans, are

Buy Now –

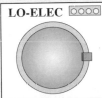

Pay November

The money to be saved by installing the new energy-saving washing machine from

Figure 3.47   Newspaper collage, dated 7 January 2050

4
The Challenge of Urbanisation

Urbanisation: the Processes and the Trends

With the exception of two continents, Africa and Asia, most of the world's population is urban. Living in towns and cities has become one of the most important trends across the globe. The growth and dynamism of urban areas has become one of the biggest challenges facing people in many countries. Urbanisation is a process which is steadily gathering momentum, particularly in the economically less-developed countries, as Table 4.1 and Figure 4.1 show.

The economically less-developed and more-developed worlds

From the tables, and your enquiry, it is clear that percentages of urban population are much higher in the latter than in the

Table 4.1 Percentage of urban population, by regions, 1960–2020

	1960	1980	1990	2000	2020
World total	34.2	39.6	42.6	46.6	57.4
Developed regions	60.5	70.2	72.5	74.4	77.2
North America	69.9	73.9	74.2	74.9	76.7
Europe incl. CIS	56.9	67.7	70.9	73.4	76.7
Oceania	66.3	71.5	70.8	71.4	75.1
Developing regions	22.2	29.2	33.6	39.3	53.1
Africa	18.8	27.0	32.5	39.0	52.2
Asia	21.5	26.6	29.9	35.0	49.3
Latin America	49.3	65.4	72.0	76.8	83.0

Source: United Nations, *Urban and Rural Population Projections 1950–2025: The 1985 Assessment* (New York, 1986)

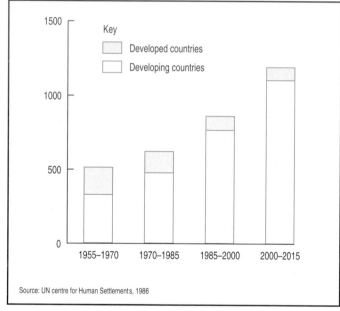

Source: UN centre for Human Settlements, 1986

Figure 4.1 Urban population increment, 1955–2015 (in millions)

former. It follows that the rate of urbanisation in the next thirty years will be much slower in the Western countries than in the Third World. Nevertheless, the process of urbanisation, whereby increasing numbers of a country's population choose to live in towns and cities, still operates in the West albeit at a much less feverish rate than in the Third World. Two examples follow to show the vast differences that exist between the urbanisation process in Western and Third World countries.

STATISTICAL ENQUIRY: WORLD URBANISATION

1 Consider the percentage of urban population by regions in 1960.
   a Why did the developed regions have a much higher percentage of urban population than the developing countries?
   b Why did continents such as Africa and Asia have such a relatively low percentage of urban population in 1960?

2 Calculate the respective growth rates in urban population predicted between 1960 and 2020 for North America, Europe, Africa and Latin America. Comment on the differences between these rates and attempt to explain them.

CASE STUDY *Bournemouth's Western Suburbs*

The development of new housing in a pleasant urban environment can entail a cost to the countryside – as in the case of Bournemouth and Poole, one of the most rapidly expanding urban areas in the United Kingdom. Look at the property brochure for Sandringham Park, on the western outskirts of Poole in the area known as Canford Heath (Figure 4.2), and at the population statistics in Tables 4.2 and 4.3.

The photograph (Figure 4.3) shows the new housing encroaching on the open countryside to the west of the Poole urban area. Beyond the housing lies Canford Heath itself, which is a conservation area. Because of the threat to the heath, a number of sensitive issues arise. Part of the ecologically valuable Dorset heathlands, Canford Heath now constitutes the largest stretch of unbroken heathland in the area.

Situated on the outskirts of Poole, in a conservation area abounding with wild flowers and butterflies, Sandringham Park is a wonderful location for your new Clarke Quality Home.

This superb development of exclusive 4-bedroomed luxury homes is so convenient for those working in Poole or Bournemouth, and as such offers a wealth of amenities and recreational facilities. Both towns are popular centres for entertainment, shopping and sports so whatever your pleasure, be it antique hunting or windsurfing you'll find it and so much more within easy reach of this desirable new development. Bournemouth boasts a number of theatres and cinemas as well as the many excellent leisure facilities of the Bournemouth International Centre. Poole of course, is home to Bournemouth's two world class orchestras, has a superb Arndale shopping centre, and is a region of great natural beauty. Poole harbour also has the distinction of being the world's largest natural harbour.

If you're looking for an area with a leisurely way of life yet plenty of action when you feel like it, Sandringham Park is the place for you.

Figure 4.2   Extract from brochure advertising Sandringham Park

Table 4.2   Canford Heath population figures

1971	1981	1988	1991
3110	8162	12317	13362

Table 4.3   1991 age structure

Age group	Canford Heath local plan area (%)	Borough of Poole (%)	Dorset (%)	Great Britain (%)
0–15	24.2	18.2	17.5	20.1
16–29	24.0	19.3	17.8	20.7
30–44	26.0	20.4	19.6	21.2
45–65	16.8	19.2	19.4	19.3
65+	9.0	23.0	25.6	18.7
	100.0	100.0	100.0	100.0

Source: 1991 Census

ENQUIRY: NEW HOUSING FOR CANFORD HEATH

1 Why do people find it such an attractive place to live?

2 What sort of people are moving to the Canford Heath area?

Figure 4.3   New housing to the west of the Poole urban area

Figure 4.4   New housing encroaching on Canford Heath

The newspaper extracts below indicate some of the difficulties that arise when a development like Sandringham Park is planned in an ecologically valuable area.

MORE TIME TO SAVE RARE REPTILES FROM BUILDERS
Peter Taylor

A DEVELOPMENT company has postponed plans to build homes on an area of Canford Heath following a plea from a conservation group to allow more time to save rare reptiles.

Clarke Homes will delay building on most of the area until next summer.

Company director Richard Terry met site rescue officer for the British Herpetological Society, Doug Mills, and John Milton of Poole Council on Marshwood Heath, to hammer out a compromise settlement.

Doug hopes he will now have time to move rare reptiles – including sand lizards and smooth snakes – off the 28 acre site and resettle them onto safer areas. This rescue operation could only take place when the animals ended their winter hibernation.

And his plan would also allow the company to build about six homes on a small uninhabited section of the site.

As a result, their highly regarded construction team could be kept together throughout the winter.

Mr Terry said the plan would be put to the board and all interested parties informed of their decision.

Meanwhile Friends of the Earth – who were not involved in the negotiations – threatened to occupy the site if the plan was rejected and asked residents to inform them if bulldozers moved onto the site.

The council was also awaiting the outcome because they had not yet completed the sale of the land to Clarke Homes.

Production director of Clarke Homes Derek Field said the board had accepted the compromise agreement because of its excellent relationship with the British Herpetological Society who they 'highly respected'.

He said they had listened closely to the advice of the BHS and were sympathetic after learning of the large numbers of rare reptiles on Marshwood Heath which had amazed and surprised them.

Mr Mills called it a victory for the animals and felt the message was finally getting through to people that the heath could not afford to lose its rare reptiles. 'If this happens species of sand lizard and smooth snake could die out altogether,' he said.

He is also fighting plans to sell off parts of Canford Heath – an area of Special Scientific Interest – to developers in a bid to protect the reptiles' sandy heathland home from further fragmentation.

Source: *Advertiser*, 6 October 1988

CONSERVATIONISTS BEGIN LEGAL FIGHT TO SAVE HEATH
Nicholas Schoon

A COURT case . . . will decide the fate of part of a habitat for some of Britain's most endangered species. Conservationists are trying to stop Poole Borough Council building houses on 17 acres of dry lowland heath [which it owns].

The hillside of heather and gorse on the outskirts of Poole, Dorset, is among the rapidly dwindling number of habitats for Britain's two rarest reptiles, the smooth snake and the sand lizard, as well as four rare bird species.

The council has given itself planning permission for up to 200 houses. It plans to sell the site to a developer, with part housing for low income families.

The World Wide Fund for Nature (WWF) and the British Herpetological Society argue that in making its decision the council failed in its legal duty to take nature conservation into account . . .

Simon Lyster, a lawyer on the WWF's staff, says it is the first time wildlife conservation organisations have legally challenged a planning decision on such grounds.

The 17 acres are part of a much larger Site of Special Scientific Interest, a status conferred on places which are particularly rich or unusual in the community of plants and animals living there.

Mr Lyster says Britain has an international obligation to protect the site, under the European community directive on birds and the Berne Convention, a European wildlife protection treaty. "If we can't hold the line on a place like this there's not much hope," he says. About 40 per cent of the dry lowland heath in Europe is in Britain.

The heathland once occupied huge swathes of southern England which overlay sandy, acidic soils. It was created about 3,000 years ago when ancient Britons who wanted open land for grazing, cultivation and hunting cleared the well-spaced trees by fire and felling. But the poor soils yielded little grain, and the land was used mainly for low intensity pasture.

The animals and the occasional fire kept the heathland clear of the trees which would otherwise have re-established themselves. It is a warm, fairly dry, semi-natural habitat in which all six of Britain's native reptile species can be found. The four rare birds are the nightjar, the Dartford warbler, the woodlark and the hobby, a beautiful bird of prey.

Between 1750 and the early 1980s about 85 per cent of it vanished. Much of the heathland was covered in pine plantations, converted to farmland, or built on.

The destruction accelerated after the last war and continued at brisk pace through the 1980s.

Canford Heath is the biggest

remaining fragment in Dorset. The southern half has been lost to housing. The 800 acres which remain are on the fringe of a conurbation of 500,000 people.

Much of Canford and other heaths have been damaged and degraded. Gravel and sand has been extracted and rubbish dumped in the resulting pits.

Pine trees and dense stands of bracken have invaded much of the heath. The worst damage has been done by the dozens of fires each summer, mostly started deliberately, which allow grasses and bracken to invade. The heathland can take more than 15 years to restablish itself.

Most of Canford Heath has been designated as an SSSI. Ideally it should be managed for nature conservation in consultation with the Nature Conservancy Council, although there is no compulsion.

The land is only a tiny part of Canford Heath but the conservationists are fighting because it is one of the best areas for smooth snakes and the sand lizards which form part of their diet. There is a south facing slope and the sort of bumpy terrain the lizards favour . . .

Councillors and planning officers from Poole are under legal advice not to discuss the case. But in the past they have emphasised the town's urgent need for low cost housing.

Recently they signed the Dorset Heathlands Strategy, an agreement betwen local authorities and conservation groups which sets out a way of protecting the remaining heathland.

Source: *Independent*, 14 July 1990

VALUE ANALYSIS: RESIDENCES OR REPTILES?

Much of what remains of Canford Heath is in private hands, but Poole Borough Council own a small section of 17 acres, on which they propose to build 200 houses. As can be seen from the article 'Conservationists begin legal fight to save heath' the council were taken to the High Court by the World Wildlife Fund for Nature, and the British Herpetological Trust. The Court ruled that it was lawful for the council to grant itself planning permission for the building of homes on the site. In March 1991, however, the Secretary of State for the Environment, Michael Heseltine, revoked the decision of the High Court, much to the delight of the bodies who originally brought the High Court action.

Typical reactions to the decision were:

Dr Simon Lister: 'We are frankly stunned at the news, not to say thrilled. Congratulations should go to Michael Heseltine for taking such a tough and brave decision, but the real victory goes to all the people who supported the campaign to save Canford Heath.'

Keith Corbett, of the Herpetological Trust: 'We're absolutely delighted.'

1 List the value positions that appear in the articles. How are the different positions justified?

2 Use the information in the article 'Conservationists begin legal fight to save heath' to hold a short class discussion: has the right decision on Canford Heath now been reached?

Further investigations

As the demand for quality housing in attractive environments grows, it is very likely that new housing estates are being built in your area, on the fringes of existing towns and villages. There are numerous opportunities for the study of urban fringe problems. Wherever new housing is being developed on the urban fringe, it is likely that there will be conflicts over the costs and benefits of this new form of land use. The effect of green belt restraints on the development of housing is worth investigating.

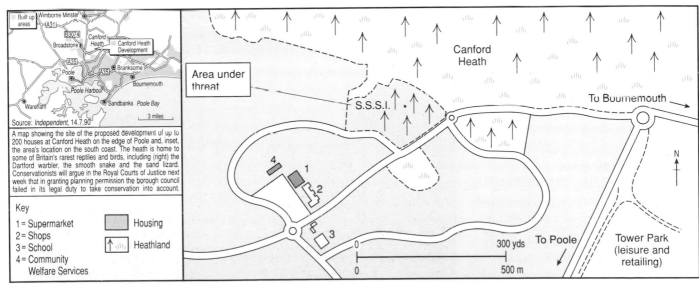

Key

1 = Supermarket
2 = Shops
3 = School
4 = Community Welfare Services

Housing
Heathland

Figure 4.5 Alternative plans for East Canford Health Housing

CASE STUDY   *The Favelas of Rio de Janeiro: 'Tudo Bem!'*

Figure 4.6   Makeshift shack on the shores of Botafogo Bay

The very poorest of the Cariocas (the inhabitants of Rio de Janeiro) have, like this woman, nowhere to live at all. She spends most of her time begging around the makeshift shack of boards and blankets on the shores of Botafogo Bay. Up to 40% of the population of Rio de Janeiro live in spontaneous squatter settlements or shanty towns (*favelas*)– a typical result of urbanisation in economically less-developed countries.

Life in the favelas

A report on the third world, published in the *Guardian* in 1988, described life in the *favelas*.

Osprazeras, near the centre of Rio, is only accessible by 363 concrete steps from the road below. The dwellings are built of pebble dash and concrete blocks. 'At the top of the stairway, alongside of which runs an open sewer, a family of goats forages around for a midday meal. Before long they are joined by a pack of dogs and a sow and her two piglets; there is more garbage than usual strung out across the city, because there have been few collections in the past ten weeks. The municipal authority stopped paying the refuse men and they went on strike.'

Sebastião do Nascimento, a bus conductor, earns 67 000 cruzados a month (£65). 'I do all my shopping for the month the minute I get the money, because I know that the currency is going to fall again. I take most of my pay to the supermarket straightaway, and spend it on the things that the family will need and that will keep.'

Elio Nunis, a labourer, doesn't know how old he is because he has two birth certificates, dated 1942 and 1946. 'Life in the *favelas* is quiet, calm.'

Giuberto Araujo, a mechanic, earns 32 000 cruzados a month (£32). 'All things in the *favela* are *tudo bem* (OK).'

Escondidhinho is a little street too small for cars, winding its way through the tatty houses. The shops are no more than crannies in the wall, like little caves with two or three shelves displaying razor blades, fruit or sweets and the bars and cafés are in slightly bigger cavities.

Divina Aldis and another, younger mother look after nine children in a dingy garret lined with breeze blocks and adorned with crucifixes. In addition to her own children, Divina looks after 17-month-old Elisa: 'It always happens here: nobody knows who the father is and the mothers always get sick, or leave.'

Daova Silva: 'You have to say *tudo bem*, but in fact things are terrible. Even beans are now 1000 cruzados a kilo, and I was buying them for 570 only last Saturday. The garbage is piling up all over the place and it is smelling.'

Ed Vulliamy wrote in the *Guardian* of these people: 'There is a gentle sensual quality to all those *tudo bems*: these people do not shed their humour, or their obsession with soccer or music, or their sensitivity to music and religion.

ENQUIRY: THE *FAVELAS* OF RIO DE JANEIRO

1 Study the two photographs shown in Figures 4.7 and 4.8.
   What is the most striking feature of the physical site of Rocinha?

2 What issues are likely to arise concerning:
   a acquisition of land in such areas.
   b land values and land ownership.
   c provision of basic services.
   d provision of some standard of physical safety.

3 Make a sketch from the photograph Figure 4.8 and mark in the likely position of the shanty towns.
   a Why are the shanty towns located in such sites?
   b What are the inherent dangers and disadvantages of such sites?

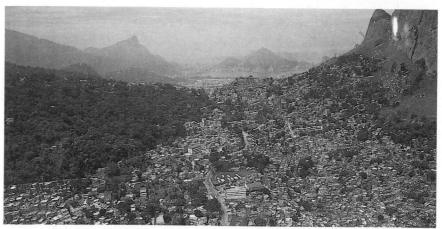

Figure 4.7   Rocinha, Rio's biggest shanty town (Population: 600 000)

4 Perception of life in the *favelas*.

  a Analyse the inhabitants' views on life in the *favelas* in the matrix below. If there is a positive mention of a particular aspect of their environment, place a tick in the appropriate box.

Person	Food	Services	Social conditions
Sebastião			
Elio			
Giuberto			
Divina			
Daova			

  b Now sum up their views of life in the *favelas*.

5 Read the following short extracts about the *favelas* from other sources:

The *Observer*, 13 August 1989: 'In the first four months of 1989, an average of 18 people a day were murdered in Rio de Janeiro, the majority in the Baixada, a poor run-down area to the north of the city. A law of silence exists in the Baixada. Those who have witnessed a murder will never admit to it. To ask for police protection is tantamount to announcing oneself as an open target – sociologists who have studied crime in the Baixada believe that more than half of the murders can be linked to the police-run death squads.'

Traveller's guide to Rio: 'No one will think you are brave if you have walked through a *favela*, they will just think you are mad. As a foreigner you run a serious risk of being kidnapped if you walk through a *favela*.'

Figure 4.8   View over Rio de Janeiro from the Corcovado

How far is it possible to reconcile these two views of the *favelas* with the residents' own perceptions, analysed above?

ENQUIRY: SQUATTER SETTLEMENTS

Study Figure 4.9.

1 Summarise the main principles of shanty town growth that it is attempting to portray.

2 In what ways does it suggest that the shanty towns and the parent city are interdependent?

3 How idealistic are the ideas portrayed in the last few frames of the cartoon? Are they likely to be realised in practice?

Study Table 4.4, which shows the proportion of population in major cities in the developing world which is found in informal settlements. Use a simple correlation test to see if there is any relationship between the size of the city and the proportion of its inhabitants living in the informal settlements. What conclusion can you draw from your result? Can you offer any explanation?

Table 4.4   Estimate of percentage of city population in informal settlements

Country	Urban %	Major city	Population (m) (1990 est.)	% in informal settlements
Ethiopia	13	Addis Ababa	1.66	85
Angola	28	Luanda	0.96	70
Tanzania	29	Dar es Salaam	1.07	60
Colombia	70	Bogotá	5.5	59
Turkey	48	Ankara	2.16	51
Zambia	55	Lusaka	0.79	50
Tunisia	61	Tunis	1.05	45
Philippines	42	Manila	5.7	40
Brazil	77	Rio de Janeiro	9.2	40
Brazil	77	São Paulo	13.5	40
Mexico	72.5	Mexico City	15.5	40
Peru	70	Lima	4.7	40
Pakistan	32	Karachi	5.0	37
Venezuela	88	Caracas	3.1	34
Kenya	23.5	Nairobi	1.3	33

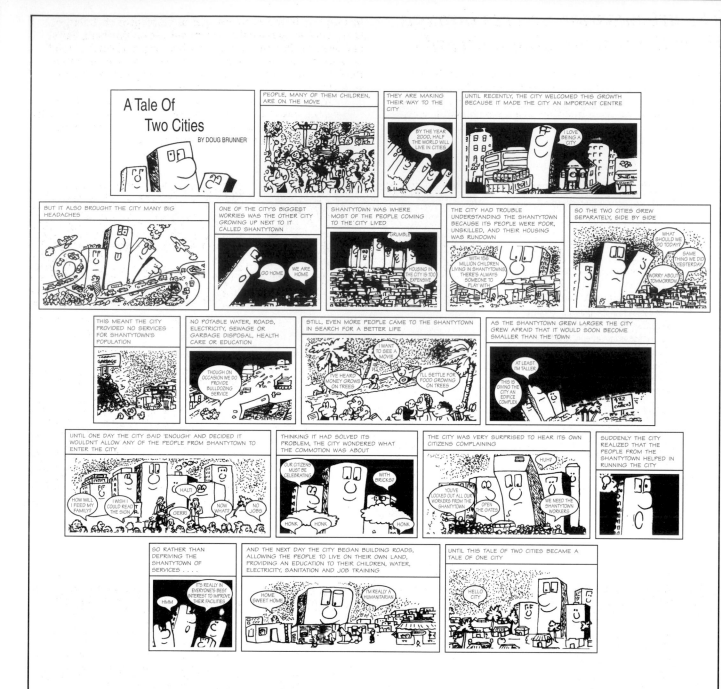

Figure 4.9   A tale of two cities

SYNTHESIS: URBANISATION CHARACTERISTICS

You have seen something of the urbanisation process at work, albeit in very different circumstances, in countries at different stages of economic development. Summarise the differences in tabular form using the following urbanisation indicators:

Provision of jobs
Land ownership
Planning agreements
Environmental
   considerations
Social conditions

Level
Rate
Social grouping
Level of organisation
Style of building
Provision of services

The urbanisation process through time: the city growing outwards

So far we have looked at the urbanisation process at the city limits in southern Engand and in coastal Brazil. However, urbanisation is a process that changes significantly over a long period of time in terms of building styles, street layout, social segregation, personal preferences, and general urban land use.

In any town or city there will be a record, although often incomplete, of the various stages of urban growth. In large cities, such as the two that we intend to examine here, Paris, and Mexico City, the history of urban settlement will extend back for hundreds or thousands of years. In the case of Paris, the first settlement in the area was probably in pre-Roman times (c. 200 BC). The Aztecs founded their capital city, Tenochtitlan, on the site of the present Mexico City in 1325.

A useful way to examine the record of urbanisation is to take an urban transect from near the centre of the city out to the fringe, where city gives way to countryside.

Figure 4.10 Paris – Total distance from the centre to the outermost location = 15 km (10 miles)

(ii) Avenue de la Grande Armée – Offices, car showrooms, apartments and supermarkets

(iii) St Germain-en-Laye – Old market town terminus of the RER (Regional Express Network)

(iv) Le Vésinet – High class residential area; fast RER link to the centre

(v) Champs Elysées – High-class shopping, restaurants and entertainment

(i) La Défense – Redeveloped office shopping and entertainment complex

Figure 4.11 Mexico City – Total distance from the centre to the outermost location = 30 km (19 miles)

(i) Indios Verdes – Metro terminus

(ii) High apartment blocks – Government rehousing

(iii) Paseo de Reforma – Office complex. High-class shopping in adjacent Pink Zone

(iv) Single-storey houses – Improved informal housing

(v) Small colonial market centre – Almost engulfed by shanty town

(vi) Unplanned development – Endless squatter settlements; no made-up roads

ENQUIRY: CITY MORPHOLOGY

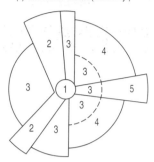
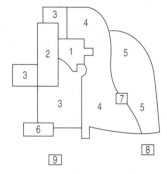

(i) The concentric model (from Burgess)

(ii) The sector model (from Hoyt)

(iii) The multiple-nuclei model (from Harris and Ullman)

1 Central business district	6 Heavy manufacturing
2 Wholesale light manufacturing	7 Outlying business district
3 Low-class residential	8 Residential suburb
4 Medium-class residential	9 Industrial suburb
5 High-class residential	10 Commuters' zone

Source: Law and Smith, 1987

Figure 4.12 Urban land-use models

1 Arrange the photographs in each set on the previous page (Figures 4.10 and 4.11) in order from the city centre outwards, giving your reasons. You will find that the innermost and outermost locations are relatively easy, the others less so. When you have completed the exercise, check that your answer is correct. You should now be able to produce a series of zones through which each transect passes. Draw a simple diagram to show these zones.

2 Now study the three classic urban land-use models above (Figure 4.12). How far do you think that the zones you have established in the transect south-west from the centre of Paris, and north from the centre of Mexico City, match any of these models? What further information would you need in order to say, with confidence, that the cities measured up to the form indicated by the classic models?

3 Now study the model of the Latin American city (Figure 4.14). How far does your model of the zones in Mexico City compare with the zones shown in this model?

4 Using a classification of urban land use devised by you, carry out a sample transect from city centre to fringe to establish the different zones which reflect the process of growth. For each zone, record the quality, cost and density of housing. You could also devise an environmental quality index to show how this varies along your transect. You should support your work with large-scale maps and small-area census statistics.

5 If you are studying a smaller city you could take a south-west and a north-east transect, and see if they are different. You can also compare your transects with the models.

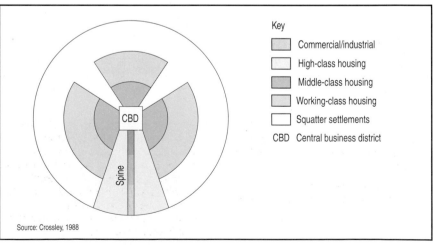

Figure 4.13 View from the Trade World Centre, Tokyo

Key

Commercial/industrial
High-class housing
Middle-class housing
Working-class housing
Squatter settlements
CBD Central business district

Source: Crossley, 1988

Figure 4.14 Generalised model of Latin America city structure

Future trends in urbanisation

Figure 4.1 showed that the proportion of people living in towns and cities will increase significantly in the next 30 years. All the signs are that, not only will the proportion increase, but the size of the very largest cities will increase at an astonishing rate. It is also likely that the spatial distribution of the very largest cities will change.

ENQUIRY: THE SIZE AND DISTRIBUTION OF MEGA CITIES

Study Table 4.5, which shows the population of the 25 largest cities in the world 1960–2000.

1 Use a dispersion diagram to work out the median size of the 25 largest cities for each of the three years. What is happening to the median size of these cities over the three years?

Table 4.5 Ranking of city agglomerations by population: 1960, 1980, and 2000

	1960		**1980**		**2000**	
	Agglomeration	Population (millions)	Agglomeration	Population (millions)	Agglomeration	Population (millions)
1	New York/NE New Jersey	14.2	Tokyo/Yokohama	17.7	Mexico City	25.8
2	London	10.7	New York/NE New Jersey	15.6	São Paulo	24.0
3	Tokyo/Yokohama	10.7	Mexico City	14.5	Tokyo/Yokohama	20.2
4	Shanghai	10.7	São Paulo	12.8	Calcutta	16.5
5	Rhein-Ruhr	8.7	Shanghai	11.8	Greater Bombay	16.0
6	Beijing	7.3	London	10.3	New York/NE New Jersey	15.8
7	Paris	7.2	Buenos Aires	10.1	Seoul	13.8
8	Buenos Aires	6.9	Calcutta	9.5	Tehran	13.6
9	Los Angeles/Long Beach	6.6	Los Angeles/Long Beach	9.5	Shanghai	13.3
10	Moscow	6.3	Rhein-Ruhr	9.5	Rio de Janeiro	13.3
11	Chicago/NE Indiana	6.0	Rio de Janeiro	9.2	Delhi	13.2
12	Tianjin	6.0	Beijing	9.1	Jakarta	13.3
13	Osaka/Kobe	5.7	Paris	8.7	Buenos Aires	13.2
14	Calcutta	5.6	Osaka/Kobe	8.7	Karachi	12.0
15	Mexico City	5.2	Greater Bombay	8.5	Dhaka	11.2
16	Rio de Janeiro	5.1	Seoul	8.5	Cairo/Giza	11.1
17	São Paulo	4.8	Moscow	8.2	Manila	11.1
18	Milan	4.5	Tianjin	7.7	Los Angeles/Long Beach	11.0
19	Cairo/Giza	4.5	Cairo/Giza	6.9	Bangkok	10.7
20	Greater Bombay	4.2	Chicago/NE Indiana	6.8	Osaka/Kobe	10.5
21	Philadelphia	3.7	Jakarta	6.7	Beijing	10.4
22	Detroit	3.6	Milan	6.7	Moscow	10.4
23	Leningrad	3.5	Manila	6.0	Tianjin	9.1
24	Naples	3.2	Delhi	5.9	Paris	8.7
25	Jakarta	2.8	Baghdad	3.9	Baghdad	7.4

Source: United Nations, 1986

2 Now calculate the upper and lower quartiles for each of the lists for each of the three years, and then the inter-quartile range. What is happening to the latter?

3 Now summarise, in general terms, what is happening to the size of the world's largest cities.

4 Use an atlas to plot, on a blank map of the world, the 25 largest cities for each of the three years.

a Work out their mean latitude for each year.

b What conclusions can you draw about the broad geographical distribution of these cities?

c Classify the cities into two groups according to level of economic development.

d Write a short account of the changing distribution of the world's mega cities.

Inequality in Urban Areas

Introduction

From the urban transects across Paris and Mexico City there is much evidence to show that distinct differences exist between various parts of cities. These variations are manifested in a number of ways: different styles of buildings, contrasting land use, varying levels of traffic and so on. They also reflect social segregation within the city. Spatial variations exist in the standards of living that people enjoy, the range of services to which they have access, and the general quality of life that they experience.

Inequality in cities is the result of a wide and varied range of factors. It often reflects decision making, whether at the personal level or at a much higher strategic level within the city. Once established, it becomes one of the major problems that city planners and managers have to face. It is likely to cause tension and conflict within the city and can sometimes manifest itself in serious social unrest.

We shall examine inequality in three different cities – Paris, Atlanta and Moscow. In Paris it is reflected in the quite stark contrasts between the east and west of the city; in Atlanta it has its origins in the racial mix of the city; in Moscow, with its socialist history, inequality should, theoretically, be less obvious.

CASE STUDY 1 *Paris Ville (Central Paris): Perceptions and Investigations of Inequality*

MAP ENQUIRY: PERCEPTIONS OF PARIS

In a survey carried out by psychologists Milgram and Jodelet, Parisians were asked about the areas of the city with which they were least familiar. The results are shown in Table 4.6

1 Trace off a copy of the blank map of the Paris *arrondissements* (Figure 4.15) and mark in the *arrondissements* unfamiliar to the middle classes (dark red to light red – highest rank darkest) and those unfamiliar to the working classes (dark blue to light blue – highest rank darkest). What conclusions can you draw about the distribution of the different social groups in Paris from your map?

Table 4.6 *Arrondissements* least familiar to middle-class and working-class Parisians (%)

Rank	Middle classes		Working classes	
	Arrondissement	%	*Arrondissement*	%
1	20	69.3	15	61.0
2	19	68.2	13	58.5
3	12	62.5	17	53.7
4	18	61.4	16	51.2

Source: Proshansky, Ittleson and Rivlin (eds), 1986

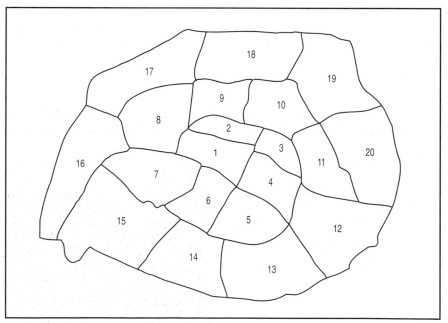

Figure 4.15 *Arrondissements* of Paris

2 Now study Table 4.7 which contains further details about Parisians' views concerning their city. Devise a map to illustrate the perceptions people hold, and use it to identify those parts of Paris that the Parisians regard as:

a Middle class and affluent.

b Working class, poor and probably having a large proportion of immigrants.

c Pleasant and friendly.

In each class try to group contiguous (neigbouring) *arrondissements*. Show these areas on another blank map of the *arrondissements*.

Table 4.7 *Arrondissements* identified with listed qualities by Parisians of all classes (%)

| Qualities | The *arrondissements* in which the quality on the left is most frequently located, ranked 1–4, and the percentage of all subjects locating the quality within this *arrondissement*. (N = 218) | | | |
	1	2	3	4
Paris of the rich	16	17	8	7
	87.6%	20.6%	18.3%	17.0%
Paris of the poor	18	19	20	13
	38.5%	31.7%	29.8%	11.0%
Dangerous Paris	18	9	10	19
	38.5%	31.7%	29.8%	11.0%
Areas you like best	6	4	1	5
	70.6%	65.1%	57.8%	51.4%
Areas in which you would refuse to live under any circumstances	18	19	10	8
	37.2%	27.1%	18.3%	17.0%
Areas you know best	6	1	5	8
	73.9%	61.5%	58.3%	57.8%
Areas you know least well	20	13	19	18
	60.1%	58.7%	57.3%	55.0%
Snobbish Paris	16	6	8	17
	49.1%	15.1%	14.7%	9.6%
'Paris des Bretons'	15	4	6	–
	50.0%	34.9%	23.4%	–
Where you would move if you became wealthy	6	4	7	16
	33.9%	31.2%	24.8%	21.6%
Friendlier, more relaxed atmosphere	6	5	4	7
	30.3%	22.5%	18.3%	14.7%
Greatest loss of pleasant qualities because of urban renewal	15	1	13	6
	43.1%	14.2%	13.8%	10.1%

Subjects were instructed to give all responses in terms of *quartiers* and not *arrondissements*. (There are four *quartiers* in each *arrondissement*.) But we have integrated the results and presented them in terms of *arrondissements* for ease of comprehension, particularly for those familiar with the city

Source: Proshansky, Ittelson and Rivlin (eds), 1986

You will appreciate that these maps represent people's opinions or perceptions of various parts of the city. In order to test the validity of these images we shall now examine two *arrondissements (administrative divisions within the city)*: the famous *seizième* or 16th *arrondissement* (seen as the Paris of the rich, and much sought after by the affluent) and the 19th *arrondissement*, in the north-east, perceived as the Paris of the poor, undesirable and dangerous to live in.

Two passages from a modern French text on Paris give contrasting impressions of the two areas.

(The 'charming' 16th) arrondissement. You just have to walk along the magnificent vista of the Champs de Mars, pass under the Eiffel Tower, cross the Iena bridge and climb up the green terraces of the Palais de Chaillot to reach the 16th *arrondissement*, the most famed in Paris for its affluence, the greenest and the most spacious.

The 19th arrondissement. In the 19th *arrondissement* there is more land given over to industry and transport than there is to housing, e.g., the SNCF, Gaz de France, all sorts of warehouses near the waterways, the stations, roads and motorway access points. What you find here … is a whole section of the road running along a factory wall. The railways and the canal create breaks in the rows of houses.

ENQUIRY: TWO *ARRONDISSEMENTS* COMPARED

1 Study the two photographs (Figure 4.16 and 4.17) of principal streets in the two *arrondissements* – the Avenue Foch in the *seizième* and the Rue de Flandres in the 19th *arrondissement*. Use the points score (Table 4.8) to determine an environmental quality index for the area. Arrange the table in two columns, one for the Avenue Foch and another for the Rue de Flandres.

2 Do your impressions of the two *arrondissements* match the Parisians' perceptions?

Figure 4.16   Avenue Foch – 16th *arrondissement*

Figure 4.17   Rue de Flandres – 19th *arrondissement*

3 To investigate the differences a little further we can examine social statistics for the two *arrondissements*. The statistics in Table 4.9 are drawn from the 1990 census for the two *arrondissements*. Examine them carefully and extract the data that you think indicate most clearly the differences between the inhabitants of the two *arrondissements*.

4 Table 4.10 shows average socio-economic data for all of the *quartiers* of Paris. Two *quartiers* – Maillot in the 16th *arrondissement*, and Villette in the 19th *arrondissement* are highlighted. Chaillot, through which the Avenue Foch runs is in the north-east of the *seizième*, near the Arc de Triomphe. Villette, through which the Rue de Flandres runs, is in the west of the 19th *arrondissement*. Examine all of the statistics: how do the differences between the two areas appear when viewed at the scale of the *quartier*?

5 Clearly there are differences in the built environments of the two areas, in the environmental quality, and in their sociological make-up. But does this add up to inequality? Summarise, in one or two short paragraphs, the main differences between the two *arrondissements*. Consider what additional information you would need to further establish the degree of inequality between the two areas. What indicators might be a useful guide to the differences in standard of living and quality of life?

Table 4.8   An environmental survey

Feature	Penalty points	Maximum score
Landscape quality		
Trees and well-kept grassed spaces	0	
Few trees and/or unkept grassed spaces	4	
No trees or grassed spaces	8	8
Derelict land		
None	0	
Small area	4	
Large area – a major eyesore	10	10
Litter/vandalism		
No litter: no vandalism	0	
Some litter or vandalism	4	
Very untidy: much vandalism	8	8
Industrial premises		
All residential properties	0	
Some industrial premises	5	
Mainly industrial premises	10	10
Traffic flow		
Normal residential traffic	0	
Above normal residential traffic	3	
Heavy vehicles and through traffic	6	6

Source: Warn and Bottomley

Table 4.9   Socio-economic statistics

	16th *arrondissement*		19th *arrondissement*	
Area (km²)	7.85		6.79	
Population	169 863		165 062	
Population density (people/ha)	216		243	
Age of population (years)				
0–19	31 594	(18.6%)	38 747	(23.5%)
20–59	928 544	(54.6%)	98 315	(59.5%)
60+	48 535	(26.8%)	28 070	(17.0%)
Foreigners	28 082	(16.5%)	29 744	(18.0%)
EC	12 060	(7.1%)	5116	(3.1%)
Non-EC	15 622	(9.2%)	24 264	(14.7%)
Unemployed (%)	Less than 8		More than 12	
Housing stock				
Before 1915	41 879	(40.2%)	21 810	(26.1%)
1915–48	28 929	(27.8%)	18 226	(21.8%)
1949–81	31 986	(30.7%)	38 739	(46.4%)
1982–90	1445	(1.4%)	4772	(5.7%)
Houses with indoor WC and bathroom	71 251	(84.3%)	64 609	(86.4%)

Source: 1990 Census, Paris

Table 4.10   Comparison of quartiers 64 and 73

	Quartier 64 Maillot	Quartier 73 Villette	Average for Paris
Area (ha)	142.5	128.6	
Population density (people/ha)	161	390	248
Non-EC foreigners (%)	Under 10%	18%	11.1%
Average age (years)	42	Less than 35	39
Unemployed (%)	Less than 8	Over 12	9.4
Houses with 5 rooms or more (%)	Over 20	Under 5	7.7
Public sector tenants (%)	Less than 5	28	12.3%

CASE STUDY 2 *Inequality in Atlanta, Georgia*

Atlanta is an interesting city in which to study the phenomenon of inequality. Twelfth in order of population size among the metropolitan areas of the USA in 1990, it had a population of 2.8 million, of whom 25% were blacks. If we focus in on the city of Atlanta itself, with a population of 400 000 at the 1990 census, 66% of the population was black. In such a city it would be a revealing exercise to examine the degree of inequality between the black and the white population.

The city is portrayed as burgeoning in its prosperity. Its thriving business district houses an impressive range of regional and national company headquarters (Figure 4.18). The city has been able to attract and keep a wide range of modern growth industries, the jewel in the crown being the successful bid for the 1996 Olympics. Amidst all of the more obvious signs of the accumulation of wealth, the history of racial segregation in the USA would suggest that such economic well-being is not evenly divided between the two communities – even though in recent decades black Americans have seen considerable improvements in their

Figure 4.18   Atlanta

standard of living, and are no longer confined to inner city ghettoes. Many enjoy a status and a quality of life which represents a considerable degree of emancipation from the poverty of their parents.

The degree of inequality between blacks and whites has continued to increase (Table 4.11). This is because the poorest blacks have remained trapped in inner-city areas. Movement into the middle class seems to have been slowed down by the current recession. Meanwhile, most whites have continued to live in prosperity.

ENQUIRY: INEQUALITY IN ATLANTA

Study the three maps which show the distribution of the black population in Atlanta for the years 1960, 1970 and 1900 (Figure 4.19).

1 Describe the changing distribution of the black population over the period 1960–80.

2 With reference to the maps, where would you expect to find (in 1980):
   a High status white areas?
   b Declining status white areas with an increasing white population?

   c High status black areas?
   d Inner city very low status black areas?
   I race a copy of the map and mark in the areas that you have selected.

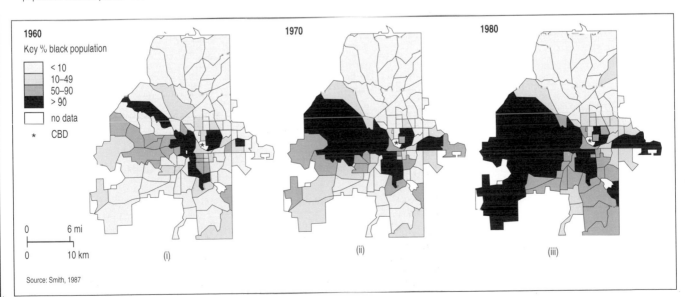

1960

Key % black population

- < 10
- 10–49
- 50–90
- > 90
- no data
- * CBD

0   6 mi
0   10 km

(i)

1970

(ii)

1980

(iii)

Source: Smith, 1987

Figure 4.19   Distribution of income amongst the black population

3 Examine the scattergram which shows the relationship between median family income and percentage of black population (Figure 4.20). What does it tell us about the differences between the black and the white communities?

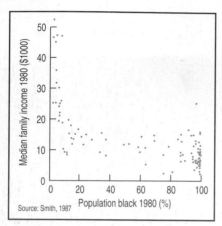

Source: Smith, 1987

Figure 4.20   Median family income for the black population in 1980

4 Consider now the set of figures in Table 4.11. Discuss what they tell us about the relative levels of inequality between 1960 and 1980. Comment on the nature and suitability of the criteria.

5 As well as the differences between the black and white communities, Figure 4.21 shows a plot of quality of life scores against percentage of black population in 1970. From this diagram, what broad general comments can be made concerning inequality within communities?

6 Summarise briefly the main features of inequality in Atlanta in the period between 1960 and 1980. Do you think that there is adequate evidence of significant improvement in the standard of living of the black community during this period? How do you think things might have changed in the decade up to 1990?

Table 4.11   Inequality between predominantly white and black tracts in Atlanta, as shown by mean values for economic and social indicators, 1960, 1970 and 1980

Indicator	Year	White	Black	Ratio
Median family income($)	1960	6380	2396	2.66
	1970	12146	5710	2.13
	1980	31612	9473	3.34
	1990	80481	16445	4.89
Median value of owner-occupied housing units($)	1960	14763	8942	1.65
	1970	22705	12124	1.87
	1980	85272	19939	4.28
Housing with more than 1.0 persons/room (%)	1960	6.48	33.06	5.10
	1970	4.55	19.74	4.34
	1980	0.83	8.80	10.60
Median school years completed	1960	11.66	7.94	1.47
	1970	12.25	9.54	1.28
	1980	15.41	10.69	1.44
Infant deaths/1000 live births	1960	22.72	37.73	1.66
	1970	19.90	32.71	1.64
	1980	13.31	21.36	1.60

Source: Smith, 1987

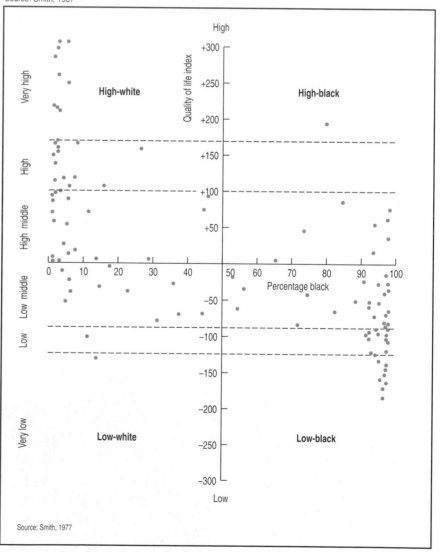

Source: Smith, 1977

Figure 4.21   The relationship between quality of life and racial composition by census tracts in Atlanta, Georgia

CASE STUDY *Is There Inequality in Moscow?*

It might be expected that in Russian urban areas there would be less evidence of spatial and social inequality than in the West. Given the egalitarian aims of a socialist society, the great and significant variations in wealth and material possessions, so obvious in cities born of capitalism, should be absent in a centrally planned and controlled state. In reality, important differences do exist between various parts of the Russian city. Segregation is perceived to exist within urban areas, and this is perhaps related to the manner in which residential accommodation is organised and allocated.

Certain privileged groups, such as members of the Communist Party hierarchy or officers in the armed forces, the KGB and the police had access to better housing, often located in areas where environmental quality is better than elsewhere. Some of this housing dates from pre-revolutionary times, and occupies prestigious locations near the centre of Moscow, with ready access to a whole range of cultural, shopping and entertainment facilities.

More than half the population live in the basic housing unit – the *mikrorayon*, a planned neighbourhood complex for between 5 000 and 15 000 people (see Figure 4.22). Within the area of the mikrorayon (see Figure 4.23) a whole range of services is provided such as nurseries, schools, basic health care, and retail, recreational and cultural facilities. A small number of mikrorayons will make up a residential complex, which will provide the next level of services appropriate to a larger number of people (similar to a town).

Impressions of Moscow housing tend to be of monotonous uniformity, although different styles reflect successive periods of building, characterised by certain features representing the main influences on building at that time. Figure 4.24 shows typical housing of the Stalin area along Smolenskaya Street lining the Moskva River. During the Khruschev era, few blocks extended above five storeys because of the regulations requiring lifts above that height resulting in the *khruschoby* (Khruschev's slums), which sprawled wherever there was suitable land. Later buildings in the 1970s and the 1980s are considerably higher, for Moscow planners have yet to follow some of their Western counterparts and reject the high-rise block as a symbol of community living. High-rise flats are seen as a means both of combating sprawl and of social control.

The range of data upon which any investigation of inequality must rest is less readily available than in the West.

However some revealing studies have shown that criteria do exist which form the basis for an examination of variations in standards of living and quality of life in different areas.

Figure 4.22 Mikrorayon

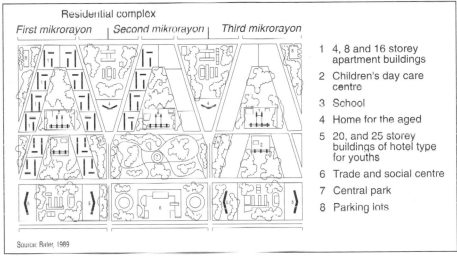

Residential complex

First mikrorayon | *Second mikrorayon* | *Third mikrorayon*

1 4, 8 and 16 storey apartment buildings
2 Children's day care centre
3 School
4 Home for the aged
5 20, and 25 storey buildings of hotel type for youths
6 Trade and social centre
7 Central park
8 Parking lots

Source: Bater, 1989

Figure 4.23 Residential complex

Figure 4.24 Stalinesque houses, Smolenskaya Street

MAP ANALYSIS: LAND-USE PATTERNS IN MOSCOW

1 Study Figure 4.25 which shows the main types of land use within central Moscow, bounded by the Garden Ring (Sadovoye Kol'tso). Photographs of locations A, B, and C on the map give an idea of the built environment (Figure 4.26).

a Identify and compare the main types of land use found within the Boulevard Ring (Bul'varnoye Kol'tso), and between the Boulevard Ring and the Garden Ring.

b How does land use differ in this central area from that in a typical Western capital city?

Key

■	Government and party buildings
▨	Central city retail and residential area
▨	1ndustrial/transport function
▨	Mixed residential and industrial land use
☐	Residential

▲ ▨	Cultural/educational facility
▨	Park
o o	Hotel for foreign visitors
•—•	Metro system
—	Railway

A = Kalinin Prospect redevelopment
B = Garden Ring off Kalinin Prospect
C = Kujbyseva St off Red Square
 I = Kremlin

0   1/2 mi
0   1 km

Source: Bater, 1985

Figure 4.25   The main types of land use in central Moscow

A   Kalinin Prospect redevelopment

B   Garden Ring off Kalinin Prospect

C   Kujbyseva St off Red Square

Figure 4.26   Moscow–central city

2 Now examine Figure 4.27, which shows land use and communications in the greater Moscow area, including the zone enclosed within the Ring Motorway, with the Forest Park towns beyond.

a Describe the distribution of the main industrial areas within Greater Moscow. Does there appear to be any concentration of these areas in any particular sector?

b Describe the distribution of green areas.

c What implications does the land-use distribution shown have for variations in the quality of life?

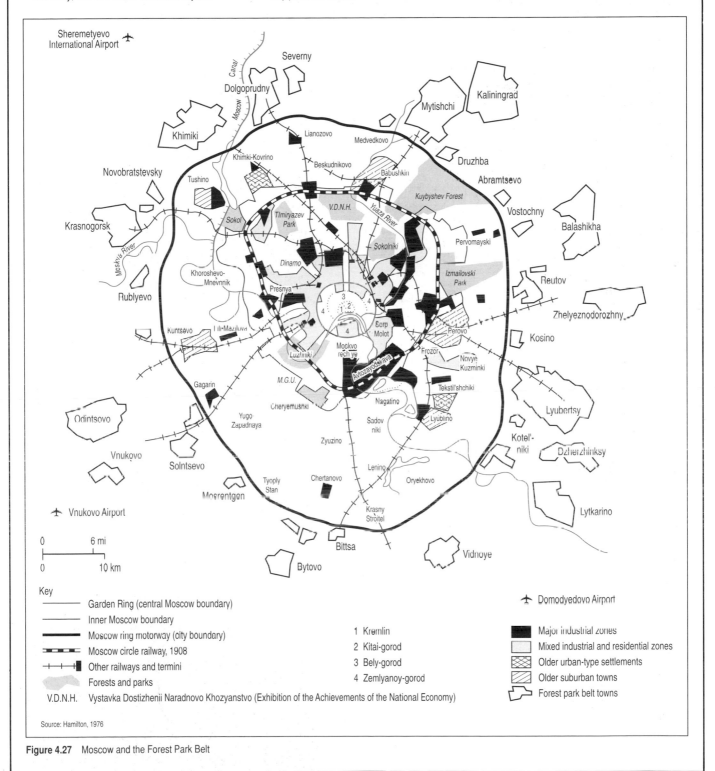

Figure 4.27 Moscow and the Forest Park Belt

You now have an idea of spatial variations in land use within the area of greater Moscow. We can go on to examine data collected by Russian geographers which describe variations in social provision and quality of life within the city. Consider what criteria Russian geographers might use to measure variations in the quality of life.

ANALYSIS: QUALITY OF LIFE IN MOSCOW

1 Figure 4.28 shows variations in occupational structure in twenty areas.

 a Which areas of Moscow show the biggest concentration of 'workers in material production', and 'specialists in material production' (factory engineers, technicians and skilled workers)?

 b Where is the lowest concentration of 'workers in material production'?

2 Maps ii, iii and iv in Figure 4.29 show qualitative indices of urban infrastructure, urban character and residential character. Use the three maps to summarise the variations in urban character and quality of life within Moscow. Which are the favoured sectors of the city, and which would appear to be those that are less privileged?

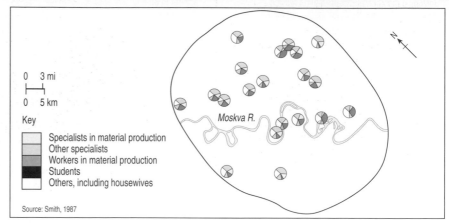

Key

Specialists in material production
Other specialists
Workers in material production
Students
Others, including housewives

Source: Smith, 1987

Figure 4.28   Socio-economic structure of parts of Moscow as indicated by occupation

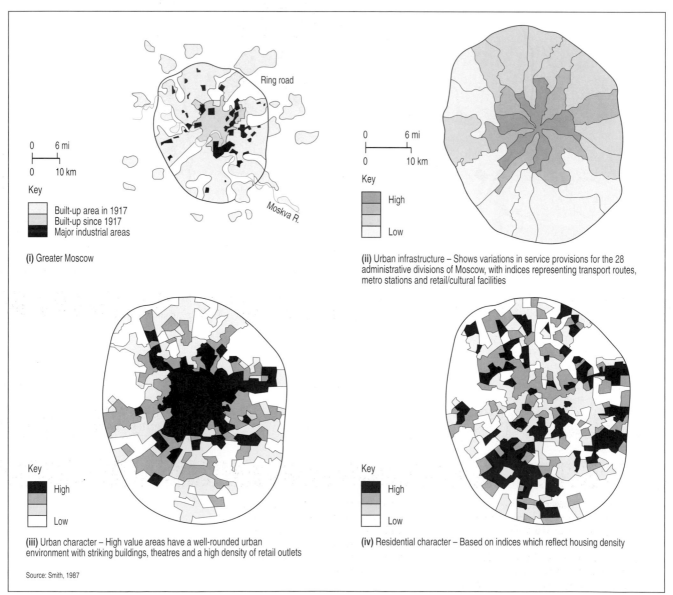

Key

Built-up area in 1917
Built-up since 1917
Major industrial areas

(i) Greater Moscow

(ii) Urban infrastructure – Shows variations in service provisions for the 28 administrative divisions of Moscow, with indices representing transport routes, metro stations and retail/cultural facilities

Key

High

Low

Key

High

Low

Key

High

Low

(iii) Urban character – High value areas have a well-rounded urban environment with striking buildings, theatres and a high density of retail outlets

(iv) Residential character – Based on indices which reflect housing density

Source: Smith, 1987

Figure 4.29   Socio-economic structure in Moscow

3 Figure 4.30 indicates the numbers of people wishing to move to a different part of Moscow by exchanging their apartment for a similar one of the same size.

a Draw a map showing the variations in 'residential desirability' in Moscow. Choose three or more categories, and then map contiguous areas together. Indicate your areas as 'high desirability', 'low desirability' and so on. How does this map compare with your maps of quality of life and urban character?

b Which areas of the city appear to be the least desirable in which to live? What would appear to be the main factors that have disadvantaged these areas?

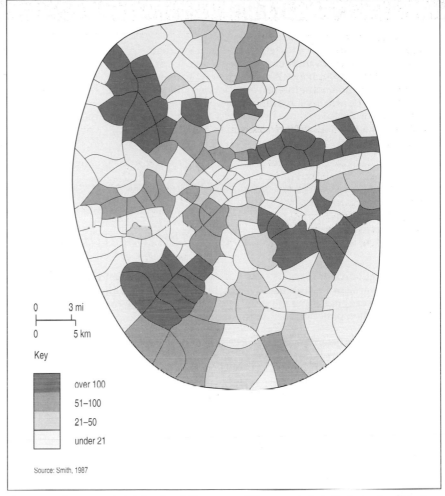

Key

	over 100
	51–100
	21–50
	under 21

Source: Smith, 1987

Figure 4.30   Relative residential attraction of different parts of Moscow, as indicated by the number of people announcing a wish to move by exchanging their present apartment for one of the same size

SYNTHESIS: DIFFERENT KINDS OF INEQUALITY?

Summarise this section by writing a short essay on the ways in which inequality in urban areas differs in the three cities that you have studied.

FURTHER INVESTIGATIONS

1 In any town or city in Britain inequalities will appear. For your town or city you could investigate the nature and extent of inequality in several different ways.

a By obtaining census statistics for all of the wards, and then developing an index of inequality to identify areas in various categories.

b By selecting areas which the index suggests would show important differences. Field work could be carried out in the areas to determine environmental equality, by using a modification of the indices that were used to compare the two *arrondissements* in Paris.

Conflict in Cities

Conflict in cities is a matter of increasing concern to urban managers and those to whom they are responsible. It can manifest itself in different ways. At group level it will appear with the organisation of local interest associations and pressure lobbies; these can be effective in bringing people's grievances and feelings to the notice of those in authority. Frustration and resentment in the city does not always seek its outlet through the formal or informal groups, however, and this may result in much more serious consequences. Petty crime and vandalism in the city are obvious manifestations of tensions resulting from underlying conflict issues. Increasing open violence on the streets of cities both in the economically more-developed and economically less-developed worlds, and more recently in the socialist and formerly socialist world, is a sign that urban conflict reflects underlying inequality and injustice.

CASE STUDY *Riots, Deprivation and Poverty in Bristol*

On 2 April 1980 there were serious riots in the inner city area of St Pauls in Bristol. Violence erupted along the narrow streets when police clashed with black youths. Cars and a number of buildings were set alight. Inevitably, there were injuries on both sides and looting was widespread. The 'Mob/Riot/Shock/Horror' newsheet (Figure 4.31) represents a local Bristol reaction to verbal and written comments about the riots.

VALUES ANALYSIS

1 Study Table 4.12 which you will use to analyse the attitudes and values involved in the reaction to the riots. Each of the column headings shows a particular attitude or value position. Along the left hand side of the table various people and media are identified. It is your task to analyse the attitudes and values that are apparent in what they had to say. Place a tick to show that there is clear evidence of their position. Use a question mark to show that this is what their assumed position might be.

2 Now consider the value positions below:
  a The community must be protected from criminals by whatever means are necessary.
  b The police understand black culture and are not biased against blacks.
  c Different communities must be encouraged to live together peaceably.
  d Better facilities for the underprivileged would do much to ease tension.
  e Employers and city managers are not biased against the black population – they have to balance the budget.

  For each of the people and the media shown in Table 4.12 assess where they would stand on each of these positions on a scale of 1–5

Table 4.12   Attitudes and values in race riots: St Pauls, Bristol April 1980

	Stronger policing	Better community relations	Respecting black culture	Better facilities	Liberal remedies
Daily Mail					
Insight Teams					
Daily Telegraph					
Sun					
Morning Star					
Chief Constable					
Rev. Kimber					
Black youth					
Peter Courtier					

(1 = strongly agree; 2 = agree; 3 = neutral; 4 = disagree; 5 = strongly disagree).
Draw up another table which shows the results of your assessment.
Where do *you* stand on all of these issues? Insert on the table your own values position.

3 This newsheet is clearly not without bias. Summarise the way in which it is biased under the following headings: political, class, colour and media.

We now look at the wider issue of poverty and deprivation in Bristol. The following extract is taken from the *Poverty in Bristol* report:
'Bristol in recent years has been seen as a city of growing prosperity, with a thriving financial sector. However this report shows that, for a growing number of people in the city, the 1980s are not a boom time at all, but years when both they and their children have suffered more poverty and more deprivation. In an immensely rich country like Britain, more people are living in poverty in 1988 than there were ten years ago. Councillors and MPs in the city will have seen more people who are cold, hungry, ill-clothed and often sick simply because they have been denied, either through low wages, lack of benefits or cuts in public expenditure, the money or the services required to achieve such basic necessities of life.'

MOB RIOTS SHOCK HORROR...MOB RIOTS SHOCK HORR

what the papers said ...

In Saturday's Daily Mail, Jane Gaskell wrote about the discussions she had in the Black and White Cafe. She really seems to have made the effort to listen to people, which is more than the television stations have done, with their endless streams of 'experts' and 'community leaders'. Even the *Daily Telegraph* has listened to heavy criticisms of its beloved Police force.

The 'Insight' teams and their ilk have come up with little more than the normal set of standard liberal remedies that are trotted out regularly on such occasions, more jobs, schools, community policemen, etc., etc. None that I have come across have dared to suggest the legalisation of cannabis, abolition of antiquated licensing laws or scrapping of 'sus', which are also liberal remedies, in that they are superficial, but which would definitely help matters.

One editorial column, that of the *Daily Telegraph*, has refused totally to bend its head to the wind. While its reporters on the streets were making some attempts to be open-minded and patient the editors were choking badly on their malt whiskies. Now I'm quite a connoiseur of the rantings of this filthy rag, but what they had to say about St Pauls was quite amazing.

The *Sun* has done its best to see light at the end of the tunnel, with its Saturday edition showing a picture of nice friendly bobbies holding hands with smiling black kids, with the title, 'The Pals of St Pauls'. It wasn't all playing on the heartstrings though, as the *Sun* has done some serious and detailed sociological research on St Pauls; a paragraph in italics gravely states that 'A special *Sun* inquiry found that young blacks want to be left alone in St Pauls to follow "our own culture" '.

'IT IS SAD BECAUSE WE THOUGHT WE HAD A GOOD RELATIONSHIP WITH THE PEOPLE OF ST PAULS, AND PUT CONSIDERABLE RESOURCES INTO THE TASK OF GETTING ON WITH THE COMMUNITY.'
Brian Weigh, Avon and Somerset Chief Constable

THE DAILY TELEGRAPH

THE EVENTS AT ST PAULS, Bristol, are only a little more melancholy than the froth of tedious advice which has been uttered since. Every kind of stipendiary benefactor has descended on Bristol with his wisdom – social workers, bishops, Mr ANTHONY WEDGEWOOD BENN, the Commission for Racial Equality and, inevitably, progressive Conservative backbenchers.

A certain 18th-century *savoir faire* and scepticism is called for, one which is free from paralytic anxiety about public images and which is rather less surprised when riots occur. They are not so remarkable nor so unmanageable as is supposed. Like fires, they are, correctly but firmly, to be stopped!

The advice-givers have made a great chorus of 'Amenity'. Is it really supposed that a craving for table tennis and coffee bars is at the bottom of this? The most serious problem confronting the police is undoubtedly a section of West Indian youth which is estranged from its families for a variety of reasons. These youths equally reject approach by the police or West Indians ... the sub-culture has a substantial criminal fringe. This Birmingham Police evidence, quoted by the all-party 1972 Select Committee, should remind us that we are dealing not with black immigrants, but with the irreconcilable worst group of those immigrants. It should discourage us all from giving advice.

REV. KEITH KIMBER

'It was bound to happen', he said. 'It has been bound to happen for a very long time, simply because of the prevailing social conditions and the lack of fundamental concern.

'It was the voice of the voiceless. It was a race riot, not in the sense of Notting Hill, but in the sense of a riot against the racialist assumptions which oblige policemen to do this sort of thing, sometimes against their better instincts.

'The police believe the law must be enforced and there are racialist pressures to make sure they do.

'This was a basic intrusion into the privacy of the black community and in a very horrific way the community has stood up to say very loudly 'I am'. These people want to drink when they want to drink, and they want to smoke ganja.'

As for the illegality of drinking alcohol after licensed hours and the smoking of cannabis are concerned, Rev. Kimber said: 'Whose law is it? These people are the disadvantaged and the poor. They are not part of the consensus which gives the law its force. Therefore, what price the law?'

MANY OF THE PEOPLE WE SPOKE TO IN ST PAULS ON WEDNESDAY NIGHT AND AFTERWARDS DEEPLY RESENT POLICE METHODS IN THEIR COMMUNITY. 'PEOPLE ARE FED UP WITH DOORS BEING BROKEN DOWN EARLY IN THE MORNING, PEOPLE HAVE A RIGHT TO THEIR PRIVACY,' ONE RESIDENT SAID.

The black youth sitting outside the Black and White feel very bitter about the society they live in, and the police in particular. 'We don't bother people; let us lead our own lives', 'There's nowhere to go, the pubs aren't ours, the Black and White is the only place left ...'

A particular grievance is the ban on cannabis, an intrinsic part of the lifestyle of many young black people. Its illegality gives the police an excuse to raid houses and detain people at will. Many are afraid to go out at night because they fear being picked up by the police ...'Police think because they wear a uniform, we should respect them. But we don't treat them any different from other people. This fight wasn't black versus white. It was us all against the police. There's too much racism in the police force.'

Two West Indian men, both with children, expressed their feeling that 'you either have to live fully or not live' and 'if life is not worth living we might as well die, and take a few policemen with us'. Other people sitting around nodded in agreement.

Peter Courtier, assistant Community Relations Officer feels that the Environment Health department also has much to answer for in its insensitive handling of many black cafes, several of which it has forced to close down. The Local Authority generally, he says, has no understanding of the black community and no strategy for the area. On Wednesday 16 he attended the meeting of Bristol City Council and found many of the councillors expressing more concern over the damage the events in St Pauls had done to the City's image nationally and internationally than over the inner city areas themselves.

They can worry and frown about the writing on the wall but they can't paint it over. Why don't they try reading it?

"So long as you stay indoors & dont cause any trouble you have nothing to fear from the police"
Commissioner Metropolitan Police

Apart from the National Front, the Tories have done more than anyone else to stoke up the fires of racism. Their immigration policies make black people second-class citizens by law.

To compound that felony, the only item on which the Tories propose to spend more, besides armaments, is law and order. And the money for this is being found by robbing the social services.

How insane can you get? It is not more police that are needed. It is more houses, schools, leisure facilities, and so on. It is creating a sense of being part of a society which cares.
MORNING STAR

Figure 4.31   Mob/Riot/Shock/Horror newsheet

MAPPING EXERCISE: CREATING A DEPRIVATION INDEX

Study the five maps (Figure 4.32) which show the distribution of various indicators of deprivation in the City of Bristol.

1 Comment on the choice of these indicators to display the distribution of deprivation in Bristol.

2 Trace off one of the maps of Bristol, and then enter on it the worst areas for each of the five indicators of deprivation.

3 When you have marked in all of the worst areas for the separate indicators of deprivation, aggregate them so that you can identify those areas that have: 5 indicators; 3–4 indicators; 2 indicators; 1 indicator; or no indicator.

4 Consider the distribution of the aggregated indicators.
Now use the map (Figure 4.33) of the wards of Bristol to identify the areas which are clearly the most deprived.

5 What general conclusions can you draw from the distribution of wealth and deprivation in Bristol?

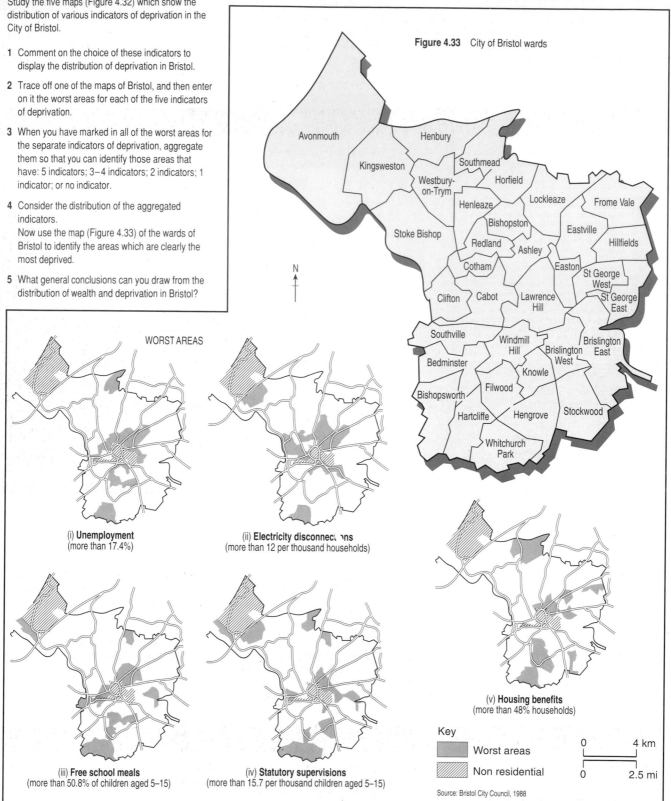

WORST AREAS

(i) **Unemployment**
(more than 17.4%)

(ii) **Electricity disconnections**
(more than 12 per thousand households)

(iii) **Free school meals**
(more than 50.8% of children aged 5–15)

(iv) **Statutory supervisions**
(more than 15.7 per thousand children aged 5–15)

(v) **Housing benefits**
(more than 48% households)

Figure 4.33   City of Bristol wards

Key

▨ Worst areas
▤ Non residential

0   4 km
0   2.5 mi

Source: Bristol City Council, 1988

Figure 4.32   Distribution of deprivation in the City of Bristol

It will be seen from the maps that you have drawn that the St Pauls riots occurred in one of the areas that suffers from the highest levels of deprivation in Bristol. The riots were in 1980, yet the statistics are for 1987. Clearly the City of Bristol confronts a major social problem. It has a responsibility to devise a programme which will tackle deprivation and alleviate the poverty that affects the people who live in the areas defined on the maps that you have drawn.

In the view of the Bristol report on poverty, 'Clearly limited, area-based policies are not a short-cut method for tackling a large proportion of the deprivation that exists in Bristol. *The problem should be thought of more in terms of the processes that lead to people being deprived rather than areas that suffer from the outcome of these processes.* Although areas are one form of targeting, the effectiveness of policies are enhanced if they are formulated to *address the processes that deprive people of secure, well-paid employment, adequate housing, decent levels of education, social services and health provision.'*

PLANNING EXERCISE: REVITALISING BRISTOL

Note the passages in italics in the quotation from the *Poverty in Bristol* report. List the processes operating in towns and cities that deprive people of the services, jobs and facilities mentioned in the article.

The following initiatives are now being undertaken by Bristol City Council, aimed at reducing the level of poverty and deprivation in the city.

1 *The Inner Area Programme* covers the inner districts of St Pauls, Totterdown, Barton Hill and Windmill Hill, and the outer estates of Southmead, Knowle and Hartcliffe and Withywood. Its objectives are creation of employment, expansion of businesses, upgrading of environmental quality, improvement of housing stock and service provision, securing better access to good quality housing for those in need, strengthening the social fabric of the inner city, and encouraging self-help.
2 *The Bristol Inner City Task Force* (administered by the Department of Trade and Industry) covers Ashley, Easton and Lawrence Hill. It focuses on enterprise and employment on the one hand; and on employability and community involvement, on the other. The essential aim is to help direct existing programmes of expenditure.
3 *The Environmental Improvement Programme* covers inner city and outer housing estates, aiming to upgrade areas of poor environment, improve open spaces and reclaim derelict land.
4 *Priority Neighbourhood Areas* and *Neighbourhood Improvement Areas* are an initiative covering Lawrence,

Figure 4.34 New housing association homes, St Pauls

Weston, Hartcliffe, Withywood, Easton, Knowle and Southmead. The aim is to upgrade publicly owned housing and the environment.

5 *Private Sector Improvement Areas* include *General Improvement Areas* in St Pauls, Easton and Totterdown; *Block Repair Schemes* in Easton, Avonmouth and Redfield; and *Neighbourhood Revitalisation Schemes* in Avonmouth and Easton. These are all aimed at improving private housing by grants from the City Council.

6 *The Bristol Urban Development Corporation* has a 900-acre site in central Bristol, from Temple Meads to St Annes. Centrally funded by the government, its objectives are to improve existing infrastructure, to create a better environment for industry and to encourage a variety of high-standard developments providing more jobs and industry.

GROUP DISCUSSION

1 What are the main criteria by which all of these initiatives should be judged?

2 Work in small groups, taking one scheme each and explaining why you would support it.

3 Which schemes are most likely to be the more successful – those that are locally funded or those that are centrally funded by the government?

4 What are the conflicts that are likely to develop if different schemes are funded in different ways?

CASE STUDY *Conflicts in Ceausescu's Romania*

Before the overthrow of the Ceausescu regime in the violent revolution of December 1989, conflict was widely evident in the country. Two particular issues are brought into focus here: the changes in the urban fabric of Bucharest resulting from Ceausescu's desire to create a socialist city to reflect his own image, and the proposals for systematisation in the countryside, which would have destroyed hundreds of villages and replaced them with agro-industrial complexes – a series of new quasi-urban units in the countryside. Conflict has been created by the urbanisation policies themselves.

Often, in a socialist country like Romania, its capital city may have undergone extensive reconstruction. The urban landscape would thus be subject to very distinctive change and renewal. Under a leader like Ceausescu much of the change, in terms of buildings and streets, was designed as a monument to socialist ideals.

Ceausescu's era will be remembered mostly for the oppression of the Romanian people, the deterioration of standards of living for both urban and rural dwellers, and finally for its violent overthrow by the Romanian people and the Romanian army. In Bucharest, the changes resulting from the post-war era of communism, and the Ceausescu years in particular, have led to social and economic conflict. With the end of the Ceausescu regime living conditions may change under the new authorities, but much of the urban fabric will remain, for the time being at any rate. Like many cities in Eastern Europe, much of Bucharest consists of monotonous blocks of poorly constructed flats – but, as in Moscow, Party officials and the *Securitate* (Secret Police) had access to better quality accommodation.

CEAUSESCU'S LEGACY THAT WON'T GO AWAY
Gavin Stamp

BUCHAREST used to be described as the Paris of the Balkans but today, thanks to the town planning projects of the late president of the Socialist Republic of Romania, the city is better compared with Moscow or Leningrad.

Neither the great Napoleon nor Napoleon III inflicted on Paris anything quite as ruthless as the Avenue of the Victory of Socialism that Nicolae Ceausescu smashed through the centre of his capital...

Bucharest is a little Balkan town, reminiscent of Istanbul, which was enlarged and embellished as a capital after the principalities of Moldavia and Wallachia became fully independent in 1878. And, conscious of its Roman past and Latin language, the new kingdom looked not to St Petersburg or Berlin, but to Paris for inspiration.

New boulevards were laid out and new public buildings erected, designed by French architects or by Romanians trained in Paris...

Most citizens, however, are obliged to live in the grim blocks of modern concrete flats that ring the centre of Bucharest. This is Ceausescu's principal legacy, of which he was proud. Last year an exhibition was mounted called 'Bucharest of the Epoch of Nicolae Ceausescu'. Apart from statistics, it consisted of depressing photographs of repetitive slab-blocks standing next to wide new roads and roundabouts. Appalling and shoddily built though these are, Ceausescu cannot fairly be blamed for them.

Urban renewal through the replacement of houses by system-built flats was conventional Modern Movement theory in Europe, both East and West. The outskirts of Bucharest look no different from, say, Leningrad or even Glasgow. Nor was this policy in Romania initiated by Ceausescu...

But the austerity of the Modern Movement was inappropriate for Ceausescu's vision for central Bucharest. This was no doubt inspired by his foreign jaunts, for if Washington and New Delhi had great wide straight avenues leading to monumental classical piles, then Bucharest must have one too.

In other cities new schemes were laid out on open ground. Ceausescu cut his Boulevard of the Victory of Socialism through built-up areas. It runs east-west for well over a mile, between the civic heart of Bucharest and Patriarchate Hill, on which stand the Metropolitan church and the old National Assembly building...

Work began in 1984 on demolishing a dozen churches, a synagogue and two monasteries, as well as thousands of old houses in the Uranus-Antim area and the old Jewish quarter. Today, the Avenue is almost finished, so it is possible to see how Ceausescu compares as a patron of architecture with Peter the Great, Louis XIV, Stalin and Hitler...

Here, in fact, is curious proof of the continuing vitality of the French connection, for these blocks of flats for party officials are reminiscent of nothing so much as the new satellite towns of Paris... The new Bucharest buildings, with their stretched columns, arbitrary detailing and rooftop pergolas and pediments, all carried out in a uniform, repulsive concrete, suggest fruitful study of the latest French architectural magazines.

But the focus of this urban megalomania is of a different order, for the so-called People's Palace, or Casa Republicii, although built of reinforced concrete, is faced in marble. This colossal structure, as wide as Viceroy's House in New Delhi but several times as tall, terminates the vista westwards down the Avenue...

The problem now facing the new Romanian government is what to do with this pile. Nothing can bring back the historic buildings that were sacrificed, but if the People's Palace is allowed to survive, [Ceausescu] will have imposed a lasting monument on Bucharest – which is just what he intended.

Source: *Independent*, 3 January 1990

ISSUES ANALYSIS: THE URBAN LANDSCAPE OF BUCHAREST

1 There is evidence in the article 'Ceausescu's legacy that won't go away', of a conflict in urban and social values. Discuss this and try to isolate the different value systems that are indicated.

2 To what extent do you think that Ceausescu was attempting to create a monument to socialism in the late twentieth century?

3 What major problems face urban planners in the post-revolution phase?

Systematisation in Ceausescu's Romania

Probably one of the most controversial of Ceausescu's proposals was the systematisation programme. Its main objective was the destruction of the majority of Romania's villages and their replacement by urban-style 'agro-industrial complexes'.

VILLAGES WIN BACK THE RIGHT TO LIFE
Victoria Clark

'WE HADN'T the heart to give the house a good springclean this year – they were going to demolish it in March.' The old woman was apologising for the shabby interior of her one-storey cottage in the village of Apahida outside the western town of Cluj. Her husband has already sold his livestock – seven chickens, some pigs – and resigned himself to moving into a concrete block. Now he will buy back his animals and she will clean the house.

The first proclamation of ... [the new] government has lifted at a stroke the nightmare threat of Ceausescu's systematisation plan, designed to gain agricultural land by herding peasants into 'agro-industrial complexes' of jerry-built blocks without running water or adequate heating. By 'eliminating the differences between the towns and the villages' systematisation also promised to remove the only remaining means of subsisting independently in a state which refused to feed the population adequately. In the past 10 years, town and country alike have come to rely on the produce of the family [plot] back in the village. 'You can't tell children there's nothing to eat, that there is nothing in the shops. They have to eat when they're hungry and there's always something in the [plot],' a mother of five pointed out to me.

Long before the revolution, every village had heard its sentence. Horror stories abound. 'In my mother-in-law's village south of Timisoara, they had begun work by laying a concrete foundation in the middle of her [plot]...'

But thankfully systematisation has affected few villages: only 10 are known to have been completely destroyed. Whether because of lack of funds or the pressure of international outrage, the demolition of up to 8,000 of Romania's 13,000 villages never materialised. It seems that 'Operation Romanian Villages' – a campaign begun by a group of young Belgians in February last year, in which nine countries, including Britain, participated – has helped. The adoption of Romanian villages by villages all over western Europe, announced on the Romanian language service of Radio Free Europe and the BBC, told Romanians of the degree of sympathy their plight was provoking outside.

But much of Apahida has not been saved. There [are] 18 new four-storey blocks in its centre, whose inhabitants relied on old houses with taps in their yards for their water supplies. 'Every day we tried our taps,' explained Florin, a 26-year-old agro-engineer, 'until a week ago when suddenly there was water at last – at the height of the troubles.' Now his wife no longer has to fill the bath with buckets of water to flush the lavatory. He reckons that those who had received less than a year's salary by way of compensation for their demolished family home would soon be returning the money to the authorities, requesting that their old houses be rebuilt...

Mariana Celac, a member of the Front for National Salvation Council in Bucharest, pointed out that there is time between now and the sowing of the first crops in February for plenty of people to take up the government's offer of an acre of land and produce enough food for the year. Envisaging a burgeoning number of smallholders with none of the technological paraphernalia for large-scale farming, she believes the way ahead lies with organic farming.

Romania's peasantry, the nation's backbone, galvanised into action by the urgent need for more and better food, will spring to life again. In the longer term, inevitable redundancies caused by the closure of the vastly unproductive prestige industries which now litter the splendid countryside, polluting the rivers and fouling the air, are likely to accelerate the move of populations back to the land and into the villages.

Source: *Independent*, 5 January 1990

VALUES ENQUIRY: SYSTEMATISATION

1 Identify the value systems that are evident in the systematisation proposals and those in the reactions against the proposals.

2 How might you seek to justify either of the value systems which led to the controversy?

3 How might rural affairs in Romania be improved without resorting to the 'urbanisation of the countryside'?

Social Justice in the City

Inequality and conflict in the city lead to a consideration of social justice in the urban environment. Achieving a more equitable distribution of accommodation and services in the city is a desirable goal but one that is difficult to achieve. Most city authorities accept some responsibility for the provision of public sector housing, although the degree to which they become involved varies enormously from city to city and from country to country. In their different ways, urban planners in both Hong Kong and the cities of the former Soviet Union have seen social justice in housing as one of their prime objectives. The extent to which they have achieved it will be studied in the two examples that follow.

CASE STUDY *Housing and the New Towns in Hong Kong*

An extract from the Hong Kong Year Book, 1988, summarises the difficulties that exist in the provision of housing in the Colony and the New Territories.

'Despite the many modern buildings and other developments in Hong Kong, it cannot be denied that, as in any large city, there are run-down areas and other environmental black spots. This is not surprising, considering how rapidly Hong Kong's economy has grown. Some areas that were developed as recently as 30, or even 20 years ago were built to lower standards when the Territory was less affluent and have since deteriorated. In most of these run-down areas, there is severe overcrowding and a general lack of space for normal amenities.'

PHOTOGRAPH AND MAP ANALYSIS: HONG KONG

1 Study the two photographs (Figures 4.36 and 4.37) which show two views of the urban area of Hong Kong. Figure 4.36 shows the urban skyline of Hong Kong Island, and Figure 4.37 shows the mainland area of Kowloon and its sprawling suburbs from the highest point on Hong Kong Island.
   a What are the striking features of the physical setting of Hong Kong?
   b For urban development, what disadvantages are inherent in such a site?
   c How might such disdvantages be overcome?

2 The map (Figure 4.35) shows the urban areas of Hong Kong, variations in population density and the position of the New Towns in the New Territories.
   a Why have the Hong Kong authorities had to look to the New Territories for a solution to the housing problem?
   b Siphoning off new population growth to the New Territories will create problems in the New Territories. What are these problems and how might they be solved?

c One particular problem will be the provision of fast and cheap transport from the New Territories to the central areas of Kowloon and Hong Kong Island. Using the map, state what means of transport are available at the moment, and suggest what others could be used in addition.

Figure 4.36   Urban skyline, Hong Kong Island

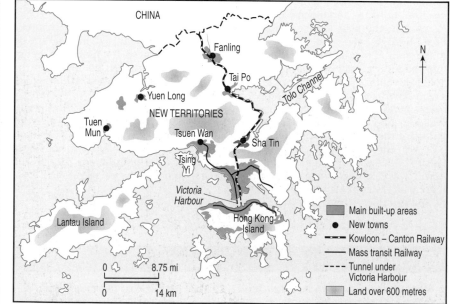

Figure 4.35   Urban areas of Hong Kong

Figure 4.37   Kowloon, from Hong Kong Island

The population of Hong Kong was reduced to about 600 000 at the end of the Second World War in 1945, but by the end of 1947 an influx of people from mainland China had swollen the figure to 1.8 million. With the establishment of the Chinese People's Republic in 1949 further immigration from the north saw the population rising to some 2.2 million in 1950. This steady influx of refugees put intense pressure on housing. Squatter settlements began to appear around the edge of the urban area, on rooftops and in sheltered bays of the much indented coastline of the mainland and the island. The squatter communities still exist and are, to a large extent, tolerated by the government;

special areas were created for some of the poorer families to build homes. Existing tenements saw a degree of subdivision which led to much overcrowding.

In 1953 a disastrous fire in a squatter settlement at Shek Kip Mei, Kowloon, left 53 000 people homeless and the government with no option but to house them. Shanties have remained, however and there is basically no systematic rehousing of squatters. They are only cleared when land is needed for redevelopment; land needed for future development is kept free of squatters and patrolled regularly. Squatters that are registered are rehoused; others are moved to temporary housing in which

they can make their own improvements to what is essentially a bare shell.

Squatting has increased in junks and sampans in Hong Kong Harbour and in small creeks throughout the colony and the New Territories. The control of these boat squatters has proved to be a particularly difficult problem for the authorities. In recent years the arrival of refugees from Vietnam has exacerbated the problem. The long indented coastline of the colony and its islands makes total surveillance almost impossible. Squatters on boats regularly petition for public housing, but as soon as some areas are cleared, new arrivals appear and the problem returns.

ENQUIRY: SQUATTER SETTLEMENTS

The map (Figure 4.38) shows the principal squatter settlements that existed in 1955.

1 Discuss the distribution of the squatter settlements.

2 Now look at the map in relation to the photograph (Figure 4.37) taken from Victoria Peak. Why are some of the squatter settlements in particularly dangerous situations?

3 Why do you think that these particular locations developed as settlements for the homeless in Hong Kong?

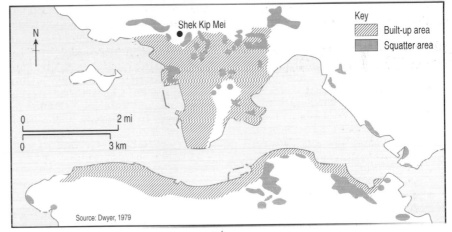

Source: Dwyer, 1979

Figure 4.38   Squatter settlements in Hong Kong, 1955

Figure 4.39   So Uk squatter village, Hong Kong

4 Study the article 'Cholera strikes at boat people camp'. Using the information in the article and the previous paragraphs, prepare a short report for the Governor of Hong Kong with suggestions for a possible solution to the squatter problem. Your report should include: (i) A review of the squatter problem, both in the past and at the present; (ii) suggestions on how the refugee problem might best be dealt with; (iii) a course of action to improve conditions, both on land and on water; (iv) a proposed programme for the eventual removal of all squatter settlements OR the upgrading of existing ones to permanent status.

CHOLERA STRIKES AT BOAT PEOPLE CAMP

Kevin Hamlin and John Bulloch

AN OUTBREAK of cholera among more than 4,500 Vietnamese boat people on the island of Tai Ah Chau off Hong Kong was yesterday blamed on unhygienic conditions and prompted warnings that an epidemic could follow.

The Hong Kong Health Department said a four-year-old boy and two women had contracted cholera and a teenage boy was suspected of having the disease. The Hong Kong director of the Save the Children Fund, Phillip Barter, said 30 per cent of boat people were suffering from malnutrition and those in the detention camp on Tai Ah Chau, an island without electricity of running water, got less than the minimum daily requirement of fresh water.

Mr Barter said the island was evacuated after a hurricane in July, and Save the Children had warned then of an epidemic should the detainees be sent back there. There were not enough tents, and sheets and blankets were being used to make shelters.

Dr Lo Wai Keh, the Hong Kong Health Department's principal medical officer, said he was not surprised by the outbreak, but an immunisation and isolation programme should prevent the disease from spreading.

The outbreak followed a 20 hour riot on the island on Sunday, when 1,000 boat people fought police with stones, iron bars and knives. Tension in the camps has risen following reports that Britain and Vietnam are nearing an agreement on the forced repatriation of boat people considered to be 'economic migrants' rather than political refugees. There are now more than 53,000 Vietnamese in Hong Kong, more than half of whom arrived this year.

Source: *Independent*, 31 August 1989

Public Housing in Hong Kong

There are essentially three phases in the development of public housing in Hong Kong.

Phase 1 1954–64. Initial rehousing of squatters from Shek Kip Mei (after the fire); acquisition of building land for redevelopment; big programme of high-rise public housing begins.

Phase 2 1964–73. Big expansion in public housing programmes; estates mainly developed on the periphery of the urban area. Planning for the new towns begins.

Phase 3 1974–present day. Reorganised housing authority has much wider powers; emphasis on the New Towns and the New territories; first provision of Government housing for middle-income families.

DECISION-MAKING EXERCISE: SOCIAL JUSTICE IN PUBLIC HOUSING?

The Hong Kong housing authority has asked an international team of experts to make an assessment of progress and achievement in its housing programme. As personal assistant to the British member of this team, you have been asked to compile a desk report that will be available for study before the team meets in Hong Kong. Your report will follow two main sets of guidelines.

1 Determining the main aims of the housing programme, where you will need to consider such things as the need to maintain some control over squatter settlements, to alleviate overcrowding, to improve old accommodation, and to accommodate new population.

2 Measuring progress and achievement, which would include comment on the types of accommodation available, the current roles of the public and private sectors, the numbers that still need rehousing, and an overview of the changing distribution of population in Hong Kong.

You are provided with photographs of various housing schemes in Hong Kong (Figure 4.40) and the following set of resources:

Figure 4.41 Diagram of the original resettlement blocks (H blocks) of the 1950s

Figure 4.42 Plans for the conversion of the H blocks in the 1970–1980s

Figure 4.43 Map showing the different types of accommodation in 1961

Figure 4.44 Population change in the metropolitan area, 1961–71

Figure 4.45 Distribution of housing estates, 1981

Figure 4.46 The overall housing situation, 1981

You should conclude with an assessment of the degree to which social justice in housing has been achieved by the Hong Kong Housing Department.

(i) Aberdeen

(ii) South side of Hong Kong Island

(iii) Sha Tin New Town

(iv) Happy Valley

Figure 4.40 Housing in Hong Kong

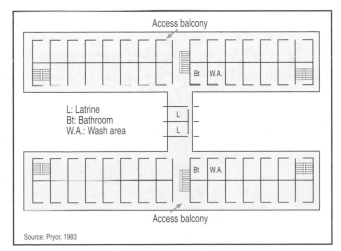

Access balcony

L: Latrine
Bt: Bathroom
W.A.: Wash area

Bt W.A.

L
L

Bt W.A.

Access balcony

Source: Pryor, 1983

Figure 4.41 Diagram of the original resettlement blocks (H blocks) of the 1950s

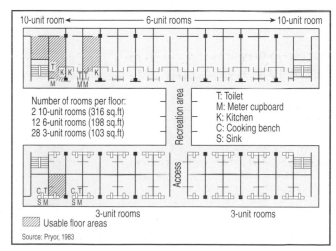

10-unit room ← 6-unit rooms → 10-unit room

T: Toilet
M: Meter cupboard
K: Kitchen
C: Cooking bench
S: Sink

Recreation area

Access

T K K
M   M M

C T   C T
S M   S M

Number of rooms per floor:
2 10-unit rooms (316 sq.ft)
12 6-unit rooms (198 sq.ft)
28 3-unit rooms (103 sq.ft)

3-unit rooms   3-unit rooms

▨ Usable floor areas

Source: Pryor, 1983

Figure 4.42 Plans for the conversion of the H blocks in the 1970s–1980s

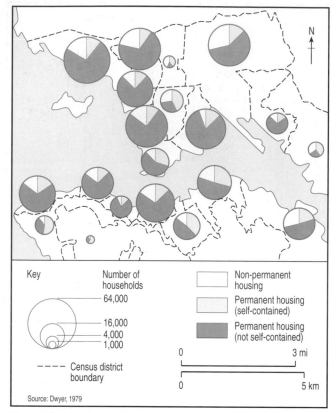

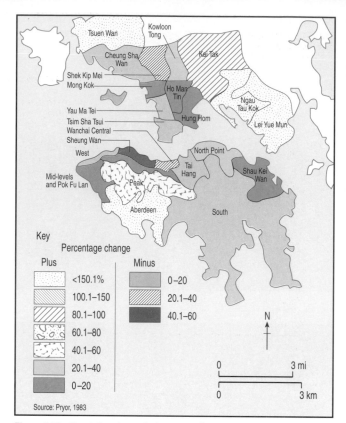

Figure 4.43   Map showing the different types of accommodation in 1961

Figure 4.44   Population change in the metropolitan area, 1961–71

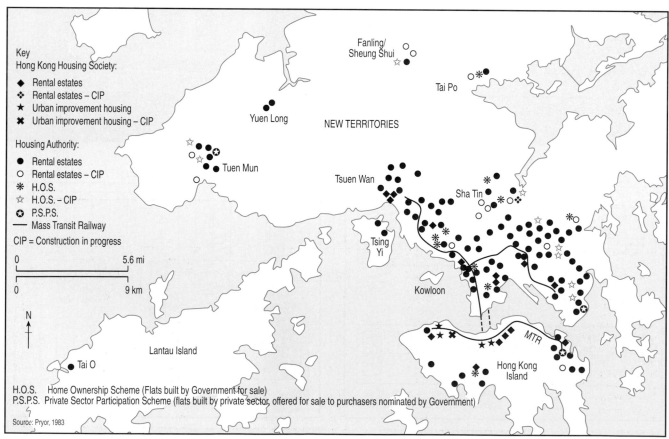

Figure 4.45   Distribution of housing estates, 1981

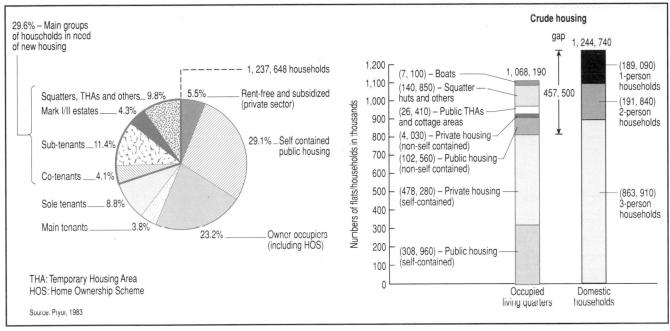

Figure 4.46   The overall housing situation, 1981

Table 4.13   Distribution of permanent domestic units by main sources of supply in the Hong Kong metropolitan area, December 1970

	Pre-war	Post-war	Total	Percentage of grand total
		Private sector		
Houses and large flats	1450	8200	9650	1.6
Medium flats	1500	13 700	15 200	2.5
Small flats	950	59 100	60 050	10.1
Tenement floors	24 500	172 000	196 500	32.9
Workers' quarters		4600	4600	0.8
Sub-total	28 400	257 600	286 000	47.9
	Government and government-aided housing			
Hong Kong Housing Authority		33 100	33 100	5.6
Hong Kong Housing Society		18 800	18 800	3.1
Government low-cost housing		33 600	33 600	5.6
Resettlement housing		214 700	214 700	36.0
Government quarters		11 000	11 000	1.8
Sub-total		311 200	311 200	52.1
Grand total	28 400	568 800	597 200	100.0

Source: Commissioner of Rating and Valuation, 1971

Table 4.14   Percentage distribution of different types of living quarter by area, 1971

Type of living quarter	Hong Kong Island	Kowloon	New Kowloon	Tsuen Wan	Rural New Territories	Total
Private self-contained flats	37.3	42.6	9.8	2.0	2.0	20.7
Private tenement floors	27.7	41.7	10.3	6.9	5.5	19.1
Non self-contained units in public housing	5.5	1.3	30.6	31.1	–	15.9
Self-contained units in public housing	4.6	2.4	29.6	34.4	2.2	16.0
Units in Housing Authority or Housing Society block	10.3	5.4	9.2	10.8	–	7.9
Houses	0.6	0.2	0.4	0.6	6.3	1.1
Simple stone structures	2.7	0.4	3.2	4.9	45.2	7.6
Other permanent structures	3.2	1.8	0.6	1.1	1.6	1.6
Temporary housing	8.1	4.2	6.3	8.2	37.2	10.1
Total	100.0	100.0	100.0	100.0	100.0	100.0

Source: 1971 Census

Table 4.15   Statistics from the Housing Department, 1991

Number of quarters

Category	Hong Kong Island	Kowloon and New Kowloon	New Territories	Total
Government quarters	8400	9200	11 800	29 400
Public housing				
Housing authority estates	61 800	269 500	292 400	623 700
Housing authority cottage areas	500	400	1900	2800
Housing society estates	10 700	11 800	9700	32 200
Home ownership scheme blocks*	11 800	30 900	78 400	121 100
Sub-total	84 800	312 600	382 400	779 800
Private housing	297 900	309 700	305 300	912 900
Total permanent	391 100	631 500	699 500	1 722 100

Estimated persons accommodated

Category	Hong Kong Island	Kowloon and New Kowloon	New Territories	Total
Government quarters	20 300	23 200	26 000	69 500
Public housing				
Housing authority estates	223 100	832 700	1 095 800	2 151 600
Housing authoirty cottage areas	1600	1300	5300	8200
Housing society estates	40 200	33 400	35 000	108 600
Home ownership scheme blocks*	41 600	109 900	269 000	420 500
Sub-total	306 500	977 300	1 405 100	2 688 900
Private housing	888 800	968 500	804 000	2 661 300
Total permanent	1 215 600	1 969 000	2 235 100	5 419 700
Temporary				197 300
Marine				19 400
Total population				5 636 400

*Includes private sector participation scheme and middle income housing
Source: *Hong Kong Yearbook 1991*

The move to the new towns. As the government housing plans gathered impetus, it became apparent that available space in the Kowloon Peninsula and the north shore of Hong Kong island was rapidly becoming exhausted. If the population was to be housed adequately, a radical solution had to be found. The only suitable land for future development was in the New Territories, beyond the central mountain barrier and around the eastern and western coasts. Population nuclei already existed and it was to these small rural and coastal centres that the authorities looked to fulfil the next stage of their programme. However, if population growth was to be stimulated in the new locations the problem of accessibility to the inner metropolitan areas would have to be solved. In the early stages of the development of the New Territories the majority of employment opportunities would still be on the Kowloon Peninsula and Hong Kong Island. The success of the creation of the new towns in the northern and central New Territories would be tied to the development of a fast and efficient transport system cutting through the central mountain complex. Such a service is provided by the fully electrified Kowloon-Canton Railway and the Mass Transit Railway (see Figure 4.47), which links Tsuen Wan into the metropolitan area and has three lines, 36.6 km of track and 37 stations, with interchange facilities at five.

Table 4.16   New Towns in the New Territories

New town	Present population	Target population	Transport link
Tsuen Wan	500 000	800 000	Mass Transit Railway
Sha Tin	300 000	750 000	Kowloon–Canton Railway
Tuen Mun	300 000	500 000	LRTS and Hovercraft
Yuen Long	110 000	180 000	LRTS and Hovercraft
Tai Po	150 000	290 000	Kowloon-Canton Railway
Fan Ling	110 000	220 000	Kowloon-Canton Railway

LRTS: Light Railway Transit System

ENQUIRY: THE SIX NEW TOWNS

Comment on the position of the six new towns in terms of:

1 Location within the New Territories.

2 Access to the metropolitan area of Kowloon–Hong Kong Island.

3 Potential for future growth.

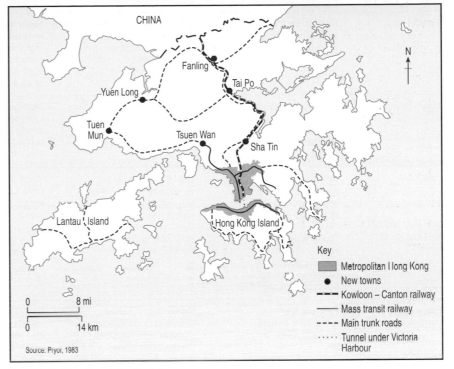

Figure 4.47   Hong Kong's New Towns

DECISION-MAKING EXERCISE: MORE NEW TOWNS

The present six New Towns are likely to be outpaced by the population growth in Hong Kong and the New Territories. The maximum size of the largest (Tsuen Wan) is 800 000, and it is not thought desirable to exceed this figure. Three New Towns are required for second generation population growth.

On Figure 4.48 five possible sites are shown for new town development. Using this map and the information provided in Table 4.17, select the three you consider would be most appropriate for New Town development.

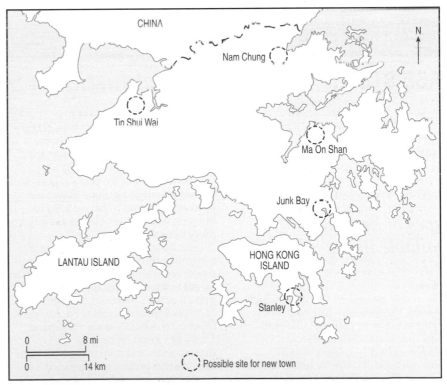

Figure 4.48   Five sites: three more New Towns

Table 4.17 Descriptions of New Towns

Site	Physical geography	Existing settlements	Land use	Communications
Tin Shui Wai	Mudflats and low-lying surrounds: reclamation needed	Series of small villages involved in market gardening, fish culture and fish ponds	Mostly rice cultivation and market gardens. High environmental value of mudflats – wildlife much prized – nearby areas are protected	Nothing to prevent extension of Light Railway from Yuen Long and Tuen Mun. Rather isolated on north-west of New Territories
Ma On Shan	Low-lying floodable land on flanks of Tolo Harbour. Backed by high mountains rising to over 2000 feet (702 m)	Small fishing settlements on Tolo Harbour	Mostly rice cultivation: some market gardens. Wildlife reserves Ma On Shan Country Park	Main Kowloon-Canton railway on other side of Tolo Harbour. Possible link to Sha Tin New Town – road needs upgrading
Junk Bay	Deep inlet east of Kowloon. Flat land at north inland end: some reclamation possible	Two small fishing villages Tseung Kwan O and Rennies Mill. Very close (2 km) to eastern suburbs of Kowloon	Mostly scrub covered; some rice cultivation; wooded hills surrounding main inlet	Close to the suburban transport net of metroplitan Hong Kong. Possible extension Mass Transit Railway
Nam Chung	Low lying land around head. Starling inlet – some reclamation will be needed. High wooded hills to north (Robin's Nest)	Small villages of Nam Chung, Wo Hang and Luk Keng	Mostly market gardening, fish ponds and duck ponds. Wooded hills surround	Good quality road to Fan Ling on Kowloon-Canton Railway
Stanley Bay (Hong Kong Island)	Peninsula site: wooded hills to north, sloping down to Stanley Bay	Stanley Town – market centre and tourist attraction. Scattered settlements over hillsides: some shanty towns	Mostly wooded hills interspersed settlement, little cultivation	Tortuous route to north via Repulse Bay linked to main Aberdeen Road into Wan Chai and Causeway Bay

CASE STUDY *Was There Social Justice in Soviet City Housing?*

'If by social justice in housing we mean the equitable allocation of available living space, it may fairly be said that the situation in the Soviet Union is far better than in most countries.' (Bater, 1989).

Types of housing available in the Soviet city

All land was owned by the state, which, therefore, theoretically had control over the allocation of housing. Such control means that social differentiation, regarded as highly undesirable in communist society, can be reduced to a minimum if not prevented. In a 'classless' society such as the former USSR, however, there was a considerable range of incomes, simply because differentials are inevitable when levels of skill and responsibility are taken into account. Furthermore, influence could be brought to bear, and certain privileged groups may have been in a position to have access to housing which was of better quality and more desirably located.

Broadly speaking, the state sector controlled the majority of the housing stock, probably about 70% according to recent estimates. This does not mean that all of the sector came under the control of city authorities. Nearly two-thirds of the state's share was in the hands of various enterprises, departments and ministries who were extremely reluctant to relinquish control, since the offer of housing was often a vital factor in attracting labour.

Three types of housing may be identified.
1 State sector housing mostly organised in the mikrorayon (Figure 4.49). Few families had a choice in which mikrorayon they live, because of the chronic housing shortage, although they were allowed to exchange with other families.
2 Cooperative housing (Figure 4.50) was available to the better-off members of Soviet society. It was privately financed, but state authorities loaned up to 60% of the cost of construction.
3 Private housing did, surprisingly, still exist in the USSR (Figure 4.51). Detached wooden homes, often surviving from pre-Soviet times, could be found in most Soviet cities. In 1987 nearly 23% all Soviet housing was still in private hands.

Figure 4.50   New flats: cooperative housing

Figure 4.49   Mikrorayon

Figure 4.51   Private housing

ENQUIRY: SOCIAL JUSTICE IN SOVIET HOUSING ALLOCATION

1 Table 4.18 shows the variations in living space in different republics. Use a suitable method to represent these figures on an outline map of the former Soviet Union.

  a What are the main spatial variations apparent from the completed map?

  b What factors might account for these variations?

2 Table 4.19 shows the amount of living space available in various cities in the former Soviet Union. Use a suitable correlation technique to discover if there is a relationship between size of city and the amount of living space available. Comment on the results of your analysis.

Table 4.18   Urban housing stock by republic, 1987

Republic	Living space* per person (m^2)
Slavic	
Russia	9.5
Ukraine	10.1
Belorussia	9.2
Baltic	
Lithuania	10.3
Latvia	11.2
Estonia	11.7
Caucasus	
Georgia	10.2
Armenia	8.6
Azerbaydzhan	7.8
Middle Asia	
Kazakh	8.2
Uzbek	7.3
Kirgiz	7.4
Tadzhik	7.3
Turkmen	6.6
Moldavia	8.4
USSR average	9.4

*Living space has been calculated as 67% of useful space
Source: *Narodnoye Khozyaystvo*, 1987

Table 4.19   Housing stock in selected cities 1983

City	Population (000)	Living space* per person (m^2)
Slavic		
Moscow	8396	11.2
Leningrad	4779	10.9
Kiev	2355	10.1
Kazan	1031	8.7
Gorkiy	1382	9.3
Novosibirsk	1370	8.9
Irkutsk	582	8.9
Baltic		
Tallin	454	11.2
Riga	867	10.6
Vil'nyus	525	9.3
Caucasus		
Tbilisi	1125	9.2
Yerevan	1095	7.7
Baku	1638	7.4
Middle Asian		
Tashkent	1944	7.1
Frunze	577	7.8
Alma Ata	1023	8.7
Dushanbe	530	7.2
Ashkhabad	338	7.1

*Living space has been calculated as 67% of useful space
Source: *Narodnoye Khozyaystvo*, 1984

3 Study the figures in Tables 4.20, 4.21 and 4.22 which show aspects of housing allocation and segregation.

  a Analyse the distribution of the different social groups in Ufa (Table 4.20) and show graphically the proportions that are located in the three different areas.

  b Comment on the distribution of the different types of housing occupied by the different socio-economic groups in Table 4.21.

  c What does Table 4.22 tell us about the allocation of living space to workers in a Siberian city, compared to the mean living space for (i) the city as a whole; and (ii) Russia (in which Novosibirsk is located)?

Table 4.20   'Social configuration' of Ufa districts 1968

Characteristics	Central	Newly built	Outskirts
Occupation of groups (%)			
Workers	33.5	47.1	57.4
Employees	9.0	17.8	12.2
Intelligentsia (ITR)	12.0	10.9	6.2
Intelligentsia (Others)	32.4	14.9	11.8
Pensioners	13.1	9.3	12.4
	100.0	100.0	100.0

Employees – low grade manual
I T R – engineers and other middle/high grade technicians
Source: Mathews, in French and Hamilton, 1979

Table 4.21   Types of accommodation inhabited by socio-economic groups of:
(a) Urals Chemical Machine Building Works and (b) Bogosloviskiy Aluminium Works (%)

	Private rent	Hostel	Self-contained flat (well built)	Communal flat (well built)	Any flat poorly built	Own house
ITR (a)	2	6	64	9	14	7
Workers (a)	11	3	38	17	21	7
ITR (b)	8	3	81	5	4	8
Workers (b)	8	2	54	14	8	17

Source: Mathews, in French and Hamilton, 1979

Table 4.22   Distribution of workers by amount of living space (Novosibirsk sample)

Amount	Men	Percentage	Women	Percentage	All	Percentage
1–3 m^2	155	12.7	70	15.5	225	13.5
4–6 m^2	440	36.0	178	39.5	618	36.9
7–9 m^2	265	21.6	67	14.8	332	19.8
Over 9 m^2	106	8.7	40	8.9	146	8.7
No accommodation or no indication given)	257	21.0	96	21.3	353	21.1
Totals	1223	100.0	451	100.0	1674	100.0

Source: Mathews, in French and Hamilton, 1979

SUMMARY ESSAY

Reconsider the quotation from *The Soviet City* by J. Bater on page 180. Write a short essay in which you discuss critically the statement that there was a greater degree of social justice in housing in the USSR than in most countries. How do you think this will change now the USSR has broken up?

Managing the City

We have considered some of the major problems and issues that face those responsible for the management of cities. Rarely can these problems be dealt with in isolation. Solutions to difficulties in one part of an urban area may well have repercussions in other locations within the city.

Increasingly, the city has to be treated as one dynamic unit, and seen in its relationship with the surrounding countryside. This is particularly true of the largest cities, whose managers are concerned with the problems of the present, but must also plan for a future that may be very different from the present.

CASE STUDY *Planning for the Future in Paris*

Those responsible for planning the future form and function of Paris are faced with a wide range of problems. Within the planning region of the Ile de France live more than 10 million people: 2.17 million live within the city of Paris, 3.9 million live within the inner suburbs (or *Petite Couronne*), and nearly 4 million live in the outer suburbs (or *Grande Couronne*). Densities of population vary enormously within this urban region, from the tightly packed tenements of the working class *arrondissements* of the Ville de Paris (397 per hectare) to the more spacious settlements on the commuter fringe of the *Grande Couronne* (28 per hectare), where housing mingles with open woods and fields.

John Ardagh, writer and commentator on French life, sets some of these problems in perspective in the following extract, taken from his book *France Today*.

Anyone arriving in Paris from London is at once aware of the difference in tempo. Parisians drive more aggressively, they are always hurrying from one appointment to another, often they are snappy down the telephone or too busy to stop and help a stranger. The brighter side of this medal is a zestful nervous vitality that can be stimulating, and somehow harmonises with the urban landscape of gaily lit streets, crowded terrace-cafés and smart shop-windows. But Parisians' curse is that their city is too physically congested. The Ville de Paris (the city proper, 'within the gates') has twice the population density of the equivalent area of central London; and apart from the boulevards, most streets are narrow and canyon-like. This congestion leads to tensions in daily living which the Parisians' second curse – their own restless, intolerant, self-willed temperament – is peculiarly ill-suited to coping with. It is a vicious circle.

No wonder that Parisians' feelings have grown so fiercely ambivalent towards a city that has always inspired deep loyalties and whose personal spell, even today, is not lightly broken. 'Paris, what a monster!' people say, almost lovingly. And so the two Parises coexist: the tiring modern town of practical daily life, and the secret personality of a city whose insidious beauty and vitality still survive and even renew themselves. For these reasons, many foreign francophiles like myself find Paris a fascinating and exciting city to visit for a month or two, but we do not want to live there as so many expatriates chose to do before the war. And even Parisians are in growing numbers moving to the provinces.

The city in fact is still paying the price of nearly a century of neglect of town-planning, up until the early '60s. The *Ville Lumière* that the tourist sees is today bright with new paint and scoured façades, but it hides other realities: the congested older commercial districts, the scarcity of green parks and the ugly sprawl of the pre-war suburbs. As the population of greater Paris swelled rapidly after the war, its new suburbs were not provided adequately with services, and the problems grew. But then the Gaullist planners of the '60s set to work on the whole shape of the city, colouring their maps with grandiose designs for garden cities and urban freeways. The French do not do things by halves: after years of total disregard, the future of Paris has become a public obsession. And up through the waste land of the old slums and suburbs the shoots have appeared of a new, daring and impressive city . . .

One of the problems of town-planning is that the organic links have never been adequate between inner Paris and its suburbs; the two are entirely distinct, administratively and even physically, separated by the wide sweep of the Boulevard Périphérique (ring motorway) and the vacant zones beside it. Within this ring, and within the old city gates lies the single commune of the Ville de Paris with its twenty *arrondissements*; its population, though still dense, has been falling steadily from 2.9 million in 1911 to 2.1 million today. Outside, the hundreds of suburban communes have mostly been growing rapidly, so that the population of the whole conurbation has risen since the war from 5 million to about 10 million, and today more than three Parisians in four are *banlieusards*. There is no overall co-ordinating body in the manner of the former Greater London Council, nothing other than the Ile-de-France Region which reaches fifty miles into the countryside – and the communes jealously hug their autonomy.

Let us look first at the wider conurbation. Baron Haussmann's rational replanning of central Paris in the 1860s was never extended to the new industrial suburbs which after 1870s grew up higgledy-piggledy outside the gates. Aubervilliers, Les Lilas, Issy-les-Moulineaux – lovely names for ghastly places – these and scores of other townlets arose while Paris was sucking the blood from the rest of France, and they became, as the planning expert Peter Hall put it, 'a vast, ill-conceived, hastily constructed emergency camp to house the labour force of Paris, presenting almost the limit of urban degeneration'. Renoir's pastoral canvas of the Seine at Argenteuil, painted in the 1870s, was soon blotted out beyond recognition.

After 1918 this kind of growth slowed down. But, with land prices so low, a different type of excrescence now appeared in the suburbs, the individual *pavillon*. The Parisian *petit bourgeois* found that he could afford to realise a dream that he shares with the Englishman: a suburban cottage with a garden. But instead of the English ribbon-development of that period, there was anarchy. Some 80,000 little red-roofed *pavillons* spread their ungainly rash of assorted shapes across the outer suburbs, and were among the few new buildings in greater Paris between the wars. Then after 1945 the population again rose rapidly, and new blocks of flats were flung up piecemeal to cope with it. Over 2 million dwellings have been built in greater Paris since the war, to house or rehouse well over half the population. But only since the 1960s has much attempt been made to plan the new suburbs coherently; at first, stray blocks of flats were planted anywhere, usually in vacant gaps where land was cheap; nor was much effort made to provide these sad new dormitories with proper equipment such as hospitals, playing-fields, even schools. Suburban public transport was appalling too, and when the housing crisis was at its worst, in the 1950s, the difficulty of finding a flat near one's work often made matters worse. A worker might have to get up at 5 a.m. to make a two-hour train journey via central Paris to his factory on the far side of town, arriving back home at 8 p.m.

Banlieusards: suburban dwellers, commuters

Source: Ardagh, 1987

ISSUES ANALYSIS: PLANNING FOR THE FUTURE OF PARIS

1 Read the extract and then attempt to list some of the major problems that face the city managers of Paris in the late twentieth century.

2 What appear to be the main stages of growth in the inter-war and the post-war years?

3 Is there any evidence that urban planning played any important part in the growth of the city?

4 What, in your opinion, are the main objectives that should exercise the planning authorities?

STATISTICAL ANALYSIS: POPULATION GROWTH IN PARIS

1 Consider the index graphs for population growth in the Ile de France (in which Paris is located, see Figure 4.54) and in Paris itself (Figure 4.52). What comments can you make about the relative rate of growth in the two areas?

2 Now consider the growth of population by *département* in the Ile de France (Figure 4.53). The various *départments* making up the *Petite Couronne* and the *Grande Couronne* as shown below:

No. of *département*

Paris	75	⎫
Hauts de Seine	92	
Seine St Denis	93	*Petite Couronne*
Val de Marne	94	
Seine et Marne	77	⎭
Yvelines	78	⎫
Essonne	91	*Grande Couronne*
Val d'Oise	95	⎭

Compare the changes in population in the different sections of the Paris conurbation.

3 To summarise the work on population changes, study the average annual rates of change in Table 4.23. A blank map of the *départements* in the Ile de France area is shown in Figure 4.54. Choosing appropriate intervals to divide up the range of percentage changes, draw choropleth maps to show the variations in population change for 1975–82 and 1982–90.

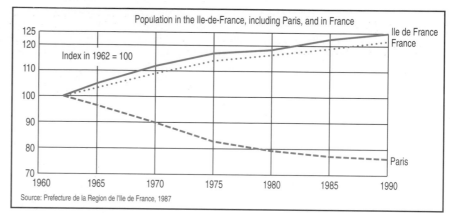

Figure 4.52   Population in the Ile de France and in France

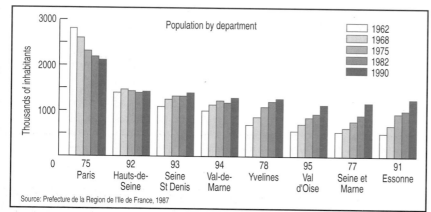

Figure 4.53   Population by *département* (county)

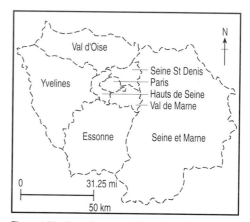

Figure 4.54   Ile de France administrative regions

Table 4.23   Population change 1975–1990, Ile de France

Départements	Total population			Population change		Population change (%)	
	1975	1982	1990	1975–82	1982–90	1975–82	1982–90
Paris	2 299 800	2 176 200	2 152 400	−123 600	−23 800	−5.4	−1.1
Hauts de Seine	1 438 900	1 387 000	1 391 700	−51 900	+4 700	−3.6	+0.3
Seine St Denis	1 322 100	1 324 300	1 381 200	+2200	+56 900	+0.2	+4.3
Val de Marne	1 215 700	1 193 700	1 215 500	−22 000	+21 900	−1.8	+1.8
Petite Couronne	3 976 700	3 905 000	3 998 400	−71 700	+83 400	−1.8	+2.1
Seine et Marne	755 800	887 100	1 078 200	+131 300	+191 000	+17.4	+21.5
Yvelines	1 082 300	1 196 100	1 307 100	+113 800	+111 000	+10.5	+9.3
Essonnes	923 100	988 000	1 084 800	+64 900	+96 800	+7.0	+9.8
Val d'Oise	840 900	920 600	1 049 600	+79 700	+129 000	+9.5	+14.0
Grande Couronne	3 602 100	3 991 800	4 519 700	+389 700	+527 900	+10.8	+13.2
Ile de France	9 878 600	10 073 000	10 660 600	+194 400	+587 600	+2.0	+5.8
New towns	273 900	443 600	653 800	+169 700	+210 200	+62.0	+47.4

Source: 1990 Census, Paris

IMPACT ANALYSIS: SCHÉMA DIRECTEUR

1 Analyse the main features of the *Schéma* in terms of the plans for the *Petite Couronne* and the *Grande Couronne*.

a What strategy has been used in the *Petite Couronne*?

b What major changes are envisaged in the *Grande Couronne*?

Plans for the development of the Ile de France

The first main proposal for the greater Paris area was the PADOG plan of 1960 which aimed principally at limiting growth around the existing conurbation. This was succeeded in 1965 by the *Schéma Directeur*, which, although it has been modified several times since, is still the basic plan on which the future of Paris is to be modelled. The main features of the *Schéma Directeur* are shown in Figure 4.55.

A separate scheme for the Ville de Paris (Figure 4.56) is subsumed in the main *Schéma Directeur*. As with the plan for the whole of the Paris region, this scheme has undergone some revisions, but the basic thrust of the proposals remains unaltered.

La Ville de Paris: renewal and renovation in action

We shall now examine four schemes for urban renewal and renovation in greater detail: Fronts de Seine (*arrondissement* 15); La Villette (*arrondissement* 19); Les Halles (*arrondissement* 1); and Le Marais (*arrondissements* 3 and 4). The locations of these schemes are shown in Figure 4.56 and photographs of each location in Figure 4.57.

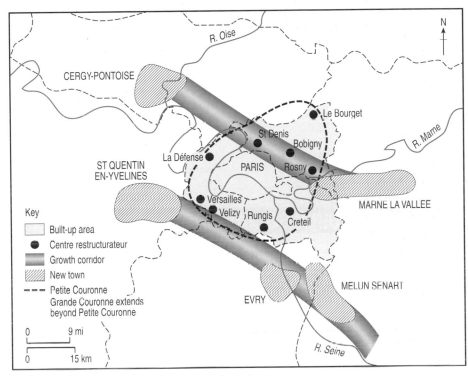

Figure 4.55 The master plan for development and urbanisation

(i) Seine waterfront

(ii) La Villette

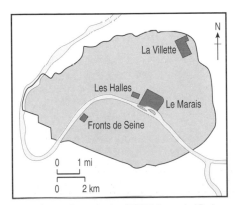

Figure 4.56 Structure plan (SDAU) for central Paris

(iii) Les Halles

(iv) Le Marais, Place des Vosges

Figure 4.57 Four redevelopment schemes

1 *Fronts de Seine*: Old inner urban area with mix of small workshops, working class residences, cafés and corner shops. It has been replaced by a prestige development for middle-class managers and professional/scientific classes: 15 multi-storey apartment blocks overlooking the Seine (4000 apartments); 4 office blocks (110 000 m³ of office space); 6500 garages; the Nikko luxury hotel; a covered shopping mall with social and sports clubs and gymnasia.

2 *La Villette*. A 166-hectare site in north-east Paris formerly occupied by disused abattoirs and warehouses lining an old canal basin, the Bassin de la Villette and the Canal de l'Ourcq. In the south-west the edges of the basin have been redeveloped with an emphasis on leisure and recreational facilities. The old abattoirs have been converted into a prestigious Science Museum, with the adjacent Géode housing a panoramic cinema. Beyond lie other features of the arts-science complex. This site will also eventually contain the new Cité de la Musique, with a huge concert hall, practice rooms, workshops and studios.

3 *Les Halles*. Site of the old wholesale markets and a surrounding area of old working-class housing, seriously congested. Redevelopment began with the futuristic Centre d'Art et de la Culture Georges Pompidou. To the west a new shopping centre, the Forum des Halles, was opened, linked to a vast underground complex served by the new RER (Regional Express Network). Aimed principally at the Parisian middle classes, the turnover of the Forum is one of the highest in Europe for this type of development. The last phase of the development includes a sports and leisure complex and gardens.

4 *Le Marais*. An area of attractive mansions and town houses much favoured in the Middle Ages by the French nobility. Most of it is arranged along narrow streets or around squares of great architectural merit, such as the Place des Vosges. Once the courtiers and nobles began to move out of the area it fell into some disrepair and some parts were almost abandoned. Now its architectural and social value has been recognised, and much restoration has been carried out. It is now regarded as the prime area for urban restoration in inner Paris and there are extensive plans for maintaining and improving the fabric of both its buildings and its streets.

GROUP ENQUIRY: SOCIAL AND ENVIRONMENTAL VALUE

Each of these four schemes has its merits, although each has very different objectives. It is your task to assess the schemes and rank them in order of their value to the rebuilding and restructuring of inner Paris. Using the information given and the photographs (Figure 4.57) you should assess the schemes under a number of headings: architectural merit; improvement of the social fabric; cultural value; improvement to the urban environment; opportunities for job creation; opportunities for housing local people.

For each of the measures above, use a scale of 1–5: 1 for low value, 5 for high value. If you think that one of the measures of assessment is worth more than the others, then you can give it extra weighting. This can be undertaken as an exercise in groups, with each group dealing with a particular development.

Restructuring the inner suburbs

Within the *Petite Couronne*, the *Schéma Directeur* designated nine *centres restructurateurs* to be the centres for the creation of new employment, for the provision of better housing, and for the development and extension of retail, welfare and cultural facilities. Their location varied enormously: some were in old industrial areas, like St Denis; others, like La Défense and Créteil, were in areas that were in desperate need of reorganisation of their infrastructure and housing; others, like Versailles, were in attractive settings on the edge of the *Grande Couronne*.

Much of the success of redevelopment in the *Petite Couronne* depended on the ability of the *centres restructurateurs* to attract new jobs, both in the manufacturing sector and in the tertiary service sector. Location of jobs in the *Petite Couronne* has been constrained by a number of problems as shown in Table 4.24, the result of a questionnaire given to managers in industry in the *Petite Couronne*.

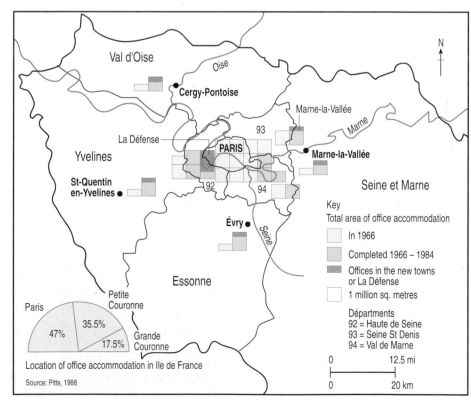

Figure 4.58   Office accommodation in the Ile de France between 1966 and 1984

ENQUIRY: REGENERATION IN *LA PETITE COURONNE*

1 Analyse the reaction of the industrialists to the questionnaire.
  a Which advantages might most easily be lost if the firm moved out of the Paris area?

  b Which disadvantages might be easily be remedied if the firm moved out of the Paris area?
  c On balance, do you think that the advantages outweigh the disadvantages?

2 The growth of office accommodation is often the key to providing new jobs in a range of the tertiary services. Figure 4.58 shows the growth of office accommodation in the Ile de France between 1966 and 1984.
  a Work out the percentage of new growth in the period 1966–84 for (i) City of Paris (ii) the *Petite Couronne* (Départements 92, 93, and 94) and the *Grande Couronne* (Départements 77, 78, 91 and 95).
  b Would you say that there was any evidence of decentralisation from Paris out to the *Petite* or *Grande Couronnes*?

Table 4.24   Advantages and disadvantages of running a business in the *Petite Couronne*

	Large firms (%)	Small firms (%)
Advantages		
Easy recruitment of labour	76	46
Ease of local communications	60	39
Ease of international communications	12	5
Disadvantages		
Transport difficulties	32	13
Labour costs	24	6
Social climate	24	6
Difficult to expand	12	0
Taxes too high	32	39

Source: Pitte (ed.), 1988

La Défense

La Défense is a *centre restructurateur* in the west of Paris. Conceived as a major new centre of business and commerce, the area's high-rise office blocks are set amidst boulevards, promenades and open squares.

Profile m²	
Office space	1 550 000
Office employment	65 000 (1989)
Residential population	100 000
Shopping	108 000 m²

ENQUIRY: THE POTENTIAL OF LA DÉFENSE

Read the extract from the brochure to La Défense that is given to visiting business executives. What kind of a place is La Défense to:

a work in?
b live in?

Figure 4.59   *La Défense*, Paris

A BOLD INNOVATION

It was at the start of the 1950s that the idea of building up an area for offices, dwellings and leisure centres at La Défense was first put forward. Like all truly innovative ideas, it left no one indifferent. Some welcomed the project enthusiastically, being aware of its outstanding advantages, while others felt concern over its very size and novelty.

In spite of various reservations, criticisms and difficulties, La Défense has come into being and its creation has gradually won over the greatest sceptics. La Défense is already an unquestionable success and continues to be one of the most wonderful urban blocks of the twentieth century.

La Défense is a living structure that is constantly developing and on the move: equipment continues to be fitted up, traffic and traffic-signalling conditions are constantly improving, the Quatre Temps shopping centre is under construction and many building programmes for offices and dwellings have been or are soon to be launched.

La Défense present a shifting – and manifold – picture: it is not a single landscape but rather a cluster of superimposed images that complement and answer one another. Among them, the now familiar outline of CNIT, the varied profusion of tall buildings, the dull polished granite brilliance of the Tour Fiat, the changing reflections of the Tour Roussel-Nobel, the Tour Manhattan and the Tour Générale, the central esplanade descending level by level towards the Seine and the monumental fountain of Agam. It would be equally impossible to try and pin down the typical lifestyle of La Défense: executives and housewives work and live here; the inhabitants of Chatou and Saint-Germain-en-Laye, having come together as neighbours, [do not find it easy] to describe this district which is so varied and undergoing so much change. Describing what exists already and letting you imagine how it will be tomorrow: this is what our brochure sets out to do.

Source: Promotional brochure for La Défense

Créteil

'I will quote the example of Créteil which I visited the other day. Créteil has resisted the flood of housing and there are, in the middle of the town, 100 hectares of conservation land, with a lake, a sailing school, and 60 hectares of open space. Along the lake there is a new area of community housing which clearly has no social or racial problems. If all the suburbs were located like this, human relationships would be very different. We need to create a civilised atmosphere in our towns.' (François) Mitterand, May 1988).

Créteil lies in south-east Paris. It embraces ambitious plans to create an entirely new focus of urban life in the south-east suburbs. The development is bordered on the west by an attractive lake, is served by an extension of the Metro, and includes the large new Regional Hospital Henri-Mondor and the campus of the University of Paris – Val de Marne.

Profile

Office space:	400 000
Office employment	20 000 (est.)
Residential population	80 000
Shopping	99 500

ENQUIRY: THE POTENTIAL OF CRÉTEIL

A questionnaire on the quality of life, circulated among the inhabitants of Créteil in January 1989, is a revealing document. Figure 4.60 shows the results.

1 Analyse the questionnaire in terms of:
  a What were the Cristoliens most satisfied with?
  b What were they least satisfied with?
  c In eight out of the 20 questions those without an opinion amounted to more than 33% of the sample. Check these questions carefully and then suggest a reason for such apathy.

2 Study the photographs of Créteil (Figures 4.61 and 4.62) and the layout of the development (Figure 4.63).
  a What do they suggest about the quality of life in Créteil?
  b How do you think it compares with La Défense?

3 What kind of a place is Créteil:
  a To work in?
  b To live in?

4 To summarise: how do the two *centres restructurateurs* compare? Do you think that a place like Créteil has finally banished the image of south-east Paris as a run-down area? Where would you prefer to live, given the choice, La Défense, or Créteil?

What the inhabitants of Créteil think

Question: On the whole, are you satisfied or dissatisfied with life in Créteil?

Very satisfied	38%
Quite satisfied	50%
Not very satisfied	7%
Not at all satisfied	5%
Don't know	0%

Question: Do you feel the present local authority of Créteil has, in the last few years, achieved excellent, good, mediocre or bad results?

Excellent	14%
Good	73%
Mediocre	7%
Bad	1%
Don't know	5%

Question: Some people speak of a way of life in Créteil based on tolerance, solidarity and friendliness. Do you, yourself, feel that such a statement about Créteil is justified or not?

Justified	50%
Not justified	25%
Don't know	25%

Question: With regard to each of the following points, will you indicate if you feel that the present local authority of Créteil's action is adequate or inadequate?

	Adequate	Inadequate	Don't know
Entertainment and culture	83%	5%	12%
Help for the underprivileged	46%	12%	42%
Building of council houses	51%	23%	26%
Information about municipal matters	85%	9%	6%
Opportunities for sporting activities	89%	5%	6%
Green open spaces (town parks)	92%	6%	2%
Leisure opportunities for children and young people	73%	11%	16%
Creches	36%	25%	39%
Immigrants	36%	23%	41%
Public transport	62%	24%	14%
Town planning (the new Créteil)	78%	12%	10%
Quality of life in Créteil	77%	14%	9%
Aid for sports associations and clubs	61%	5%	34%
Help for children of school age (youth centres, holiday groups, canteens, sporting and cultural activities)	60%	7%	33%
Aid for the elderly	49%	8%	43%
Safety for the citizens	39%	43%	18%
Local taxes	20%	67%	13%
Pedestrianised streets	83%	14%	3%
Help for primary and nursery schools (state of buildings, furniture, general funds)	43%	15%	42%
Reception of children in schools	42%	12%	46%

Figure 4.60   Results of a questionnaire circulated among inhabitants of Créteil in 1989

Figure 4.61   The lake at Créteil

Figure 4.62   Office block at Créteil

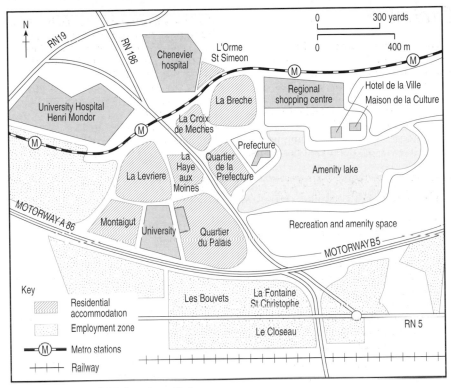

Figure 4.63   Layout of Créteil, south-east Paris

Moving to St Quentin-en-Yvelines

St Quentin is one of the five new towns developed under the SDAU Plan for the Ile de France (see Figure 4.54). In its ten years of existence it has seen quite remarkable growth and is clearly a major node of attraction in the southern corridor identified in the *Schéma Directeur*.

REPORT: THE POTENTIAL OF ST QUENTIN-EN-YVELINES (NEW TOWN)

You have been appointed to the Research and Development staff of a medium-sized electronic company with a major plant in the south of England. The company, mindful of the opportunities presented by the single European Market after 1992, wishes to locate an advance factory unit in Western Europe.

Your first assignment is to act as personal assistant to the managing director and she has asked you to accompany her to St Quentin-en-Yvelines to examine a possible site for an advanced factory. Before you go to France she has asked you to prepare a brief about the general infrastructure, benefits to industry, and quality of life in St Quentin-en-Yvelines.

You are provided with the following: map of the south-west Paris region including the *Petite Couronne* and the *Grande Couronne* (Figure 4.55); map of St Quentin-en-Yvelines (Figure 4.66) general information on St Quentin-en-Yvelines and comments from other industrialists already located in the town (Figure 4.67); photographs of housing, industries and transport in St Quentin (Figure 4.65).

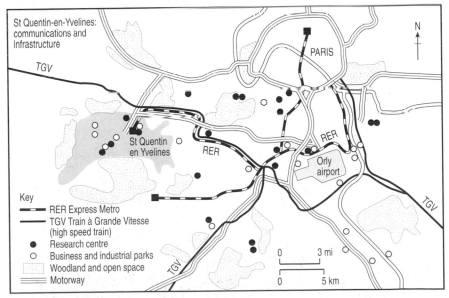

Figure 4.64   St Quentin-en-Yvelines: communications and infrastructure

Your brief for the managing director should have the following broad structure:

1 What are the main features of the community and the environment in the south-west Paris region?
2 What are the main attractions of St Quentin-en-Yvelines as an industrial base for an electronics company?
3 What sort of quality of life could managers and employees expect when living in St Quentin-en-Yvelines?
4 A balanced appraisal of the opportunities that St Quentin-en-Yvelines would offer your company.

(i) High-tech industry

(ii) RER link to Paris

(iii) Housing

Figure 4.65   Scenes from St Quentin-en Yvelines

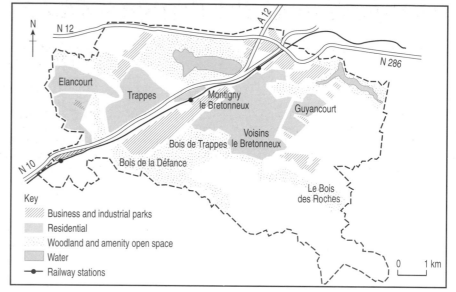

Figure 4.66   St Quentin-en-Yvelines: functional zones

Key
- Business and industrial parks
- Residential
- Woodland and amenity open space
- Water
- Railway stations

0   1 km

SAINT-QUENTIN-EN-YVELINES

The future in the present
Its ideal geographical location and its privileged situation close to one of France's major historic cities, as well as the quality of its urban development, mean that Sain-Quentin-en-Yvelines is already a leader in the Paris region in terms of housing and employment.
Over the past decade, 75 000 people have come to live in the new districts and 500 businesses have set up here.

Population
The town has a young population (60% of the inhabitants are aged between 20 and 40), with a high activity rate, mainly directed towards the service industries (38% of the working population holds management or supervisory positions). This population is growing by 7 000 to 7 500 inhabitants per year, corresponding to the annual construction of 2 000 homes.

Employment
40 000 people are currently employed in Saint-Quentin-en-Yvelines. 40 firms set up here every year, creating some 2 500 new jobs.
The 500 firms already established here are representative of all economic sectors; electronic data processing, electronics, mechanical engineering, building and civil engineering, banking and finance. The presence of the European headquarters of major corporations such as MILLIPORE, INTEL and POLAROID make Saint-Quentin-en-Yvelines a genuine international business center.
Today, Saint-Quentin-en-Yvelines boasts 865 acres of business parks and 5.3 million sq. ft. of office accommodation.
Its economic potential will double over the next ten years, making it the leading business center to the West of Paris.

Employment structure
- clerical employees 35%
- management and supervisory staff 38%
- manual workers 27%

Saint-Quentin-en-Yvelines: a good corporate image
Jérôme Huret of Sperry adds: 'Ours is a corporation which has evolved very fast and today feels the need to centralise its corporate headquarters. Not only is Saint-Quentin-en-Yvelines less expensive than La Défense, it is also good from the corporate image point of view.
Saint-Quentin-en-Yvelines already has good references: Intel, Polaroid, Matra, BMW... What is more, its geographical location is ideally suited to staff allocation.'

MILLIPORE

Saint-Quentin-en-Yvelines: a strategic base for the future
Pierre Thomas gives the following reasons why Polaroid chose to locate here: 'In moving to Saint-Quentin-en-Yvelines, we found just what we were looking for. Close to Paris, with reliable postal and telephone services, it is a strategic base for the future. We then set up our European headquarters in the Polaroid France offices, at the end of 1984.'

Saint-Quentin-en-Yvelines: a good place to live
Yves Macaire of BMW adds: 'When we moved to Saint-Quentin-en-Yvelines from Bagneux in the Southern suburbs of Paris, the majority of our staff came with us. Most of them took advantage of this opportunity to find housing locally, thus improving their life-style.'

Saint-Quentin-en-Yvelines: a town for expansion
This is the opinion of René Develay of Fuji Film France: 'By moving here, we have been able to rationalise our organisation whilst enjoying the best possible conditions for expansion.'

Saint-Quentin-en-Yvelines: an excellent address
Stating that the decision to locate here was endorsed by all the Intel staff, Patrick Chancerelle went on to add: 'We chose Saint-Quentin-en-Yvelines in order to be near all our French clients and because it is an excellent address for our corporate image, a major consideration for the European headquarters of a corporation such as ours.'

BOUYGUES

Saint-Quentin-en-Yvelines: a technology center
Charlie Vican of Millipore explains: 'We are an American high-technology corporation. In the Paris region, all technology is located in the West. We chose Saint-Quentin-en-Yvelines because we needed a good address for our European headquarters.'

Figure 4.67   General information and industrialists' comments

---

FURTHER INVESTIGATIONS

In most towns and cities there are plans for change. Some may be relatively small scale, involving no more than a site redevelopment; others may be conceived on a much grander scale and can involve whole sectors of the urban area.

1 Select a small plan for redevelopment, and then carry out some field work at the site. You could map the present land use, carry out an environmental quality survey and generally assess the present character of the site. Then the proposals could be measured against the existing qualities of the site.

2 Select one particular aspect of a town's transport policy, such as a park-and-ride scheme, and then attempt to assess its effectiveness.

Urbanisation at the Fringe – and Beyond

Much of our discussion so far has focused on what is happening inside towns and cities. It is\at the margins of urban areas and in the rural areas beyond that some of the most important issues connected with urbanisation are likely to arise in the future. In areas where urban population is increasing there is immense pressure for extra housing. Some additional housing can be built by 'recycling' land that has already been used for housing – using derelict land within urban areas or demolishing housing that is too old or dilapidated to be worth renewing. This land within cities rarely provides enough space for all the housing needs, so, inevitably, housing authorities and builders look towards the land beyond the urban fringe.

Such land is often part of areas that are protected by green belt or similar policies and is subject to special planning controls. However, such is the demand for building land in south-east England that areas outside the green belts have to be considered for housing, and it is in these areas that controversy is likely to be fiercest and rival claims to the land most hotly contested. Decisions have to be taken as to whether the housing that is needed is built adjacent to existing towns and villages or concentrated in completely new greenfield sites. An example of the controversies that can arise in such a situation was the proposal of Consortium Developments to build a new town at Foxley Wood in north-east Hampshire.

CASE STUDY *Foxley Wood: New Town for North-East Hampshire*

Population change in south-east England shows that there are marked differences between different parts of the region. It is likely that these differences will be accentuated in the next decades and housing forecasts adjusted accordingly.

Much of Hampshire is seen as an important area of significant population growth.

VALUES ENQUIRY: SHOULD FOXLEY WOOD GO AHEAD?

Study the map that shows population change in south-east England in the period 1981–91 (Figure 4.68).

1 Which areas appear to be losing population?

2 Which areas appear to be gaining population?

3 Make a copy of the outline of the map, and then mark in the zones that will indicate:

   a Areas where recycling of land would provide land for housing.

   b Areas under intense pressure that will need greenfield sites to be released if the demand for housing is to be satisfied.

   c Areas that are under less intense pressure, but will still have to release considerable quantities of land for housing.

4 How would knowledge of the extent of the green belt in south-east England help you to produce a more accurate map?

Note: You should refer to an atlas of Great Britain so you can name the areas.

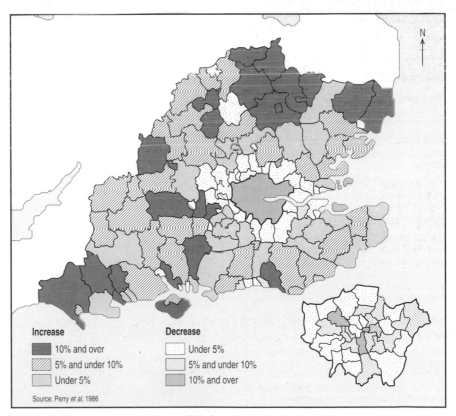

Increase
- 10% and over
- 5% and under 10%
- Under 5%

Decrease
- Under 5%
- 5% and under 10%
- 10% and over

Source: Perry et al, 1986

Figure 4.68 South-east population change 1981–91

The proposals, 1984

The plan for Foxley Wood centred on a 700-acre site in a disused gravel pit, surrounded by pine trees. The site on long lease to the Forestry Commission, is one mile to the west of Eversley. It lies within easy commuting distance of both Reading and Basingstoke, and has relatively easy access to the M3 and to the main rail links into London.

The proposal was to build 4800 homes, two schools, a community centre, a library, a leisure centre, a health centre and to create a nature reserve, with a total population of 12 500. The site was outside the green belt so it was regarded as an important test case for the preservation or development of land of high environmental quality.

Figure 4.69   Old gravel pit, Foxley Wood

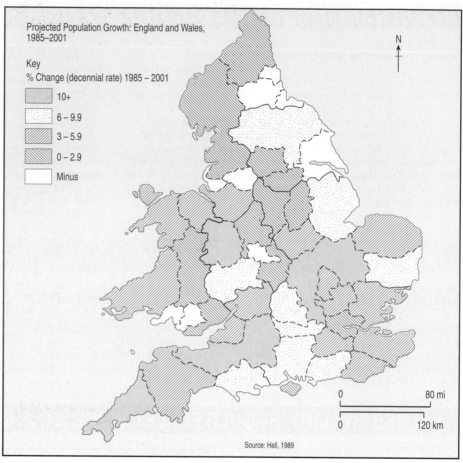

Figure 4.70   Projected population growth: England and Wales, 1985–2001

What they said

Estate agent, Yateley, of Foxley Wood: 'I have to be honest: as a local I wouldn't really want it. I like a bit of green space around me.'

Estate agent, Yateley: 'Everybody wants to live in Yateley. There's a big premium on prices in Eversley.'

Chief executive, Consortium Developments Limited: 'If there's anything like Foxley Wood in the whole of the south-east, I'd be amazed. It is quite unique in southern England.'

Chief planner for Hart District Council: 'The whole of the south-east is being peppered with such schemes and inquiries in the hope that one might get through. There isn't a blade of grass in our area that someone hasn't got their eyes on. The developers know that they would make millions and millions if any proposal were to be allowed. A consortium spent £600 000 on one previous inquiry.'

Retired couple living in Hartley Wintley, four miles from Foxley Wood: 'We would like to see the prosperity of the south-east spread to the north. You should see the queues of people trying to get on to the M3 in the morning; you can't get on it. The whole area is completely swamped: the M25 is completely clogged.'

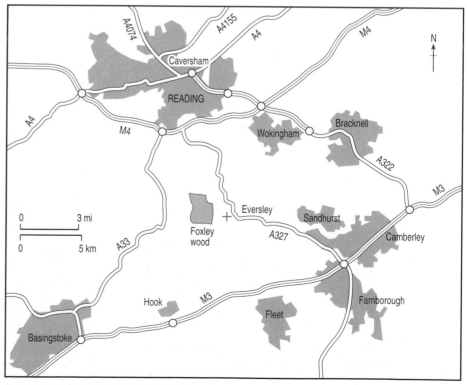

Figure 4.71   Locational sketch of Foxley Wood

Hart District rejected the Foxley Wood scheme, and it went to public inquiry in June 1988. The Inspector of the public inquiry rejected the appeal of the consortium of developers, and the Secretary of State for the Environment was asked for a decision. On 7 July 1989 he allowed the appeal by Consortium Developments Limited for the building of the new settlement at Foxley Wood.

This decision caused uproar in Hart District, and the local Council published a leaflet setting out its strongest possible disapproval of the Minister's action. In the summer of 1989 a new Minister for the Environment was appointed. Would he agree with his predecessor or would he overturn the decision?

On 4 October 1989 the Secretary of State for the Environment Chris Patten announced a revised interim decision on the Foxley Wood proposal, indicating that he was now minded to dismiss the appeal of Consortium Developments Limited against the original Inspector's decision to reject the scheme.

What they said: the controversy continues

Hart District Councillor – 'If Patten agrees to the plantation plan in our area, the developers will be free to pick the next bit of land that falls free, irrespective of where or what it is, and say, "You like the idea. Here's some land with planning constraints – overrule them." It is totally against the democratic process.'

Spokesperson for SPISE (Sane Planning for the South-East) – 'The irony is that it is Conservative local authorities that are campaigning against the government. People have become aware of a whole number of environmental issues, not just the big ones, but immediate ones on their own patch.'

Spokesperson for CPRE (Council for the Protection of Rural England) – 'With the change at the DOE we would hope to see greater sympathy for environmental issues and the views that people are expressing.'

Moving away from the cities: counterurbanisation

Movement away from rural areas to urban centres has been a major component in urban growth, both in the economically more-developed world and in the economically less-developed countries. In the latter it is still a powerful force in the continued growth of both modest towns and the largest cities. In the former, however, as we have already seen, the pace of urbanisation is already slackening, and in countries such as those of Western Europe the rate of urbanisation is now very small indeed. Moreover, there is now increasing evidence that people are leaving the cities in order to live in the rural areas. Some of the country areas are still within easy commuting reach of the urban centres, but others are sought because they offer a change of workplace, a chance to work at home (increasingly so in an era of rapid and effective telecommunications) or the opportunity to retire to more pleasant surroundings. Clearly, this new process of counterurbanisation has important implications for planning in both urban and rural areas, whether the latter be adjacent to urban areas or more remote. The ripples of urbanisation in south-east England can be seen to be spreading to places like Foxley Wood, but in the sense of counterurbanisation much further in every direction. People in Dorset villages now live there for a variety of reasons: they can commute to London in two hours; they can work in attractive surroundings in modern service industries in towns like Bournemouth or Southampton in the outer south-east; they can work at home surrounded by modern computer technology giving a ready link to the capital.

A study was carried out in West Cornwall to investigate the process of counterurbanisation in that area. It confined itself to the following locations, each with different characteristics. These locations are shown on the map (Figure 4.74).

1 St Just: remote tin-mining settlement in the far west.
2 The Lizard: farming area, tourism and a large naval air station.
3 Carbis Bay: holiday and retirement centre, adjoining St Ives.
4 Feock: area with prosperous villages in wooded valleys.
5 South Redruth: old mining and industrial town, somewhat run down.
6 Tregolls: prosperous suburb of Truro.
7 St Stephen: centre of china-clay industry, population still declining.

ENQUIRY: THE PHASES OF URBANISATION

1 Draw up a table showing the 'push' and 'pull' factors that are responsible for:
   a Urbanisation in an economically more-developed country in the early twentieth century.
   b Urbanisation in an economically less-developed country in the late twentieth century.
   c Counterurbanisation in an economically more-developed country in the late twentieth century.

2 Draw flow diagrams to show the various stages of these population movements, incorporating the major decisions that have to be made. The first one is drawn as an example (Figure 4.72).

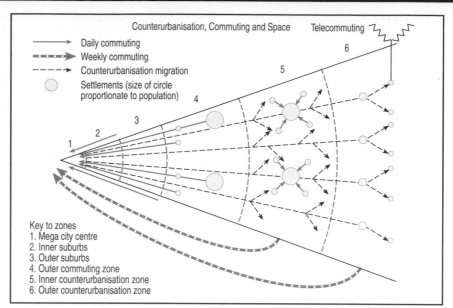

Key to zones
1. Mega city centre
2. Inner suburbs
3. Outer suburbs
4. Outer commuting zone
5. Inner counterurbanisation zone
6. Outer counterurbanisation zone

Figure 4.72   Flow diagram of urbanisation

ENQUIRY: COUNTERURBANISATION IN WEST CORNWALL

Study Figure 4.73 which shows the main changes in population in Cornwall 1961–71 and 1971–81.

1 With the help of a good atlas map, analyse the changes that have taken place.

2 Isolate all those areas that are showing population increasing at a faster rate.
   a Classify these areas according to their location (e.g., Atlantic Seaboard, Channel Coast).

   b Explain why these areas, in their different ways, have grown faster in population.

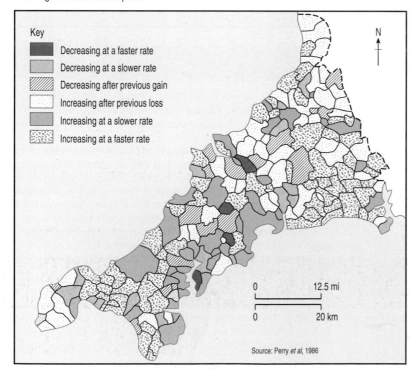

Key
- Decreasing at a faster rate
- Decreasing at a slower rate
- Decreasing after previous gain
- Increasing after previous loss
- Increasing at a slower rate
- Increasing at a faster rate

Source: Perry et al, 1986

Figure 4.73   Cornwall: change in population trends 1961–71 and 1971–81

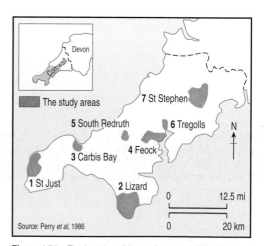

Figure 4.74   The location of the study areas in West Cornwall

VALUES ANALYSIS: REASONS FOR COUNTERURBANISATION

1 Study Table 4.25, which indicates reasons quoted by migrants for moving to Cornwall.
  a How do these reasons compare with the ones that you gave in the first part of this section for people moving from towns to rural areas?
  b Summarise the reasons why West Cornwall is attractive to the migrants.

2 Study Table 4.26. How far does the type of area that they moved to reflect their reasons for moving?

3 Study the Table 4.27 which analyses migrants' reactions after they had made the move.
  a What are the main values that seem to have influenced their perceptions after moving?
  b To what extent have the migrants adjusted to their move?

Table 4.25 West Cornwall interview sample: important reasons for moving, all migrants

	Socio-environmental	(%)
Pull	Preferred environment	42
	Rejoin relatives/friends	40
	Enjoyed previous holidays	38
	Return to homeland	30
	Preferred climate	23
	Better for children	21
	Better for retirement	10
	Better for health	8
Push	Escape urban rat race	39

	Economic	(%)
	Better job prospects	34
	Cheaper housing	12
	Better wages	3
	Better housing	3
	Posted/Transferred to Cornwall	11

Source: Perry, Dean and Brown, 1986

Table 4.26 West Cornwall interview sample: important reasons for moving by study areas

	Previous holidays		Preferred environment		Employment prospects		Escape urban rat race	
	Return migrants (%)	New migrants (%)	Return migrants (%)	New migrants (%)	Return migrants (%)	New migrants (%)	Return migrants (%)	New migrants (%)
Feock	8	46	31	37	39	60	15	34
Carbis Bay	15	53	39	47	31	19	8	48
Lizard	15	53	41	60	30	49	26	38
St Just	18	49	24	51	24	23	35	47
Tregolls	29	38	32	53	29	59	26	53
Redruth	31	42	38	37	19	42	50	47
St Stephen	18	57	18	30	27	30	18	61

Source: Perry, Dean and Brown, 1986

Table 4.27 West Cornwall interview sample: social life and cultural perceptions of migrants in seven study areas – a summary

		St Just Penwith (%)	Carbis Bay and Lelant (%)	Lizard (%)	Feock (%)	Redruth (%)	Tregolls (%)	St Stephen (%)
Positive perception of a distinct Cornish culture	RM	59	85	89	65	69	81	64
	NM	59	71	72	69	58	81	39
Development of many new friendships since moving	RM	71	77	59	50	66	55	57
	NM	59	57	72	69	44	56	45
Most or all of new friends also migrants	RM	18	0	15	35	6	13	9
	NM	11	10	21	54	11	16	17
Affinity for migrants' new residential environment	RM	88	92	93	96	59	97	73
	NM	89	90	92	97	58	94	70
Perception of conflict between locals and newcomers	RM	12	15	22	8	34	29	9
	NM	33	28	26	14	16	16	43
Right decision to have moved	RM	94	85	78	89	81	90	100
	NM	91	93	94	94	79	88	91

RM   Return migrants
NM   New migrants
Source: Perry, Dean and Brown, 1986

FURTHER INVESTIGATIONS: IMPACT OF COUNTERURBANISATION ON GROUPS AND INDIVIDUALS

Investigate the way in which the essential functions of a group of villages (or just one village) alter as a result of a changing population base. The villages could be those adjacent to a fairly large town, or those in a much remoter area. In both cases some of the effects of counterurbanisation could be investigated.

It is very likely that in your area there will be some planning controversy over the development of building land, albeit on a much smaller scale than Foxley Wood. A fieldwork project could look at the environmental quality of the area, and attempt to measure the impacts the new development would have on the local area.

The Future of the City

Much thought and considerable ingenuity have been devoted to the form that urban settlements should take. Every town and city has tended to reflect its era, its architects and planners, and the country of its location. Western cities, Third World cities and socialist cities are all the result of planning, or the lack of it, as are varying degrees of success and failure in urban style and living.

The world's urban people are likely to reach nearly 60% of the total global population in the early twenty-first century and the need for sensible and realistic planning is all too apparent. Apart from the creation of new settlements, there will be much need for restructuring, renewal and restoration in existing towns and cities.

We shall examine here two examples of urban planning, with the future very much in mind. Both contain a strong element of idealism, but this is perhaps where any similarity ends. We shall examine the Prince of Wales' scheme for an extension to Dorchester on his land in the Duchy of Cornwall on the outskirts of the town. On an entirely different scale and in one of the world's most rapidly developing countries, we shall attempt to evaluate the success of city planning on a vast and spectacular scale in the city of Brasilia.

CASE STUDY *Poundbury: a New Vision of the English Country Town*

This newspaper report echoes a common enough cause for concern in southern England at the end of the twentieth century. Extra housing is badly needed in Dorchester, but providing it at a price that young couples can afford is increasingly difficult. Against this background a new proposal for extending Dorchester has been put forward by the Prince of Wales and his architect, Leo Krier.

Discussion of the original proposals for Poundbury led to a considerable degree of revision of the plans for this new development. Phase one, which has received planning consent, is scheduled to begin in 1993. It will consist of the expected mix of land uses with:
- 244 houses and flats of various sizes
- 1610 m² of offices
- 1020 m² of retail space
- 785 m² of light industrial workshops
- Tower, market hall, inn, public house and restaurant.

An artist's impression of a street scene in the new development is shown in Figure 4.75.

ROGER Ranson is a Dorchester mortgage broker, kept going only by the flourishing trade on his hi-tech photo-copying machines – his colour copier was financed by a remortgage deal on his house.

He's arranging about one mortgage a week in Dorset, and turning away nine out of 10 potential customers, after facing them with the bald reality that on two salaries, on a 100 per cent mortgage, there is little in the county they can afford to buy.

He wasn't aware that Dorset was near the top of the league in the Association of District Councils' study of first-time buyers unable to afford anything, but he was no more surprised by it than anyone else in Dorchester yesterday.

His typical would-be-client might be a Dorchester shop worker, earning about £6 000 a year, married to an office worker earning about £7 000. Their absolute maximum mortgage – 'and that would be really stretching them, I'd have to warn them' – would be £39 000.

Source: *Guardian*, 9 August 1989

Figure 4.75   Artist's impression of a street scene, Poundbury

ENQUIRY: POUNDBURY: PROPOSALS AND RESPONSES

1 Study the cartoons by Leo Krier in Figure 4.76.
  a Explain how he has caricatured the present Western city and its functional zones.
  b What is he proposing in the cartoons on the right-hand side?

2 Study the artist's impression of Poundbury in the future (Figure 4.75). How does it fit in with the ideas that are suggested in the cartoon?

3 The essence of the plan is that different functions of the town should not be segregated: there should be a mix in different areas (e.g. small computer workshops could be housed in the same units as residential accommodation and retail facilities).
  a How do you react to this fresh approach to urban planning?
  b What arguments might be raised against it?

4 The Poundbury Planning Weekend, held in June 1989, attracted much attention from the local community and the media. Comments from both groups are shown below.
  a Do you think that the weekend had a good press? Were any notes of caution sounded?

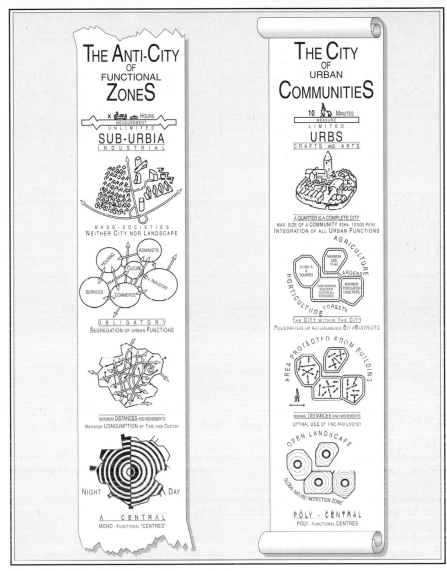

Figure 4.76 The functional city versus the community city

Media Coverage, 16–18 June 1989

Is Dorchester being greedy? As a weekend of discussion on Dorchester's future began last night it became very clear that the path forward would not be easy.
– *Dorset Evening Echo*

Deep in Dorset, the Prince's vision of a small country town.
– *The Times*

The Prince's plans for Dorchester add up to a bold experiment which should be given a chance. If it works, it really could form the basis for future urban planning elsewhere. And it would be rather nice for Dorchester to set an example on a world-wide scale, wouldn't it?
– *Dorset Evening Echo*

The Prince of Wales practised what he preaches yesterday when he initiated one of Britain's largest examples of 'community planning'.
– *Daily Telegraph* 17.6.89

'It won't work' – Krier told.
– *Dorset Evening Echo*

Leon Krier's master-plan for Dorchester represents a striking attempt by the Prince of Wales to translate his architectural theories – centred on classicism and community architecture – into practice.
– *Daily Telegraph*

'We can show it is possible to regenerate and rediscover urban living on a civilised basis' The Prince of Wales.
– *Dorset Evening Echo*

Hundreds help to scheme a vision
– *Sunday Telegraph*

Following Krier's presentation, a massive community consultation exercise has taken place over this weekend under the aegis of the excellent community architect John Thompson. Experts in everything from electronic communications to workshop management have been bussed in. Such brainstorming sessions are common in inner city trouble spots but nobody has tried it in a rural district before. Ebenezer Howard never did.
– *The Sunday Times*

If built as planned over the next fifteen years, Poundbury could be the model that Britain's almost overwhelmed market towns are seeking.
– *The Sunday Times*

b Look at the community response (only a selection, but a fair one). Ten comments are shown: divide them into those definitely in favour, those expressing some qualified approval, and those uncertain. What values are inherent in these comments?

5 Write a short summary of the ways in which it would be different to live in Krier's Poundbury from your home town. Is this the future that our urban areas badly need?

Community response

The most important things for me are health and happiness – most other values change – quality of life is what matters. If this development ensures a better quality of life then I'm all for it.

I admire the vision but how easy will it be to put into practice? How will it protect local interests? It's a lovely idea not to do everything but to leave some spaces blank so they can be built later.

I think it's great to get the macro and the micro view but it needs to be a Dorchester-generated scheme. We don't want to be used as guinea-pigs.

The master-plan is beautiful, civilised – I imagine it would be a joy to be in. It's somewhere I'd like my children to grow up in. I'm sure it will work but I hope it goes slow. The great cathedrals took 200 years!

A rigid masterplan can stifle opportunity, change, expansion and contraction. I am concerned that there should be a balance between an overall vision and lots of opportunities for flexible planning.

The idea is wonderful. People who want to live here can't. I think people here are cautiously excited – I honestly think it's because they identify with the Prince's views.

I think the whole idea is wonderful. I've lived in Dorchester all my life (I'm 74 now).

I think the cars parked in the streets is an awful idea. Why can't there be parking underground?

I like the idea of workshops inside the town and think there ought to be a commitment to a pollution-free environment. By pollution I mean noise as well as fumes.

I don't understand why there is all this emphasis on creating jobs – Dorchester does not have an unemployment problem!

CASE STUDY *Brasilia: Success or Failure?*

'On 20 April 1960, Brazil, a land full of magic, performed its most amazing trick when from the vast plains of the Central Plateau it brought forth a brand-new city, matchless in its beauty.'
– Brazilian Guide book, 1978

'It looked like I always expected Heaven to look at night. It was difficult to tell where the building lights ended and the stars began. They seemed to be put there to show off the others.'
– Old Brazilian peasant woman

'Most visitors to Brasilia take an early plane from Rio – there are flights from 6.30 onwards – land in Brasilia before noon, take a sightseeing tour around the main buildings, and have lunch at one of the two good hotels; in the afternoon they continue their tour, this time visiting the old free city, and are delivered at the airport in time to catch a flight back to Rio and dinner.'
– American Tourist Guide Book, 1987

'It must be a marvellous place to be if you are a building or a motor car for this is a city masterfully designed to cater for everything except people. Twenty years on I found it very depressing.'
– Simon Hoggart, *Guardian*, 1980

'The first impression is emptiness with few cars and even fewer pedestrians, with just a handful of tourists and souvenir stands.'
– Tony Morrison, *Sunday Telgraph Magazine*

'Brazilians, from the centre of this nation I bring you my thoughts and address to you my greetings. Explain to future generations above all else – for them this city is being constructed, the precursor of a revolution of prosperity. For these generations will, one day, stand in judgement on us.'
– Joscelino Kubitschek, President: Inauguration Day, 21 April 1960

Figure 4.77   Exotic Brasilia

ENQUIRY: BRASILIA – THE PROMISE AND THE PERFORMANCE

Brasilia, capital of Brasil, celebrated its thirtieth anniversary in 1990. Kubitschek said that future generations would stand in judgement on Brasilia when he spoke on Inauguration Day, 1960. What do the future generations think, thirty years on?

1 Study the map of Brasilia, Figure 4.77.
   a Discuss its form in terms of city structure. In what ways is it revolutionary?
   b Now study the photograph taken from the Television Tower looking along the principal axis of the city (Figure 4.78). Try to identify the main features represented on the map. Then consider the first four comments on Brasilia – which one most nearly fits the view of the city in the photograph? How do the others fail to match up to reality?

2 Study the map of Brazil (Figure 4.79) which shows the position of the capital in relation to all the state capitals.
   a How far can it be a truly central capital?
   b Now compare its position to that of Rio de Janeiro, the old capital that it replaced in 1960. How far were the Brazilians justified in moving the capital to Brasilia?
   c Refer to Table 4.28, which shows the road distances from all the main Brazilian cities. Does this confirm the visual view of Brasilia's centrality?

3 One of the most telling comments from Tony Morrison: 'Flights to the coast are fully booked months ahead.' This is particularly true of Friday nights, when everyone wants to get back to Rio. An English tourist commented: 'The airport on a Friday night is absolute bedlam. Nobody seemed to know when the flights were leaving, least of all the airport officials; if you got on the wrong plane you could finish up two and a half thousand kilometres from where you wanted to be!' Why do you think so many of Brasilia's inhabitants are weekend commuters to Rio?

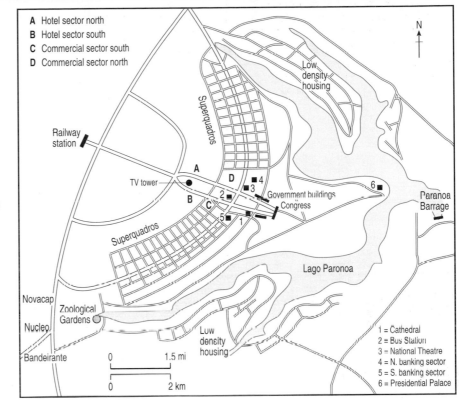

Figure 4.77 Brasilia, urban form and function

Figure 4.78 Aerial photograph of Brasilia

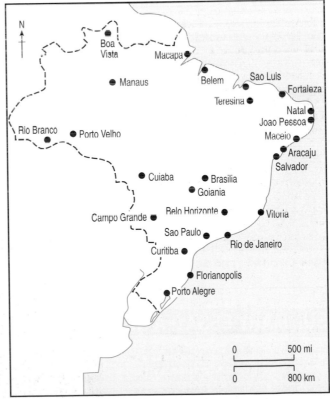

Figure 4.79 The location of state capitals in Brazil

Table 4.28   Road distances between principal cities in Brazil

ROAD DISTANCES IN KILOMETRES	Aracaju	Belem	Belo Horizonte	Brasilia	Campo Grande	Cuiaba	Curitiba	Florianopolis	Fortaleza	Goiania	João Pessoa	Maceio	Natal	Porto Alegre	Recife	Rio de Janeiro	Salvador	São Luis	São Paulo	Teresina	Vitoria
Aracaju		2368	1548	2375	3273	2895	2638	2944	1266	2580	602	265	773	3345	498	1985	345	1902	2230	1442	1289
Belem	2368		2868	1945	3230	2945	3364	3656	1595	2010	2252	2346	1923	4070	2116	3338	2048	966	2960	972	3240
Belo Horizonte	1548	2868		718	1428	1617	994	1286	2470	917	2250	1847	2450	1701	1952	470	1335	2745	586	2290	540
Brasilia	2375	1945	718		1420	1140	1420	1713	2446	200	2446	2132	2587	2127	2342	1188	2048	2240	1012	536	1258
Campo Grande	3273	3230	1428	1420		719	1045	1337	3819	1220	3835	3523	4010	1766	3698	1473	2870	3245	1043	3196	1994
Cuiaba	2895	2945	1617	1140	719		1764	2056	3585	935	3867	3260	3740	2486	3454	2015	2625	2914	1585	2928	2157
Curitiba	2638	3364	994	1420	1045	1764		292	3507	1318	3237	2902	3408	722	3133	838	2358	3771	408	3298	1349
Florianopolis	2944	3656	1286	1713	1337	2056	292		3799	1610	3529	3194	3701	465	3425	1120	2650	4064	701	3591	1642
Fortaleza	1266	1595	2470	2446	3819	3585	3507	3799		2645	650	1015	480	4214	795	2609	1384	1076	3100	632	2576
Goiania	2580	2010	917	200	1220	935	1318	1610	2645		2646	2321	2787	2025	2542	1387	2258	1979	910	1993	1487
João Pessoa	602	2252	2250	2446	3835	3867	3237	3529	650	2646		325	175	3945	105	2400	965	1728	2830	1273	1899
Maceio	267	2346	1847	2132	3523	3260	2902	3194	1015	2321	325		605	3609	230	2250	630	1896	2495	1194	1654
Natal	773	1923	2450	2587	4010	3740	3408	3701	480	2787	175	605		4115	286	2560	1150	1535	3000	951	2074
Porto Alegre	3345	4070	1701	2127	1766	2486	722	465	4214	2025	3945	3609	4115		3840	1534	3065	4478	1115	4005	2056
Recife	498	2116	1952	2342	3698	3454	3133	3425	795	2542	105	230	286	3840		3155	828	1599	2725	1144	2010
Rio de Janeiro	1985	3338	470	1188	1473	2015	838	1120	2609	1387	2400	2250	2560	1534	3155		1690	2933	430	3269	521
Salvador	345	2048	1335	2048	2870	2625	2358	2650	1384	2258	965	630	1150	3065	828	1690		1555	1950	1124	1192
São Luis	1902	966	2745	2240	3245	2914	3771	4064	1076	1979	1728	1896	1535	4478	1599	2933	1555		2889	455	2547
São Paulo	2230	2960	586	1012	1043	1585	408	701	3100	910	2830	2495	3000	1115	2725	430	1950	2889		2890	941
Teresina	1442	972	2290	536	3196	2928	3298	3591	632	1993	1273	1194	951	4005	1144	3269	1124	455	2890		2092
Vitoria	1289	3240	540	1258	1994	2157	1349	1642	2576	1487	1899	1654	2074	2056	2010	521	1192	2547	941	2092	

ENQUIRY: HOUSING IN BRASILIA

Study the three photographs (Figure 4.80) of housing conditions in Brasilia, (i) the Superquadros – self-contained apartment blocks for government officials and civil servants; (ii) high-quality housing near the lakeside of Lake Paranoa; (iii) housing in Nucleo Bandeirante – one of the satellite cities that house some 40% of Brasilia's workers.

1 Compare housing quality in the three areas (you could use a bi-polar semantic approach or a housing quality index).

2 Are the housing inequalities evident here an inevitable consequence of Brasilian society – regardless of the idealism of the new capital?

(i)   Superquadros

(ii)   High-quality housing, Lake Paranoa

(iii)   Housing, Nucleo Bandeirante

Figure 4.80   Housing conditions in Brasilia

SUMMARY ESSAY: A REVIEW OF BRASILIA

Brasilia was designed as a new capital because conditions in Rio de Janeiro made the old capital increasingly unable to discharge its function. Using all of the evidence from the material presented above, write a short review of Brasilia's success or failure as a capital. What recommendations would you make to improve its weaknesses as a capital city and the deficiencies in its quality of life?

Is this the end of the city?

The articles 'A capital case of British rot' and 'Electronic requiem for our cities' summarise the main thrust of this chapter. Read them thoroughly and use their contents as a broad structure for an essay on the topic 'Do our cities have a future?'

A CAPITAL CASE OF BRITISH ROT

Until now, cities in acute economic decline have been in a minority. Their problems have often been serious and have taken a heavy toll in social and political turbulence (witness the rise of Militant in Liverpool and, separately, the tensions of Toxteth). But it has been reasonable to think of them as having specific problems in need of specific solutions. Liverpool and Glasgow, for example, found themselves stranded on the wrong side of Britain when our main trade route switched from the Atlantic to the Straits of Dover.

What is now happening carries an awesome potential. Liverpool, Glasgow and Detroit might prove to be not extremes, to be pitied, subsidised and isolated, but harbingers of general urban decline. So far the evidence is anecdotal rather than statistical, but it points remorselessly in one direction.

Here is a parochial example. Until, say, 10 years ago, I would have had to spend most of my working week in London. Now, with my fax machine and my computer modem, I can both receive and send information electronically. This column is not only being written but, in effect, typeset at home. After being processed by the newspaper's features staff, it is transmitted to printing plants in Portsmouth, Bradford and Northampton. Modern technology has made modern journalism infinitely more flexible than it used to be. The result has been something close to a collapse in the number of jobs printing and typesetting newspapers in London.

Here is another, less parochial, example. Last September, the United States' fifth largest insurance company, New York Life, opened a new claims office – in a small town in Ireland's County Kerry. It does not deal with Irish, or even European, claims, but with American customers. Every day claims letters are air-freighted to the new office, where they are processed. The replies are transmitted by computers and satellite back to New York, where they are printed and posted to claimants.

More routinely, many organisations, from banks to Civil Service departments, find that modern technology makes it possible to separate policy work (which often still needs to be done in a major city, but which employs few people) from administrative and clerical work (which can now be done almost anywhere and employs many people). This is opening the way to some remarkable cost savings. Rent and business rates, now running at £60 a square foot for a modern office in the City of London, can be reduced to £20 by moving to the suburbs and £12 or less west of Swindon. In rent and rates alone it is £1 a week cheaper to keep a wastepaper bin in Bristol than in Throgmorton Street.

This lethal combination of technology and economics poses a severe threat to cities like London. Their main attraction – indeed, their main purpose – is as centres of employment. It used to be the case that goods and services could be provided more efficiently if the people who supplied them worked closely together. Cities offered their residents a bargain: we shall provide the work and the wealth if you put up with the dirt and the danger.

As long as enough people had to choose between city and poverty, this was an offer millions could not refuse. Now, increasingly, they can and do. Wherever it becomes possible for people, and cheaper for employers, to transfer work elsewhere, many will choose – are already choosing – to do so. Suddenly the centuries-old rationale for cities is vanishing. Residents depart, their retreat sounded not by trumpets but by the warble of electronic pulses.

Two sets of consequences ensue. The first concerns cities themselves. Unless they become cleaner, safer and more attractive, they will spiral into a destructive decline, with their contracting populations increasingly polarised between rich and poor. Shortages of key people, such as teachers and nurses, will become endemic. Local public finances will suffer, and public services will decline.

Racial tensions will increase. Already black and Asian Britons are concentrated in the poor parts of inner cities. They live in worse houses, go to worse schools and have worse career prospects than whites. They will have fewer chances to join the flight from the cities; instead they are likely to become a larger and larger proportion of the residents who get left behind.

The second set of consequences concerns the places that are already growing, and likely to expand further. The pressures on the south-east of England are already immense. If many more homes are built, the character of towns and villages will change, in some ways for the worse. But if not enough are built, then the price of housing will escalate, upsetting the balance of today's country communities and deterring some of the very people, such as teachers and nurses, who are needed to sustain a high quality of life. Some of the long-term problems of city life will reach out to the suburbs and beyond; in parts of the south-east they are already doing so.

As far as I am aware, nobody is suggesting that these large strategic matters can be settled purely by market forces. Wherever markets have had too much influence in urban development (especially in the United States), the results have been disastrous. Here in Britain, the most committed Thatcherite MPs would think twice before suggesting that developers have untrammelled power to turn their home counties constituencies into a concrete moonscape of houses, shops and offices.

Instead, some kind of long-term planning is needed. The P-word, I know, causes dread on the right and, these days, nervousness on the left. It should not. Every successful organisation looks at its future environment and works out how to adjust to it. Not to look, and not to plan, is to risk disaster. I doubt whether anyone could offer a detailed plan for the future of city – and non-city – life at this moment. Some of the forces at work are too new to have been fully charted. My point at this stage is simpler but more urgent: just as with the ozone layer and the greenhouse effect, some large changes in policy and behaviour may be needed, and we do not have much time to get it right.

Source: *Independent*, 7 August 1989

ELECTRONIC REQUIEM FOR OUR CITIES

Peter Kellner

Is your city really necessary? Last week I argued here that London had become a tatty, unpleasant place, and that this helped to explain why people like me had moved out. My article provoked readers into a variety of responses, but two themes recurred: that a London-is-nasty article could have been written at any time during the last 200 years; and that many other cities are also shoddy.

Both points are right, of course. In some ways London is more civilised (although in other ways less so) than in Dickens's time: fewer drunks fall in the Thames these days and more fish swim up it. But there is nothing we can do today about the state of Victorian London. We start from where we are now.

As to the why-pick-on-London argument: it is by far the biggest British city, and this fact alone magnifies its problems. But, yes, many of its problems apply to other cities. What is more, these problems are likely to get worse. Social forces already at work will have a startling impact on the lives of hundreds of millions of people throughout the world.

Until recently, cities globally were things that grew. In most of the third world they still are. In 1950 Africa had only one city (Cairo) with a population of more than one million; by 2000, according to the latest United Nations estimate, there will be 60. Across the Atlantic, Mexico City's population has doubled to 20 million in less than 20 years, and is likely to reach 30 million by the turn of the century.

Cities in the developed world also used to grow inexorably; but no longer. London's population is now 20 per cent below its peak (8.6 million in 1939). Its decline, which has accelerated since the 1960s, has been matched elsewhere. Examples include Birmingham, Paris, Hamburg, New York and Chicago.

Other cities, dominated for generations by smokestack industries, have declined even faster. Liverpool's population is now 470,000, 40 per cent less than in 1951. Manchester's population has fallen by 37 per cent and Glasgow's by 34 per cent during the same period. America's Motown – Detroit – has experienced a 41 per cent loss, from 1.9 to 1.1 million, since 1950.

Two distinct forces have been at work. Some people choose to commute further to work. In cities like London and New York the contraction of the urban population has been matched by an increase in the numbers living in the outer suburbs and towns and villages 20-50 miles away. The host city has lost residents in far greater numbers than it has shed jobs. The second trend, seen in Glasgow, Liverpool and Detroit, is for economic decline to prompt a sharp reduction of job opportunities. Here, a flight to suburbia has been compounded by an exodus to find work elsewhere.

Source: *Independent*, 14 August 1989

5
Changing Agricultural Systems

Global Issues in Agricultural Geography

Sudden impact

'If you go down to the woods today, you're sure of a big surprise' – Splat! Sudden Impact! You won't find a teddy bears' picnic on this Hertfordshire farm. Instead, you will be watching or taking part in an action-packed survival game over 25 acres of farmland. This is how the brochure describes your 40-minute game: 'Feel the adrenalin pump through your veins as you and your team-mates, equipped with splatmaster guns, battle to capture the "enemy" flag, rescue a leading politician from armed captors or capture a bridgehead!'

Survival games on 'set-aside' farmland around our major towns and cities are growing in importance, as farmers respond to changes in society. This British issue is part of a wider chain of events that links eco-development and the diversity of products produced in tropical rainforests to the diversification of agriculture in Europe. What are the links between farmers in the economically more- and economically less-developed worlds? How do these links affect us and the environment around us? We shall be trying to answer questions like this in Chapter 5

The agricultural chain

What did you have for breakfast today? We could ask this question anywhere in the world and the answer would be different every time. The point about breakfast, or any meal, is that the food we consume is part of the 'agricultural chain'. At the simplest level this is a chain of events linking the cultivation of crops or tending of livestock to the bowl of muesli or plate of bacon on our breakfast table. The chain can be a relatively simple one if the farmer's family eats all that it grows. If the rural community was characterised by this type of chain, we would call them 'subsistence farmers'. On the other hand, the chain might be extremely complex if it involved different people in the growing, collection, packaging and distribution of foodstuffs. If one company, like Birds Eye, was involved in all of these activities then we might say that farming was characterised by agribusiness. It is important to remember that the chain is not just about food production – it can also involve a multitude of products (see 'Fruits of the forests'). Products that are cultivated are not always consumed by those that need them most; there are risks of food contamination at the growing and packaging stages; population or business pressures may affect either end of the chain.

BRAINSTORMING

1 Read the articles on pages 204-205. How do the ideas expressed in these articles fit into the concept of an 'agricultural chain'? What are the limitations of these ideas?

2 Make a list of the 'fruits of the forest'. How important are these forest products? Why are they being destroyed? Working in pairs, suggest what could be done to check this destruction.

3 Why did the EC encourage the stockpiling of surplus food in the past? Produce a list of arguments, for and against GATT, that you think farmers in the economically less developed and economically more developed world might use.

PRACTICAL ENQUIRY

Working in pairs, visit a supermarket on a 'family shopping expedition' (make up your own shopping list) and try to find the place of origin and of processing and packing of the products you would have purchased. Present your findings using an annotated map. Outline the likely environmental impacts at each stage of the chain that you are able to identify.

FRUITS OF THE FORESTS

• A potential treasure trove of plants is going up in smoke. Norman Myers reports

DOWN TO EARTH

When the new Director of Kew Gardens, Dr Ghillean Prance, returned from Amazonia recently, he brought with him a suitcaseful of rainforest plants for Anita Roddick, the enterprising head of Body Shop. They were potential sources of new fragrances and perfumes. If just one were to go into production, it could transform the fortunes of its habitat, giving it a considerable – and more importantly a sustainable – economic value.

With a little management, plant products like these, small in volume but high in value, can be harvested without damaging either the species themselves or the rainforests where they grow; and there is no reason why the harvesting should not go on indefinitely. To exploit them would therefore be a very different matter from the other kind of exploitation in these parts, the clearing of the forest for cattle pastures and other agriculture.

There are thousands of such plants. According to Brazilian scientists, fewer than 200 of Amazonia's 30,000 plant species (two-and-a-half as many as in the whole of Europe) have been assessed for their potential contributions to modern industry and medicine. Yet as far back as 1979, Brazil's exports of essential oils and other perfumery compounds and associated resinoids were worth $21.5 million.

So why are the fruits of the tropical forests not being extracted? Why are these potential pharmaceuticals factories being put to the torch? Why, when the forests offer a sound economic argument for their conservation, are they still being ravaged?

The potential is not limited to chemist's products. The rainforests offer myriad sources of new foods... In western Amazonia a team of American scientists, headed by Dr Charles Peters of the New York Botanical Garden, has found that an acre of forest can generate a sustainable harvest of wild fruits, rubber, fibres, natural oils and medicinal plants with six times the commercial value that would be achieved through logging...

More extensive assessment in India shows that non-wood forest products have been accounting for well over 50 per cent of the value of all forest products.

The best way to engage in methodical harvesting of these self-renewing products is through 'extractive reserves' of the sort pioneered by the late Chico Mendes in Brazil. In 11,000 square miles in just the Amazonian state of Acre more than 13,000 people have been harvesting wild rubber and other products, supplying an annual income far above what could be derived through cattle ranching and small-scale agriculture.

Yet of Acre's 59,000 square miles of

Figure 5.1   Brazil: tilling the land

forest, well over 2,000 have been destroyed and another 11,500 grossly degraded in the past few years. The problem is not confined to Brazil; it applies throughout the tropical forests, largely due to the Cinderella status of 'minor forest products', as they are still termed...

The fault lies not with the forests, but with experts' perceptions. Until the shades fall from the eyes of forestry leaders, the forests themselves will continue to fall. Commercial timber, unfortunately, supplies a pretty solid beam.

Source: *Sunday Times*, 14 October 1989

FARMERS PAY PRICE OF RICH HARVEST

British farmers face "fines" totalling £200 million from the Common Market and an automatic cut in the support price of cereals next year as part of their reward for bringing in this year's harvest.

Although this year's crop is expected to be substantially below the record 26.6 million tons of 1984, it is expected to top 22 million tons,

roughly the same as last year, and contribute to a Common Market harvest of more than 160 million tons.

At this level, farmers suffer stiffer penalties under the so-called co-responsibility levy scheme designed by the EC Commission in Brussels to curb production and pay for the disposal of surpluses. The latest penalties, based on this year's crops,

take effect next season.

Britain's farmers are expected to have to pay just over £10 a ton in levy, about £3 more than this year's charge, on 19 million tons of cereals. They are exempt from levy on crops grown for seed and for grain used on the farm as animal food.

Source: *Daily Telegraph*, 10 August 1991

A NEW DEAL FOR PEOPLES AND THE LAND

The 1992 GATT (General Agreements on Trade and Tariffs) have strongly encouraged European farmers to trade freely in the world's agricultural markets and carry out a radical reform of the CAP (Common Agricultural Policy) (see article below). GATT has been trying to secure a fairer deal for farmers outside Europe. This has been partially achieved by reducing the level of government financial support that farmers in the economically developed world once used to enjoy. The new support system which has emerged is very controversial: it is now paying farmers to be better custodians of the landscape instead of producers of surpluses. One example of the changes is 'set-aside'.

Set-aside was first introduced in the EC in 1985. Until 1992 farmers could withdraw (voluntarily) a minimum of 20% of their land from arable production for five years receiving compensation in return. Under the May 1992 arrangements the minimum is 15% and unless farmers withdraw this amount they will not be eligible for the annual cereal subsidy. In effect many farmers feel they have been forced into the scheme. They also have to meet the costs of mapping their land as up-to-date maps are required before any grants are given.

Land under set-aside may be kept fallow with green cover as well as grazed or converted to woodland. Farmers may also use the land for tourism or as a game or nature reserve. Land must be maintained in good agricultural condition and there are restrictions on the use of fertilisers and pesticides.

CAP in the 1980s – Mountain Madness

Mountain madness was the result of the CAP in the 1980s. In Britain in 1985 there were 200 warehouses, as big as cathedrals, where thousands of tonnes of beef, butter, cereals and skimmed milk were kept, not in readiness to feed famines, but for release when the market was right. Produced by subsidy and stored at the taxpayer's expense, the surpluses were often wasted because the price was never right. In 1983 the EEC spent £7 million disposing of its over-production. Every minute of the year, from 1983–1984 the amount of food destroyed from intervention stocks included: apples 134 lb, apricots 2091 lb, Cauliflowers 4 lb, oranges 5266 lb, peaches 1579 lb, pears 53 lb, tomatoes 19 lb.

In the same year as Live Aid focused on famine in Ethiopia there were 3.2 million tonnes of cereals stored in 130 warehouses in the UK; 30 000 tonnes of beef; 58 000 tonnes of butter and 32 000 tonnes of skimmed milk powder.

The mountains existed because the CAP guaranteed a certain price to farmers for milk, beef, grain, peas, beans, etc. buying all that they could produce. What farmers grew was not determined by people's needs or demands but by profit margins unrelated to the real situation. It was all connected with power politics: rich countries storing food and people in the Third World dying of starvation.

BITTER HARVEST

The Samaritans estimate that farmers are now killing themselves at the rate of 200 a year. According to the last survey made by the Office of Population Censuses and Surveys – covering the years 1979 to 1983 – farmers were even then twice as likely to commit suicide as the average member of the population. It was the second most common cause of death among farmers between the ages of 15 and 44, whereas 10 years earlier it had been the sixth. Farmers are second only to doctors in terms of occupational risk of suicide....

Something is wrong in the countryside. For those of us who make up the 98 per cent of the population outside the farming community, it does not mean much, yet the malaise behind the suicide figures affects all of us. The issue matters more in Europe, where most people have some farming connection, an uncle in the south, a cousin in Bavaria... Here, more than 30,000 farmers have left the land in the past 10 years, and over 10,000 farm workers are departing every year.

Nor are farmers a uniform group. There are still agri-businessmen... who can now set aside 15 per cent of their land for £208 a hectare; and part-timers who keep sheep as a hobby. Many dairy farmers admit to doing reasonably well. But there is a majority who are not: tenant farmers, and landowners who, once encouraged to borrow for investment, carry massive mortgages.

For these farmers, their income is often less than half what it was in the good years before 1984. In 1991 interest payments alone on loans to agriculture added up to £1 billion, the equivalent of the total borrowing 10 years earlier. [Farmers'] spendable income is no longer coming out of profits but from precarious overdrafts. In the past two years they have had to comprehend the reforms of the CAP, the implications of the talks on GATT and the effects of more than 260 pieces of legislation. Exhorted to intensify since the last war, they now find themselves a target for stringent new controls on environmental pollution and animal welfare...

Edwina Currie's remarks about eggs, the alarming revelations about "mad cow" disease, BSE, have damaged the public's view of the farmer, already diminished by the animal welfare lobby and conservationists. Much of the criticism currently levelled at farmers is undoubtedly true. But much of it is not.

When Jackie Samuels, from Ledbury, near Hereford, saw a magazine article about the BSE scare... she felt she had to do something. Sparking with anger, she says "BSE wasn't *in* beef cattle. It isn't now. It's in the dairy herd. Yet when did anyone think twice about drinking milk, even at the height of the scare? No, it was beef they stopped buying."

So she founded a group called Agricultural Awareness, to challenge such misconceptions and look at the reality behind the scare stories....

Source: *Sunday Times Magazine*, 1 November 1992

Agriculture modifies the natural world

We can use statistics to try to investigate the pattern of global agriculture. Statistical information is often collected by the governments of the countries concerned and published by organisations like the United Nations or World Bank. A word of warning about such statistics: the accuracy of the information can vary a great deal – some of it may be falsified for political purposes and much of it may be incomplete. The statistics shown in Table 5.1 are, however, unlikely to be subject to any sort of bias. Why?

Agriculture modifies the natural world. It is important to understand how the natural world operates if we are to understand agricultural problems and processes. Paterson's Index of Plant Productivity is one way of investigating these links. The index allows us to calculate, for a specified area, the level of natural plant productivity (without any human intervention) and contrast this with the actual pattern of agricultural productivity. The hypothesis that we are trying to test is 'is there a significant relationship between natural plant productivity and agricultural productivity?'. If agriculture is in step with what is happening in the natural world, then we might expect only a little modification of existing natural environments. On the other hand, if agriculture is less closely linked to natural processes, then we may expect to see more dramatic environmental impacts.

Table 5.1   Climatic data for the calculation of the plant productivity index

Continent	Place	Map number	Temperature (°C)	Precipitation (mm)	Growing season (months)	Solar radiation (%)	Annual range of average temperature between coldest and warmest months (°C)
South America	Manaus	1	28.2	1771	9	41	1.7
	Rio de Janeiro	2	26.1	1099	9	44	5.7
	Buenos Aires	3	23.1	962	12	49	13.7
	Medellin	4	22.0	1493	12	42	1.4
	Arica	5	22.8	1	0	44	6.6
	Santiago	6	20.4	350	5	48	12.8
	Tucuman	7	24.9	959	7	46	12.9
North America	New Orleans	8	27.4	1460	12	50	15.1
	Memphis	9	26.7	1212	12	50	21.9
	Chicago	10	23.1	833	8	54	26.8
	Edmonton	11	16.3	435	7	66	30.6
	Phoenix	12	31.9	198	0	50	21.5
	Baffin Island	13	8.3	422	4	81	36.3
	Acapulco	14	28.3	1380	5	43	2.9
Africa and Middle East	Yaundé	15	23.3	1579	10	41	2.1
	Freetown	16	26.6	4431	8	42	2.5
	Mombasa	17	27.7	1217	9	41	3.4
	Aswan	18	30.0	180	0	44	13.0
	Algiers	19	25.3	765	7	49	18.3
	Beira	20	27.4	1567	6	44	7.4
	Luderitz	21	20.4	23	0	44	7.1
	Lamu	22	27.4	775	5	41	3.7
	Pretoria	23	21.4	660	3	45	10.3
Europe and CIS	Paris	24	18.6	328	10	60	16.1
	Seville	25	29.4	471	6	50	18.2
	Catania	26	26.4	533	6	50	15.6
	Moscow	27	18.0	615	7	67	28.8
	Kabul	28	24.8	285	2	49	25.5
Asia	Mangalore	29	29.5	3251	7	43	2.6
	Darjeeling	30	16.4	1050	8	46	11.9
	Bangkok	31	28.6	1487	8	43	4.8
	Manila/E.Indies	32	29.6	1927	8	43	3.6
	Tomsk	33	17.8	478	5	68	37.2
	Verkhoyansk	34	15.1	128	3	85	65.2
	Beijing	35	26.0	633	9	52	30.7
Australia	Darwin	36	29.9	1545	6	42	4.7
	Melbourne	37	19.8	646	10	51	10.5
	Alice Springs	38	28.5	276	0	45	17.0
	Perth	39	23.3	878	6	48	10.5
	Marble Bar	40	33.8	330	1	41	14.6

STATISTICAL ENQUIRY

You will need a calculator for this exercise. Work in groups of three or four.

1 Calculate Paterson's Plant Productivity Index (I) for the areas shown in Figure 5.1. To save time, split the calculations equally between the people in your group. Use the formula below:

$$I = \frac{Tm \times P \times G \times S}{1200 \, (Tr)}$$

where Tm = temperature of the warmest month
P = precipitation in mm
G = growing season in months
S = amount of solar radiation
Tr = annual range of average temperature between coldest and warmest months
1200 = constant value

2 Using the rating zones below (and a tracing of the base map, Figure 5.1), produce a choropleth map of I.

Index Value	Product zone rating
5000+	A
1000–4999	B
300–999	C
100–299	D
25–99	E
0–24	F

3 Compare your map with the map (Figure 5.2) showing zones of actual agricultural potential for different agricultural regions (the method used to construct this map was to award a maximum of 4 points for each of the following: relief suitability; soil adequacy; temperature adequacy; precipitation adequacy; precipitation distribution; weather reliability; market accessibility. Make a list of the major contrasts. What reasons can you think of to explain these differences?

4 Can we accept or reject our original hypothesis? What are the weaknesses of Paterson's Plant Productivity Index? Discuss this in your groups and try to suggest some suitable modifications.

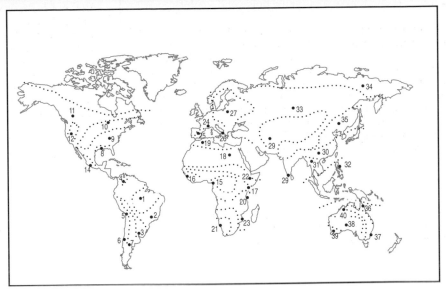

Figure 5.1   Base map

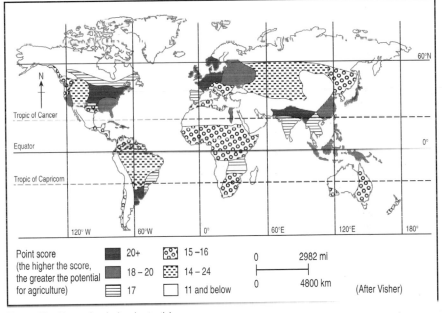

Figure 5.2   Zones of agricultural potential

The changing countryside

In this country the great majority of us only come into direct contact with agricultural activity when we use the rural landscape. Driving, walking, riding, sailing or jogging through the countryside can give people enormous pleasure. However, we may rarely see the farmer who has created and managed the environment that we are using. Popular rural areas are visited by thousands of people during holiday periods and at weekends: in August 1988 police closed the A66, a main routeway into the Lake District, after the area was overwhelmed by visitors on a sunny bank holiday.

Modern farming methods have a great deal to do with landscape change and agricultural impact. If you read John Betjeman's poem 'Harvest Hymn' (see Figure 5.3) you will be able to recognise some of today's trends and problems. It is important to remember that people's perceptions of landscape have changed through time. Yi-Fu Tuan, writing in 1961, has pointed out that: 'In the course of time Europeans have viewed mountains as the dwelling place of Gods, ugly blemishes on the smooth body of the earth, sublime scenery, or health and tourist resorts.' In the past, a 'tamed' countryside of orderly farms and gardens was highly valued; a remote, untouched landscape was not. Even with industrialisation in Britain, and

Harvest hymn
(sung to 'We plough the fields and scatter')

We spray the field and scatter
   The poison on the ground
So that no wicked wild flowers
   Upon our farm be found.
We like whatever helps us
   To line our purse with pence;
The twenty-four-hour broiler-house
   And neat electric fence.

All concrete sheds around us
   And Jaguars in the yard,
The telly lounge and deep-freeze
   Are ours from working hard.

We fire the fields for harvest,
   The hedges swell the flame,
The oak tree and the cottages
   From which our fathers came.
We give no compensation
   The earth is ours today
And if we lose on arable,
   then bungalows will pay.

All concrete sheds . . .
John Betjeman

Figure 5.3 *Harvest hymn*, John Betjeman

the movement of people to the cities, a strong attachment to the countryside has remained. More recently, environmental quality has become an issue of concern and now 'wildscapes' (see Figure 5.4) have come to be regarded as important unspoilt areas of land providing recreational release from urban lifestyles.

Figure 5.4 Wildscape

ENQUIRY: VIEWS OF THE COUNTRYSIDE

Study the information in Figure 5.5, taken from a Gallup Poll for the *Daily Telegraph*.

1 Chose a suitable graphical technique (bar chart, pie chart, etc.) to help represent this information.

2 What are the top 3 and bottom 3 'pleasures'? Do you agree with these ratings? Discuss your views with the rest of the class.

3 How closely related are the 'threats' and the 'farmers'?

4 Do you feel that the information collected from the survey has been fairly presented? Discuss your views.

5 How far are John Betjeman's sentiments echoed in the Gallup Poll results?

Pleasures		Threats				Farmers				Voters		
What we like		**What we fear**				**How we see them**				**How they split**		
	%		Is a threat	Is not	Don't know		Agree	Dis-agree	Don't know		Con. voters	Lab. voters
Countryside is more peaceful	71	Pollution of rivers, lakes and waterways	93	4	3	They are poisoning the land by using too many chemical fertilisers and such-like	79	12	10	Would prefer to live in the country	76	66
Like feeling of space	54	Farmers using too many herbicides and pesticides	87	8	5	They pollute the country's rivers by allowing pesticides, slurry and waste to run into them	77	11	12	Associate Britain more with cities	29	40
Like trees and forests	50	Acid rain	80	9	11	They produce high-quality food at reasonable cost	58	29	14	Say their families' roots are in the countryside	48	36
Like flowers and wildlife	48	New housing developments	77	18	5	They are very efficient	54	23	22	Live in a city	17	27
Countryside more natural	46	The building of new motorways	76	21	3	They pay their workers badly	52	18	29	Share the view that the countryside is in danger	72	82
There aren't as many people	42	Too much traffic	73	23	4	They do not take sufficient precautions to make sure the food they produce is clean and free of disease	46	36	17	Regard acid rain as a threat to the countryside	74	85
Like mountains	29	Farmers digging up hedgerows	63	29	7	Because of changes in policies from London and Brussels, many farmers are suffering	46	24	30	Believe Britain's farmers produce high-quality food at reasonable cost	65	54
The country hasn't changed as much as towns and cities	24	Too many people moving into the country from towns and cities	48	45	7	The subsidies they receive from the British Government and the European Community are too big	35	33	32	Believe the Government is not doing enough to protect the countryside	74	91
Like feeling in touch with the past	19	The planting of non-traditional plants like rape or conifer trees	37	49	15					Are concerned enough about the countryside to consider voting for another party in a General Election	31	42
Like farms and farming	16	Too many visitors and tourists	35	57	8							
Like fishing	11											
Like hunting or shooting	3											
Source: *Daily Telegraph*, 14 August 1989												

Figure 5.5 Views of the countryside

In many parts of the world the countryside is a *place of work* for the majority of the population rather than a recreational resource. For some communities their experience of rural areas is their only environmental experience. In some areas only a few farmers will have visited towns or cities and their relationship with the land is to do with physical exertion, toil, sweat and often hunger, rather than personal feelings. In areas where the environment is hostile farmers and their families may be involved in a daily struggle for survival. They may have to face problems ranging from flood, famine, drought and disappearing soils to encroaching desert and locust plagues. The whims of the commodity markets, for example, a change in the price of coffee or sugar in London, may bring poverty for thousands of farmers.

SYNTHESIS

1 Look carefully at the newspaper reports ('Aid today, but what tomorrow?' and 'Poor pay the price') and the cartoons in Figures 5.6 and 5.7. Make a list of the main problems faced by agriculturalists in the Third World. What 'other' problems exist that are not described by these sources?

2 Agricultural change brings with it modifications to the countryside. How do the problems you have outlined show themselves in the rural landscape? What can be done to reduce their impact in the short and long term?

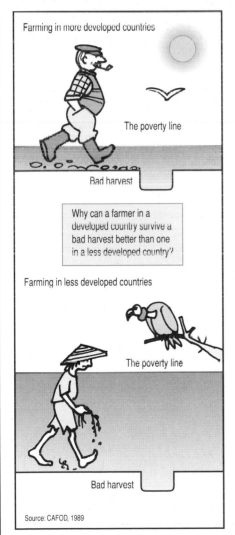

Figure 5.6 Bad harvests in developed and less developed countries

Farming in more developed countries

The poverty line

Bad harvest

Why can a farmer in a developed country survive a bad harvest better than one in a less developed country?

Farming in less developed countries

The poverty line

Bad harvest

Source: CAFOD, 1989

AID TODAY, BUT WHAT TOMORROW?

FAROUK EL-BAZ

IF a picture is worth a thousand words, a televised report is worth a million. Films of the drought disasters in Ethiopia, the Sudan, Mozambique, and other African countries are heart-wrenching. Almost as disturbing are the perceptions of cause and effect that pervade most comments on the situation. . .

We are repeatedly told that it is the nomads in these parched lands that ruin the environment. They misuse the land, we are told, chop down the trees and allow their animals to overgraze. Thus, the place becomes a desert. . .

[This] suggests that the people that live in the dry parts of the world ruin their environment because they do not understand it. With this assumption goes the arrogant notion that academics and development planners know the desert better than local inhabitants do. It insinuates that our new technologies and scientific techniques can surely fix it. . .

Today's deserts used to be kinder places in which there was life.

Once there was rain. Then the clouds gradually disappeared. These places dried up and were deserted by plants, animals and man. The deserts are where they are because of the rhythmic patterns of global circulation of air masses in the earth's atmosphere, which are fueled by energy from the sun. . .

Today's misery in the arid lands of Ethiopia and Mozambique is caused by an enduring drought.

The answer is not 'aid projects' that result in settling of the nomads around overcrowded towns as happened following the drought in the Sahel a decade ago. . .

Rain in the geologic past left behind vast areas of arable land that may be hidden by sheets of sand. Some of that rain water seeped through the rock to be stored in giant underground aquifers. Today, we have the means for locating such hidden resources.

Nasa's space shuttle is useful in this area. In November 1981 a shuttle-borne radar instrument unraveled the terrain beneath the sands in the southern reaches of the western desert of Egypt. In an area that is now bone-dry without a single blade of grass, the radar revealed ancient river courses as wide as the Nile Valley. Nearby a region was selected to drill for water. Eight wells were dug and all brought fresh water from depths between 25 and 250 feet. Today there is an experimental farm that may be the nucleus for a vast agricultural settlement in this parched land. . .

We should study the ways of desert nomads and try to reinstate their age old practices and desert-born wisdom. Nomads roam the land followed by their meagre herds not because they are a restless lot. They do so because theirs is the only way of using the scarcest and most inconsistent of resources: rain. In the desert, when it rains, it does so in one small place and not in others. And when the occasional rain clouds return, it rains in some other place. Desert dwellers have developed a remarkable sensitivity to such happenings.

The Bedouin also know when to make their animals stop grazing to preserve the range because they know that they will have to return to it someday.

We should accept the cyclic pattern of mother nature's moods. Part of the harvest in years of abundance should be stored for the lean years.

Source: *Guardian*, 6 December 1985

POOR PAY THE PRICE

Victor Keegan

BRITAIN – along with most of the rest of Europe – has had a bumper grain harvest this year and can look forward to a slowing down of inflation over the next 12 months... But a price fall for the industrialised countries (however temporary) means even lower incomes for Third World producers. And this at a time when their debt repayments are an increasing burden because of high interest rates and when countries like Britain are reducing their aid programmes.

To be forced to pay ever-increasing debt interest (and capital payments) out of diminishing income is a sure-fire formula for bankruptcy and social turmoil.

It is absolutely absurd that there is now a large (net) transfer of funds from developing to developed countries as the Third World pays the cost of high interest rates totally outside its own control. This may look good on the West's balance sheet but the mirror image of declining real incomes among the poorest nations in the world is bleak. A bit like curing haemophilia by demanding payment in blood...

The United States has a particular responsibility since it was the result of lax fiscal policy (causing the gargantuan US budget deficit) which pushed interest rates up so high. The vast majority of Third World debts are denominated in dollars.

The mirror image of Europe's bumper harvest... is falling per capita production of food grains in Africa below the Sahara and worsening famine.

The situation is helped by voluntary actions like [the] Live Aid programme. But this can only be temporary. Aid like this, though vital in an emergency, can undermine the even more vital business of putting local agriculture on a sounder footing. The reality is that local farmers have no incentive to invest in agriculture if they have to compete with 'free' grain from overseas.

Donor countries have been slow to realise that the most cost-effective aid is... projects which improve food output by the poor.

In other words, what Africa needs is a common agricultural policy of its own, one which encourages output of key commodities. Europe's CAP was remarkably successful in its pristine aim of removing the continent's post-war food shortages. But it has now grown into a nightmare for Europe and the Third World in which heavily subsidised over-production strains the EEC's budget to breaking point and shuts out agricultural produce which could be more economically grown in the Third World.

Of course, not everything which grows in Europe can be planted elsewhere. But the dismantling of the CAP is the nearest thing to a free lunch for everyone. European governments would have more tax revenues to spend on other things and consumers would benefit from much lower prices as imports were stepped up from outside.

Source: *Guardian*, 6 December 1985

Source: *New Internationalist*

Figure 5.7   The green revolution

DISCUSSION

1 Is it more important to think locally or globally when seeking solutions to Third World problems?

2 How useful are cartoons as a method of presenting environmental issues? What kind of audience might cartoons have?

3 To what extent are the images shown a fair representation of the farmer's fortunes?

In order to feed growing populations and to satisfy interest payments for increasing levels of foreign debt, many Third World countries have embarked upon a 'technological response' to the difficulties of farming. They have tried to use a range of new technologies to raise the low levels of productivity. The technology of the 'green revolution' (see Figure 5.7) has brought riches to some farmers and increased poverty to others. The new high-yielding varieties have also created their own environmental problems through the overuse of chemical pesticides, herbicides and fertilisers. Whilst productivity in some areas has increased, the cost has also soared. Farmers who have become too reliant on the new technologies may be subject to increasing levels of debt. The use of dangerously toxic agrochemicals has damaged the health of some farmers.

ENQUIRY: GLOBAL ISSUES

1 Using all the resources in this section and other relevant maps, books and periodicals, produce an annotated world map to show the major global issues in the geography of agriculture.

2 Using the evidence you gathered in **1** discuss in groups the major factors responsible for the most important issues. Try to produce a flow diagram to show the relationship between issues and factors.

3 'To understand global agriculture we must look beyond the natural world.' Use the resources from this section to help you write an essay on this topic. It may also be useful to consult some of the standard reference books (see Further Reading).

LOCAL RESEARCH ENQUIRY

1 Using Figure 5.8 as a starting point (it is possible for you to prepare a more detailed questionnaire) and working in pairs, conduct a local survey on attitudes to the rural landscape. Try to interview 10–20 people.

2 Using the data you have collected, write a report presenting and summarising your findings. Use graphical techniques to display your data and to investigate interrelationships.

3 How do your survey results match up with those from the *Daily Telegraph* Gallup Poll (page 208)?

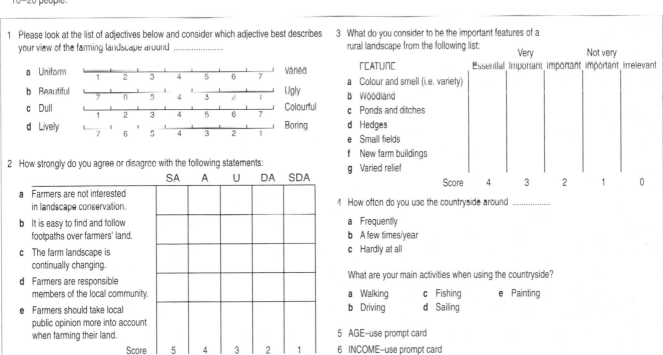

Figure 5.8 Local survey sheet

Understanding Agricultural Landscapes

Farming and the landscape

Agricultural geography is concerned with the description and understanding of farming activities. As we have already seen from the *Telegraph* Gallup Poll (Figure 5.5), farming has an impact on the rural landscape. The word 'landscape' needs a little consideration (see Figure 5.9). During the Middle Ages 'landscape' was the name given to a district owned by a

particular person or group and had nothing to do with the visible features of an area. It was not until people could travel more freely during the seventeenth and eighteenth centuries that a popular interest in landscape developed. Travellers wanted to record what different places looked like and did so by writing or painting. Our own response to the rural landscape is very personal. Often it can be related to a particular experience we may have had in the countryside or to

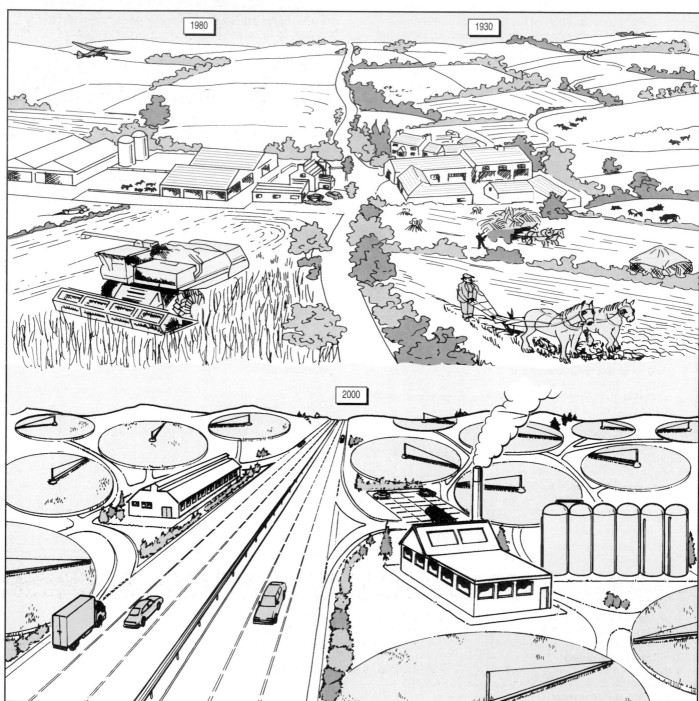

Figure 5.9   The farm – today, yesterday and in the future

an 'image' created by novelists or television programmes. For example, an enjoyable holiday can help us 'fall in love' with a landscape while programmes like 'Last of the Summer Wine' and 'All Creatures Great and Small' have helped to popularise the Yorkshire area.

Farming has expression in the landscape through particular enterprises: these enterprises may consist of crops, grasses and livestock products; they may be specialist producers, concentrating on one crop; or show signs of diversification. Enterprises may affect the size of farms and the shape, colour, noises and smell of fields as well as the structure and range of farm buildings. There are also elements of agricultural activity that may not be directly 'visible' in the landscape but are expressed through particular customs or rituals: for the Kayapos Indians of the Xingu region of Amazonia, the cultivation of the soil symbolises a bond between nature and society and the Kayapos clearly show this spiritual association through their stories, dancing and body painting (Figure 5.10). The Kayapos, like all cultivators, are essentially ecosystem managers although the way they use the tropical rainforests is very different from intensive cultivation of cereal crops in East Anglia. Different farming systems thus reflect the different management skills, expertise, investment, commitment and level of development of particular farming groups.

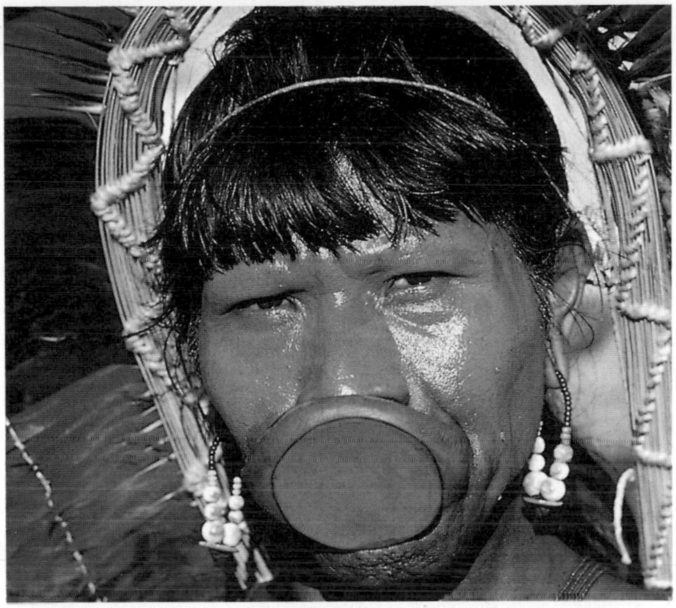

Figure 5.10 Kayapos – Amazonian Indians

ANALYSIS: FARMING AND THE LANDSCAPE

1 Study Figure 5.9. What appears to be the relationship between farming activities and the landscape?

2 How has the farmscape changed from 1930 to 2000? Make a list of the major differences. What possible reasons might there be for these changes?

3 Is it possible to measure the 'scenic value' of landscapes? One method is outlined in the chart. Use this method to try to evaluate the scenic value of Figures 5.4 and 5.9. You will need to estimate the area of the view in miles. Compare your results with the rest of the class. How valid is it to use an 'objective' method to measure 'scenic value'?

SVI = LC + NC − MC
where LC = landscape characteristics,
NC = natural characteristics,
and MC = artificial characteristics.
These characteristics are detailed in Table 5.2.

Table 5.2 Scenic value

	Scores* 5	4	3	2	1
Landscape characteristics					
Convex landforms	Dominant mountain or hill	Isolated mountain or hill	Variety	Somewhat repetitious	Monotonous repetition
Concave landforms	Dominant steep-walled canyon	Isolated canyon or valley	Variety	Somewhat repetitious	Monotonous repetition
Relief (feet)	>400	200–400	100–200	50–100	<50
Natural characteristics					
Land covered with indigenous vegetation and natural rock or soil (%)	80–100	60–80	40–60	20–40	0–20
Miles of natural stream per square mile	>8	4–8	2–4	1–2	<1
Artificial characteristics					
Number of buildings per square mile	<5	5–10	10–20	20–40	>40
Miles of road per square mile	<1	1–2	2–4	4–8	>8

* It is possible to weight these if required
Source: Keller, 1976

LOCAL ENQUIRY

Try to visit a number of local viewpoints overlooking agricultural landscapes, or look at a number of different slides. It would be useful to have an OS map of the relevant areas for this exercise. Use the SVI to evaluate these landscapes. How far do your views compare with others in the class, and is it possible to explain any similarities or differences?

Prior to visiting these sites, chose three pastel colours from a selection of 12 and whilst at the site produce an 'impression' of the landscape from one of the views. Compare and discuss these results. Which is a better personal record – the SVI or the pastel sketch?

DISCUSSION AND GROUP ENQUIRY

Read the extract from the various writers shown in 'Agricultural views'. What sentiments are being expressed here? How do these change with time? In groups of four write a sentence which summarises the views expressed in each extract. Next, rank this list of sentences in order of your group's strength of agreement. Conduct a classroom discussion to see who agrees with your top and bottom ranks.

Agricultural views

I like to look at the winding side of a great down with two or three numerous flocks of sheep on it, belonging to different farms: and to see, lower down, the folds in the fields, ready to receive them for the night . . . The sheep principally manure the land. This is to be done by folding, and to fold, you must have a flock. Every farm has its portion of down arable and meadow . . .
– W. Cobbett (1830) *Rural Rides* (Penguin, 1967)

Our countryside is like a multicoloured chequerboard. Its chief characteristic is its attractive patchwork appearance, with an infinite variety of small odd shaped fields of brown ploughland or green pasture, bounded by twisting hedges, narrow winding lanes, small woodlands and copses and isolated trees and hedgerow timber.
– G.M. Young (ed.) (1943), *Country and Town: A Summary of the Scott and Uthwatt Reports*, (Penguin)

Farm practice has, through generations of experience, been adapted to suit the natural environment, but there are of course other factors which influence the type of agriculture. Tradition, the character and outlook of the individual farmer, his capital resources, government policy and a number of external economic pressures bring about changes from time to time. Between 1935 and 1955, for example, many farmers turned to the production of liquid milk for sale in an area long associated with store rearing and some fattening. Since 1955 a number of men have changed back to cattle rearing, in response to a favourable demand for beef and to changes in the regulations governing the production of milk.
– W.M. Williams (1963), *Ashworthy: A West Country Village* (Routledge & Kegan Paul)

A new agricultural revolution is under way. If allowed to proceed unhindered, it will transform the face of England. Already a quarter of our hedgerows, 24 million hedgerow trees, thousands of acres of down and heathland, a third of our woods and hundred upon hundred of ponds, streams, marshes and flower rich meadows have disappeared. They have been systematically eliminated by farmers seeking to profit from a complex web of economic and technological change.
– Marion Shoard (1980), *The Theft of the Countryside*, Temple Smith, London

If British farming is so efficient, why does it need so much protection? Subsidies taken from public money make up something like two-thirds of farming's net income in Britain today. Yet even with subsidies running at almost £400 million per year, farm incomes are still well below those in other industries. Where is the efficiency here?
– P. Cheshire and J. Bowers (1969), *New Scientist*

The fact has got to be faced that farming is a backward industry by contrast with all other activities of the nation. If offers no opportunity to ability and ambition: it cannot retain its workers. The discoveries of science are too slowly applied; the experience of other industries and other countries is unheeded.
– C.S. Orwin (1942), *Speed the Plough* (Penguin)

Never mind the surpluses, just keep on producing as much as possible – that's the message to arable farmers from senior ADAS farm management adviser Bill Mitchell.
   He told Lincs and Humberside farmers last week to forget about reducing crop inputs to help cut Common Market surpluses.
   'Will the chap in Germany or France cut back if you do? The answer is no, so you get on and produce it,' he said.
– *Farming News*, 20 January 1984

'There'll always be an England, where there's a country lane.' This seems to me one of the bigger of the big lies invented by propaganda, but it is fervently believed . . . the rural self-depiction of the British is particularly strange because we were first nation to leave the land, and we did very well in material terms by doing so . . . when we British say how much we love country we are really saying that we want the best of both worlds. We want 'rus in urbe' – trees and gardens and peace and quiet; but we also want shops, electricity, telephones and fast roads.
– Adapted from Charles Moore, *Daily Telegraph*, 19 August 1989

'Countryside Chief warns of Green threat to farming': such was the *Financial Times's* somewhat sensation seeking headline . . . [about] . . . the speech given in January by Sir Derek Barber, the chairman of the Countryside Commission. Bearing in mind that he is first and foremost a farmer, with an estate in the Cotswolds, and that his audience consisted almost entirely of farmers, his critique of the Green movement's approach to farming was fairly standard and predictable: 'naive', 'insular' 'impractical' 'neurotic', 'non-scientific', 'lay-doomsters', 'hypochondriacs', and various other epithets thrown in for good measure. The main thrust of Sir Derek's speech was to question the move towards 'extensitication' on low input and organic farming systems. He contrasts such half-cocked farming with the 'high-pitched buzz production' of modern, intensive farming.
– Adapted from Johnathan Porritt, *Daily Telegraph*, 10 February 1990

The farm system

For all farmers the management of soil and grass ecosystems is a major concern.

Soil and grass management have also come to dominate the technical development of agriculture in the economically more developed world over the last 50 years. The story of George Stapledon (see 'Tsembaga, "Stapes" and Standbridge') and his important work on grasslands which led to the founding of the Welsh Plant Breeding Station near Aberystwyth are evidence of such involvement. Both the Tsembaga Maring and 'Stapes' would have recognised that good ecosystem management involves careful planning for 'seasonal rhythms'. These are the life cycles of particular crops and involve the farmer in sowing and harvesting, activities which affect labour demand and the time that equipment, seed and fertiliser must be used. The appearance of the landscape closely reflects these natural cycles. There are also non-seasonal rhythms, such as the need for twice daily milking, which can have similar effects.

Figure 5.11   Tsembaga Maring – Papua New Guinea

Tsembaga, 'Stapes' and Standbridge

Tsembaga

The Tsembaga Maring, who are shifting cultivators in the tropical rainforest of Papua New Guinea, have adapted land-use practices which are particularly siuted to local conditions. Crops are interplanted 'gardens' which allow for the slight variations in garden habitats to be taken into account and protects the thin tropical soil. Simple erosion control is carried out by placing logs along the contours of the slope to retain the soil. The regeneration of the forest is encouraged by the farmer, who removes useless weeds, but protects and encourages tree saplings which grow amongst his crop. Pig herds are kept, partly to provide a source of meat in the diet, but also as a status and religious symbol. Pigs graze parts of abandoned gardens, encouraging regeneration of secondary forest and fertilising the ground with their manure.
– Adapted from Bayliss-Smith, 1982

Stapes

Sir George Stapledon was part scientist, part wizard, part practical man, part poet. Stapledon bridged the gap between the old craft farming of the Norfolk four course rotation and the new industrial farming of fertilisers, chemicals and machinery by championing the grass ley. Rye grass and clover, examples of leys, when ploughed, release very large quantities of nitrogen essential to secure high yields of wheat and barley. By first fertilising the grasses with slag, and then allowing livestock to graze on the clover and manure it, Stapledon effectively manipulated the nitrogen cycle. As the first director of the Welsh Plant Breeding Station in Aberystwyth he searched the world for varieties and strains of grasses which could flourish. As a result, the first Aberystwyth bred grass was put on the market in 1932, and from then on the Station produced a stream of new ryegrasses, clovers, cocksfoots and timothys suitable far British farming.
– Adapted from Seddon, 1989

Stanbridge

Paul Stanbridge farms 446 acres of the north-west Hertfordshire countryside. Great Revel End Farm has doubled in size since 1970 while the number of fields has fallen from 25 to 12 during the same period. Stanbridge's main crops are wheats and oil-seed rape which are sold to merchants locally. The farm has been worked by the family for several generations. Stanbridge and his family provide the main labour input together with one full-time employee. Stanbridge is a great believer in the value of leys which occupy 21 acres of his arable farm. A three year ley mix is used to provide pasture for grazing and as hay for local riding schools. Soil fertility elsewhere is managed by using over 80,000 tonnes annually of nitrogen and herbicide. Soil erosion on the undulating clay and flints is a problem: Stanbridge's answer has been to plant one mile of new hedgerow.
– (For more detail on Stanbridge's farm see Figure 5.12 and Table 5.3).

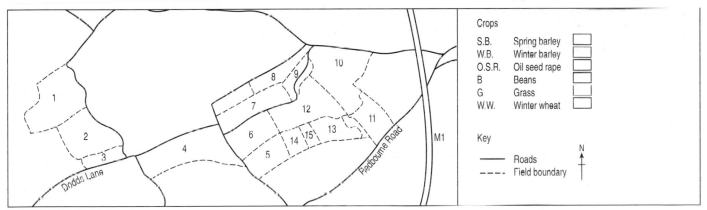

Figure 5.12   Great Revel End Farm (proposed cropping 1992–93)

Table 5.3   Great Revel End Farm accounts 1992–93

FIELD: ACRES CROP		SEED£	FERTS£	SPRAYS£	VC	YIELD	£/TONNE	£/ACRE	GM/ACRE	FC	PROFIT
1. RE27: 27	WW	19.95	42.36	30.12	92.43	2.8	113	316.4	223.97	110	113.97
2. AUBREY: 20	WW	20.21	41.48	30.9	100.59	2.7	110	297	196.41	110	86.41
3. BAIRNS: 20	WW	19.82	41.42	38.18	99.42	2.5	112	280	180.58	110	70.58
4. AGNELLS: 60	WW	20.34	35.38	37.25	92.97	2.6	113.5	295.1	202.13	110	92.13
5. CLARIES: 11	GRASS	10	38.34	0	48.34	3.5	40	140	91.66	110	–18.34
6. GADDS: 30	WW	19.43	40.91	48.36	108.7	2.5	112	280	171.3	110	61.3
7. MERRYC: 30	WW	19.43	40.91	36.16	96.5	2.7	110	297	200.5	110	90.5
8. LRE: 21	OSR	12.38	49.4	25.99	87.77	1.45	270	391.5	303.73	110	193.73
9. BIGP: 60	BEANS	25.92	8.26	7.53	41.71	1.4	170	238	196.29	110	86.29
10. RE35: 35	OSR	13.06	49.47	25.56	88.09	1.4	270	378	289.91	110	179.91
11. RE30: 30	OSR	12.7	52.32	25.22	90.24	1.3	270	351	260.76	110	150.76
12. EASTR: 40	SB	22.25	32.41	12.33	67.00	1.5	110	165	107.11	110	–2.89
13. DODDS: 10	SB	21.53	24.55	12.23	58.31	1.5	110	165	106.69	110	–3.31
14. NEWP: 42	WB	25.33	28.55	34.07	87.95	2.14	95	203.3	115.35	110	5.35
15. PARK: 10	PPAST	0	0	0	0	1.5	45	67.5	67.5	110	–42.5

TCINCOME	120 364.00	SPRAY TOTAL	11816.70	TCOSTS	84550.50	TFARM SIZE	446		AV. FC	110.00	
STOTAL	8657.89	VCTOTAL	35490.50	TPROFIT	35813.40	AV. INCOME/ACRE		269.87	AV. TCOST/ACRE		189.58
FTOTAL	15015.90	FCTOTAL	49060.00			AV. VC	79.58		AV. PROFIT/ACRE		80.30

Key
Field = field name
Crops: WW = winter wheat, OSR = oil seed rape, SB = sugar beet, PPAST = permanent pasture
Seed£ = cost seed per field acre
Ferts£ = cost fertiliser per field acre
Sprays£ = cost sprays per acre
VC = variable costs per acre
Yield = yield per acre
GM/Acre = gross margin per acre
FC = fixed costs

PROFIT = 35 813.40
FARM VALUE (£2500/ACRE) = 1 115 000
ROCE = 3.2%

PRACTICAL ENQUIRY

1   Using the information contained in Figure 5.12 and Table 5.3 select appropriate cartographic techniques to show the pattern of land-use and selected inputs and outputs. (If you have access to a spreadsheet or graphics package in school it may be possible to use this to help you with your investigation.)

2   What is the relationship between inputs and outputs? Use a suitable statistical technique to test this relationship.

3   Produce a SWOT table showing the Strengths, Weaknesses, Opportunities and Threats for each of the case studies. An example is given below:

S	W
O	T

How similar are the farm systems? Explain your answer.

Where farming is predominantly a 'commercial' activity, food is produced for sale and farming is a means of earning a living, then it is rather more than ecosystem management. It is also the management of a manufacturing process through the careful use of inputs. The farm system (see Figure 5.13) has a number of distinctive features: parts or elements (buildings, land, machinery, etc.); the links between these; inputs and outputs. The farm operates as a planned economic system. The farmer has to decide what to produce and how to manage the available resources to achieve this. Some of the resources, such as the amount of land, the climate and the type of soil, are 'fixed'. The farmer only has limited influence over these. The farmer also has to consider how much capital is available and how this can be organised and what labour is necessary and where it can be obtained. These factors tend to be variable. He is also the person who decides on the physical layout of the farm and its general appearance. Farms are both managed ecosystems and economic systems (see Figure 5.14).

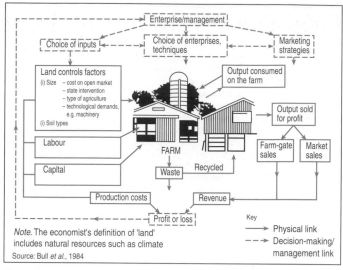

Note. The economist's definition of 'land' includes natural resources such as climate

Source: Bull *et al.*, 1984

Figure 5.13   The farm system

ENQUIRY

1 Study Figures 5.14 and 5.30.

  a Working by yourself, produce a table to show the main differences and similarities between natural and agricultural ecosystems.

  b Which of the two ecosystems do you think is more efficient? (To help you investigate efficiency you could use Figure 5.18)

  c What would be the likely effect of a sudden increase in 'pests' or 'urban people' in the agricultural ecosystems?

  d It would be possible to rearrange the agricultural ecosystem, although this may require a significant change in social attitudes. What particular attitudes may have to change and what could the new system look like?

2 Read 'Tsembaga, "Stapes" and Stanbridge' carefully. What was George Stapledon's major contribution to agricultural change? Why is grass 'difficult'?

3 Look at Figure 5.13. The boxes containing land, labour and capital are collectively known as the 'factors of production'.

  a Produce a table for each factor to show its most important aspects. Add details to show how each factor is regulated, changed or acquired. Some information has already been included in the 'land' box to help you.

  b What are the differences between the 'physical links' and the 'decision-making/management links'? How might a profit or loss affect the working of the system? What could a farmer do to reduce losses from one year to the next?

  c The farm system is characterised by 'feedback loops'. Feedback is the name that we give to the process where a change in one component of the farm system may lead to a change in others. If the change 'regulates' the farm system and keeps it in equilibrium then this is known as

'negative feedback'. However, if the changes disrupt the farm and eventually lead to its destruction, then this is called 'positive feedback'. How could these two different types of feedback operate on the farm system?

4 The farm system is a part of a much larger 'agricultural system' within any given country. Figure 5.15 tries to show the relationship between these two systems.

  a Working in pairs, try to produce a flow-line diagram like Figure 5.12 for an agricultural system in an economically more-developed country. What differences would you find in the agricultural system of an economically less-developed country?

  b What effect might 'scale' have on agricultural investigations?

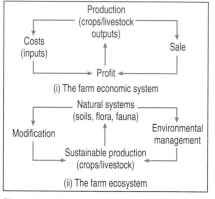

(i) The farm economic system

(ii) The farm ecosystem

Figure 5.14   Simple systems

GROUP ENQUIRY

1 Using Figure 5.15 'The agricultural system' as a starting point make a large sketch of the diagram and add the missing labels given below:
Economic limitations   Land tenure and organisation   Soils
Government action   Land-use decision
Access to market (transport costs)

2 Using this figure as a guide, re-draw the diagram to scale for farming in the USA, Brazil and Papua New Guinea. Do this by working out how important you think each of the outer rings (including Government action) is along a scale of 1 to 5 where 1 = a very small limiting factor and 5 = a major limiting factor. For example, if you give climate a score of 3, increase the size of the climate part of the physical limitations by 3 cms. Describe your results.

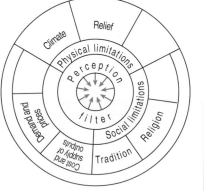

Figure 5.15   The agricultural system

CASE STUDY *The Farm of André Molines, Massif Central*

André Molines has never had a holiday. Now aged 60, he has left the Massif Central only once – to visit, briefly, a relative in Lyon. When asked if he wanted to move to another area where farming is easier and he could earn twice as much money as he does now, he smiles and shakes his head. Finiels, he replies, has all that he requires; there is no need to look elsewhere.

André Molines is the owner occupier of his farm. It has been a family farm for just over two hundred years and was given to the Molines family after the revolution of 1789. He cultivates an area of 113 hectares, renting some 60 hectares from the Parc National Cevennes (PNC). Since he has been running the farm he has tried slowly to increase its size and reduce the high level of land fragmentation. There are still 126 fields on the farm. In 1986 he purchased 18 hectares from his uncle (on his mother's side). Buying land is very difficult in this area: there are many small graveyards which cannot be touched and it is often impossible to trace the owners of small fragments which have become subdivided on inheritance several times down the generations.

The farm is classified as a pastoral enterprise: Molines has thirty cows and two bulls. It is the 'suckling cows' or young calves (there are eleven of these) that provide the farm with an important income. The market is Italian and the product is veal. In addition, there are twenty chickens, five pigs and some rabbits. These are for personal consumption. Labour is supplied by André and his family. André works 10–12 hours a day during winter, repairing and servicing machinery and checking on the health of his cattle, which are kept permanently in the large barn during this period. In the summer he may work 16 hours a day. The busiest time of year is July, when the whole family (his two sons, his wife and his parents) work late into the night cutting grass in the fields to provide a store of fodder for the long winters.

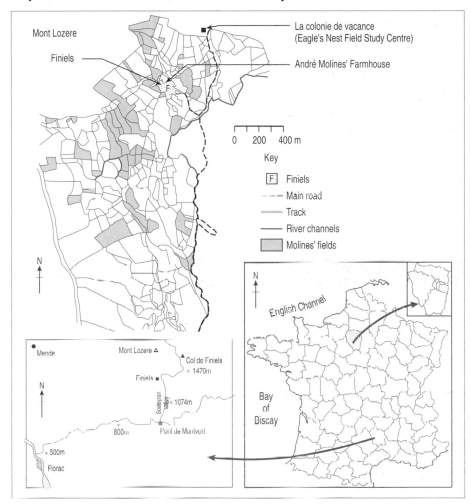

Figure 5.16   André Molines' land in the Souteyran Valley

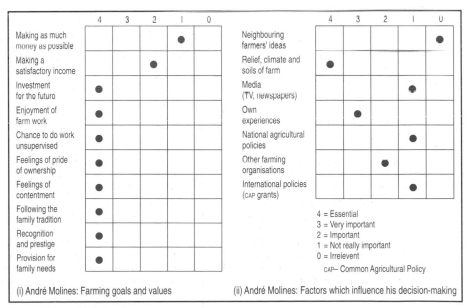

(i) André Molines: Farming goals and values

(ii) André Molines: Factors which influence his decision-making

4 = Essential
3 = Very important
2 = Important
1 = Not really important
0 = Irrelevent

CAP– Common Agricultural Policy

Figure 5.17   André Molines Farm

Physical characteristics of the farm

Relief
Undulating surface ranging from 1100 to 1450 m. The underlying rock is granite and the fields have emerged gradually as the granite boulders and stones have been cleared to form boundaries, although the largest boulders remain. The farmhouse is located at the bottom of the Souteyran Valley, the sides of which rise steeply to meet impressive granite tors.

Soils
Acidic – 4–5 pH. They are relatively well developed on the valley bottom but much thinner on the sides.

Climate
Mediterranean influence. This means hot, dry summers, with a mean temperature in July of 28˚C. Rainfall during the summer months is irregular and unpredictable with a mean total of 60 mm in July. Winters are cold with heavy snowfalls and strong, icy winds which effectively isolate the village and freeze water supplies for three months of the year. In February the mean temperature is 0.5°C and the mean rainfall 250 mm.

Personal characteristics

André Molines left school at 14. He then worked on the farm, studying at agricultural college during the winter months for four years. He still attends winter update courses. He has five children, two of whom intend to continue farming in the future.

Economic characteristics

Capital (variable)
Gross farm income (including all grants) was 150 000 francs (net 25 000 francs) in 1990. Total grants fell between 1991 and 1992 from 131 675 francs to 47 000 francs. Main income comes from the sale of animals. Recent attempts at diversification. Rents out skiing equipment in winter and offers accommodation. Major cash shortage in summer and winter before cattle are sold. Cash surplus in summer after sale.

Capital (fixed)
New barn – finished 1986. Cost 155 000 francs. Grant from EC for 80% of cost.

The main source of capital is the Credit Agricole – which has a monopoly on agricultural lending. There is talk of a change in this arrangement – M. Molines considers this ill-advised.

Machinery

Type	Purchase date	Cost (FF)
Tractor	1981	150 000
Tractor	1983	150 000
Baler	1981	40 000
Trailers (2)	1981	70 000
Transporter	1974	n/a
Truck	1982	30 000
Steam cleaner	1986	10 000
Grass cutter	1982	2500
Chainsaw	1986	8000
Snowplough	1981	10 000
Mill grinder	1979	5000
Muck spreader	1985	10 000

Grants
Grants used to come from three sources: the *Parc Nationale de Cévenne* (PNC), the French Government, and CAP. Money is still available from PNC, usually in the form of grants to encourage 'eco-development' e.g. to reintroduce traditional Aubrac cattle. Support from the French Government may come in the form of subsidies but few are available to mountain farmers. The CAP Mountain Grant disappeared on 1 January 1993.

Chemicals
Apart from cattle tick sprays, these are not used on the farm because M. Molines rejects them for environmental reasons. Slag from a steel works, rich in phosphates, and dung from the cattle are spread on the fields.

Land use
Cereals are planted over 14 hectares. Woodland (for fencing and fuel) accounts for 2 hectares. There are 40 hectares of pasture (for hay making) and 57 hectares of rough grazing.

Livestock sales
These are the only source of income.

Farm incomes (francs)

1980	126 000	1986	146 000
1981	138 000	1987	146 000
1982	144 000	1989	146 000
1983	158 000	1990	150 000
1984	174 000	1991	173 708
1985	149 000	1992	190 500

M. Molines points out that these fluctuations reflect changes in French government policy.

The energy question

One of the ways in which a farmer is linked to his or her crops and animals is by the flow of energy. Energy is the capacity to do work. One of the most important characteristics of energy is that it cannot be created or destroyed, only transformed. It is during this process of change that energy may be 'lost' from the farm system. Energy inputs in agriculture, which can come from solar radiation, human labour, the work of machines and applications of fertiliser and herbicide, can be converted into energy values. In the same way outputs from the system – various vegetable and animal products – can also be expressed

Table 5.4   Energy inputs and output for the Tsembaga Maring of Papua New Guinea

Inputs	Work input (person hours per year)	Rate of energy expenditure (MJ per hour)	Total input (MJ per year)
Clearing & burning	7340	1.271	9329
Fencing & erosion control	4460	0.951	4241
Planting & weeding	18 960	0.619	11 736
Harvesting	7340	0.488	3582
Transporting	6440	0.876	5641
Herding	17 000	0.397	6749
Hunting & gathering	1340	0.830	1112

MJ: Megajoule

Outputs	% of diet	Food supply (MJ per year)
Gardens		
Tara-yam	91.0	721 000
Sweet potato		
Abandoned gardens		(24% fed to pigs)
Domestic pig	8.0	48 180
Forest		
Wild pigs		
Small mammals		
Birds		
Fruit		
Nuts		
Timber	1.0	6020
Animal and vegetable fibres		
Vines		
Dyes		

Source: adapted from Bayliss-Smith, 1982

in energy terms (see Figure 5.18 and Table 5.4). It is then possible to compare different kinds of agriculture and see how much energy they use and how much is created. This is known as the energy efficiency ratio (EER).

There are only two ways in which farmers can increase productivity from the same unit of land. The first method would involve the selection and breeding of high-yielding plants and animals, i.e., those with the potential to convert a large proportion of the available energy into food products.

The second method is to increase or change the inputs into the agricultural ecosystem. This would be an attempt to provide the right sort of environmental conditions in which plants and animals can achieve their highest yields. Inputs can be thought of as a means of subsidising energy. The use of fossil fuels, such as oil to drive machinery, is a 'direct subsidy'. There are also 'indirect subsidies' in the form of seeds, fertiliser, pumped water and the machinery itself. This is because fossil fuel energy may have been used to produce each of these.

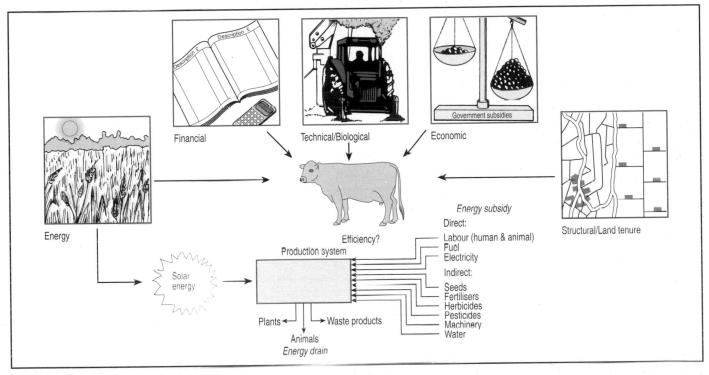

Figure 5.18   Energy inputs and efficiency in agriculture

STATISTICAL ENQUIRY: USING THE ENERGY EFFICIENCY RATIO

For this enquiry you will need to calculate the energy efficency ratio (EER). The formula is:

$$EER = \frac{Energy\ (food\ output)\ per\ hectare}{Energy\ density\ (input)\ per\ hectare}$$

First use Table 5.4 to complete the totals for work input, rate of energy expenditure, total input, diet, and food supply. Which activities require the greatest work input and which require the greatest energy expenditure? Try to explain these differences.

Now use the EER formula to calculate the EER for the Maring system of farming and the other systems shown in Table 5.5. Plot your results on a scatter graph against percentage of energy derived from fossil fuels (x axis). Divide the graph into three zones based on the following classification:

Zone 1   Pre-industrial system – very low dependence on external energy sources.

Zone 2   Semi-industrial system – some dependence on external energy sources.

Zone 3   Full industrial system – very high dependence on external energy sources

What conclusions can you draw from this enquiry?

Table 5.5   Energy inputs and outputs for different foods and farming systems

Type of farming system / foodstuff	Energy input / hectare (MJ)	% energy from fossil fuels	Energy output hectare (MJ)
1 Shifting cultivation, PNG cassava	103	0	1460
2 3-field rotation, UK in 1820s/cereals	183	2	7390
3 Polynesian atoll/coconuts	1079	54	14 760
4 Traditional paddy-field cultivation, S. India/rice	3255	58	42 280
5 Paddy-field cultivation from HYVS, S. India/rice	6878	77	66 460
6 Cereals, Mexico/corn	2903	66	14 150
7 Collective farming, Russia/cereals vegetables, cattle	6145	96	8060
8 Mixed farm, UK/cattle, sheep, poultry, cereals	21 870	97	44 890
9 Corn Belt, USA/corn	29 850	99	76 910

Source: adapted from Bayliss-Smith, 1982

DEBATE

If you look back at Figure 5.18 you will see that there are other approaches to measuring efficiency in agriculture. Use these to help you prepare for a debate on the motion, 'This house believes that only those agricultural systems which are energy-efficient have a long-term future in feeding the world's growing population.'

The decision-makers

Farmers are decision-makers. They must decide how best to use their land and how to organise their working day (see 'A week in the life of Farmer Giles' – although Farmer Giles may not be typical!). On a daily basis, farmers may be required to make decisions about sick animals, machinery breakdowns or the need to repair field boundaries. These decisions are short-term and can be called 'organisational decisions'. Over a longer time period, the farmer must make more significant decisions about how the farm will run. These 'planning or policy decisions' will usually involve decisions on levels of borrowing investment, or they may involve a more radical decision to move from one enterprise to another. Policy-making requires careful and original thought, whereas organisational decisions frequently require snap judgements.

A week in the life of Farmer Giles

Monday
We were awakened before dawn by the dogs barking. No. 1 son Desmond, twelve-bore under his arm, was first outside. By the light of the lamp we could see a fox in the chicken run. After shooting the brute – a big vixen – we counted the casualties: eleven hens, most with their heads torn off.

Tuesday
Market day again. Bill, our pig handler, loads up three litters of weaner pigs into the horse box. We wait for the 27 little blighters, all plump, pink and shiny to be auctioned. They fetch a good price and happily we return home to service and repair the Massey Ferguson.

Wednesday
A long, hard day stockproofing hedges and repairing fencing. Our young farm labourer lacks the skill of coppicing and has to be shown how to thicken a hedge. An article in the *Guardian* about 'sustainable organic farming' infuriates me and I scribble a hasty letter that evening to the editor. The only way farming can survive without raping the environment is for the public to pay the full economic price for the food they eat.

Thursday
Muck-spreading. Not my favourite of days. Desmond and I return home for tea covered in bull shit. If that isn't organic farming, what the hell is it? During the meal there is an unexplained power-cut. Searching for the source we discover a 180-year-old oak lying scorched and powerless across an overhead cable. The wind speed is increasing.

Friday
A sleepless night. We spent most of the time hammering down anything that looked as if it may fly away. Not a good time to meet my MP in London. Over a drink in the Members Dining Room we discussed the future of farming. He waffled on about subsidies and the need to exchange our featherbed for one of nails. Irritated beyond measure I return home to examine the weekly accounts. The computer screen reassures me of a successful week.

GROUP ENQUIRY

1 Read 'A week in the life of Farmer Giles'. What type of farm is described in this article?

2 Is there anything 'unusual' or 'unexpected' about the activities of this farmer? Discuss this with the rest of your group.

3 Copy and then complete this table by listing possible decisions that a farmer may have to make for each of the time periods.

	Daily	Weekly	Monthly	Yearly
Decisions				

Understanding decision-making

Farmer decision-makers, like all decision-makers, are influenced by a number of factors (see Figure 5.19). Two important starting points in helping us to understand this process are the 'real world' and the farmer's 'learning experiences'. It is not possible for farmers to have a complete picture of their farming environment. Only limited information can be collected by them or provided by others. This forms their environmental 'image'. The image is often related to their past 'learning experiences' and, when making decisions, farmers will often follow a pattern already established by themselves or by someone else. One good example of this is where a neighbouring farmer may have started a new enterprise, such as 'Pick Your Own', which appears to be successful, and the adjacent farmer follows suit. Personality may be very important here: in some farmers there is a reluctance or 'inertia' to experiment with new practices.

The importance of values

Values are the principles or standards that influence the way that we conduct our lives. Values are a bit like the layers of an onion: the outer skin represents the values held by society, while the inner core contains values that an individual may only admit to herself or himself. If you peel an onion you will know how difficult it is to get to the core! The values that a farm decision-maker may have are shown in Figure 5.20.

The effect of values on farm decision making is twofold. Values can affect the type of decision directly: for example, a farmer who gives top priority to instrumental values, such as maximising incomes, will make very different decisions from a farmer who puts social values, like continuing family traditions, first. Values can also affect the 'image' because they may 'condition' the farmer to ignore some types of information. If you look at Figure 5.20 you can see examples of different farmers' values.

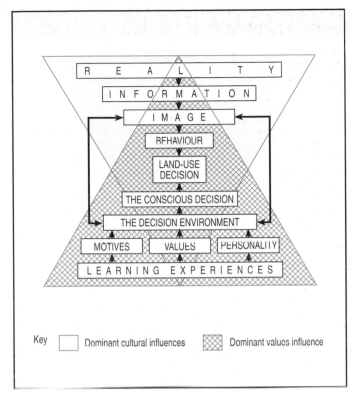

Figure 5.19 Agricultural decision-making: the farmer

Making maximum income
Making a satisfactory income
Safeguarding income for the future
Expanding the business
Being able to arrange hours of work

} *Instrumental* – where farming is viewed as a means of attaining income and security in flexible working conditions

Independence
Doing the work you like
Leading a healthy, outdoor life
Purposeful activity, value in hard work
Control in a variety of situations

} *Intrinsic* – where farming is valued as an activity in its own right

Meeting a challenge
Being creative
Pride of ownership
Self-respect for doing a worthwhile job
Exercising special abilities and aptitudes

} *Expressive* – where farming is valued as a means of self-expression or personal fulfilment

Belonging to the farming community
Gaining recognition, prestige as a farmer
Continuing the family tradition
Earning respect of workers
Working close to family and home

} *Social* – where farming is carried out for the sake of personal and family relationships

It is the ordering of these groups of values relative to one another which is important.

Source: Gasson, 1970

Figure 5.20   Values in farm decision-making

ANALYSIS: AGRICULTURAL DECISION-MAKING

1 What does Figure 5.19 tell us about agricultural decision-making?

2 The farmer is the decision-maker but sometimes the important decisions about change in agriculture have been made elsewhere. Who or what may be responsible for such decisions?

3 Try to produce a diagram similar to Figure 5.19 to show the different organisations which may affect the farmer. Carrying out some background research will be very helpful here. Look for the chapters or sections on the role of government in agriculture in some of the general agricultural geography textbooks in your library.

VALUES ENQUIRY

1 Working individually and using Figure 5.20 as a starting point, list the values that you consider to be important in your future working career. Rank these from 1– 20. Carry out a class survey to compare the top and bottom three ranks. Discuss your results.

2 Working in pairs, decide which of the main value headings apply to the following types of agriculture:
A – Rubber plantations in Malaysia.
B – Lemon groves in Cyprus.
C – Beef production in France.
D – Nomadic sheep and goat herding in the Sahara.
E – Shifting cultivation in Indonesia.
F – Wheat farming in the USA.
G – Sheep rearing in Australia.
H – Rice farming in South East Asia.

Whilst every farmer has his or her own set of values, it is often the case that groups of farmers with the same cultural background will have similar values. There are many examples of the way in which culture may affect the organisation of rural societies and decision-making. In 'The poorest of the poor; women's lot' you can read about the harsh struggle experienced by women in the Third World.

THE POOREST OF THE POOR: WOMEN'S LOT

Women constitute the largest group of landless labourers in the world. Though they do a great deal of work on the farm in most regions, they are almost everywhere little better off than the tenants or employees of their husbands, with no title to the land they work and even less security than most tenants would have. They may be evicted by their husbands on divorce or by their husband's male relatives on his death. Landownership is invariably vested in men. In Indian custom, all males belonging to a joint family become co-owners of its land at birth but females do not. Under Islamic law, women can inherit and own land. 'But if they choose to make over to you a part of it' the Koran tells husbands, 'you may regard it as lawfully yours.' And this, of course is the common practice. Dowries and brideprices implicitly admit that the woman has a right to a notional share of the family land but both practices commonly hand over her share to her husband or her father. Even land reforms and schemes to allot individual titles to communally held land usually assign ownership only to males assuming that women automatically benefit. This lack of title is a grave handicap when the woman is, in practice, the main farmer, as in the many areas where men migrate to work. It leaves her with no collateral security to obtain loans, no power to take managerial decisions and no incentive to improve the land. Indeed, in many legal systems she may be debarred from entering into contracts separately from her husband.

They have also been the victims of gross discrimination in agricultural development programmes which have often worsened their relative incomes. Membership of co-operatives is frequently restricted to men. Cash crop programmes have boosted men's incomes but women are called upon to help with the extra work – and their own food crops may be shifted onto more distant or less fertile plots. Agricultural extension services are almost exclusively staffed by men and addressed to helping men. The net effect of these biases is that men's productivity and incomes are increased, while women's stagnate or decline, and those agricultural operations in which women specialise such as weeding, harvesting or storing food become bottlenecks, negating much of the benefit from improvements in male operations, such as ploughing or water control.

In addition, the notorious double day, in which women work as a full unit of economic production *and* do all the unpaid housework and child care, is spreading in agrarian societies as well as industrial ones. The double day is often the result of cultural lag biased in favour of men. Thus, in pre-colonial days, Africa's women grew the food crops while men hunted and warred. Now there is little left to hunt and professionals do the warring but women still grow the food. They produce an estimated 70 per cent of subsistence food supplies in Africa.

The double day is the most long-lasting of all women's oppressions.

Source: adapted from Harrison, 1982

CASE STUDY: *Dairy goat project in Ethiopia*

Centred on the Shoa, Harage, Bale and Welaita districts of Ethiopia, this project is improving the living standards of some of the country's poorest women by helping them move into dairy goat production. FARM (Food and Agricultural Research Management) provides good quality local goats to give to the women on credit. The goats are either tethered or stall fed which ensures maximum production and minimum environmental damage. Once the basic elements of goat husbandry have been mastered the women are provided with more productive cross-bred animals. The project was launched in 1989.
Cost: £205,000 a year
Donor: The British Government's Overseas Development Administration (ODA)

Figure 5.21 Dairy goat project

Decisions and agricultural location

The decisions that a farmer makes have a direct impact on the agricultural landscape (see page 213). Farmers don't usually reach decisions quickly. It takes time, and they must search through the alternatives carefully. You can have a go at the sort of searching that a farmer may undertake by completing the decision-making enquiry on this page. If you carried out this sort of exercise frequently, then you would have been able to make very quick decisions. In the same way, a farmer's ability to make decisions can improve over time. You don't repeat a wrong decision! The behavioural matrix in Figure 5.22 shows the link between the ability to use information, quality and quantity of information and time.

Locational decisions are very important in the success of farming. Farmers who locate a long way from markets have to pay the extra costs of transporting goods to the market and in moving material, such as machinery or fertilisers, from the market to the farm. To compensate for high costs they may produce crops which require low inputs (Crop 2 is an example in Figure 5.22). The result may then be a series of production zones based on distance from the market, with each production zone containing a particular type of crop or enterprise.

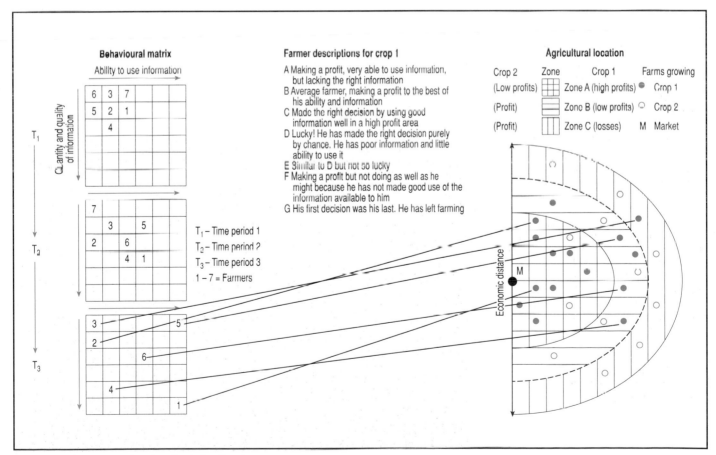

Figure 5.22 The behavioural matrix and agricultural location

DECISION-MAKING ENQUIRY

1 Work individually for this enquiry (an atlas would be helpful). Time how long it takes you to make your decisions. Use the information on the climatic data for five locations and the flow chart in Figure 5.23 to decide which crops can be grown in each of the locations. When you have done this, try to suggest a real world location for each crop identified. Compare times with the other students in your class. Discuss what other factors would have to be considered to make this exercise more realistic.

2 Work in groups of 2–4. Study Figure 5.22. What happens to the famers over time? For each farmer, (1–7), allocate the right description, (A–G), and produce a written list. Compare your results with the other groups.

3 The theories of land-use zoning were developed by Johann Heinrich Von Thünen in the nineteenth century. Using your school, college or other libraries carry out some research into Von Thünen's ideas and include these in a report titled 'Von Thünen's model of agricultural land use'. Some helpful sources are: Grigg, *An Introduction to Agricultural Geography* and Bradford and Kent, *Human Geography*.

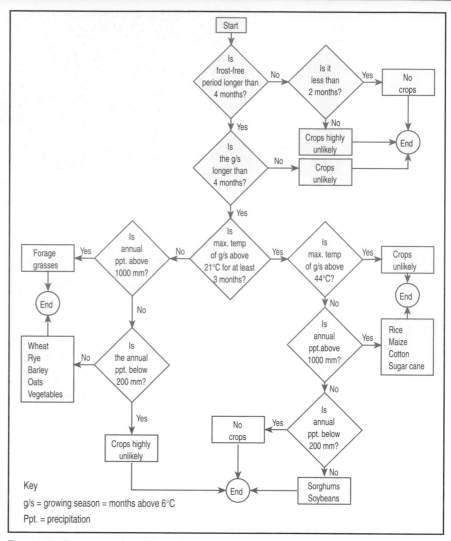

Figure 5.23   Flow chart for determining the broad influence of temperature and precipitation on agricultural crops

Table 5.6   Searching and decision-making

		Jan	Feb	Mar	Apr	May	Jun	July	Aug	Sept	Oct	Nov	Dec
Location 1	Temp.	4	5	5	8	12	14	16	16	14	10	6	4
	Ppt.	38	33	38	33	46	53	56	58	41	61	48	48 (553)
Location 2	Temp.	1.4	2.4	5	5.56	9	13.2	13	13.5	11.7	7.4	2.9	2.2
	Ppt.	60	83	152	43	108	159	139	67	153	113	165	256 (1498)
Location 3	Temp.	2.3	5.1	5	7.1	11.4	15.4	14.6	14.9	14.1	11.1	5.6	4.3
	Ppt.	31	72	24	48	28	71	83	62	14	68	97	61 (639)
Location 4	Temp.	3	4	6.5	13	16.5	20.5	24.5	25	21.5	13.5	10.5	5
	Ppt.	42	75	98	144	118	189	130	134	221	215	97	62 (1525)
Location 5	Temp.	-11.5	-11.5	-8.5	-1.5	3.5	9	12.5	10.5	6	-0.5	-6	-10.5
	Ppt.	20	18	15	20	25	33	48	51	56	56	36	25 (403)

Temperature – °C
Precipitation – mm (figure in brackets = total annual precipitation)

CASE STUDY *Cyprus: Investigating an Agricultural Landscape*

Putting theory into practice is the aim of this last section. There are, of course, several ways in which this could be achieved. One method would be for you to carry out your own fieldwork investigation by visiting a local farm. Some suggestions and advice about this approach are given on page 211. The alternative is to link together some of the theoretical ideas that we have looked at through a case study. Since we already have an understanding of some individual farms (see pages 215, 217 and 218) this investigation considers the evolving agricultural landscape of one country, Cyprus.

Cypriot landscapes – past to present

The agricultural landscapes of Cyprus have shown continual change since the Neolithic period some 3000 years ago. At one time large forests of 'golden oak' covered much of the island. These gradually disappeared as the trees were cut down for building materials and fuel, and to provide land for increased food production. The removal of forest and scrub has seen the gradual appearance of cereals, vines, carobs and a range of irrigated crops. New settlements or 'agro-towns' have also developed in a variety of coastal and mountain settings, each with its own distinctive Cypriot architecture (see Figure 5.24).

Into the last 40 years Cyprus has packed an economic revolution which took most European countries five times as long to achieve at the end of the last

Figure 5.24 Cypriot architecture

century. The land and its water sources remain the main natural resources. The users of the land, mostly the farmers, are part of a solid peasantry with a long and chequered history and a mentality that reflects their background and environment. Some of the most recent changes have their origin in the Turkish invasion of 1974 which has left the island divided: a third in the North under Turkish occupation in the self-proclaimed Turkish Federated State of Cyprus, and two thirds in the South under Greek Cypriot rule. Whilst the northern agricultural landscapes have stagnated, those in the south have undergone enormous change. One reason for this is that the Greek Cypriots

had lost some of their most valuable and productive agricultural land, and consequently needed to raise production to cope with increasing population pressures in the south. Agriculture has long been viewed as the basis for economic growth and significant amounts of development aid, stimulated by the Turkish invasion, and in the form of capital injections and foreign expertise, have accelerated the agricultural transformation. The result has been a startling landscape change bought about by two events: the expansion of the irrigated area and land-tenure reform. These two related topics are discussed below.

ENQUIRY: CHANGE AND THE FUTURE IN CYPRIOT AGRICULTURE

Using Table 5.7 describe the importance of agriculture in the Cypriot economy from 1960 to 1990. Remember that the figures for GNP show absolute change. You will need to change these to percentages to show relative change so that you can compare each year. What explanations can be offered for any of the changes that you have identified? How would you expect these trends to develop in the future?

Table 5.7 Cyprus: GNP (£CY millions) and employment (%) by sector

Sector	1960 GNP	1960 EMP	1970 GNP	1970 EMP	1980 GNP	1980 EMP	1990 GNP	1990 EMP
Agriculture	14.6	44.4	36.0	39.8	70.1	25.0	164.2	21.0
Manufacturing	9.5	14.4	25.2	14.6	125.2	21.9	365.9	22.9
Construction	4.8	9.6	16.9	10.5	100.8	10.3	206.8	11.3
Wholesale and retail	9.9	7.6	31.9	8.8	107.6	10.9	391.9	12.8
Transport and storage	7.4		19.8		53.4		198.0	
Banking and insurance	2.2	21.5	11.1	14.8	38.2	16.3	272.3	19.2
Public administration	7.4		11.4		47.4		239.2	
Services	6.9		21.7		50.1		103.3	
Other activities	24.7		34.7		52.0		73.2	

Employment = % economically active population (1990 estimates)
Source: adapted from *Official Statistics 1990*, Bank of Cyprus

STATISTICAL ENQUIRY

Table 5.8 Cyprus – selected agricultural statistics, 1977 and 1985

Agro-economic region	A		B		C		D		E		F	
	1977	1985	1977	1985	1977	1985	1977	1985	1977	1985	1977	1985
1	3.3	3.7	19.5	16.8	48.8	33.3	17.9	18.5	29.5	28.1	8.2	14.4
2	8.4	9.4	29.4	31.8	18.8	19.7	27.6	25.6	23.2	24.9	15.0	19.2
3	15.4	12.1	76.6	47.1	47.9	37.4	21.0	18.6	43.0	39.7	9.8	16.7
4	7.2	4.5	66.7	36.9	68.9	59.9	6.0	8.4	66.2	69.6	6.0	12.1
5	10.8	9.7	55.8	44.2	49.6	49.9	16.9	16.6	37.0	35.0	14.8	21.3
6	4.3	4.4	27.9	23.4	57.2	49.9	33.2	17.8	34.6	30.1	10.4	12.2
7	3.5	3.6	33.6	30.6	72.8	68.4	18.6	16.9	32.0	33.0	7.1	12.6
8	3.0	3.6	12.1	13.4	22.9	18.7	13.7	9.8	43.1	48.0	8.2	9.8
9	2.6	2.6	15.8	14.1	35.6	26.5	8.9	8.1	59.6	66.4	6.2	3.5
10	1.8	1.9	23.8	20.6	81.1	74.9	14.3	10.4	45.0	54.7	14.1	4.1
11	3.4	3.0	12.8	9.5	6.7	7.6	22.4	16.5	33.8	39.0	8.5	8.0
12	4.8	4.9	37.7	32.9	63.5	59.6	18.5	17.2	38.3	35.4	11.3	13.4
13	13.0	7.8	38.1	22.9	31.2	25.4	15.8	11.3	25.7	29.0	5.7	8.2
14	4.0	4.6	37.8	28.1	66.5	42.5	18.1	20.1	48.3	45.1	8.6	10.3
15	4.3	4.7	36.7	32.0	59.8	48.5	15.8	15.0	50.7	52.5	7.1	9.2
16	3.6	3.5	36.7	18.3	44.0	26.9	9.7	3.5	60.0	64.0	8.0	6.5
17	4.8	5.1	36.9	37.2	56.6	49.6	10.0	6.7	59.4	67.4	5.8	5.5
18	11.2	11.6	45.4	43.7	25.9	22.1	20.8	15.5	36.6	41.3	7.8	12.3
19	7.2	8.0	32.8	29.8	39.4	23.0	16.4	16.5	39.6	36.3	6.8	10.5
20	7.5	6.8	24.3	20.0	27.7	18.3	20.9	15.8	28.8	29.6	7.9	9.6
21	4.7	4.9	40.8	40.9	64.6	60.5	13.6	9.9	50.2	56.1	6.3	7.1
22	8.6	7.9	31.4	21.2	25.8	11.1	24.6	23.4	30.8	26.1	9.1	9.3
23	6.6	8.6	40.5	46.6	42.3	38.5	19.0	12.5	51.8	57.6	9.5	10.3
24	5.3	5.8	21.8	23.7	12.5	16.3	18.8	14.6	35.0	42.8	10.5	9.9

Agro-economic region	G		H		I		J		K		L		M		N	
	1977	1985	1977	1985	1977	1985	1977	1985	1977	1985	1977	1985	1977	1985	1977	1985
1	n/a	31.7	55.0	62.6	18.9	28.3	16.6	19.0	44.2	58.7	6.66	5.36	117	306	n/a	45.5
2	–	23.7	28.0	39.0	50.8	50.8	1.4	1.1	78.8	89.7	46.25	38.31	499	1127	–	45.9
3	–	18.6	38.5	41.7	10.5	18.6	11.7	7.4	47.3	73.8	28.77	19.86	205	715	–	33.6
4	–	16.2	42.0	40.0	1.7	6.7	49.4	33.4	2.4	4.0	3.82	59.7	54	336	–	41.4
5	–	25.5	51.9	61.1	2.8	5.2	8.3	3.5	57.5	80.2	15.45	11.12	161	461	–	34.5
6	–	38.9	61.2	71.1	19.6	21.0	8.0	8.0	42.8	54.9	7.33	10.39	114	320	–	43.8
7	–	31.1	50.2	60.6	32.2	34.8	7.6	3.9	62.2	71.2	27.55	38.99	251	680	–	39.6
8	–	37.4	67.9	63.2	32.4	24.5	25.3	29.2	12.2	31.0	2.65	4.37	52	421	–	50.2
9	–	27.2	55.3	48.9	8.3	17.5	27.7	41.0	0.4	0.5	0.89	1.54	44	221	–	56.3
10	–	13.7	60.3	57.5	10.6	12.8	30.7	36.7	3.21	5.6	0.77	1.68	167	707	–	63.6
11	–	21.5	64.6	62.6	20.4	24.8	35.4	24.4	2.2	0.3	6.15	6.79	39	108	–	53.4
12	–	26.6	61.0	66.1	8.6	8.7	14.6	10.6	41.3	57.1	12.75	12.29	147	424	–	35.9
13	–	71.0	80.0	83.7	11.8	11.7	2.8	3.5	67.6	19.1	23.81	31.8	58	115	–	36.4
14	–	10.3	43.3	49.4	10.7	19.6	25.7	31.4	6.3	3.8	9.28	12.52	107	725	–	48.6
15	–	15.3	44.6	53.5	7.1	7.3	17.7	32.0	3.9	2.9	3.27	3.37	359	117	–	57.2
16	–	16.3	46.7	49.1	15.6	15.4	25.6	29.4	0.8	0.9	0.29	0.25	311	788	–	51.0
17	–	9.1	26.3	31.9	1.6	1.6	12.6	25.4	5.0	6.9	0.89	0.62	335	853	–	49.5
18	–	19.5	29.3	37.3	16.3	20.2	28.2	33.9	11.5	24.5	1.50	0.33	293	810	–	41.0
19	–	32.2	60.7	67.4	3.0	5.1	22.8	29.8	12.6	19.2	11.47	9.99	123	355	–	44.8
20	–	43.7	66.5	76.4	42.8	26.2	18.4	38.0	18.9	9.9	106.65	143.45	136	348	–	43.2
21	–	16.8	26.9	34.2	2.5	3.3	14.0	21.0	21.4	11.9	7.78	10.94	446	1433	–	52.5
22	–	52.3	60.8	71.7	29.2	45.7	9.9	14.6	49.3	34.7	15.19	36.41	141	508	–	45.6
23	–	18.2	34.4	41.3	3.8	5.5	14.2	19.7	38.7	24.7	7.19	10.68	148	1052	–	49.3
24	-	29.0	51.2	52.9	36.3	36.0	2.2	10.3	56.5	40.0	10.35	23.88	131	467	–	51.9
Total											356.69	441.62				

Source: adapted from *Census of Agriculture 1977* and *1985*, Republic of Cyprus

Variables

A – Average size of parcel (donums)
B – Area per holding (donums)
C – % holders with more than 10 parcels
D – % holders less than 35 years old
E – % holders more than 55 years old
F – % holdings with more than six persons per holding
G – % holders with secondary or higher education (1985 only)

H – % holders that are part-time farmers
I – % of agricultural land irrigated
J – % of agricultural land uncultivated
K – % of agricultural land under temporary crops (cereals, fodder, vegetables)
L – agricultural land under citrus ('00s donums)
M – number of tractors per 1000 holders
N – % females working in agriculture (1985 only)

1 This enquiry requires the use of data from the Cypriot Censuses of Agriculture of 1977 and 1985 (see Table 5.8) The aim is to investigate selected aspects of the Cypriot agricultural landscape. The first step is to look carefully at the list of variables. Some of these variables can be grouped together. Try to group them under the following headings: Land-use variables, Farm structure variables, Social aspects of the rural population, Technological aspects of the rural population. Collectively, these groups describe the 'agrarian structure' of Cyprus.

2 Using a tracing of Figure 5.25 construct an isoline map to show the distribution of holding sizes in 1985 (assume that the data parts for each region are given by the numbers 1–24). Select your own cartographic technique to *add* to the map information on the average size of parcels, 1977 to 1985. Next, examine land use. Select suitable cartographic techniques to show the pattern of land use in 1985 and the change in selected variables from 1977 to 1985 (try to use only those variables which show the most striking changes).

3 Now divide up your agro-economic regions into the four zones shown in Figure 5.25. For these zones (*not* for the individual agro-economic regions) produce a series of graphs to show the changes in age structure from 1977 to 1985. Carry out a similar exercise for *one* of the 'technological' variables. Some of the agro-economic regions of Cyprus suffer from rural deprivation. There are several types of deprivation – we are concerned with social deprivation. Calculate the Index of rural social deprivation (RSD) for 1985 using the formula below:

$$RSD = \left(\frac{e}{\bar{x}E} + \frac{f}{\bar{x}F} + \frac{o}{\bar{x}O} \right) \times 100$$

where e, f and o are social variables for each agro-economic region from Figure 5.25 (o is the percentage of holders with no secondary or higher education and can be calculated from variable G) and $\bar{x}E$, $\bar{x}F$, and $\bar{x}O$ are the mean values for all of Cyprus. Produce a table of your results and a deprivation map.

4 The next part of this enquiry involves the setting out of hypotheses and the testing of relationships. Use only the data for 1985. You will need to familiarise yourself with correlation coefficents and the relevant tables of significance. The question that you have to answer here is what are the relationships between the four groups of variables that make up the agrarian structure of Cyprus? For example, what effect does farm structure appear to have on the use of technology? Is there a statistically significant relationship? Carry out an investigation to answer this question. Try to look for other interrelationships between the variables.

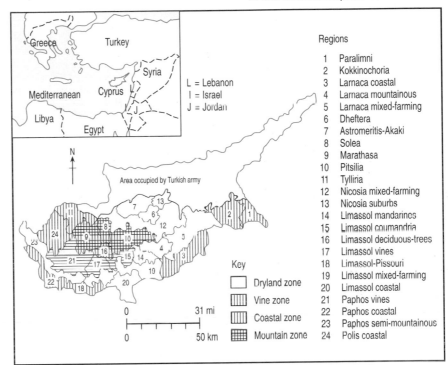

Regions

1	Paralimni
2	Kokkinochoria
3	Larnaca coastal
4	Larnaca mountainous
5	Larnaca mixed-farming
6	Dheftera
7	Astromeritis-Akaki
8	Solea
9	Marathasa
10	Pitsilia
11	Tylliria
12	Nicosia mixed-farming
13	Nicosia suburbs
14	Limassol mandarines
15	Limassol coumandria
16	Limassol deciduous-trees
17	Limassol vines
18	Limassol-Pissouri
19	Limassol mixed-farming
20	Limassol coastal
21	Paphos vines
22	Paphos coastal
23	Paphos semi-mountainous
24	Polis coastal

L = Lebanon
I = Israel
J = Jordan

Key
Dryland zone
Vine zone
Coastal zone
Mountain zone

Figure 5.25 The agro-economic regions of Cyprus

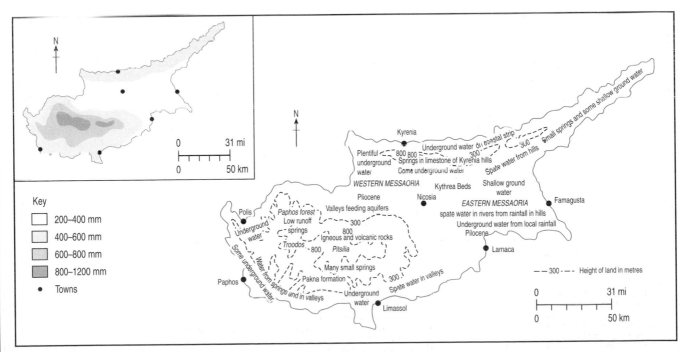

Figure 5.26 Water resources of Cyprus

5 Use the following headings to complete a report entitled 'The changing agricultural landscape of Cyprus'.

   a Description and explanation of the pattern of holding size and changes 1977–85 (use Figures 5.26 and 5.27).

   b Description and explanation of the pattern of land use in 1985 and changes in selected variables, 1977–85.

   c Description and explanation of the pattern of age variables in 1985 and changes 1977–85.

   d Description and explanation of rural social deprivation in 1985.

   e Construction of a flow-line model to show the interrelationships that make up the agrarian landscape of Cyprus.

   f Maps of the agrarian structure of Cyprus 1977 and 1989. It is possible to complete this exercise using spreadsheets and mapping programmes such as *QUEST* and *Q-map*. The aim is to produce a composite map using six of the variables from Table 5.5, with at least one from each of the four groups. If it is not possible to use IT, rank each of your selected variables from 1 to 24, where a rank of 1 = a positive aspect of agrarian structure and 24 = a negative aspect. Add together all ranks and divide by six. This will give you the average ranking. Divide your ranks into groups suitable for chloropleth mapping.

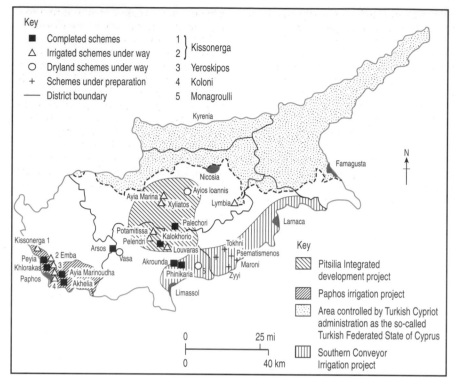

Figure 5.27   Main areas of land reform and irrigation schemes, Cyprus

The importance of water

In many areas of the world water is a key natural resource. The productivity of land, labour and capital depend on the available water supply. In Cyprus one is constantly reminded of the need for water and can see the remnants of Roman aqueducts and rain-collecting systems, Turkish chain-of-wells, massive concrete dams, open irrigation ditches, miles of iron pipes of various ages, and modern wells. Cyprus has no perennial rivers and few underground sources (see Figure 5.26). All water supplies have their origin in the rain that falls upon the island in a single short season each year. Every Cypriot is well aware of the value of water; it may mean the difference between poverty and prosperity. Of the total annual rainfall, 64% is lost through direct evaporation and evapotranspiration from non-agricultural areas, and 20% is utilised by cropped land. Water captured by

boreholes, dams and springs accounts for 9% of the rainfall while surface losses to the sea account for 7%. The demand for ground water has increased enormously over the last twenty years and agriculture is having to compete directly with industrial, tourist and domestic users. At the same time, the Turkish occupation of northern Cyprus has disrupted the Republic's attempts at developing an overall plan for water development, and also created serious water shortages; the capital, Nicosia, experiences strict water rationing in the summer months.

Two basic problems affect water use in Cyprus: the regional imbalance in the potential supply and demand for water, and the chaotic system of private water rights.

Water rights, like rights to land, are inheritable and over generations the process of equal division between heirs has created a water tenure pattern that is

frequently more fragmented than the land. In his famous book *Bitter Lemons* Lawrence Durrell described the situation graphically:

'Water is so scarce in Cyprus that it is sold in parcels. You buy an hour here and an hour there from the owner of the spring – needless to say no quantity measure exists. The trouble lies here: that water rights form part of the property titles of citizens and are divided up on the death of the owner among his dependents. Families being what they are, it is common for a single spring to be owned by upwards of thirty people ... The whole problem is then one of common consent – usually one has to pay for the signatures of thirty people in order to achieve any agreement that is binding. Otherwise one dissident nephew or niece can veto the whole transaction. As may be imagined the most elementary litigation assumes gigantic proportions – which explains why there are so many lawyers in Cyprus.'

ENQUIRY

Use Figure 5.26 and the results of your earlier enquiry on pages 226–28 to try to explain the regional water imbalance. Variable I in Table 5.8 may be particularly useful here.

Private rights exist on nearly all rivers and act as a brake on agricultural improvement and development. For example, water distribution may be carried out to a predetermined time period and not to crop needs. The multiplicity of demands and rights often blocks and delays major water development projects: in one dam-building operation the existence of a complicated pattern of water rights prevented the use of dam water for eight years. Any new irrigation plan involves formidable legal, social and economic problems which, combined with poor physical sites, makes dam building in Cyprus the most costly in the world.

The development of water resources has assumed major importance in the planning that has taken place since the Turkish invasion. A look at Figure 5.25 should explain why. The objectives of this planning were the expansion of the total irrigated area by new dam-building and water distribution systems, extensive surveying for new water reserves and the saving of additional water for industrial and domestic users. Three long-term schemes can be seen in Figure 5.27.

The role of values

Attitudes to land ownership (Tables 5.9a and 5.9b) have had an important bearing on the success of origation projects and a land-tenure reform. (Tenure is the word that we use to describe the rights of ownership or of use (or both) of a piece of land.) Land tenure and its reform are key elements in the agrarian landscape: farming behaviour and associated landscape changes are strongly associated with the motives and attitudes of the people involved (for more detail see Figure 5.19 on page 221).

Table 5.9a Land ownership values in Cyprus

Value and rank		Total point score	% A	% T	% I
1	Making a satisfactory income	777	93.5	77.7	83.1
2	Pride of ownership	764	92.0	76.4	83.0
3	Contentment	700	88.5	70.0	79.0
4	Dowry	690	81.5	69.0	84.6
5	Family tradition	658	90.5	65.8	72.7
6	Investment for future	639	79.5	63.9	80.4
7	Enjoyment of farm work	615	86.0	61.5	71.5
8	Recognition and prestige	605	77.5	60.5	78.1
9	Chance to work unsupervised	582	79.5	58.2	73.2
10	Making as much money as possible	551	71.5	55.1	77.1

%A – Percentage applicability (the number of times where a value applied, as a percentage of the total number of cases)
%T – Total percentage score (the total score, as a percentage of the maximum possible score for all cases investigated)
%I – Percentage importance (the total score, as a percentage of the maximum possible for all those cases where the value was applicable)
Dowry – Land given as part of a marriage contract

Table 5.9b Land ownership values: selected villages

Value	Palechori (n = 50)					Akrounda/Phinikaria (n = 50)				
	Rank	Score	% A	% T	% I	Rank	Score	% A	% T	% I
Making as much money as possible	9	53	56	26	47	9	54	47	34	47
Making satisfactory income	6	118	84	59	70	6	104	63	52	70
Investment for future	8	61	50	30	61	5	158	84	71	88
Enjoyment of farm work	5	160	90	80	89	4	166	80	70	94
Work unsupervised	7	67	52	33	64	10	49	35	26	57
Pride of ownership	3	173	96	86	90	8	62	49	31	61
Contentment	2	180	94	90	96	7	68	50	49	57
Family tradition	4	166	90	83	92	2	176	92	90	93
Recognition, prestige	1	180	98	90	92	1	178	96	90	92
Dowry	10	50	38	25	65	3	173	80	85	90

Value	Kissonerga (n = 50)					Khlorakas (n = 50)				
	Rank	Score	% A	% T	% I	Rank	Score	% A	% T	% I
Making as much money as possible	9	85	66	42	64	2	120	94	60	85
Making satisfactory income	2	170	96	85	88	3	119	98	59	61
Investment for future	3	130	86	65	76	4	118	96	59	61
Enjoyment of farm work	8	90	80	45	56	10	75	44	37	40
Work unsupervised	7	114	84	57	68	6	95	98	47	48
Pride of ownership	4	141	86	70	82	5	109	100	54	54
Contentment	5	124	80	62	77	7	92	100	46	46
Family tradition	6	121	86	35	62	8	90	100	45	45
Recognition, prestige	10	70	56	35	62	9	88	100	44	44
Dowry	1	174	98	87	89	1	132	94	66	69

%A – Percentage applicability   %I – Percentage importance
%T – Total percentage score
n – Sample size

VALUES ENQUIRY: FIELDWORK SUGGESTION

1 Visiting a local farm can provide you with an important small-scale study. The farmer can often give you statistical information which you can use to construct land-use maps and look at crop or livestock changes over a period of time. (Sometimes this can be obtained in advance of a visit.) Some of the most valuable information can be collected from an interview with the farmer, particularly information on his or her attitudes to farming and his or her 'values'. One method is to use a 'point score scale'. An example is given below:

Question: How important are the following factors in your farming operation?

As well as a total score for each farmer three other statistics can be calculated (these are shown in Tables 5.6a and b). In the example above the total score is 5; percentage applicability is 66.6 (one factor or case was irrelevant); percentage total score is 41.67 (total possible score is 12: to get the right answer divide 5 (total score) by 12 and multiply by 100); percentage importance is 62.5 (since only two factors applied – one was irrelevant – the total applicable score is 8; to get the right answer divide 5 (total score, by 8 and multiply by 100). You can see from this example that each of these statistics is measuring different things. Which is the most 'sensitive' statistic and why?

2 Use Table 5.9 to complete the following tasks:
a The total point scores from Table 5.9a have already been ranked for you. Referring back to Figure 5.20, construct a values profile by working out which groups of values are the most and which the least important. Now rank percentage importance. Is there a difference? Try to explain your answer.
b Locate the villages in Table 5.9b by using Figure 5.27. For each of the villages construct a values profile using the percentage applicability columns. What variations exist between the villages? How do you think these values will be reflected in the rural landscape? How might such values affect the land reform and irrigation programmes shown in Figure 5.27?

Factor	Point score scale				
	Essential (4)	Very important (3)	Important (2)	Not really important (1)	Irrelevant (0)
1 Enlarging your farm					
2 Using more chemicals	✓				✓
3 Planting hedgerows			✓		

The Impact of Agriculture

Images of farming

We all have different images of the types of farming found in various parts of the world. Some are stereotyped, a bit like the cartoon shown in Figure 5.6 on page 209. Others may be more realistic. Any viewpoint will be affected by our experiences, beliefs and knowledge. Some countries have been particularly successful in creating a positive image of agriculture. The USA, for example, is seen by many people as a model producer: efficiency and self-sufficiency are the cornerstones of its agricultural policy. Some organisations have created very skilful images to present the diverse areas of their business and the links with the communities that they work for (see Figure 5.28)! Many of us have negative images of economically less-developed countries: backwardness, inefficiency and an inability to feed a growing population.

On paper one of farming's greatest impacts has been its ability to feed a world population growing exponentially. As Table 5.10 shows, world food output increased by 29% between 1969 and 1981 while world population increased by only 20% during the same period. Reality, however, contradicts the statistics: there are many parts of the world where food is not readily available and where rural populations suffer from malnutrition and starvation.

The production of food, whether for home consumption or for sale, has a number of impacts. These may, for example, be economic. In the United Kingdom agriculture is a major contributor to the economy: in 1990, 645 000 people (2% of the total workforce) were employed on farms. Receipts from agriculture totalled £14 264 million and accounted for around 2% of gross domestic product. There can also be political impacts: collectives and communes have been important in furthering the ideologies of communism and socialism. In this section our enquiries focus on two themes which have been developed gradually in earlier sections: the impact on ecosystems and the impact on landscape.

Table 5.10 Indices of food production by regions (1979–81 = 100)
For each region A = total food production   B = food production per capita

		1980	1981	1982	1983	1984	1985	1986	1987	1988	1989
World	A	99.2	102.4	105.8	105.7	111.2	114.1	116.1	116.3	117.6	121.2
	B	99.3	100.6	102.2	100.2	103.7	104.6	104.6	103.0	102.3	103.6
Africa	A	99.9	103.1	104.5	101.5	103.3	111.8	116.6	114.9	119.5	121.7
	B	99.9	100.1	98.5	92.9	91.8	96.5	97.7	93.4	94.3	93.2
North & Central America	A	96.1	105.3	105.3	91.8	103.4	108.6	105.2	102.8	96.6	106.9
	B	96.1	103.8	102.3	88.0	97.7	101.3	96.8	93.3	86.5	94.5
South America	A	99.6	104.1	108.1	105.6	109.3	115.6	113.4	118.3	125.1	125.2
	B	99.6	101.8	103.4	98.9	100.1	103.6	99.5	101.7	105.3	103.3
Asia	A	99.9	103.7	107.6	114.4	119.6	123.0	126.2	127.9	133.0	136.2
	B	99.7	101.8	103.6	108.1	111.0	112.1	112.9	112.4	114.7	115.4
Europe	A	101.1	99.6	104.8	103.3	109.7	107.4	110.0	109.6	109.0	108.8
	B	101.0	99.2	104.0	102.2	108.3	105.7	108.0	107.2	106.2	105.7
Oceania (incl. Australasia)	A	94.7	100.8	94.0	110.0	106.4	107.2	108.2	106.0	110.7	106.8
	B	94.7	99.2	90.9	104.8	100.0	99.3	98.7	95.4	98.2	93.5
Former USSR	A	99.6	97.4	105.0	110.0	110.6	110.3	118.3	119.0	118.8	122.8
	B	99.6	96.6	103.3	107.2	106.8	105.5	112.1	111.6	110.3	113.0

Source: FAO Yearbook (Production), 1990

Figure 5.20 Advertisement for Shell

DISCUSSION AND GROUP ENQUIRY

1 Look carefully at the images shown in Figure 5.29. What 'impacts' do they suggest that agriculture can have?

2 In groups of 2–4 examine each image in more detail. Produce a table to show the characteristics of each image. What effect does text have? Discuss your results with the rest of the group.

3 List the information sources which give us a global or national picture of agriculture. Add a + or –, or both, to each source to indicate whether the source views are generally positive or negative.

Figure 5.29 Two images of world agriculture

ANALYSIS

1 Examine the information in Table 5.10. Using graphic techniques (constructing a spreadsheet and using a graphics package would be useful here) describe the regional variations. Suggest reasons why such variations may have occurred.

2 In groups select a suitable statistical text to investigate the relationship between total food production and food production per capita. How and why do these relationships vary?

3 Outline the major problems that would face an economically less developed country in its attempts to increase food production per capita. Suggest how these problems could be overcome.

BRAINSTORMING

What are the main similarities and differences between natural and agricultural ecosystems? Use Figure 5.30 to help you to produce a class list. Next decide what impacts agriculture can have on natural ecosystems. Widen the discussion to include the effects that agriculture might have on its own agro-ecosystem. Now try and produce a general diagram to show these impacts.

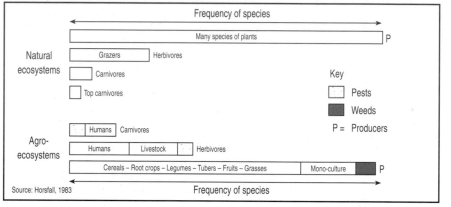

Source: Horsfall, 1983

Figure 5.30   Natural ecosystems and agro-ecosystems

The drainage of wetlands

Wetland environments form a special kind of habitat for a host of plants and animals. They also present a challenge to the farmer concerned with agricultural intensification. Technology allows the farmer to drain anything that is wet – but at a price! Drainage can be achieved in two ways: firstly, by using electrically powered pumps which are able to artificially lower the water table; and, secondly, by the construction of drainage ditches or dykes which carry water away.

The drainage of wetlands creates conflict: we have few wetland areas left in Britain (see Figure 5.31); thousands of hectares of wetland have disappeared this century; remaining areas are under threat from drainage operations such as afforestation, reclamation for agriculture and chemical enrichment of drainage water (see Figure 5.32 and also Figure 2.37 on page 92).

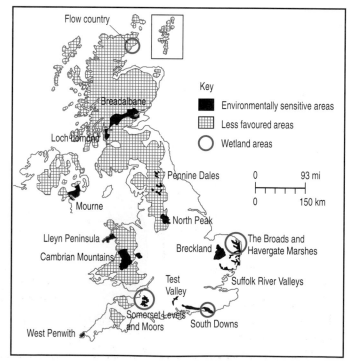

Figure 5.31   Location of wetland and environmentally sensitive areas

CASE STUDY *Halvergate Marshes: Wetland under Threat*

In 1985 changing agricultural policies threatened Halvergate Marshes with extinction. This Case Study, and the role play that follows, highlights the conflicts between agriculture, concern for the environment, and the economy.

The situation

Halvergate Marshes occupy an area of about 5000 acres within the Broadland district of Norfolk (Figure 5.32). The marshes have been partially drained but remain a wetland area. They are a unique habitat for some birds and rare plants, and have long been a place in which traditional rough grazing of cattle has been practised. In the Land Classification maps of the Department of the Environment the marshes are listed as Grade 1 (most valuable); a part of the marshes is also designated a SSSI (Site of Special Scientific Interest) because of the rare flora and fauna.

The future of the marshes is, at present, in the hands of the farmers who own the land and use it for agricultural purposes. There is a body known as the Broadland Authority which is roughly equivalent to a National Park Planning Board: it has advisory status and some financial influence (for example, it can offer payments to farmers to do certain

things) but it is unable to impose ultimate sanctions. The Wildlife and Conservation Act (1981) allows central government to purchase land for conservation purposes in exceptional circumstances, but the Broadland Authority could not afford to do this.

The issue

Traditionally farmers have reared cattle on the marshes: the profit from this is about £123 per hectare per year. They are now seeking to use the land to grow cereal crops because this is more profitable. They can get a subsidy of £246 per hectare per year from the EC to do this and *also* make another £123 per hectare in profits each year from wheat at current prices.

The Broadland Authority seeks to retain the marshes in their original form: they have reached a temporary agreement with the farmers not to plough, but this will expire by the end of this role play. The farmers are asking for compensation payments of £492 per hectare per year (£250 000 per year for the 2025 hectares) if they agree to the Broadland Authority's request not to plough.

The Broadland Authority could not afford such a sum. It has a *total* budget – to cover all its conservation projects – of

only £200 000 per year. Central government (the Department of the Environment) may help, but it is their rule never to fund more than 75% of such compensation payments (in this case, a limit of £750 000). The Broadland Authority says that it can find no more than £100 000 of the £250 000 shortfall that would remain if central government paid out.

The questions to consider

In the simulated public inquiry that follows, these are the questions which the commissioners will have to decide:
1 Is it worth saving *all* of Halvergate Marshes from the plough?
2 Is it worth saving *some* of the marshes from the plough (or is that to accept defeat)?
3 If some or all of Halvergate Marshes is to be saved, who pays?
   a Should the farmers be persuaded to reduce their compensation demands?
   b Should the Broadland Authority use some or all of its budget?
   c Should the Department of the Environment be persuaded to give more than 75% of the compensation payment?

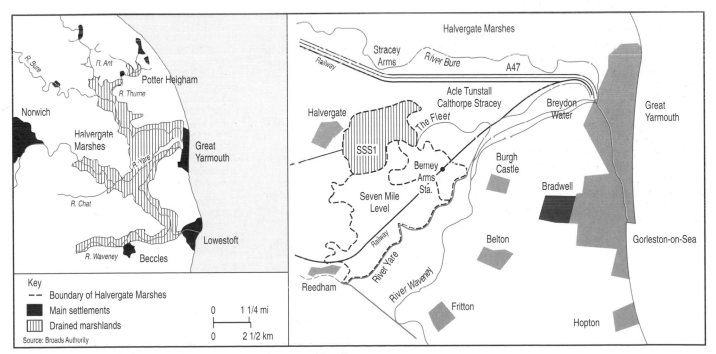

Figure 5.32 Halvergate Marshes

ROLE PLAY: PUBLIC ENQUIRY – THE DRAINAGE OF HALVERGATE MARSHES

This activity will take approximately 60 minutes and will need to be prepared in advance. On the day of the inquiry the classroom must be arranged to simulate an 'Inquiry Chamber': the commissioners should sit behind a table at one end; on one side there should be a single table and chair; at the other end of the room have a semi-circle of eight chairs and desks; each witness's desk should have a nameplate, visible to all present. Witnesses should be called out by the commissioners one by one when it is their turn for the spotlight. The commissioners may ask them questions. The rest of the witnesses must wait until the final witness has been questioned before they in turn can ask questions and debate amongst themselves. This is a quasi-courtroom procedure. The commissioners then leave the chamber for a few minutes and return to make recommendations. At the end of the simulation, take two votes on the commissioners' recommendations, one still assuming the allocated roles and the other with the roles discarded.

The following witnesses are asked to give evidence:

1	Jo Anderson	A member of the Broadland Authority
2	Sam Bryant	A senior official of the Department of the Environment
3	Ronnie Chatterton	A farmer who owns land on Halvergate Marshes
4	Hilary Downing	Chief Executive of Country Landowners Association
5	Chris Evans	East Anglian organiser of Friends of the Earth
6	Les French	Honorary Secretary, Norfolk Ramblers Association
7	Pat Grenville	Director, Norfolk Conservation Trust
8	Val Hartwell	President, Third World First

As a *witness* you will be asked to present your case to the commission for 2–3 minutes and then answer questions about it. As a *commissioner* you will hear the witnesses present their views and should then seek to question them closely. Take notes about what each witness says and compare their views.

In addition it may be useful to have a *recorder* who acts as a secretary during the inquiry and can produce a set of minutes for distribution to all those taking part.

Jo Anderson, MEMBER OF BROADLAND AUTHORITY

The Broadland Authority is the planning authority for the region and is financed mainly by the *local* government councils in its area. It has advisory powers but no legal power to tell farmers what to do with their land.

It has a budget of £200 000 each year for conservation projects – cleaning up the Broadland rivers, preserving historic windmills, etc. To spend *all* that money on one project (such as saving Halvergate) would be a very bold step.

Yet the Authority would like to save the historic and unique 'wetland' environment of Halvergate. Indeed the symbol of the authority is a rare dragonfly which breeds in the marshes and which might well become extinct if the marshes are ploughed.

The chief executive of the Broadland Authority recently said: 'Halvergate Marshes is part of our national heritage. To buy the marshes from the farmers would cost about £3 million pounds – well beyond your budget. The only other alternative is to seek some kind of agreement with the farmers and offer them compensation in return for not ploughing.

The Department of the Environment is likely to support you financially, but as we have seen their '75%' rule still leaves you with a lot of money to find – money which you simply don't have in your budget.

Questions to consider:

1 Can you persuade either the farmers to ask for less or the Department of the Environment to give you more (or both)?

2 Would it be worth trying to save *some* of the Marshes but not all of them? This would bring it within your budget – say, if you spent £100 000 a year.

Remember – it is in your best interests to get *some* kind of agreement before the commission decides, otherwise the farmers may go ahead and plough anyway on 1 April.

Sam Bryant, SENIOR OFFICIAL, DEPARTMENT OF THE ENVIRONMENT

The Department of the Environment has overall responsibility for the countryside of Britain. It can *aid* local planning authorities (such as the Broadland Authority) by providing funds for compensation to farmers, if the cause is a worthy one. But it is usual to pay a *maximum* of 75% of the cost of such compensation – leaving the Broadland Authority to find the rest.

The Minister of the Environment has been to look at the Halvergate Marshes and is sympathetic to the case made to 'save them from the plough'. However, he knows that money is tight in the government's budget and has told you that the Department can only afford a maximum of £500 000 for the project – and hopefully it will be *less*. He urges you to persuade everyone to compromise and tells you that you will be very unpopular if you commit the government to *more* than £500 000. (You may even lose your job for incompetence as a negotiator!)

After all, there are 3 million people unemployed – projects like saving Halvergate Marshes must be seen as luxuries against the needs of the regions in decline, the unwaged and the poor.

Questions to consider:

1 You don't have the money to save *all* the Marshes *unless* the Broadland Authority can provide more *or* unless the farmers can be persuaded to accept less compensation. (If the farmers could be persuaded to accept only £100 per acre, then the whole 5000 acres might be saved – the cost would be £500 000 and you would certainly be willing to provide 75% of that.

2 If the Broadland Authority can't find more money and if the farmers won't take less, is there a case for trying to save *some* of the Marshes from the plough? Or is that not good enough? Wouldn't a piece of Halvergate saved be better than nothing – whatever the hard-line conservationists say?

Remember – try to seek a solution *before* the commission is asked to make a judgement. Otherwise it might recommend that the Department of the Environment pays *more* than £500 000, and that will make you very unpopular with your minister!

Les French, HONORARY SECRETARY, NORFOLK RAMBLERS ASSOCIATION

As secretary of the Norfolk Ramblers Association, you have also agreed to speak for all those who use the countryside for recreation (walkers, anglers, joggers, field sports enthusiasts, etc.).

You know Halvergate Marshes well and often go there at weekends. It's a wide, open area, but with a wonderful sense of space; honeycombed with footpaths, it's the ideal place to exercise the dog, gaze across the meadows, and generally enjoy the peace and quiet of the countryside. It is almost the only place in the whole of East Anglia where you can get a sense of freedom as you walk about.

The proposal to plough up the fields does not affect you or your fellow Ramblers directly, since the footpaths would be preserved by law; still you are concerned since your 'experience' of other areas suggests that some farmers 'forget' about rights of way if they aren't in constant use.

Questions to consider:

1 If the fields are ploughed, would that make the general area *less* attractive for those who use the area for recreation? Would it put any constraints on *some* leisure activities?

2 Would you accept a situation in which *some* of the land was ploughed up, but not all of it?

3 Would you seek to save the Marshes as they are at *any* cost?

Chris Evans, EAST ANGLIAN ORGANISER, FRIENDS OF THE EARTH

Friends of the Earth (FOE) is a campaigning organisation, promoting policies which protect the natural environment. FOE believes that Britain's natural countryside is disappearing at an unacceptable rate.

Halvergate is an obvious and important example of the rape of the countryside by farmers. To plough one acre of it would be a crime. The whole area has an essential unity which needs to be preserved. If arable farming takes place in this area there will be a catastrophic decline in marshland wildlife. Water levels in the drainage channels will be lowered and the associated flora and fauna will become impoverished; the increased use of herbicides and fertilisers will pollute the water. The main ditches will be filled in to accommodate prairie-like farm machinery. Tall reeds, unchecked by cattle grazing, will grow unchecked at the edges of fields and eventually crowd out smaller plants. These drastic and irreversible changes will also drastically reduce the variety of bird life.

For Halvergate, there should be swift action – no deals, and no loss of any part of the area.

Questions to consider:
1 Should the marshes be saved for cattle grazing at *any* cost?
2 If the world is short of grain, shouldn't we be encouraging its growth in the UK somewhere?

Ronnie Chatterton, FARMER WHO OWNS LAND ON HALVERGATE MARSHES

You and your family have farmed on Halvergate Marshes for generations. There is no question of you not caring or not knowing about the place.

For many years you have reared livestock on the grasslands of the marshes – but it has been getting less profitable. It now yields only £50 profit per acre per year. If you were to plough up the marshlands that you own, you could grow winter wheat; with the current level of EC subsidy, that would bring you a total profit of £250 per acre per year.

Or course, if someone would pay you the £200 difference you would be willing to save the Marshes from the plough.

There are some zealous conservationists about who seem to think that land uses must never be changed; there's been a lot of fuss about 'preserving Halvergate from the plough'. But if you look at the history of British agriculture, land uses have always been changing. Anyway . . . the Marshes aren't 'natural'; they were partly drained last century. If they were left to go *really* natural (without cattle grazing) they would just be a jungle of reeds, rough grass and scrub growth within a very few years.

Questions to consider:
1 The Broadland Authority and the Department of the Environment may offer you some compensation money for not ploughing – but supposing they offer you *less* than £200 per acre for this. Will you take what they can afford or bargain with them? Go ahead and plough up the marshes if you *don't* get the full £200 per acre per year?
2 Would you accept a solution for the Marshes in which *some* land was saved for marshland and other parts farmed?
3 Do you have any wider duty to the community as a whole – or should you only consider your own economic interests?

MEMBER OF THE SPECIAL COMMISSION ON THE HALVERGATE MARSHES

You will need to decide:
1 Whether you think the marshes should be ploughed up.
2 The nature of any restrictions which should be recommended, if they are not to be ploughed up.
3 The amount (and source) of any compensation which should be paid if they are not ploughed up.
4 How to resolve any other disputed issues. Clearly, it will be best if you can suggest an agreement which meets the wishes of all parties. However:
1 Some witnesses will be in favour of ploughing, and others not.
2 If the Marshes are not to be ploughed – *either* the land will have to be bought for public ownership *or* the farmers will have to be compensated.
3 There is a gap between what the Authorities seem able to offer as compensation and what the farmers are demanding. Can you bring the two sides to an agreement?
4 Is it a solution to allow some of the marshes to be ploughed up but to save 20% in its original state?

In the end your recommendations do not have to have the agreement of the parties concerned. However:
1 Any recommendation about finance beyond what the Department of the Environment and Broadlands Authority can actually offer will have to be considered by the Minister of the Environment. He is known to have already overspent his budget.
2 Any recommendation about buying the land for public ownership will also have to be considered by the Minister of the Environment.
3 Any recommendation which does not have the agreement of all parties is likely to lead to the immediate ploughing of the land by farmers – who have been waiting two years for an agreement.

Pat Grenville, DIRECTOR, NORFOLK CONSERVATION TRUST

The Norfolk Conservation Trust is one of the affiliated groups to the CPRE (the Council for the Protection of Rural England). The CPRE is very concerned about conservation of the countryside, but it seeks to defend the *whole* of the countryside, rather than simply particular features or elements in it. It seeks to work *with* farmers in developing constructive policies for the protection of valuable habitats.

You are aware of the impossibility of preserving everything – but nevertheless it is important to remember that the uprooting of a hedge or the ploughing of a field can destroy an ecosystem which has taken centuries to develop.

Halvergate Marshes is a clear example of a very delicate issue. It is a flower-rich lowland meadow area – a 'wetland' – and a recent report by the Nature Conservancy Council showed that 95% of such areas have been destroyed by ploughing since 1950. Halvergate is the last *large* area of unspoilt 'wetland' in Britain.

It is not a place of picture-book beauty but it does have an austere attraction, it is important to preserve lonely places like this for urban dwellers to visit and enjoy. And its birdlife is unique.

It is important to work out a solution in which the interests of farmers, visitors and the conservationists can all be satisfied.

Questions to consider:
1 Would you be happy to see *some* of the land ploughed if a guarantee never to plough was given on the rest?
2 Should the land be saved at *any* price?
3 If the Broadland Authority and the Department of the Environment don't offer enough money as compensation to the farmers, who would you persuade to 'give ground' in the first instance?

Val Hartwell, PRESIDENT, THIRD WORLD FIRST

Third World First is an organisation which seeks to campaign for a greater understanding of Third World countries and of the problems of underdevelopment. It raises funds for educational programmes and for supplies and equipment needed in these areas. It has recently been very active in working for aid for the Ethiopian famine.

You live in Norfolk and know the Halvergate Marshes area well; you sometimes go there on summer Sundays, and enjoy a walk in the pleasant open countryside. But isn't it rather an irrelevant argument to worry about whether or not the fields should be ploughed – when millions are dying of starvation all over the world, and when two thirds of the world's population does not get enough to eat?

If anything, the balance is *against* saving the Marshes – the world needs more grain and the farmers want to plough. Their wheat could be part of the world's contribution to the starving millions. And instead of taxpayer's money being spent on compensation payments to the farmers, it could be diverted to the Overseas Aid Budget.

Questions to consider:
1 How could you be sure that Halvergate wheat would actually *reach* the world's starving millions?
2 Some farmers have recently *not* helped the 'Send a tonne to Ethiopia' campaign believing that there is inefficiency and corruption in Africa and that the aid would not reach its proper destination. Is that a sufficient reason not to help?

The use of fertilisers and pesticides

The first agricultural revolution came from the introduction of machinery into the countryside. The second agricultural revolution was based on chemical inputs (see Chapter 2, page 91). The third revolution, still really in its infancy, is linked closely to biotechnology and genetic engineering. The impact of the first revolution was to drive people from the land and slowly change the landscape to accommodate larger and larger machines. The results of the second revolution have been to radically increase productivity. This affects both the visible and invisible aspects of the landscape (see page 213) and has a major impact on ecosystems.

Fertilisers

Before 1945 the essential inorganic nutrients removed by crops came from a number of sources: the breakdown of rocks, soil eroded from elsewhere, manure, legumes and, increasingly, manufactured chemicals. This is still largely the situation in many Third World countries. Today in economically more-developed countries high amounts of inorganic fertilisers are used. Phosphates, one important fertiliser, are manufactured from ores imported from Morocco and Florida: their use has increased by 50% since 1949. Potassium-based fertilisers which come from the UK, Russia, Israel, France, Germany and Spain, have more than doubled in use. Nitrogen fertiliser is used in greater quantity than potassium or phosphate because more is needed. 1.5 million tonnes of synthesised nitrogen fertiliser are used in the UK annually, a sixfold increase since the 1950s.

It is difficult to find comparative data on the use of fertilisers in Third World countries. We have seen that the generally high level of energy efficiency of these agricultural systems results from a low input of chemicals. In 1985 economically more-developed countries were using an average of 100 kg of all fertiliser types per hectare, while Asia was using 31 kg, Latin America 34 kg and African countries an average of only 4.8 kg. In certain areas the arrival of the green revolution has had some impact on chemical use, although not all farmers are able to benefit from the introduction of inorganic fertilisers (see Table 5.11 and Figure 5.38). In Wangala village in Southern India the use of inorganic fertilisers has become more widespread with the introduction of high-yielding varieties of rice (Table 5.11c). This contrasts strongly with the situation 20 years ago when no inorganic fertilisers were added and farmers relied on the natural nitrogen cycle of a flooded environment to produce the necessary nutrients for crop growth.

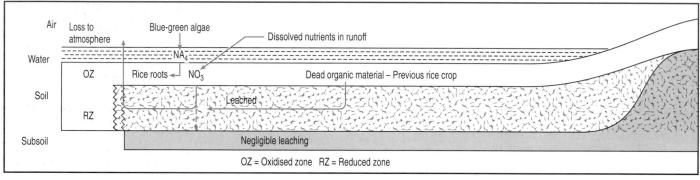

Figure 5.33   Nitrogen cycle of flooded paddy terrace

Table 5.11a   The effect of farm size in Nigeria

		Farm size and incomes (naira)					
		Small (2 hectares)		Medium (6 hectares)		Large (10 hectares)	
Year	Harvest	+fertiliser	−fertiliser	+fertiliser	−fertiliser	+fertiliser	−fertiliser
1	Very good	240	200	720	600	1200	1000
2	Poor	160	150	480	450	800	750
3	Very bad	60	80	180	240	300	400
4	Bad	100	100	300	300	500	500
5	Fair	180	160	180	160	900	800

Source: Bayliss-Smith, 1982

Table 5.11b   Effect of fertiliser cost in Nigeria (in naira)

		− Fertilisers			+ Fertilisers		
Year	Harvest	Income	Cost of fertiliser	Net income	Income	Cost of fertiliser	Net income
1	Very good	100	0		140	20	
2	Poor	75	0		100	20	
3	Very bad	40	0		50	20	
4	Bad	50	0		70	20	
5	Fair	80	0		110	20	

Source: Bayliss-Smith, 1982

Table 5.11c   Effect of the green revolution in Wangala Village, Karnataka State, South India

Land use	Input/ output	Quantity (1975–76)	Energy value (MJ)	Change since 1955 (%)
Dry land Finger millet (0.20 ha)	Human work	26 days	166	Nil
	Millet	98 kg	1250	Nil
Wet land Sugar cane (0.81 ha)	Human work	524 days	3354	+26
	Fertiliser	585 kg	12 324	+138
	Irrigation	5.4 kWh	78	Nil
	Sugar cane	100.2 t	165 425	+41
Rice (0.71 ha)	Human work	225 days	1440	+3
	Fertiliser	166 kg	3526	Innovation
	Pesticide	7 kg	650	Innovation
	Irrigation	4.7 kWh	68	Nil
	Paddy	4.259 kg	43 084	+190
Waste land Bullock grazing	Human work	20 days	128	Nil
	Milk		280	Nil

t = Metric tonnes
MJ = Megajoules (1 MJ = 10^6J = 239 kilocalories)
Source: adapted from Bayliss-Smith, 1982

The Second World makes greater use of fertilisers than the Third World. In the FSU collective or *kolkhoz* they are an important input. One *kolkhoz*, Moscow Oblast, which forms the agricultural hinterland of Moscow City and provides food for 8 million people, uses inorganic fertiliser together with large inputs of animal manure. Wheat receives typically one tonne per hectare of manure in addition to chemical fertiliser, while potatoes and fodder get four tonnes of manure and no chemical fertiliser. It is not certain whether this is sustainable in the long term. In China using 'night soil', human excrement, is still the dominant method for maintaining soil fertility although many communes now contain small chemical fertiliser plants.

The use of nitrate fertilisers came under close scrutiny in the late 1980s as evidence was assembled which demonstrated some of their negative effects. More recently in economically more-developed countries nitrate use has been reduced and managed more effectively, partly as a result of 'green' pressure and new government policies. The problem with nitrates is that not all the chemical is used by the crop. Some of it is leached through the soil and finds its way into streams (see Figure 5.34). Three problems may be caused by the use of nitrates. Firstly, there are ecological effects: nitrates washed into streams continue to act as a fertiliser causing rapid aquatic plant growth which has some undesirable implications. Secondly, there is a risk to drinking water and to human health. Finally, there is an economic effect as the loss of nitrate is also a loss of money to the farmer.

The view of a fertilizer manufacturer

Of the fertilizer nitrogen applied to major crops each year, less than 10% is leached to drainage water. Thus the vast proportion of the nitrogen in drainage water is derived from the soil's own nitrogen reserves.

Of the total nitrate consumed in the UK, some 70% does in fact come from foodstuffs and only 30% from drinking water. (Note – the foodstuffs themselves may be richer in nitrates as a result of fertilizer use.)

Methaemoglobinaemia is extremely rare in Britain with only 14 suspected cases attributable to nitrates in drinking water in the past 35 years.

In spite of the increase in nitrate levels in drinking water, stomach cancer is declining steadily worldwide. In the UK, deaths from stomach cancer are the lowest in East Anglia though in fact this region has the country's highest nitrate levels.

The DHSS's Chief Medical Officer has stated "*Although a theoretical risk of a relationship between nitrate and cancer, based on experiments in animals, remains, the epidemiological evidence looked at as a whole gives no support to the suggestion that nitrate is a cause of cancer of the stomach or any other organ (in the body) in the UK.*"

The UK government has granted the water industry time-limited derogations (temporary exemptions) on 52 water sources which fail to meet standards laid down by the EC Directive on Water Quality which came into force in 1985. (This set the maximum acceptable limit for nitrates in EC drinking water at 50 mg nitrate per litre.) Better water treatment and improved agricultural practices provide better means of meeting EC standards than does reduced fertilizer use. The effectiveness of taxes and controls on fertilizer use has not been demonstrated whereas it is proven that fertilizers help produce more food of a higher quality and at a lower cost to the nation.

Source: Imperial Chemical Industries

The view of a Regional Water Authority

Nitrate levels are rising.

Water supplies have been, and will continue to be, maintained within safe limits.

Nitrate pollution originates mainly from arable agriculture.

It is possible to control nitrate levels by changing agricultural practices; such changes will be extensive in the worst affected areas. In less affected areas changes will be smaller and agricultural restrictions could be the cheapest control measure.

Any measures to restrict nitrate losses by agriculture will help the nitrate situation and should show economic advantage to the farmer.
The "polluter pays" policy should be applied to agriculture to recover the costs of remedial measures taken by Water Authorities to control nitrate levels.

Source: Anglian Water, 1986

The view of a journalist

In December 1986 a report from the Nitrate Co-ordination Group (officials from MAFF, DoE and representatives from water, fertilizer and farming industries) blamed nitrate pollution of drinking water on the overuse of fertilizers by farmers.

A report by the Steering Group on Food Surveillance (MAFF) in July 1987 accepted a link between some nitrate compounds and cancer.

While the average consumption of nitrates from water is only 20 mg/day the maximum is probably around 460 mg/day for an energetic, male vegetarian living in Lincolnshire.

The UK government is reluctant to comply with the EC safe water directive because:
i) it wants to privatise the water authorities, cleaning up water to meet EC standards will cost £300 million.
ii) reducing nitrate pollution means cutting fertilizer use. The Government is reluctant to offend the NFU and ICI.

Even with exemption from EC standards, Anglian Water can only guarantee 80 mg/l maximum concentration by blending water in some areas.

The NFU has agreed (July 1987) to reduce nitrate use in trial water protection zones, but seeks a "key role" in designating the zones and drawing any conclusions. It is strongly resisting the "polluter should pay" principle.

The 80 mg/l concentration limit to be met in exempted areas is only realized on the basis of three month averages. On bad days the limit is still broken.

According to EC rules, areas should only be exempt if nitrate pollution results from "the nature and structure of the ground" (i.e. where naturally occurring nitrates abound). In the UK, exemptions include areas of high artificial fertilizer use.

Sales of bottled water and water filters are booming in southern Britain.

Source: James Erlichman, 'Designer water may be OK for Yuppies but the rest of us are about to turn off the taps', *The Guardian*, 18.7.87.

Figure 5.34   Nitrates and the environment – three viewpoints

BRAINSTORMING

For this enquiry work in groups of up to six. In your groups decide what 'messages' are conveyed by the posters shown in Figure 5.35. Produce two statements of fact and two statements of opinion you find in each of the posters. Next, imagine that you are a member of the board of directors of a major fertiliser manufacturer. Produce a policy or 'mission' statement using some of the words from your characteristics list. Compare your results with the other groups. Return to your groups and produce a table showing the advantages and disadvantages of organic and inorganic fertilisers.

Fertiliser type	Impact	
	Positive	Negative
Organic		
Inorganic		

If you've ever wondered whether fertilisers really do any good, take a look at these two carrots. One is noticeably larger than the other. They illustrate the Wellesbourne Research Institute's finding of an average 66% yield reduction across all crops in unfertilised soils. What explains this difference?
The answer is: diet.
The nitrogen, phosphate and potash that occur naturally in fertile soil are as essential to plants as protein, carbohydrates and vitamins are to people. If they get enough of these plant foods, they reach their fullest potential. Too little, and growth is stunted. The problem is, each crop uses the food it needs, and takes it away when harvested. The more plants a soil must feed, the more help it must have if it is to feed them all adequately. Something must put back what growing plants take out.

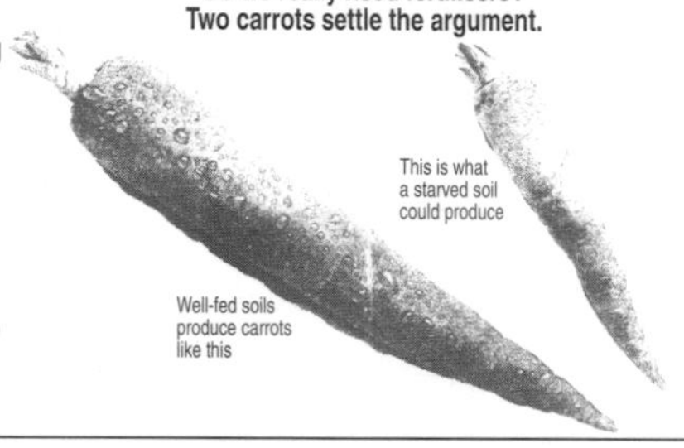

Do we really need fertilisers?
Two carrots settle the argument.

This is what a starved soil could produce

Well-fed soils produce carrots like this

And that something, is fertilisers. Whether organic or manufactured, they provide the identical plant foods found in naturally fertile soils. Nitrogen. Phosphate. Potash.
Organic fertilisers – such as farmyard manures and composts – release theirs slowly as bacteria cause them to decompose. In manufactured fertilisers – necessary because there simply aren't enough organic fertilisers – they're entirely natural and taken from the air, and ancient deposits left by long-dried seas. Whichever is applied, they help crops grow as well as they would in naturally nutritious soil. Fertilisers can do no more. Plants use only the nutrients they need, so applying an excess wastes not only plant foods, but the money fertilisers cost. Over-fertilisation is rare in Britain. Do we really need fertilisers? Yes – used properly, they're the natural alternative to smaller food supplies.

If the potatoes you see here look as good as one another, that's hardly surprising. Both were raised in nutritious, healthy soil, and enjoyed rich, natural diets. If they needed essential plant foods like nitrogen, phosphate or potash, the soil provided them. It might just as easily not have done. Had previous crops been harvested, the nutrients they'd used would have left the soil along with them. The soil's natural reserves of nitrogen, phosphate and potash would have been depleted, and each successive crop would deplete it still further. Eventually plants would starve.
What prevented this unhappy fate befalling the two potatoes in our illustration?
The answer is: fertilisers.

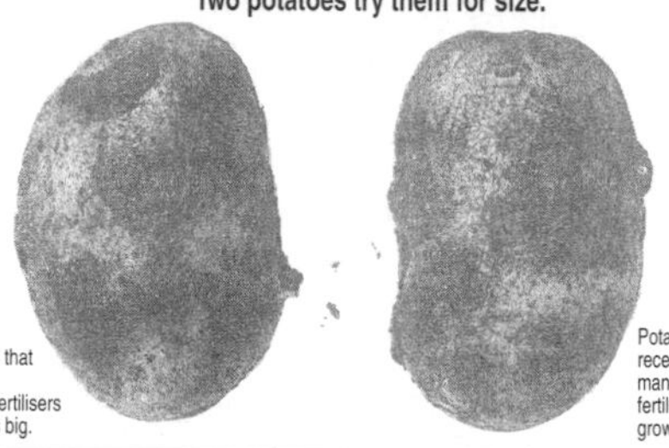

Are all fertilisers equally good?
Two potatoes try them for size.

Potatoes that receive organic fertilisers grow this big.

Potatoes that receive manufactured fertilisers grow this big.

All fertilisers, whether organic or manufactured, work for the simple reason that they replenish the nitrogen, phosphate and potash naturally found in fertile soil. Bacteria cause organic fertilisers to release them slowly; with manufactured fertilisers they're available immediately. The difference is not what's provided, but how it's provided. Their names might suggest laboratories, but nitrogen, phosphate and potash are naturally abundant in such sources as the air, and ancient deposits left by long-dried seas. Plants could not exist without them. Yet, fertilisers help plants achieve their potential, nothing more. Plants use only the nutrients they need, so nothing is gained by applying any excess. Land must be used carefully to ensure nutrients benefit the soils – and crops – for which they're intended. We must put back what crops take out. And fertilisers, used properly, are exactly what we need to feed the soils that feed us.

All fertilisers, whether organic or manufactured, contain nitrogen, phosphate and potash. If these sound like products from some laboratory, rest assured they're not. They're nothing more than nature's plant foods. Fertile soils are naturally rich in them, and plants release them as they decompose. The air we breathe is 80% nitrogen. Even water must contain plant foods, or aquatic plants could not grow. The question is, do these nutrients occur in such quantities that they pose a threat to human health? On a condition known to be linked to high nitrogen levels in bacterially contaminated water, the informed view is: "Blue Baby Syndrome does not occur in Western Europe." Exhaustive research by separate independent bodies has led to the same essential conclusion: "The current balance of evidence would suggest that the range of nitrate intake

Are fertilisers harmful to humans?
Two greens suggest the answer.

Plants which receive only the nutrients nature provides feed on nitrogen, phosphate and potash.

Plants which receive fertiliser feed on nitrogen, phosphate and potash.

which we face in the United Kingdom is unlikely to be associated with an increased stomach cancer risk." 'Nitrate' is the form of nitrogen in which plants take up their food. There is, in fact, evidence that the incidence of stomach cancer is actually lower in areas with high levels of nitrate in drinking water. Evidently then, we are not getting 'too much of a good thing'. The fertiliser industry, nonetheless, accepts the maximum nitrate level set by the EEC of 50 parts per million in drinking water. Old levels were safe, any reductions brought about by improved use of farmland will make them safer still. Far from being harmful, fertilisers promote health by ensuring we enjoy sufficient food, of high quality, at reasonable prices. They are not over-used, and help crops achieve maximum potential by providing a nutritious supply of natural plant foods. There can be no doubt our diet would suffer without them. And, used properly, fertilisers should never give anybody cause for alarm.

Source: Fertiliser Manufacturers Association

Figure 5.35   Fertile thoughts

ANALYSIS FERTILISERS AND THE THIRD WORLD

Table 5.11 shows some of the effects of using fertilisers in the Third World. Look carefully at this information and then answer the questions below:

1   What happens when fertilisers are used in good and bad years? Explain your answer.

2   What effect does farm size have on the 'potential' use of fertilisers?

3   What must the small farmer do if he or she wishes to use fertilisers?

4   Why should Third World farmers be cautious about using inorganic fertilisers?

5   Which land use was affected by the green revolution in Wangala village?

6   Apart from fertilisers, what other farm inputs have increased in the village since 1955?

7   How was nitrogen produced in the traditional wet – rice system and how would this have changed with inorganic fertilisers? What are the advantages and disadvantages of the traditional system?

VALUES ENQUIRY: DEBATE ON NITRATE USE ACTIVITY: ISSUE IDENTIFICATION

Look carefully at Figures 5.34 and 5.36 and use these and any other resources to prepare for a debate. This debate is a little unusual: as well as 4 speakers and a chairperson, there are also 3 expert witnesses.
Organise the debate in this way:
Chairperson – Introduces the motion; calls upon first speaker for the motion, then first speaker against.
Speakers – Two for and two against, to speak for a maximum of three minutes.

Chairperson – When the speeches are over, calls the three witnesses, each of whom will speak for a maximum of three minutes.
Witness 1 – Journalist.
Witness 2 – Water Authority.
Witness 3 – Fertiliser manufacturer.
Chairperson – Opens debate up with questions from

the 'audience' (expert witnesses can ask questions, but not the speakers).
Speakers – At the end of the questions session (allow 10–20 minutes) one speaker from each side must sum up (allow only one minute).
The motion: 'This house believes that the benefits to farm productivity outweigh the environmental risks of the use of nitrates.'

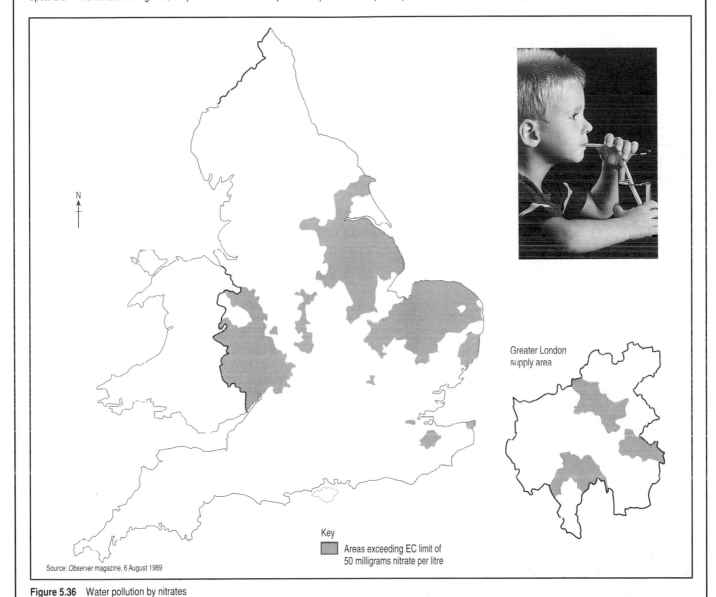

Greater London supply area

Key

Areas exceeding EC limit of 50 milligrams nitrate per litre

Source: *Observer* magazine, 6 August 1989

Figure 5.36   Water pollution by nitrates

DECISION-MAKING

Using all the information available produce a poster to raise public awareness of the difficult balance between the benefits and the risks of nitrogen fertiliser use in the UK. Produce a second poster,

looking at the same issue for the Third World. Make careful decisions here about design, language, colours, etc. If possible, produce your poster using the desk-top publishing software available on your

school computer network.
For the first poster you will need to use an atlas to link together the map on Figure 5.36 with geology, ground water and farming practice.

Pesticides

The other major chemical input comes in the form of pesticide. It is considered that although fertilisers increased yields significantly, pesticides have made an even more vital contribution by reducing crop losses from disease and pests, and by improving the appearance of many products, for example apples. For convenience we are including herbicides (weedkillers), fungicides (which kill parasitic fungi), nemotacides (which kill soil fauna) and molluscides (which attack slugs) within this group. These chemicals are essentially poisons and as such can represent a threat to all natural life systems (see Chapter 2, page 92). Pesticides may be particularly toxic to a target group of pests and less toxic to other creatures (see 'Pesticide poisoning'). For example, some sprays against bean aphids (greenfly) are less lethal to bees which pollinate the bean flowers, but must inflict some harm on the bees in the long term. They may also kill ladybirds and spiders which help to control aphid and fly populations. Nor can damage to other plants sprayed in the field be avoided. There is an additional problem here of indiscriminate or accidental spraying. This affects wildlife and humans in areas adjacent to fields which are attacked by 'spray drift', a possible result of spraying from the air by helicopter or fixed-wing plane. There may also be 'vapour drift' or 'volatilisation' which comes from the evaporation of chemicals already on plants, and 'subsequent drift' which is the blowing of soil particles and chemicals attached to them in strong winds. Some chemicals may also be transportable by living animals to other areas where their effects can be serious. For example, a peregrine falcon in Scotland may eat a migratory bird infected with insecticidal seed in England and so be poisoned. Chemicals may also move quickly through the soil and into rivers, ponds or lakes. Once there the chemicals can become concentrated in fish, with fatal results. Some of the chemicals are not stable and may combine with other chemicals to produce potentially lethal cocktails.

Some pesticides are capable of altering the genetic make-up of pests and other populations by killing only the weakest individuals, so that resistant strains are produced. New or more chemicals must be applied, although the genetic impact is the same. This presents serious problems: pests become more difficult to control and 'superpests' emerge. There may also be a genetic effect on non-pest species.

A frightening impact of pesticide use occurs in the Third World (see Figure 5.37). An Oxfam researcher in 1977 calculated that there were 6700 deaths in the South from pesticide poisoning every year (this was 82% of the world figure). By the early 1980s this figure had gone up to 10 000 and in 1987–89 it was estimated that there were around 20 000 deaths and well over 1 million accidents. In 1978, 15 504 people were admitted to government hospitals in Sri Lanka with pesticide poisoning and 1029 of them subsequently died. Most

PESTICIDE POISONING

On 14th July 1977, farmer Enfys Chapman was sprayed by a helicopter treating a pea field bordering her smallholding near Ely, in Cambridgeshire. The pilot was using Hostathion, a trade name for the pesticide triazophos marketed by Hoechst. Mrs Chapman was covered in spray herself, and probably further contaminated while she treated her rapidly sickening cattle over the next five days.

A number of cattle died quite quickly, from a combination of bloat (where they lost all strength in their back legs), mineral deficiencies induced by poisoning (especially selenium) and fatty livers. MAFF autopsies also showed bone deterioration. Some 'surviving' cattle became sterile and had to be culled.

Five days after the incident, Mrs. Chapman became so ill herself that she was admitted to Addenbroke's Hospital. When I met her, in 1984, she was still virtually confined to a wheelchair, and had been warned by the Health and Safety Executive to move to an urban area so as to avoid spray drift, because the poisoning had made her sensitive to pesticides. She had been forced to move into Cambridge. She suffered spasms if affected by drift, and one of these attacks had resulted in a coronary in 1983.

Mrs. Chapman had also suffered periods of delirium, in which she forgot the English language and reverted to her native Welsh. Her memory was dulled, she had difficulty in concentrating and described herself as a 'victim of premature ageing'. For years she had muscular cramps several times a night, sometimes lying rigid for up to an hour or being thrown completely out of bed.

Source: Dudley, 1987

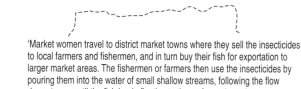

'Market women travel to district market towns where they sell the insecticides to local farmers and fishermen, and in turn buy their fish for exportation to larger market areas. The fishermen or farmers then use the insecticides by pouring them into the water of small shallow streams, following the flow downstream until the fish begin floating to the surface where they are collected for salting and smoking... Everyone agrees that fishing with poison is bad. Most don't realise how bad... The same fishermen who use the method complain that they are now in a vicious circle: they cannot catch enough using nets and hooks to pay for or maintain the very costly nets and fishing gear. Actually, poison presents the cheapest, easiest, most convenient and therefore most profitable method of fishing available... The fish population is dropping by about 20% per year... People in fishing villages complain of blurred vision, dizziness and vomiting, but none makes the connection between these symptoms and the poison.'

Figure 5.37   Fishing with pesticides in Ghana

of the poisonings were thought to be caused by organophosphate.

Farm workers who mix and apply the chemicals are most at risk. They may fail to wear protective clothing, often because this is impractical in hot and humid conditions (such clothes have been designed for cooler environments), and they may re-enter fields too soon after spraying. Around 40% of accidental poisonings are occupational. Other cases include children drinking pesticides by mistake; families using pesticide containers for storing food or water and for cooking; and the contamination of individuals and food by chemicals stored in the same room that is used to cook, sleep and work in. Other deaths come from illegal sales and uses such as the common practice of fishing with pesticides in Ghana (Figure 5.37).

Some farmers in the Third World have discovered that the application of a pesticide can produce exactly the opposite of the intended effects. Research in the USA has supported this. By experimenting with carefully timed and measured applications of pesticide it is quite possible to increase the pest population by as much as 1250 times! If farmers mistakenly apply the wrong amounts or use the wrong chemicals the result can be disastrous. The small farmer, with little time and money, is particularly susceptible. Sometimes even the pests themselves are necessary in the maintenance of the agriculturial ecosystem: control by natural enemies is extremely energy-efficient, since it runs on the energy of the pest itself! The pest is thus the food supply of its own enemies. Cut off this food supply, the natural enemies may be depleted too much to deal with a later outbreak.

In the economically more-developed world pesticides are a common weapon used by farmers in their management of agricultural ecosystems. This method of control is encouraged by the agrochemical companies (see Figure 5.38) products are heavily marketed. There are controls over product development and testing. Pesticides in Britain are normally subject to careful scientific scrutiny before they are available to farmers. An Agricultural Chemicals Approval Scheme is operated by the scientific staff at MAFF and products are eventually included in a booklet (*The green book: UK pesticides guide*). Any firm wishing to add a new chemical to this list must have made thorough field and laboratory investigations indicating the likely effects on wildlife as well as crop pests. This scheme was voluntary but now under the Food and Environment Protection Act (1985) it is a legal requirement.

Many of the problems associated with pesticide use in the Third World are also found in economically more-developed countries. There are the usual problems of drift and accidents during handling. But perhaps most worrying is the way that pesticides are able to get into our food supply. In 1984 FOE launched a 'pesticide-free food campaign'. This used glossy posters to put across the message about pesticide residues in food. In the FOE survey 13 out of 32 lettuce samples showed contamination by Lindane (Table 5.12b). Lindane is a highly persistent organochlorine pesticide which has been identified as potentially carcinogenic. It had been banned and severely restricted in 15 countries including Argentina, Hungary and New Zealand. Other products contained residues of DDT and Aldrin in spite of the fact these should not have been used. Aldrin is thought to cause birth defects and to be carcinogenic.

Bayer: Expertise with Responsibility.

Crops need protection. We have a responsibility to protect the environment as well.

One third of the world's potential crops is lost to pests, weeds and disease — every year.

With the world population growing by over 200,000 every day, providing enough to eat is problem enough, without waste on such a scale.

We still need to improve yields and protect quality; with crop protection products that are increasingly specific, effective in smaller doses and, when their work is done, bio-degrade safely, leaving beneficial predators and other benign creatures in peace.

A balance has to be found between economics and ecology. We are making our contribution.

If you would like more information, please write to:
Bayer UK Limited,
Department A, Bayer House,
Newbury, Berks. RG13 1JA.

Figure 5.38   An advertisement for Bayer UK

Table 5.12a   Pesticide contamination in fruit

Fruit	Number sampled	Number contaminated	Number of different pesticides present
Apples	42	9	5
Blackcurrants	11	4	2
Cherries	11	5	6
Gooseberries	11	5	4
Grapefruit	13	2	2
Grapes	23	6	6
Lemons	12	3	3
Oranges	20	8	5
Pears	37	19	5
Plums	15	4	2
Raspberries	17	10	5
Rhubarb	3	3	2
Strawberries	35	14	17
Tomatoes	33	11	6

Table 5.12b   Pesticide contamination in vegetables

Vegetable	Number sampled	Number contaminated	Number of different pesticides present
Artichoke	1	1	1
Aubergines	3	2	2
Beans	4	1	1
Beetroot	1	1	1
Cabbage	17	2	3
Carrot	4	2	2
Cauliflower	13	3	4
Celery	4	2	2
Courgettes	5	4	3
Cucumber	16	6	2
Lettuce	32	13	7
Mushrooms	39	12	8
Onions	3	2	1
Peppers	5	1	2
Potatoes	5	5	2
Spring onions	3	1	2
Turnips	2	1	1
Watercress	3	2	3

Source: Dudley, 1987

ENQUIRY

Use Figures 5.39 and 5.40, and Tables 5.13 and 5.14 to write a report for a newspaper on the problems of pesticide resistance. Your report must include the following:

1 Case study of (resistance) problems in the Gezira Scheme.

2 A map to show resistance in mosquitoes (this must show all the information in the table).

3 An explanation of Figure 5.40.

4 A diagram to show the pesticide treadmill.

5 Your suggested solutions to these problems.

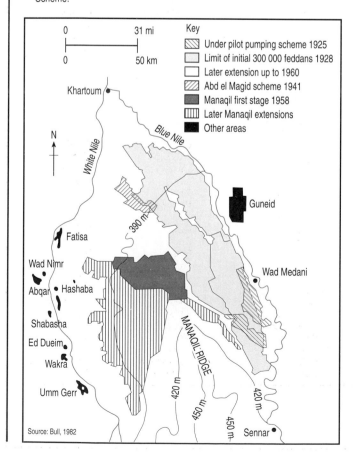

Source: Bull, 1982

Figure 5.39   Pesticides in Gezira. The massive Gezira scheme in the Sudan grows cotton which brings in nearly half the country's foreign exchange. But production costs have quadrupled in the last ten years while yields have fallen by 40 per cent. The pesticide treadmill has played an important part in this disaster on the world's largest farm. Other factors include difficulties in maintaining irrigation channels, and management problems. A large irrigated scheme such as this can operate successfully only if the distribution of inputs is efficient and farm operations properly coordinated.

The two million acres of the Gezira are farmed by tenants who grow ten acres of cotton each as well as a few food crops. In the Gezira the use of pesticides has led to resistance and the destruction of natural enemies. The number of applications has increased seven to nine times since chemical pesticides were introduced in the 1940s, and some pest species have arrived on the scene in unprecedented numbers. One of these, the whitefly, excretes a sticky substance which makes it impossible to process the cotton in modern mills. According to a United Nations panel of experts, a rescue operation has begun, but the Gezira remains a classic example of the potential ill-effects of the pesticide treadmill.

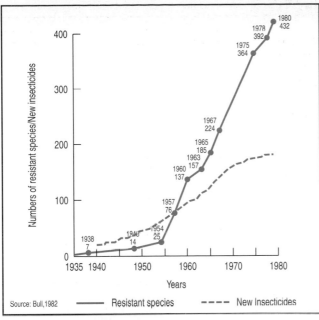

Source: Bull, 1982 —— Resistant species ----- New Insecticides

Figure 5.40 Resistant species of arthropods and new insecticides 1938–80

Table 5.13 Gezira pesticide record 1946–79

Year	Cotton sprayed (ha)	Cotton sprayed (% of area)	Average number sprays/year
1946	600	0.7	1.0
1947	3500	4.0	1.0
1948	14 500	17.0	1.0
1949	32 700	37.0	1.0
1950	53 000	60.0	1.0
1951	70 000	80.0	1.0
1954	98 000	100.0	1.0
1959	158 000	"	1.0
1964	213 000	"	2.5
1969	246 000	"	4.9
1974	247 000	"	6.0
1976–7	"	"	6.5
1977–78	"	"	8.1
1978–9	"	"	9.3

Source: adapted from Bull, 1982

Table 5.14 Cases of resistance to insecticides in mosquitoes

Species	Country	Crop	Insecticide resistance
Anopheles acconitus	Java	Various crops, rice	Dieldrin, DDT
A. albimanus	El Salvador, Nicaragua	Cotton, rice	Parathion Me. parathion Malathion Fenitrothion Propoxur Carbaryl
	Mexico, Guatemala, El Salvador, Honduras, Nicaragua	Cotton	DDT Dieldrin
A. culcifacaes	India (A.P. and Haryana)	Cotton	Malathion
A. gambiae s. l.	Ivory Coast	Coffee, cacao	Dieldrin
	Nigeria	Groundnuts	Dieldrin
	Ghana	Cacao	Dieldrin
	Mali	Cotton	Dieldrin
	Upper Volta	Cotton	DDT
	Sudan, Ethiopia, Togo, Senegal	Various crops	DDT
A. maculipennis	Romania, Turkey	Crops	Dieldrin
A. melanoon subalpinus	Turkey	Crops	Dieldrin
A. melas	Zaire	Bananas	DDT
A. pharoensis	Egypt	Cotton	Dieldrin, DDT
	Sudan	Various crops	Dieldrin, DDT
A. quadrimaculatus	USA	Cotton	Dieldrin
	Mexico	Cotton	DDT, dieldrin
A. rufipes	Mali	Cotton	Dieldrin
A. sacharovi	Greece, Turkey	Cotton, rice	DDT, dieldrin
A. sinensis	China	Rice	OC and OP
Aedes aegypti	Tahiti	Coconut	Dieldrin
Aedes nigromaculis	USA	Various crops	DDT, dieldrin, OP
Culex pipiens fatigans	USA	Various crops	OP

OP = organophosphates
OC = organochlorines

Source: Bull, 1982

SYNTHESIS

1 Select a suitable graphic technique to display the information in Table 5.12. Identify those fruits and vegetables with more than 50% contamination. Explain why these products contain high levels of pesticide.

2 How do pesticides get into our drinking water? Use Figure 5.41 to produce a diagram showing the possible pathways. Which parts of England and Wales are most at risk? Explain your answer.

3 Essay: 'The advantages of inorganic chemicals in agriculture outweigh their disadvantages. Discuss with reference to examples from economically more-developed and economically less-developed countries.'

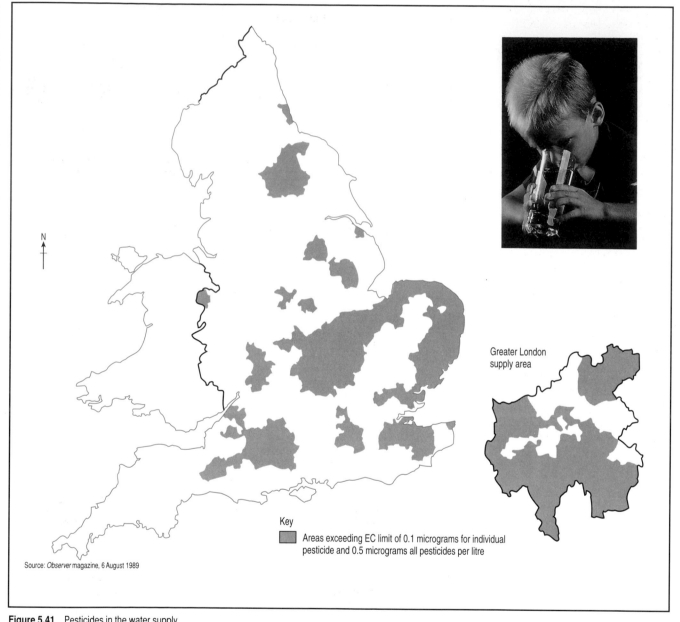

Greater London supply area

Key

▨ Areas exceeding EC limit of 0.1 micrograms for individual pesticide and 0.5 micrograms all pesticides per litre

Source: *Observer* magazine, 6 August 1989

Figure 5.41   Pesticides in the water supply

The impact on landscape

The link between agriculture and the landscape was discussed on pages 208, 212–13. In the last 50 years agricultural changes throughout the world have transformed rural landscapes. Some of these changes have improved the visible landscape. The Gezira scheme (page 242) changed an area of semi-desert into a productive cotton zone while at the same time creating some unforeseen difficulties. In Cyprus a combination of irrigation and land tenure reform has brought a new landscape to the Cypriot countryside. The introduction of of HYVs (high-yielding varieties) in Africa, India and South East Asia, and the use of new machinery (both for cultivating and processing), have affected the farmscapes of the South.

CASE STUDY *Land Consolidation and Landscape Change in Cyprus*

Land consolidation is a type of land reform. A land reform involves a change in the land tenure system of a particular country. (Land tenure is the right to hold or use land – see page 246.)

Cyprus's programme of land reform began in 1969 with the passing of the Land Consolidation Law. Land consolidation seeks to overcome the difficulties experienced by farmers trying to work in a fragmented farm landscape. Fragmentation, which is present in many rural areas throughout the world, has two interrelated aspects. Firstly, there is the breaking up of farms into smaller and smaller units until they become so tiny that they cannot be exploited economically. Secondly, there is the break-up and scattering of plots belonging to a single holding. The causes of fragmentation are complex. Excessive fragmentation is usually regarded as an irrational aspect of farm structure. Some countries have devised their own terminology to describe the situation: the French use *morcellement* for subdivision and *parcellement* for scattering; the Spanish call fragmentation *polverizzazione*.

Responsibility for carrying out land consolidation in Cyprus now rests with the Ministry of Agriculture and its Land Consolidation Authority (the latter was an independent body until 1986). The organisation and process of consolidation is shown in Figure 5.42.

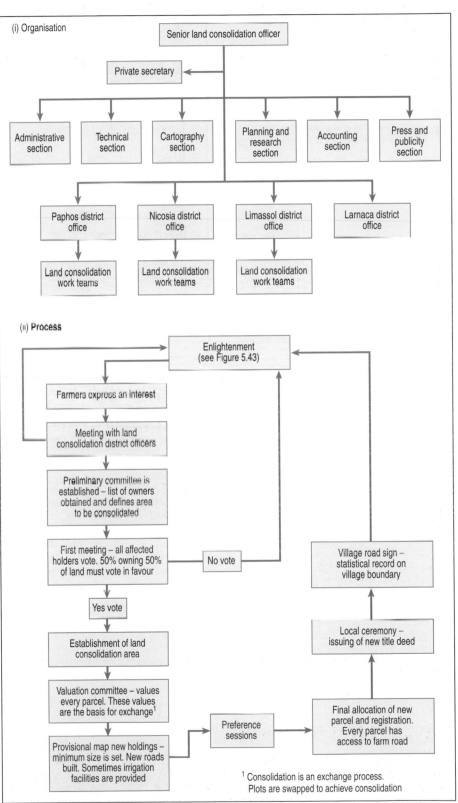

Figure 5.42   Organisation and process of land consolidation

BRAINSTORMING

1   Work in groups (up to six per group) for this enquiry. Think of ways in which agricultural practices can have a negative effect on the landscape. Produce a list.

2   Consider Figure 5.43. What message is conveyed by this poster? In your groups list all the possible disadvantages of a fragmented landscape, firstly for the farmer and secondly for the country. Compare your lists with those from other groups.

3   Return to your groups and now consider the possible advantages of a fragmented farm (produce a similar list and compare your findings).

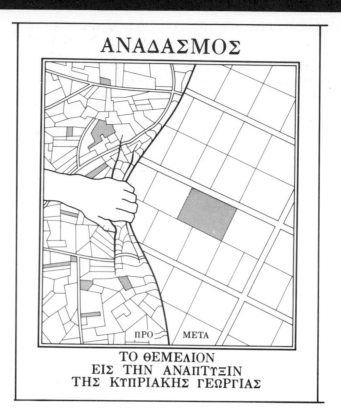

ΑΝΑΔΑΣΜΟΣ

ΠΡΟ   ΜΕΤΑ

ΤΟ ΘΕΜΕΛΙΟΝ
ΕΙΣ ΤΗΝ ΑΝΑΠΤΥΞΙΝ
ΤΗΣ ΚΥΠΡΙΑΚΗΣ ΓΕΩΡΓΙΑΣ

Figure 5.43   Poster used by the Land Consolidation Authority in Cyprus to educate farmers as to the advantages of land consolidation. The Greek lettering reads 'Land Consolidation: the fundamental effects for the Cypriot farmer'

THE CYPRIOT LAND TENURE SYSTEM

The present land tenure structure in Cyprus is the result of a long historical evolution. Each of the island's colonisers – Greeks, Romans, Byzantines, the Lusignan family, Venetians, Ottomans and British – left a contribution to the evolving rural landscape. In the early Christian period farming was dominated by large estates. The Ottoman (Turkish) conquest, dates from 1581. Conquered land became, in theory, state land and was allocated to peasants to cultivate in return for a proportion of their produce. Peasants were serfs to the state but the use of the land was inheritable. During this feudal period the church amassed large amounts of property from donations. Most were from people who feared the loss of their land to the Ottoman regime; they knew that once it passed into the name of the church it would be safe!

Feudalism was abolished when the new Ottoman Land Code of 1857 came into being and private rights of use became more widespread amongst peasants. Rights of possession were registered, inheritable and transferable through sale, exchange or gift but were lost if land was left uncultivated. Under the 1857 Land Code land was classified into five types: (i) *Arazi Mirie*, or state land (as well as state forests and pastures, this included the bulk of peasant-farmed land noted above); (ii) *Arazi Memlouke*, or private land (this comprised house and garden plots as well as trees and vines planted or grafted on land in category (i); (iii)

Arazi Metrouke, or communal land; (iv) *Arazi Mevcoufe*, or religious lands; and (v) *Arazi Mevat* or 'dead' lands (these were waste lands, usually remotely located, and were effectively state-owned). This code remained in force until 1946.

The trend towards smaller and more fragmented holdings continued to be viewed with alarm by the government in 1945. The 1946 Immovable Property Law, the final phase in the evolution of the tenure system prior to the current consolidation programme, simplified the various categories of land, and outright private ownership replaced the rights of use established in 1857.

In 1960 the new Cyprus Republic, safeguarded private ownership rights. But the progressive fragmentation of viable holdings and the dispersion of farmers' plots continued to severely hamper agricultural development. The drastic political events of 1974, which resulted in the Turkish Cypriots, supported by Turkey, seizing total control of the northern 38 per cent of the island, have not significantly changed the tenure structure of that part of the island remaining under Greek Cypriot control. Tenure data for northern Cyprus are not available. A Land Consolidation Law was passed in 1969.

Source: adapted from Burton and King, 1982

TECHNIQUES ENQUIRY: THE STATISTICS OF FRAGMENTATION IN CYPRUS

1 Study 'The Cypriot land tenure system' and Tables 5.15 and 5.16. Choose a suitable graphic or statistical technique to examine the changes in holding size and fragmentation from 1977 to 1985. What has happened to both these variables?

2 Using Table 5.8 on page 226 calculate the average number of plots per holding in 1977 and 1985 for the agro-economic regions. Using a base map from Figure 5.24 on page 227 choropleth this information for 1985 and select an alternative cartographic technique to show changes in fragmentation, 1977–1985. Which areas of Cyprus have the lowest and highest levels of fragmentation? Explain your results. It might be appropriate here to investigate the statistical relationship between fragmentation and the variables H, F, L and K.

3 Based on your analysis, try and outline the possible causes of land fragmentation.

Table 5.15 Distribution of holding size by number and area (donum = 0.33 acre/0.133 hectare)

Holding size class (donums)	Number of holdings 1977	1985	% 1977	1985	Area covered (donums) 1977	1985	% 1977	1985
0–1	896	798	2.1	1.7	442	406	0.1	0.05
1–2	1771	1481	4.1	3.0	2186	812	0.2	0.1
2–5	5167	2909	11.8	6.0	16 214	3701	1.1	0.3
5–10	6452	7139	14.7	14.9	45 006	22 439	3.0	1.7
10–15	5228	8050	11.9	16.8	61 912	56 467	4.1	4.2
15–20	4042	5531	9.2	11.5	68 033	66 302	4.5	5.0
20–40	9740	4079	22.2	8.5	272 219	69 427	18.1	5.2
40–60	4628	5554	10.6	11.6	222 341	134 208	14.8	10.0
60–80	2370	3630	5.4	7.6	161 084	124 429	10.8	9.3
80–100	1308	2592	3.0	5.4	114 654	114 467	7.6	8.6
100–150	1365	1591	3.1	3.3	160 990	86 203	10.7	6.4
150–200	406	1846	0.9	3.8	67 898	126 289	4.5	9.4
200–500	340	1034	0.8	2.2	92 927	91 764	6.2	6.8
500–1000	43	1025	0.1	2.1	28 215	122 060	1.9	9.1
Over 1000	51	342	0.1	0.7	186 579	58 303	12.4	4.4
		341		0.7		98 239		7.3
		66		0.1		45 519		3.4
		38		0.1		118 141		8.8
Total	43 807	48 046	100.0	100.0	1 500 700	1 338 779	100.0	100.0

Note: there are, in addition, 715 'landless holdings' recorded in the Census; these consist of livestock units with very little or no associated land
Source: adapted from *Census of Agriculture 1977* and *1985*, Republic of Cyprus

Table 5.16a Fragmentation of holdings

	Number of plots per holding	Number of holdings	Number of parcels	Total area (donums)	Average area per parcel (donums)	Average area per holding (donums)
	1	8737	8737	81 604	9.3	9.3
	2–3	10 360	25 304	183 822	7.3	17.7
1977	4–5	7113	31 689	176 196	5.6	24.8
	6–9	8250	59 926	298 224	5.0	36.1
	Over 10	9347	156 034	760 854	4.9	81.4
	Total	43 807	281 690	1 500 700	5.3	34.3
	1	12 508	12 508	105 562	8.4	8.4
	2–3	12 980	31 502	206 470	6.4	15.9
1985	4–5	7225	32 024	181 610	5.7	25.1
	6–9	7614	55 330	278 282	4.8	57.2
	Over 10	6921	113 321	566 855	4.9	90.4
	Total	47 248	245 135	1 338 779	5.5	28.3

Source: *Census of Agriculture 1977* and *1985*, Republic of Cyprus

Table 5.16b   Changes in land use after consolidation: first-phase projects

Crop type	Before consolidation (1971) Donums (area)	%	3 years after consolidation (1977) Donums (area)	%	7 years after consolidation (1991) Donums (area)	%
Vegetables	1597.75	29.30	1557.01	31.15	421.09	10.48
Cereals	1046.44	19.82	766.25	15.33	680.23	16.93
Vines	245.15	4.44	170.60	3.41	73.83	1.84
Carobs	9.00	0.16	51.00	1.02	12.00	0.30
Cultivated trees	3.48	0.06	74.30	1.48	307.64	7.66
Bananas	107.10	1.36	219.00	4.38	829.76	20.65
Citrus	40.05	0.73	141.07	2.66	341.30	8.49
Strawberries	0.00	0.00	0.00	0.00	42.21	1.05
Uncultivated	2406.33	44.13	2018.07	40.37	1309.74	32.60
Total	5452.30	100.00	4997.30	100.00	4017.80	100.00

Table 5.16c   Net farm incomes and farm expenditure before and after land consolidation (£CY)

Farm income	Before consolidation (1972) Mean/ holder	Mean/ operator	After consolidation* (1980) Mean/ holder	Mean/ operator
Palechori	40.2	57.4	323.0	345.9
Kissonerga	166.5	189.2	445.3	473.9
Khlorakas	362.0	411.3	484.0	515.0
Akrounda/Phinikaria	38.3	44.5	379.5	403.7
Overall mean	183.8	225.1	422.5	450.6
Farm expenditure				
Palechori	22.1	31.5	76.0	80.8
Kissonerga	126.2	143.4	176.1	188.1
Khlorakas	248.0	326.0	390.0	433.8
Akrounda/Phinikaria	17.8	24.1	111.6	193.9

*   1980 figures adjusted for inflation 1972–89

Table 5.16d   Change in farmer typology

	% holders before consolidation who were			% holders after consolidation who were		
	Non-farmers	Part-timers	Full-timers	Non-farmers	Part-timers	Full-timers
Palechroi	30	58	12	6	58	36
Kissonerga	12	50	38	6	44	50
Khlorakas	12	38	50	6	36	58
Akrounda/Phinikaria	20	58	14	10	52	38

Table 5.16e   Changes in material possessions (%)

	Palechroi Before	After	Kissonerga Before	After	Khlorakas Before	After	Akrounda/Phinikaria Before	After
Radio	94	100	90	96	90	94	84	100
Television	24	60	24	78	40	96	8	62
Refrigerator	32	80	42	94	66	94	14	78
Washing machine	6	26	14	52	14	32	2	30
Car	22	50	42	66	32	36	24	48
Van/pick-up	4	20	8	20	10	16	4	22
Motorcycle	0	4	10	22	2	6	2	6
Donkey	70	58	48	20	68	38	72	54

Source: Burton, 1983

ANALYSIS: THE IMPACT OF LAND CONSOLIDATION

Use the information in Figure 5.44 and Tables 5.16 a–e to analyse the impact of land consolidation on the Cypriot landscape. The location of each of the schemes is given on Figure 5.26, along with the different phases of consolidation.

1 What differences in 'impact' exist between the schemes and how can you explain them? (Use the results of your earlier enquiries into farmers' land-values for each of these schemes.)

2 From the Cypriot evidence what are the effects of land consolidation (use Figure 5.42 in your answer)?

3 How do you think the 'process' of land consolidation could be improved?

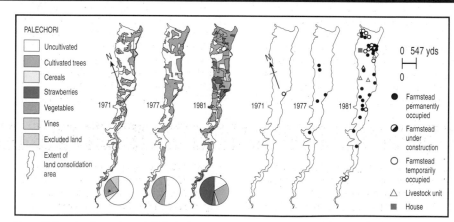

Figure 5.44a   Land use change in Palechori   **b**   Distribution of farmsteads, Palechori

Figure 5.44c   Kissonerga – area of land consolidation

Figure 5.44d   Khlorakas – bed in a field

Figure 5.44e   Kissonerga – new road network

CASE STUDY *The Green Revolution in South Asia*

The introduction of the green revolution has altered the rural landscape of many countries in the developing world. Part of this impact, as we mentioned in an earlier section, is due to the use of chemicals on the land. The other landscape impacts come from the introduction of double and triple cropping (possibly because the HYVs have a much shorter growing season), mechanisation and irrigation.

Seed breeding had been going on in South Asia for more than fifty years before the introduction of HYVs. These gave higher yields and were more resistant to diseases than the traditional varieties. The adoption of HYVs varied considerably in this area (see Table 5.17). Increased mechanisation and the growth of chemical applications followed their introduction. The most important form of mechanical innovation has been the water pump which has allowed the cultivation of irrigated varieties. In 1951 there were 82 000 oil engines and 26 000 electric pump sets in India. By 1971 the respective figures were 471 000 and 1.6 million; and in 1981 they were 2 million and 4.3 million. The number of tractors has also slowly increased. There were 400 000 of these in India in 1981, but 60 per cent were in the states of Punjab and Harayama. In South Asia as a whole there were nearly 500 000 tractors.

At a national scale the impact of the green revolution can be seen in the changing pattern of land use, altering the traditional subsistence nature of the agricultural economy. In the more favoured Punjab the use of HYVs of the main food grains has led to yields of wheat and rice which are at least twice the national average. It was an area of longer holdings, with a well-developed irrigation system. Punjab has been able to supply other food-deficit states with these crops.

RESEARCH ENQUIRY: GREEN REVOLUTION – SUCCESS OR FAILURE?

Using the school and other local libraries, carry out further research on the green revolution and then write an essay on the following topic:

'The failure of the green revolution has highlighted the inadequacy of applying technological solutions to Third World agricultural problems.' Discuss. Refer to standard texts such as D. Waugh, *Geography: An integrated approach*, F. Slater, *People and environments: Issues and enquiries* and R. Prosser, *Human systems and the environment* for more information.

Table 5.17 Adoption of high-yielding varieties in South Asia

India

| Crop | 1966–7 | | 1975–6 | | 1978–9 | |
	HYV ha (millions)	% of total crop	HYV ha (milions)	% of total crop	HYV ha (millions)	% of total crop
Wheat	0.54	4.2	13.45	65.8	16.10	71.1
Rice	0.89	2.5	12.74	32.3	16.90	41.7
Sorghum	0.19	1.1	1.95	12.1	3.10	19.2
Bajra	0.06	0.5	2.89	25.0	2.90	25.5

Bangladesh

| Crop season | 1969–70 | | 1975–6 | | 1980–1 | |
	HYV ha (millions)	% of total crop	HYV ha (milions)	% of total crop	HYV ha (millions)	% of total crop
Aman rice	0.012	0.2	0.557	9.7	0.962	15.9
Aus rice	0.017	0.5	0.353	10.3	0.486	15.6
Boro rice	0.234	26.4	0.642	56.1	0.747	64.4
Boro wheat	–	–	0.088	58.7	0.429	99.0

Pakistan

| Crop | 1967 | | 1970–1 | | 1974–5 | | 1978–9 | |
	HYV ha (millions)	% of total crop	HYV ha (milions)	% of total crop	HYV ha (millions)	% of total crop	HYV ha (millions)	% of total crop
Wheat	0.96	16.0	3.13	52.0	3.72	63.0	5.10	76
Rice	0.004	0.3	0.55	37.0	0.63	39.0	0.97	47

Sri Lanka

| Crop | 1972 | | 1981 | |
	HYV ha (millions)	% of total crop	HYV ha (millions)	% of total crop
Rice		0.507	69.7	0.683	80.8

Source: Bradnoch, 1984

STATISTICAL ENQUIRY: HYV IMPACT ON SOUTH ASIA

The way that a new innovation, such as HYVs, is adopted is known as diffusion. Some farmers are more likely to adopt a new method than others and some countries adopt at a faster rate than their neighbours. In this enquiry we are analysing the rate of HYV adoption in South Asia.

1 Produce a line graph to show changes in the percentage area under HYV crops from 1966 to 1979 for each country shown in Table 5.17. Concentrate on wheat and rice for this analysis. Comment on your results. Why do you think that some countries adopted at a faster rate than others?

2 Using a tracing of Figure 5.45, select appropriate cartographic and statistical techniques to show the pattern and impact of HYV use in India. Which states have adopted the new varieties most widely? Suggest reasons for this and outline the likely social and environmental changes brought about by HYVs (use pages 216 and 240–243).

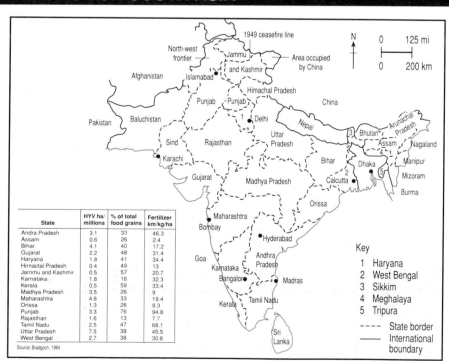

State	HYV ha/ millions	% of total food grains	Fertilizer km/kg/ha
Andra Pradesh	3.1	33	46.3
Assam	0.6	26	2.4
Bihar	4.1	40	17.2
Gujarat	2.2	48	31.4
Haryana	1.8	41	34.4
Hirnactal Pradesh	0.4	49	13
Jarnmu and Kashmir	0.5	57	20.7
Karnataka	1.8	16	32.3
Kerala	0.5	59	33.4
Madhya Pradesh	3.5	26	9
Maharashtra	4.6	33	19.4
Orissa	1.3	26	9.3
Punjab	3.3	76	94.8
Rajasthan	1.6	13	7.7
Tamil Nadu	2.5	47	68.1
Uttar Pradesh	7.5	38	45.5
West Bengal	2.7	38	30.6

Source: Bradgoch, 1984

Figure 5.45 A map of the states in India

Farm size and landscape change

There are two ways in which farmers can increase the productivity of their holdings. They can intensify, using chemicals and HYVs to produce a greater yield from the existing area. The other alternative is to enlarge the farm, either by amalgamating with other farms in some sort of co-operative, or by the purchase of land. However, there is some evidence to suggest that there is an upper limit on size, and that if farms increase above this optimum then the disadvantages outweigh the advantages. In Western Europe the number of farms has declined rapidly. Between 1900 and 1980 there was a 42% fall in farm numbers in the UK and a 39% fall in Sweden during 1946 to 1977. Similarly, in North America, the number of farms in the USA fell by 63% from 1930–81. This trend has been accompanied by a corresponding increase in average farm size. For England and Wales farm size rose from 25 hectares in 1900 to 57 hectares in 1980. In the USA the increase was from 61 hectares to 174 hectares between 1930 and 1981. However, not all parts of the USA or the UK have experienced such significant changes (see Figure 5.46). Changes in farm size are often the result of amalgamation. Amalgamation tends to be greatest amongst larger farms.

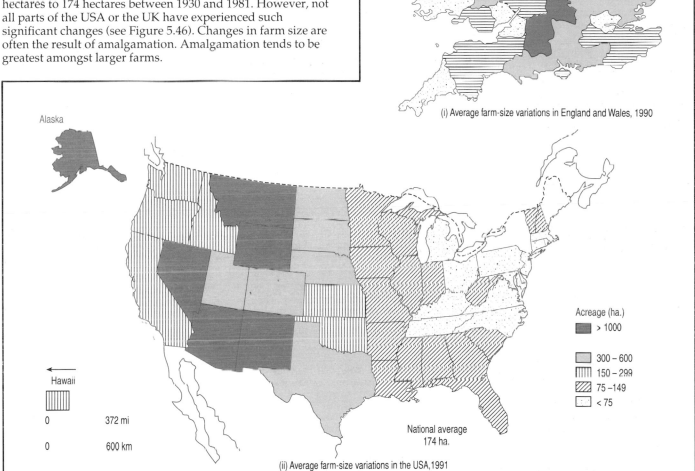

Figure 5.46   Farm size variations in England and Wales and the USA

ENQUIRY: FARM SIZES IN THE UK AND THE USA

1   Study Figure 5.46 and, using an atlas, identify those areas of England and Wales with an average farm size of more than 60 hectares and less than 40 hectares. Carry out a similar analysis for the USA, naming states with an average farm size of more than 1000 hectares and less than 75 hectares. Describe the general pattern of farm size distribution in the UK and the USA. Using your atlas, try to account for this pattern.

2   Refer back to the Cypriot case study. Can the same explanations be used for this example? What additional factors may be important?

3   What are the likely effects on the landscape of increasing farm size?

Hedged out. With increasing farm size have come significant changes in the agricultural landscape. In the UK the hedge has been disappearing at an alarming rate (see 'Hedged out by progress'). Between 1945 and 1970, 8000 km of hedge were removed each year in England and Wales. By 1990 this figure had been reduced. Between 1984 and 1990 78 000 km were lost through neglect, and 39 000 km through removal by building developers, farmers, etc. In 1993 a bill was introduced making it illegal to remove a hedge or impair its quality. The great majority of hedges are, however, relative newcomers to the countryside. They were planted during the Enclosure Movement between 1760 and 1820 when common land was enclosed as a result of various Acts of Parliament. Some hedges are much older, having certainly existed from Saxon times. These hedges often mark parish boundaries or were deliberately planted to make fields stockproof. A few of the hedges which date from this time are the remnants of woodland or 'assarts' when clearances for farming were made

HEDGED OUT BY PROGRESS

THE face of the countryside has changed over the years. The patchwork quilt landscape of small fields split by rustic hedgerows has largely been obliterated in the name of progress.

Since the war, improved transport, factory farming methods and government pressure for higher production have encouraged farmers to uproot ancient hedgerows to grow vast open fields of one-crop type.

Conservationists have fought a losing battle against the destruction, arguing that the often historic hedges provide shelter not only for hundreds of species of plants, birds and animals, but also for the soil, defending it from wind and rain erosion.

Farmers and developers in the south-east have been among the worst culprits, axing 20,000 miles of hedgerow in the region since 1947 – Hertfordshire alone has lost about a quarter of its hedges.

Now the Council for the Protection of Rural England (CPRE) has produced a free leaflet, sponsored by BP, explaining the value of hedgerows and the threat to them.

Andy Wilson, assistant secretary of the CPRE said: 'Many established hedges date back to the middle ages and even Roman times.'

'They are a living reserve for plants, insects and animals but are not protected by law. The only way is if all the trees in a hedge are given tree protection orders.'

'The law can protect trees and houses which might be a couple of centuries old, but at the moment little is being done for hedgerows, which can date back more than 1,000 years. They are as much a part of our heritage as a work of art.'

Source: C. Richmond, Hemel Hempstead *Gazette and Express*

DISCUSSION

Using Figure 5.47, discuss the advantages and disadvantages of the hedge. On the evidence presented here, should hedges be retained? Hedges are very costly to maintain properly. Why was this not such a problem in the past? What technological advance has replaced the stockproofing role of the hedge? What does hedge management involve and how might its management affect the suitability of a hedge as a wildlife habitat?

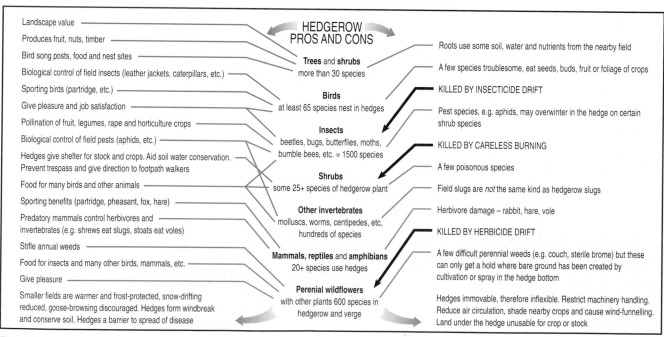

Figure 5.47   Hedgerows, the pros and cons

in the forest. These may contain rare and important species and are known as 'ancient woodland'. Other hedges developed spontaneously from the scrub growth which began to appear along the edge of field boundaries.

Grassed over. Apart from hedges there are other aspects of the landscape which have been lost through the modernisation of farming. Grassland areas in England and Wales have been affected in a number of ways and 80% of our chalk and limestone grasslands have been lost since the Second World War. In Hertfordshire more than 96% of the county's old grasslands disappeared (see Figure 5.48).

A shady story. A third of ancient woodlands in England and Wales have been destroyed since 1945 with the loss of some very important scientific and historical records: timber was used in these woods in the past for a wide variety of agricultural, domestic and industrial purposes, and whole communities based their existence on such woods (see Thomas Hardy's novel *The Woodlanders*). As Marion Shoard (1980) writes:

'Every single tree in an ancient woodland can embody a wealth of information about what has gone on around it; its

---

Old Grassland in Hertfordshire

Have you ever wondered why you no longer see fields full of wild flowers and butterflies in the countryside? A recent survey carried out by Hertfordshire County Council has shown that more than 96% of the County's old grasslands have disappeared during the last 50 years.

1934   Rate of loss – 9.5 acres every day   1984

What do old grasslands look like?

Although old grasslands differ in looks they can be recognised by certain characteristics:
Colour: they vary in colour but lack the bright green appearance of artificially fertilised grasslands.
Presence of anthills: old grasslands are frequently covered with low grassy mounds made by the yellow meadow ant.
Archaeological remains: the presence of burial mounds, hillforts, ridge and furrow show that a field has been left undisturbed for many years.
Animal life: many old grasslands support important populations of birds and insects.
Flowers: there is a high proportion of wild flowers to grasses. Many of these flowers are unable to survive on artificially enriched ground.

Where can old grasslands be found?

They are likely to be found on poorer or less accessible farmland, in particular
– on steep and rough ground
– on poorly drained, infertile soils
– on remote forgotten corners, often surrounded by hedgerows
– on common land and village greens.

What do we mean by old grasslands?

Old grasslands are areas of land that over the years have been grazed or mown rather than ploughed or treated with artificial fertilisers and other chemicals. There are many different types of these grasslands due to variations in climate, soil, location and usage. However they all share the common feature of having a turf which has never been 'improved', not ploughed for several decades if not centuries.

As a result these habitats support a rich variety of wild flowers and animals, many of which cannot survive in today's intensively managed countryside. Unless these valuable and irreplaceable parts of our heritage are conserved, many of our native flowers and insects will be lost for ever.

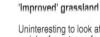

'Improved' grassland

Uninteresting to look at, consisting mainly of one type of grass and a very limited range of flowers, usually buttercups, clover, thistles and docks.

Old, undisturbed grassland

Can support over 100 different types of wild flowers, together with a large and varied population of insects – especially butterflies – and birds. Flowers characteristic of these grasslands include harebell, common spotted orchid, primrose, cowslip and quaking grass.

Conservation and management of grasslands

All old grasslands require regular management to restrict the natural growth of coarse grasses, bushes and trees, which would otherwise take over and destroy the grassland habitat. Most of the plants and animals can be retained simply by following traditional management practices based on grazing and cutting, and avoiding the use of artificial fertilisers and other chemicals.

Old chalk downland – one of our richest grassland habitats, supporting as many as 40 different types of plants per square metre, including: Yellow Rattle, Birds-foot Trefoil, Pyramidal Orchid, Fragrant Orchid, Bee Orchid, and Quaking Grass. The Six-spot Burnet Moth and Marbled White Butterfly can also be seen.

Figure 5.48 Grasslands in Hertfordshire

very existence, its shape and branching, the scars of old injuries, embody information about land use and woodland management.'

In addition, the demand for softwood has led to the coniferisation of many broadleaved woods leading to the gradual elimination of what was once the 'traditional English wood'. For example, between 1946 and 1973 almost a third of broadleaved woods in Lincolnshire were felled and replaced with conifers. Coniferisation can threaten wildlife and damage landscape aesthetics. Today, the rate of coniferisation has slowed down since the government abolished tax concessions for the mass plantation of conifers in the March budget of 1988 and introduced grants to encourage the plantation of broad-leaved trees (see also Figure 2.19 on page 75).

In the developing world the loss of woodland to accommodate agricultural expansion is enormous. Perhaps the best known example is the destruction of the Amazonian rainforest, one of the richest biological ecosystems on Earth. Three types of agricultural activity are responsible for the destruction although the greatest loss must be attributed to the growth of large scale ranching.

Perishing ponds. Ponds have also disappeared at an alarming rate from the British countryside. The majority of ponds were dug to provide water for livestock to drink; others supplied the clay needed to fill the spaces between the beams of seventeenth-century houses. Village ponds were important as a source of water for villages. Water was used for drinking, for washing down farm vehicles, for ducks, for putting out fires in thatched houses (these were quite common) and for watering cattle. Some farm ponds were built only for cattle watering and were located where several fields met, so that animals grazing in any of them had access to water. The ponds tended to become colonised by plants and animals, developing into valuable wildlife habitats. Unfortunately, during farm modernisation many farmers have filled in ponds. In other areas the ponds that have remained have become rubbish dumps, and may contain all sorts of domestic refuse including old motor cars. The disappearance of ponds is strongly correlated with the decline in the number of frogs and dragonflies in many parts of England.

LOCAL ENQUIRY

1 For the first part of this local enquiry you will need to obtain maps of a local farm showing present-day field boundaries and the boundaries 40 years ago. Use the statistical techniques below to examine the changes.

a Hedge Index = $\dfrac{\text{Total length of hedge}}{\text{Area of farm}} \times 100$

b Fragmentation Index (FI)

$FI = \dfrac{\sqrt{\Sigma a}}{\Sigma \sqrt{a}}$ where a = area of each field

O = extreme fragmentation
I = no fragmentation

c Field Shape (FS)

$FS = \dfrac{Pa}{PA}$ Pa = area of field

PA = area of smallest circle which fits in the field

A circular plot has a value of 1.0 and a square a value of 0.73.

2 The second part of this enquiry involves a visit to a local farm to investigate hedges. It is possible to calculate the age of a hedge using Hooper's Hedgerow Hypothesis. The method is outlined below.

a Walk 30 yards along a hedge and count the number of species of shrub.

b For each species multiply by 100 (if you count 5 species of shrub in the hedge then it is 500 years old!)

NB The age of a hedge is important because new species only develop slowly; an old hedge will therefore contain a great variety of plant species such as dog's mercury, bluebells and primroses.

INDIVIDUAL ENQUIRY

1 Using Figure 5.48, produce a table to show the difference between improved and old grassland. Why did the mechanisation of farming herald the destruction of old grasslands?

2 Evaluating all the information in this section, write an essay with the following title:
'The English landscape is under sentence of death. Discuss.'

Managing agricultural systems

Management of the agricultural system is needed if we wish to avoid some of the negative environmental impacts described in the last section. Two levels of management are important. The first concerns the effect that agriculture can have on the physical environment and the interrelated and complex nature of such impacts. The second concerns the relationship between the farmer, the economy and other users of the rural landscape. In terms of practical and effective management it may be necessary to consider both levels simultaneously. Management at the farm level, as we have seen in an earlier section, is an important aspect of the farmer's decision-making process. At a regional or national level management may result from the introduction and enforcement of government policies or the action taken by agribusiness. Some countries, particularly those in the South, may be unable to manage their agricultural systems without help from outside agencies located in the North.

Controlling chemicals – the options

Attempting to overcome the harmful effects of modern agriculture on people and on physical systems is gradually becoming a part of good management practice in the developed world, but can still be lacking in the economically less-developed world. The alternative to the chemical package is to produce crops and livestock using only naturally produced inputs. This is known as organic farming. In the UK this type of farming is growing in popularity (see Figure 5.49).

Figure 5.49 Visions of organic farming

It is of course possible to manage chemicals more effectively on the farm in order to reduce their impacts on the ecosystem. In the UK the Game Conservancy Council has suggested that farmers leave a one-metre pesticide-free strip around the edges of their fields in an attempt to repopulate the dwindling stocks of partridge. Consumer organisations have become more aware of the dangers of cosmetic spraying, and some large supermarkets no longer accept certain products that have been treated in this way. Careful labelling, stringent testing, thoughtful selection and reduced spraying may all help to lessen the impact of pesticides. The quantity of nitrogen used should be carefully matched to the needs of the crop and the soil for both ecological and health reasons. In the Third World, controlling the use of chemicals is more problematic.

One world-wide solution to the pesticide problem has been Integrated Pest Management (IPM). IPM still involves the use of chemicals, but at lower levels and with other ecological methods (see page 257). Some of the responsibility for IPM must lie with the manufacturers of pesticides. They need to ensure that pesticides are correctly and carefully labelled and that pesticides banned in the West are automatically banned elsewhere. Along with the governments of those countries using pesticides, manufacturers should concern themselves with education for safe use and with the design of appropriate safety clothing which suits tropical and other environments. Primary responsibility must of course lie with the appropriate authorities in each Third World country who should provide strict legislative controls over the import, formulation, distribution, advertising, promotion and use of pesticides. Oxfam has produced a number of recommendations.

ENQUIRY: ORGANIC FARMING

1 Organic farming is concerned with the soil and its management. Why is waste particularly important in the organic system? Draw up a table to list the advantages and disadvantages of organic farming.

2 What would be the effect on:
   a The farmer
   b The landscape
   c The economy, and
   d The consumer if a national system of organic farming was implemented?

3 In your local supermarket, carry out a survey similar to the one demonstrated in Figure 5.49.

DISCUSSION

Using Figure 5.50, discuss the ways in which nitrate use could be controlled to avoid the pollution risks.

What other methods are available? (Use the results of your enquiries above and on page 249.)

Nature gives us nitrate, the equivalent to plants of protein to humans.

Without it, nothing could grow – in soil, or in water.

Unquestionably, it is one of life's essentials.

Why, then, are so many people so concerned about it?

Against this, there is no evidence of an increased risk of gastric or any other sort of cancer associated with nitrate.

The incidence of stomach cancer is declining and less common in areas with high nitrate levels.

Where there is concern, however, there must be caution.

High nitrate levels existed in some water long before manufactured fertilisers ever did.

Which begs the question: if nitrate occurs naturally in such quantities, why do we need to add more?

Starving soils.

Fields used to be left fallow, decaying matter

Nitrate is as vital to food production as safe water is for drinking.

Here is why manufactured fertiliser could be the best way to have both.

Waste not, want not.

Fertiliser manufacturers know precisely what goes into their fertilisers.

We've been blamed for putting nitrate in water. Here's why that's not entirely fair.

Nitrate and water.

Like anything in excess, nitrate has a down side.

It is highly soluble, so can be carried into lakes and rivers.

What is good for plants on land, can be too good for plants in water.

In some parts of the world, nitrate, along with phosphate and other nutrients, can so stimulate growth that other water dwellers are denied oxygen.

Evidence of adverse effects on human health is hard to find.

In combination with bacterially polluted water, high nitrate levels can lead to a temporary inability to absorb oxygen in bottle fed infants.

This is known as 'Blue Baby Syndrome'. There has not been a case in the United Kingdom since 1972.

Nitrate alone cannot cause the syndrome; a lower nitrate level reduces the risk, as does an absence of bacteria.

Under certain circumstances a little nitrate is converted into nitrosamines – a suspected carcinogen – in the stomach.

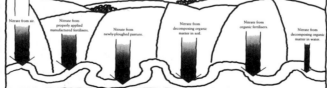

Sources of nitrate, excluding pollutants from sewage and industry.

Less of a good thing.

The solution to the nitrate problem seems obvious.

Use less, and less will end up in water.

It's not that simple.

Nitrogen is naturally present in soil, in such quantities that ploughing a pasture can raise nitrate levels in water coming off it for years.

Nitrate occurs whenever organic matter decomposes. Even air is 78% nitrogen, the element from which nitrate is manufactured.

slowly replacing the nitrate used by crops.

Too little land feeds too many mouths to permit this today.

High yield crops are essential simply to fulfil demand.

The more a plant produces, the more nutrients it requires.

Without a ready supply of nitrate, these crops would starve.

Food surpluses would become shortages. Prices would rise.

They know how plants use it, during which part of a growing season they use most, and how much will be used.

Amounts are designed and timed to ensure all nitrate put onto the soil, is used by the crop.

Growing season over, little then remains to carry into water.

The Fertiliser Manufacturers' Association devotes substantial funds to research and to promote this proper use of manufactured fertiliser.

Farms can stay economic, food will remain cheap and plentiful.

Nitrate is a naturally occurring substance, and fertilisers merely supplement sources in the soil.

And anyone who says fertiliser manufacturers are careless about how it's applied, is being less than entirely fair.

Fertiliser Manufacturers Association

The Fertiliser Manufacturers Association was established in 1875 to promote the proper use of fertilisers. For further information, write to Barry Higgs at The Fertiliser Manufacturers Association Ltd, Greenhill House, Thorpe Wood, Peterborough, PE3 6GF.

Figure 5.50   Extract from a leaflet published by the fertiliser Manufacturers Association, 1990

ANALYSIS

1 Look carefully at the chart and article on IPM and produce a matrix to show the physical, economic and social benefits of this approach (see also 'Alternatives to the agrochemicals' and Figure 2.39 on page 94).

2 Why is it difficult to promote IPM in the economically less-developed world?

The elements of IPM

1 Biological controls including both planting patterns to maximise the usefulness of existing predators of pests in the environment (e.g. not using pesticides in a way that also kills the predators), and the deliberate introduction of pest predators into a farming system.

2 Timing crop planting to avoid the time of the season when pests will be most active.

3 Mechanical methods of killing or avoiding pests, such as use of miniature flame nozzles to kill weeds between crop rows, mechanical strippers for harvest, physical barriers against certain pests, etc.

4 Removing dead plant material to avoid build-up of pests or their survival over winter.

5 Rotation of crops to avoid build-up of crop-specific pests in the soil.

6 Computer technology to accurately assess precise times of pest infestation, numbers of pests, comparisons with other occurrences, etc., to best plan a control strategy.

7 Pesticides applied at the time of maximum usefulness.

Source: Dudley, 1987

IPM IN INDIA

India rice and cotton

In India, experimental IPM programmes for rice have been carried out since 1975 at six locations in five States. At each location nearby villages using IPM and conventional pest control are compared. The largest project is in Cuttack district in Orissa where eleven villages with an area of 2,500 acres under IPM are compared with a 300 acre control village. The project stresses the importance of gearing control measures to individual plots, where rice is grown by a large number of small farmers. Pest populations are monitored by the project team and by the use of light traps by individual farmers. On the basis of such monitoring, insecticides are applied according to pre-determined threshold levels. Cultural methods used include ploughing in of stubble, adjustment of planting times and avoidance of over-fertilization. Pesticides are chosen and applied so as to inflict minimum damage on natural enemies. Varieties resistant to some of the major pests are also used.

The project is explicitly inter-disciplinary and attempts to take full account of 'the socio-economic constraints operating in adoption of the modern technology by rice farmers'. The farmers are directly involved in the project through monitoring and through weekly training classes.

'The main emphasis of the programme is to train the farmers themselves to use the pest management programme so that they become self reliant in the use of the technology rather than depending on experts.'

The results have been encouraging. During the rabi (October to January) season of 1979 the major pest, stem borer, reached the economic injury level in only one of the eleven villages.

The project's 1979 Annual Report stated that,

'The major gain of integrated pest management programmes in the area has been a drastic cut in the number of insecticide applications from an average of 4–6 rounds of sprays given prior to commencement of the project to an average of two rounds per crop.'

Source: Bull, 1982

Landscape controls

Whilst farmers in many parts of the world have rights of ownership, this does not exclude others from using their property. The issues which arose at Halvergate Marshes are a good example. There were other areas where the same fundamental principles applied, but because of the size of Halvergate and its national importance it became the flag bearer for policy reform. This was the start of the attempts to reconcile agriculture with conservation and demonstrated a greater public awareness of 'green issues'. In the end, the proposed new drainage scheme at Halvergate was not constructed. Part of the area was improved, although this had little effect on the landscape. It was the EEC who really saved the day when, in March 1985, agreement was reached in Brussels to provide a grant for preserving the area. The farmers, bowing to public pressure, also agreed to accept less compensation. The decision not to plough was, however, a very narrow one. Subsequently, MAFF (Ministry of Agriculture; Fisheries and Food) and the Countryside Commission joined forces under Section 40 of the 1981 Wildlife and Countryside Act to establish a three-year experimental scheme for Halvergate and other similar environments. This scheme was known as the Broads Grazing Marshes Conservation Scheme; it covered some 4000 hectares and expired in March 1988. When the scheme was in operation any farmer in the designated area was eligible for a payment of £123 per hectare. The cost of the scheme, £1.7 million, was shared by MAFF and the Countryside Commission. The scheme was extremely successful: no grazing marshes were drained; 108 out of 110 farmers signed up; one farmer sold his land to the RSPB, who were attempting to convert the area into an important wildfowl refuge; and some land producing cereals was put back to grass!

In a European context the work of the Broads Scheme comes under Article 19 of the Community Regulations on improving the efficiency of agricultural structures. This involves the designation of ESAs (Environmentally Sensitive Areas) which are based on the model established by the Broads Scheme. Under the Agriculture Act of 1986 six sites in England and Wales, amounting to 235 000 hectares (1.25% of agricultural land) were selected. Three additional sites in Scotland and Northern Ireland were later added. Each area is administered by a small unit from the relevant Agricultural Department, with support from the Countryside Commission and the Nature Conservancy Council. Landowners are eligible for payment at two levels: a base-level 'landscape maintenance' payment of around £20–£50 per acre, and a top-up payment for special management measures designed to enhance or re-establish special wildlife habitats and landscape features.

RESEARCH ENQUIRY

1 Using the library and organisations like Friends of the Earth, find out all you can about Sites of Special Scientific Interest. Produce a map of SSSIs in your county and, if possible, visit one of these. What are the advantages of making an area an SSSI?

2 Find the addresses of English Nature and Scottish Natural Heritage. Write to these organisations to obtain information on the location of ESAs. What other types of 'conservation space' exist in the UK?

What other methods are being used to control the negative effects of agriculture on the landscape:
a In the UK (use Geofiles and Figure 5.51 to help you)?
b In the economically less-developed world?

3 Evaluate the measures shown in Figure 5.51, explaining how balance is achieved.

DISCUSSION

1 What do you think the farm of the future will be like? Try to produce a sketch of this 'future farm'.

2 'Just let nature do all the work', 'Balance in the countryside', 'The biotechnology option' and 'Countryside stewardship' present alternative views of the future. What will be the likely impacts of each approach? Make sure you consider here the impact on landscape and ecosystems. What are the differences between these approaches? Which do you think is likely to be the agricultural approach of the future? Justify your answer.

JUST LET NATURE DO ALL THE WORK

The most fertile and down-to earth Green idea started life in Tasmania as a humble scheme for growing vegetables: let nature do most of the work.

Bill Mollison called it permaculture, which means permanent agriculture: lots of mulching but no digging, little weeding and no artificial inputs....

His idea is indeed simple. Take a piece of land. Identify what grows, lives or simply exists: soils, weeds, insects, worms, slugs, birds, butterflies, rocks, water sources. That's your eco-system.

Get rid of anything poisonous or wasteful like machines that cost more in energy than they earn. Add plants, animals, people, houses, workshops – whatever fits into the system and keeps it self-sustaining...

Mollison concedes that intensive agriculture has much higher yields per acre under a single crop, but he insists that permaculture grows many different things on the same acre at a fraction of the cost in energy, without poisoning the earth. The better it works the more people and animals it can support, hence his claim that food and population are no problem once we abolish mass agriculture...

Permaculture UK is at 8 Hunters' Moon, Dartington, Totnes, South Devon TQ9 6JT.

Source: *Weekend Guardian,* 7 – 8 October 1989

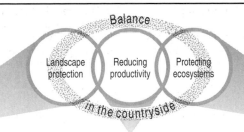

Balance

Landscape protection | Reducing productivity | Protecting ecosystems

in the countryside

ESAs – MAFFs Environmentally Sensitive Areas have been introduced to help conserve selected areas from change resulting from more intensive farming methods. The ESA scheme requires farmers to maintain or introduce traditional agricultural practices which conserve or improve the landscape.

FARM CONSERVATION GRANT SCHEME (FCGS) – this scheme was introduced in February 1989 and offers a wide range of environmental grants for: providing and improving hedges; planting trees as shelter beds; regenerating heather and controlling bracken; protecting natural woodland and heather from livestock; renovating farm buildings using traditional materials.

FARM WOODLAND SCHEME (FWS) – a joint scheme between MAFF and the Forestry Commission, this is designed to encourage farmers to plant new woodland on land currently in productive agriculture. Small broadleaved woodlands are favoured. This scheme first came into operation in October 1988 and by 1990 16 million trees had been planted (3.5 million oaks).

SET ASIDE – a minimum of 15% of arable land must now be taken out of production for a period of five years. The land set aside must be kept fallow, grazed or converted to woodland. (See below). In 1991 130,000 hectares had been taken out of production through set aside.

COUNTRYSIDE PREMIUM SCHEME (CPS) – This is also for arable farmers and allows for basic changes. There are four options: conversion to unfertilised ungrazed grass; conversion to unfertilised grazed grass; conversion to grass with limited fertiliser; conversion to grass with tree planting.

FARM DIVERSIFICATION GRANT SCHEME (FDGS) – this is a comprehensive package of assistance to farmers thinking of diversifying into non-agricultural profit-making activities on their farms. There are 3 parts:
(i) capital grant – to assist in establishing or improving a non-farm business;
(ii) feasibility grant – up to 50% payment towards a feasibility study and business plan;
(iii) marketing grant – to pay for marketing and promotional functions.

HILL LIVESTOCK COMPENSATORY ALLOWANCE (HLCAs) – this is paid to farmers in less favoured areas (LFAs) such as uplands. Payments are made to farmers farming at least three hectares of land, keeping regular herds of cows or flocks of sheep for breeding purposes.

THE NITRATE SCHEME – this has involved the setting up of Nitrate Sensitive Areas (NSAs) where farmers voluntarily enter into five-year agreements to:
(i) maintain autumn green cover (reduces the risk of nitrate leaching);
(ii) follow procedures for the timing and quantity of inorganic and organic fertilisers;
(iii) plant cover crops when needed. There are also nine Nitrate Advisory Areas (NAAs) covering 20,000 hectares giving farmers free advice on nitrate leaching. There are ten NSAs covering 11,000 hectares.

PESTICIDE CODES OF PRACTICE – in 1990 MAFF introduced two Codes of Practice; one on the storage and transport of pesticides for users, retailers and producers; the other on using pesticides safely. The Health and Safety Executive are responsible for enforcing these codes.

INTEGRATED MANAGEMENT PROGRAMMES – these programmes have been developed to reduce the use of pesticides by creating habitats which encourage populations of predators. This form of biological control has commercial and environmental benefits.

FINES – these are set out in the 1990 Environmental Protection Act. Maximum fines that can be imposed in Magistrate's Courts for water pollution offences were increased by the Act – from £2,000 to £20,000 for each offence.

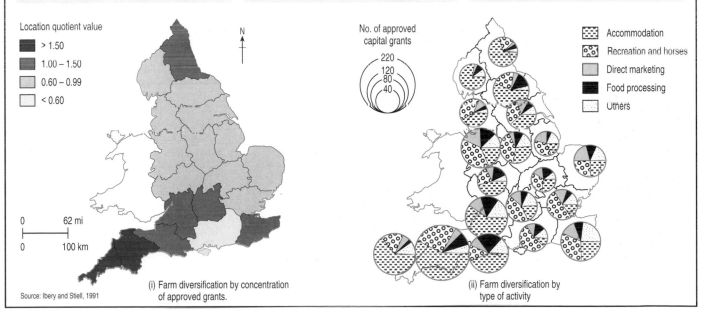

Location quotient value
- > 1.50
- 1.00 – 1.50
- 0.60 – 0.99
- < 0.60

N

0 ___ 62 mi
0 ___ 100 km

Source: Ibery and Stiell, 1991

(i) Farm diversification by concentration of approved grants.

No. of approved capital grants
220
120
80
40

Accommodation
Recreation and horses
Direct marketing
Food processing
Others

(ii) Farm diversification by type of activity

Figure 5.51 Balance in the contryside

COUNTRYSIDE STEWARDSHIP

Toby Moore

MEASURES to protect English landscapes and wildlife from the pressures of development, including a breeding programme for endangered species, were outlined yesterday by the agency which replaces the Nature Conservancy Council in England from next month.

English Nature, which has an annual budget of £32.4 million, announced schemes to pay landowners to preserve rare landscapes and pay schools to create them. About £650,000 will be spent buying land to increase the existing network of 141 national nature reserves.

Every county will have an English Nature office and wardens responsible for new "positive management agreements" with land-owners, the first of which is likely to be signed this summer. A further 124 staff will be recruited this year in addition to the 620 initially employed.

Dr Derek Landslow, the organisation's chief executive, said he wanted a new image for conservation which reflected the fact that land was no longer simply used for agriculture or forestry as it was 20 years ago.

"We want to build conservation as a core part of public policies and we need to involve a wider range of people in nature conservation, particularly local authorities, Government and industry," he said.

The new management agreements were intended to use cash incentives to better protect the 3,500 Sites of Special Scientific Interest from dereliction and development, Dr Langslow said.

"We want to show the owners and users a friendlier face in what we recognise is a harsh economic climate," he said, indicating that payments would be between £50 and £90 per acre . . .

English Nature hopes that the new scheme will fill a gap in proposals to encourage farmers not to damage landscapes. These are principally focused on cereal growers. Lowland heath and upland grazing areas are likely to be targeted . . .

A species recovery programme initially will concentrate on ensuring the survival of 12 plants and animals. Dr Langslow said these would be announced next month.

The list is likely to include the rare Lady Slipper orchid; the large blue butterfly, extinct in Britain since 1983; and stepping up the reintroduction of the red Kite. Up to 30 species eventually will become part of the recovery programme. Moves to reintroduce pupae of the large blue butterfly have begun already on four sites in the South-West.

Source: *Daily Telegraph*, 28 March 1991

AN important national move by the Countryside Commission affecting large parts of Hertfordshire was launched last week.

The Commission launched the Countryside Stewardship scheme – a new range of incentives for farmers and landowners.

It combines commercial farming and land management with conservation and public enjoyment of the countryside.

The Government is backing the pilot scheme with funds totalling £13 million for the first three years. . .

Countryside Stewardship is a voluntary scheme providing a variety of measures for managing five distinctive English landscapes – chalk and limestone grassland, lowland heath, coastal land, waterside and upland.

Landowners, private farmers including tenants, local authorities and voluntary bodies are invited to take part.

Typical annual payments range from £50 a hectare for managing limestone grassland to £275 a hectare for creating riverside meadows and opening them to the public.

Sir John Johnson, chairman of the Countryside Commission said: "Countryside Stewardship is a new flexible approach to conserving the beauty of the English countryside in that it offers a menu of conservation measures from which farmers and landowners can choose what is most suitable for their land . . .

Carol Somper, Countryside Stewardship Adviser for Hertfordshire said: "In Hertfordshire we are most keen to encourage applications in the following two key areas:

"The chalk escarpment of the Chilterns Area of Outstanding Natural Beauty (AONB) and the Ridgeway – an important feature of northern Hertfordshire is the herb-rich downland areas of scarp slopes and dry valleys.

"Secondly the river valleys of the Lea and Colne and their tributaries, whose landscapes are an attractive resource, important for wildlife, parklands and sites of antiquity.

"Traditional hay meadows, permanent pasture and their associated drainage systems are in need of conservation and restoration.

"Management of other features such as reed beds, alder carr and pollarded willows will also be supported."

Source: *Gazette and Express*, 1 January 1991

THE BIOTECHNOLOGY OPTION

The modern science of genetics was born when a fairly obscure Austrian monk called Gregor Mendel carried out some ingenious experiments which showed how characteristics were passed down successive generations of a flowering pea. It took a further, decisive step forward when two researchers at Cambridge University, James Watson and Francis Crick, showed how genes stored and passed on the necessary information for inheritance. Their discovery of the role of deoxyribonucleic acid (DNA) in the genetic code opened up the possibility of understanding and, ultimately, controlling the process of evolution.

The next step took a couple of decades to develop. This was the capacity to isolate chosen genetic material (genes) from one cell and incorporate them into another. When applied to microbes, or cells grown in tissue culture in test tubes, it opened up the possibility of radically changing the characteristics of living materials. For the first time in history, desired genetic material could be taken from one species and added to another, effectively giving the ability to 'create' new species, with physical characteristics fitted to order. This is the set of techniques which have become known as biotechnology or 'genetic engineering'...

One of the areas where biotechnology is already having the most profound effects is in agriculture, and especially crop production. At present, it takes ten to fifteen years, and a great deal of money, to produce a new crop strain. This process will be able to be enormously speeded up through a mixture of genetic engineering and tissue culture.

Tissue culture involves growing an entire plant from one cell. It allows thousands of identical plants to be produced very quickly. The Dutch multinational Unilever is already growing a million oil plantlets a year through tissue culture, which are then grown to maturity in the company's South-East Asia plantations. When combined with genetic engineering, tissue culture will allow the creation of a whole new strain of plant and, within months, the production of millions of tiny replicas of this. In the case of fast growing plants, today's invention can be this season's main crop.

The possibilities are endless, and there is much speculation about the production of square tomatoes or equal length carrots for ease of packaging, multi-coloured bananas and other science fiction ideas. (Although it must be stressed that these may soon actually exist in the real world.)

There are also more prosaic, and useful possibilities. Principle areas of biotechnological research in crops include: increased rates of growth and yields; nitrogen fixation abilities (thus reducing or eliminating the need for nitrogenous fertilisers); stress tolerance to factors like cold, drought and air pollution; and pest resistance.

• *Not such a perfect solution*
Despite the possibilities for enormous benefits, there are a number of very serious problems, and potential hazards, with biotechnology. These include physical hazards from the release of genetically altered materials, and political hazards as to how this material will actually be used.

The possibility that scientists will create something they cannot very easily control is one of the earlier and most persistent fears in our industrial society. Experience has shown that the fear all too often has some basis in reality, and many dangerous and destructive substances have been created and released into the environment. Pesticides are a prime example. Biotechnology provides extra possibilities for doing this more often, and of introducing dangerous material capable of reproducing itself. The possible hazards are such that there was a voluntary ban on certain aspects of research for a while but, despite the fact that the questions still remain undebated, the ban has now been lifted. Indeed, we are likely to see an explosion of new 'products' released into the environment, with effects which we have never really considered in much detail at all...

A more serious problem comes from the fact that ownership of research ability also bring with it the ownership of the improved plant varieties. We have already touched upon the problems of introducing high yield varieties into the Third World. Biotechnology will introduce the same dilemmas into these countries, increasing the potential profitability for those who can afford to get started and further disadvantaging everyone else.

It will also mean that many products traditionally traded from the South to the North will be capable of production in the North. For example, exporting pyrethrins, plant-based pesticides, from East African countries currently provides them with much-needed foreign exchange. The same is true of quinine from the Andes, cacao from Africa and many more plant products. These will soon be prepared in the North. It will be argued that this is an inevitable process in any development and that the net gains will benefit everybody. But history shows that when a great deal of money is made in one place, other people (and almost always a greater number of other people) suffer elsewhere...

Thus biotechnology, for all its promise, is a route fraught with dangers. It should certainly not be seen as a universal panacea, as today's optimists and advertising agents tell us. People said the same about pesticides not so very long ago.

Source: Dudley, 1987

6

The Impact of Industrial Change

Introduction

Good news ... and bad

The reports give only a glimpse of the all-pervading influence of industry in our world.

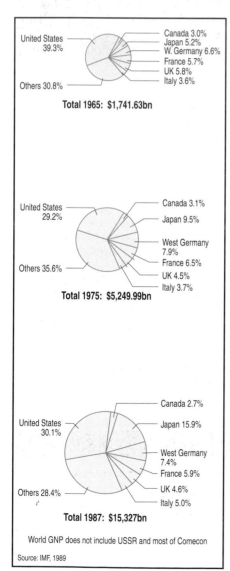

United States 39.3%
Canada 3.0%
Japan 5.2%
W. Germany 6.6%
France 5.7%
UK 5.8%
Italy 3.6%
Others 30.8%

Total 1965: $1,741.63bn

United States 29.2%
Canada 3.1%
Japan 9.5%
West Germany 7.9%
France 6.5%
UK 4.5%
Italy 3.7%
Others 35.6%

Total 1975: $5,249.99bn

United States 30.1%
Canada 2.7%
Japan 15.9%
West Germany 7.4%
France 5.9%
UK 4.6%
Italy 5.0%
Others 28.4%

Total 1987: $15,327bn

World GNP does not include USSR and most of Comecon

Source: IMF, 1989

Figure 6.1 Gross world product (percentage shares)

JOBS BOOM WITH NORTH SEA OIL

BRITAIN'S North Sea oil industry is set for another boom with huge spending and the creation of a 'substantial' number of new jobs, it was forecast yesterday.

The 10,000 jobs lost in Scotland in the 1986 oil price crash will have been recovered by the end of this year, according to the Scottish Development Agency. It estimated in its two-yearly forecast of offshore oil and gas spending plans that the oil industry will spend £27 billion in the North Sea between now and 1993, 10 times Britain's total spending on the Channel Tunnel...

'The oil and gas industry is a cornerstone of the Scottish economy and will continue to be so for many years to come,' said SDA chief executive Mr Iain Robertson...

The agency believes the current official figure for North Sea oil employment – about 60,000, half offshore, half onshore – understates the real figure, which it estimates at 70,000.

It forecasts a 'substantial' increase in this but cannot put a figure on it. The estimates are based on the assumption that the oil price will increase by 1 per cent in real terms up to 1995.

Source: *Guardian*, 31 August 1989

PLANTS CONFIRM AIR IS CLEANER
Richard Caseby

THE FIRST natural sign that British cities are breathing cleaner air has come from lichen, the world's oldest and most reliable monitor of air pollution.

Species of lichen not seen for up to 200 years are growing again in metropolitan parks after a dramatic improvement in air purity...

The shrubby, yellow lichen is spearheading an invasion in central London, Manchester, Sheffield, Leeds and Bristol after a sharp decrease in sulphur dioxide emissions, the principal product of burning coal.

Lichens absorb nutrients from the air. Many died out in the industrial revolution...

Research reveals that sulphur dioxide levels have fallen by almost two-thirds in the last eight years in west London...

Under an EC directive that came into force seven years ago, Britain must cut sulphur dioxide emissions – a big contributor to acid rain – by 60% by the year 2003.

Source: *Sunday Times*, 18 June 1989

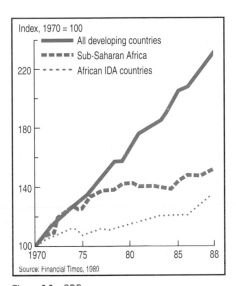

Index, 1970 = 100

Source: Financial Times, 1989

Figure 6.2   GDP

Figure 6.3   Mrs de la Vega's sewing business

AN INNOVATIVE PHILIPPINE REHABILITATION PROGRAMME CREATES NEW ENTREPRENEURS

The Philippine fishing town of Morong (population: 29,000) provides no exception to the chronic unemployment that plagues many small communities surrounding Manila.

Yet Amelita de la Vega's streetside garment shop is crowded with employees, its Singer sewing machines whirring busily almost every steamy evening...

By any yardstick, Mrs de la Vega is an extraordinarily successful entrepreneur. Her homespun manufacturing business appraised at US$160,000 employs at least 30 men and women. She travels weekly to Manila to deal with major exporters and even subcontracts additional production from other new shops that she helped establish around Morong. Her baby clothes and women's shirts and blouses are eagerly sought by buyers from New York, Panama and Hawaii.

The rise of Mrs de la Vega from poverty to business mogul is a source of hope for a Philippine economy long wracked by recession, trade deficits and widespread unemployment. What makes her story more extraordinary is that she belongs to a most disadvantaged and forgotten class of the Philippine poor, the physically disabled. Since birth, Mrs de la Vega has faced daily survival without either fingers or toes.

While exceptional, the experience of Amelita de la Vega is not unique. She is one of almost 1,500 severely disabled people throughout the Philippines who have been helped by an innovative rehabilitation project supported by the United Nations Development Programme (UNDP), the International Labour Organisation (ILO) and the Philippine Government.

Source: *World Development UNDP*, September 1988

ENQUIRY

Pages 262–65 contain reports on the effects of industrial change. For each report discuss the following questions:

1   Do you think the report contains good or bad news?

2   What is good or bad about each report?

3   For whom is the news good or bad?

4   Who is in control of the process in each case?

5   What evidence is there of the values held by the people or organisations controlling the industries?

6   Should the good effects be further distributed? How?

7   How can reparation be made for the bad effects?

8   How can the bad effects be limited in the future?

9   Which effects are caused by industrial change?

OUTCRY AS WEST DUMPS TOXIC WASTES IN AFRICA

AFRICAN leaders have strongly condemned the dumping of the West's toxic wastes in Africa, in the wake of a spate of recent revelations about this secretive and profitable trade...

'Bomb'

Nigeria was involved in a diplomatic dispute with Italy after it was discovered that over 3,500 tonnes of dangerous chemicals had been dumped at the small port of Koko by Italian ships between August 1987 and May 1988. (It has since been shown that the operation also involved Intercontract, a Swiss based company)...

An investigation of the dump was carried out by an expert team from Friends of the Earth (FoE) at the invitation of the Nigerian government. It revealed that, although the waste did not appear to be radioactive, the site was 'totally unsuited for the short or long term storage of hazardous wastes.' The team's report concludes that 'the site is extremely dangerous and liable to explode or catch fire at any time. It is no exaggeration to say that the dump is a bomb waiting to go off.'...

Profits out of poison

The Nigerian scandal, however, is only one of a number recently

Figure 6.4   Toxic waste, which was illegally exported to Nigeria, aboard the deep-sea carrier

exposed in West Africa and is a part of a lucrative trade in which Western companies export an estimated 20 million tonnes of toxic wastes a year to poor countries.

Source: *Spur*, July/August 1989

AN APPALLING ANNIVERSARY

SOME anniversaries are best forgotten. Others offer little more than a peg for a few reflections. This vintage year has, among many, come up with the Armada, the Glorious Revolution and Munich. At the weekend there was another, very recent by such standards, which was marked by a riot, a moving report on the BBC World Service and the odd

paragraph in newspapers round the world. Some 500 people were arrested when a demonstration turned into an attempt to storm the Bhopal plant of Union Carbide on the fourth anniversary of an unparalleled man-made catastrophe in which noxious gas killed 3,000 people, crippled at least 26,000 and left many others to die a more or less lingering death.

In one appalling respect the fourth anniversary is exactly like earlier ones. There is no sign of compensation for tens of thousands of shattered families.

Source: *Guardian*, 3 December 1989

GRAND CANYON SMOG CRISIS PROVES TEST FOR BUSH PLEDGE

Simon Tisdal

THE plight of the Grand Canyon has become an early test of the Bush Administration's pledge to provide clean air for every American by the year 2000.

Since the early 1970s, as a result of man-made air pollution, visibility had begun to decline sharply. Naturally-occurring mist has thickened into a dense haze formed by smog from the motorways of California and chemical smelters to the south-west.

In winter, the problem is worsened by dry, sooty sulphates produced by coal-fired power plants.

Despite its remote location, in Arizona, the canyon sucks in pollution-bearing winds from as far away as Los Angeles and northern Mexico. It is hard to see it some days.

The Environmental Protection Agency (EPA) has been ordered by a court to decide on Thursday whether an Arizona coal-fired power station is the main source of the canyon's winter smog.

If the EPA decides that Navajo is to blame, a six-month period will ensue during which countermeasures will be considered.

But since the plant's electricity is used to pump water from the Colorado river to a federal irrigation programme, either water consumers or federal funds would be tapped. That would be a precedent, and a potentially costly one, too.

Source: *Guardian*, 3 December 1989

£270M CEGB URANIUM VENTURE IN ARCTIC UPSETS ESKIMOS

Rob Edwards

THE Central Electricity Generating Board has taken a 20 per cent stake in a £270 million uranium mining and processing project in the Arctic tundra of north west Canada, it was confirmed yesterday.

Eskimos – native Inuit Indians – claim the proposed plant would threaten herds of caribou which they regard as sacred. Yesterday Friends of the Earth energy spokesman, Simon Roberts, said: 'This is just another example of the CEGB's blatant disregard for the delicate balance of the natural environment.'

In partnership with West German and South Korean companies, the CEGB has applied for permission to extract and process 55 million tons of uranium ore over the next 10 years at Kiggavik, near Baker lake in the Keewatin region.

The mine would produce 3.1 million tons of uranium oxide for use in nuclear power stations and 50 million tons of radioactive waste.

It involves digging two open pits 200 metres deep in the permafrost. A settlement for 250 workers, new roads, an airport, and a marine terminal are also planned.

Source: *Guardian*, 3 December 1989

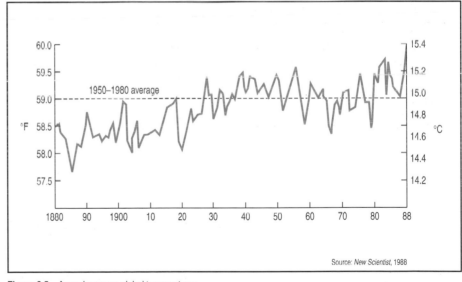

Source: *New Scientist*, 1988

Figure 6.5   Annual average global temperatures

RESEARCH

1   Search a week's newspapers and take cuttings of any reports about industry. Share these with colleagues monitoring other newspapers. Choose two 'good' news and two 'bad' news reports, and discuss the questions above with a partner or group.

2   Write a short comment on your first impressions of the impact of industry and industrial change.

Past and present

POSTMARK THE BLACK COUNTRY

CND's Bruce Kent once said: 'I've spoken twice in the Black Country – first time at Coventry, second time at Stoke-on-Trent.' Considering Stoke and Coventry are over 60 miles apart – whilst the Black Country is barely 12 miles across at its widest – this is quite a claim!

But (be honest now) how many of you reading this know that neither Stoke nor Coventry – nor Birmingham – are anywhere near the Black Country? In truth, the Black Country is a small industrial region, located today on the western fringe of the West Midlands conurbation. There are no big cities here, just a broken collection of coalfield villages, a few of which (Dudley, Walsall and Wolverhampton) have grown to be busy minor towns.

A stable peasantry

But let's skip back a bit. In the beginning, things were very quiet (400 million years ago the area was a tropical coral reef!); later, the landscape became deep and lush green and the earliest inhabitants were the Celts – a sparse, forest-dwelling people, whom the Romans promptly colonised. Then the Anglo-Saxons came, slaughtering the Celtic men and outlawing all Celt influence (Walton means 'foreigner settlement'). What was it like to be reclassified a 'foreigner' in your own land?

In Medieval times, a stable peasantry farmed the now forest-less land. Then came Capitalism's infancy, and the Industrial Revolution sharply cut its teeth. Local Silurian limestone and the exceptional Ten Yard coal seam attracted money and minds alike. According to my mother's research, some coal faces were 17 yards high – they needed scaffold to reach them! In 1700 they extracted 70,000 tonnes of coal annually; by 1860 they took 7½ million.

As the industry resulting from this onslaught of fuel began to bolt, stretch and explode, so it demanded a workforce of equal enormity – and that was the end of that stable Medieval peasantry. Lured and starved into the expanding new towns, this refugee population recomposed themselves into a new culture of immense resilience – they became the world's very first proletariat, and now they called their ruined landscape the 'Black Country'.

To enslave

Let's take an historical perspective. At a local level, the women nail and chain makers endured 17 hour days, in lethal conditions, from early childhood onwards, only to earn far reduced wages from the men who cartelled their iron supplies; they also suffered a sexual repression similar to that used against Parisian laundresses. (Working in constantly hot conditions, they preferred to work semi-clad, and were then routinely molested by men passing their workshops.)

Yet trace this perspective wider and the story actually *worsens*. Those nails they made nailed ships together, and those chains chained limbs together . . . the very technology used to enslave 100 million West Africans was therefore made, by the hour, by the ton, right here in the Black Country.

The start of the end for the Black Country came as early as the 1890s. Nomadic capital quickly collapsed a whole series of presumed 'certainties' and the twentieth century merely accelerated such upheavals; that old Black Country iconography rapidly disintegrated. The greatest change of all has been in the local population, now a constellation of cultures. Peoples of Irish, Welsh, Yorkshire, Scottish, European Jewish, Polish, Ukrainian, Jamaican, Italian, Indian, Pakistani, Turkish, Bengali, Bangladeshi, Chinese, Ugandan Asian, Kenyan Asian, Cypriot and Vietnamese origin have all migrated here.

Source: Vanes, 1989

The past is with us

'Postmark the Black Country' describes some of the historical changes in one important English industrial region. It shows the way in which one place is part of the wider world and inextricably bound to processes beyond its borders. In the late twentieth century changes in industry come thick and fast, often even more exciting and far-reaching than those experienced in the past.

Post-industrial society

The change to what has been called a post-industrial society (another special use of the term 'industry'!) is heralded by a shift in industry from manufacturing to services, and in occupations from manual (blue-collar) to non-manual (white-collar) work.

In countries with industrialised market (capitalist) economies this has been accompanied by changes in consumption patterns, with a greater demand for luxury items. It is also suggested that there is a more obvious division of labour into a favoured and a less favoured group, the privatisation of services, and the growth of an informal economy.

The *informal sector* includes waged work that is largely part-time, small-scale, local, and irregular. It also includes a *self-service* (DIY) approach by households, and goes some way to providing an alternative lifestyle for long-term unemployed or early-retired people. Much of it does not appear in official statistics. The informal economy is also very important in Third World countries.

What will the next 'revolution' bring? Maybe an 'information society' where IT leads to the replacement of labour in the service sector. What effect would this have on employment and life style?

GROUP DISCUSSION

1 Bearing in mind the perspectives suggested by Black Country history, in what ways do you consider that the changing industrial scene represents 'progress' or a series of improvements? Who benefits?

2 Discuss the divisions of industry and occupations suggested below. Are they helpful, or are there too many cases of industries or occupations that 'don't fit' the classifications? The 'hidden assumption' here is that the economic viewpoint is paramount. Are there other important ways of classifying industry and occupations – e.g. environmental, social, moral? Try one.

3 How far do you welcome the post-industrial society? Are the division of labour and high unemployment the only 'bad' aspects? What could be its main advantages?

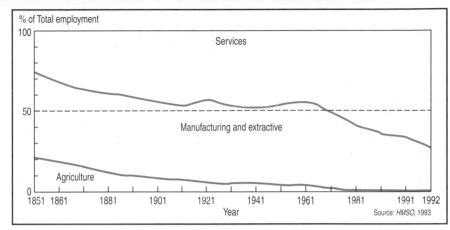

Figure 6.6 Employment in the industrial sectors: UK 1851–1986

STATISTICAL ENQUIRY

Consider Figure 6.6 and Tables 6.1, 6.2, 6.3, 6.4.

1 Comment on the importance and growth of the different sectors of industry in the UK and the trends in occupation structure.

2 Explain the relationship between industries and occupations in the UK.

3 Use the statistical data to draw an annotated map or diagram to show the importance of different sectors of industry around the world and the changes taking place.

Table 6.1 Changes in occupation, UK 1970–80

% change	Occupations
< −10	Miners and quarries (A); glass and ceramics (B)
−9 to −5	Leather; construction; drivers of cranes, etc. (A)
−4 to −1	Farmers; woodworkers; textiles; clothing; food; painters; labourers (A); transport; clerical (C)
0 to +4	Engineers (B); 'other' products (B); warehouse workers; sales (C); service and recreation (C); administrators and managers (C); professional and technical (C); armed forces
> +4	Gas, coke, chemicals (A); furnace and forge (B); electric and electronic engineering (B); paper and printing

A, B and C: Groups of occupations that have a tendency to associate spatially in the UK
Source: 1981 Census

Table 6.2 Industry and occupation in the UK, 1971

		Primary	% in each occupation group		
			Secondary	Tertiary	Quartenary
Industry	Primary	78.4	7.0	6.5	7.9
Group	Secondary	0.1	53.3	17.8	28.6
	Tertiary	0.2	22.1	52.6	24.8
	Quartenary	1.2	6.4	8.4	83.7

Source: Daniels, 1982

Table 6.3 Proportions of GDP from each industrial sector, 1965–90

Industrial market economies	1965	1990
% Agriculture	5	2
% Industry	40	34
% Service	55	64

Developing market economies		
% Agriculture	26	16
% Industry	30	37
% Service	44	47

Table 6.4 Changes in GDP in % per annum, total economy and selected activities

World	1970–80	1980–90	Developed market economies	1970–80	1980–90
Total	3.8	3.2	Total	3.4	3.1
Per capita	2.4	1.4	Per capita	2.5	2.4
Manufactures	4.3	3.7	Manufactures	3.5	3.3
Finance etc.	5.1	3.1	Finance etc.	3.8	3.0

Developing market economies	1970–80	1980–90	Centrally planned economies	1970–80	1980–90
Total	5.6	3.2	Total	5.3	3.5
Per capita	3.2	1.2	Per capita	3.6	2.8
Manufactures	6.8	6.0	Manufactures	4.9	3.2
Finance etc.	6.5	3.6	Finance etc.	5.2	2.9

...Oak is a Birmingham suburban ...opping centre where a major radial route (the Bristol Road) crosses an important ring road (the Outer Circle route) at the Triangle Site.

Since before 1970 plans to widen the Bristol Road and to improve the junction had been under discussion. From time to time the plans were changed and the uncertainty led to 'planning blight', with shops and houses on short leases sinking into disrepair and even dereliction.

The information on these two pages describes the area and the planning from 1980, and the development that resulted. Study Figure 6.7 and Table 6.5. Read the 'Development guidelines' and the 'Planning history'.

Table 6.5 Statistical data for the area in Figure 6.7

Land use	Hectares
Industry and warehousing	18
Land suitable for industrial development	19
Retail and offices	9
Hospital	11
Garden nursery	6
Housing	37
Public open space for recreation	13

Population	3587 people
Residential density	97 per ha
Retired	622 people
Economically active	1779 people
	(1059 males, 720 females)
Unemployed	10 % (1989)

Economically active people

Employment	%	Socio-economic group	%
Manufacturing	40	Professional	2
Construction	8	Intermediate	13
Distribution	17	Skilled non-manual	16
Transport	8	Skilled manual	30
Other services	27	Semi-skilled	32
		Unskilled	7

Source: 1981 Census: small area statistics

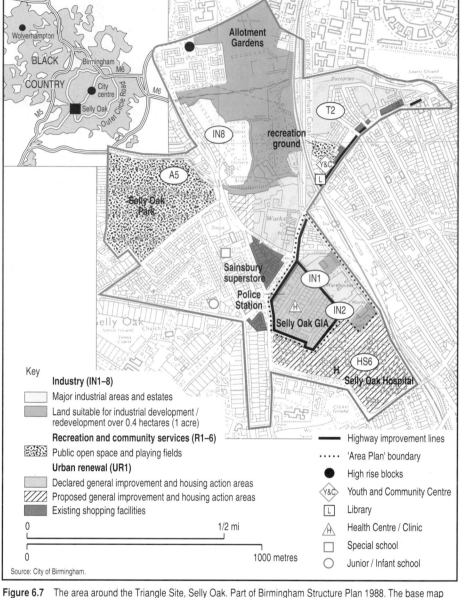

Key

Industry (IN1–8)
- Major industrial areas and estates
- Land suitable for industrial development / redevelopment over 0.4 hectares (1 acre)

Recreation and community services (R1–6)
- Public open space and playing fields

Urban renewal (UR1)
- Declared general improvement and housing action areas
- Proposed general improvement and housing action areas
- Existing shopping facilities

- —— Highway improvement lines
- ····· 'Area Plan' boundary
- ● High rise blocks
- Y&C Youth and Community Centre
- L Library
- H Health Centre / Clinic
- □ Special school
- ○ Junior / Infant school

0 ———————— 1/2 mi
0 ———————— 1000 metres

Source: City of Birmingham.

Figure 6.7 The area around the Triangle Site, Selly Oak. Part of Birmingham Structure Plan 1988. The base map shows the buildings in 1980

Development guidelines, July 1980

The Local Planning Authority recognises the urgent need to restore confidence and to revitalise the Selly Oak Area.

It is essential that any scheme should treat the area available for development in a comprehensive manner. The predominant use should be shopping. Consideration will be given to schemes comprising a large retail store provided that a number of smaller retail uses are offered in conjunction with the main unit, and adequate car parking and service facilities are incorporated within the scheme.

In addition, any scheme should make provision for the erection of public conveniences and a public house.

The planning history

'My major concern at the outline stage was that the store should be fully integrated with and relating to the existing Selly Oak shopping centre.'
– City planner

February 1982: Outline consent granted for superstore (35,000 square feet), public house, community centre, public conveniences, arcade of shops and parking area.

August 1982: Outline application withdrawn.

January 1984: Outline consent granted for retail store, ancillary facilities, unit shop, public house, car park, service area and access. Applicant advised that detailed consent would only be granted for a store incorporating an entrance and frontage to Bristol Road.

November 1984: Detailed consent granted for scheme, omitting main entrance and frontage to Bristol Road.
'A petition was submitted, signed by all local traders, expressing full support for the scheme.'

– Planners' report, November 1984

1985

Sainsbury's was built in 1985, with a large car cark and a public house on the Triangle Site. The traffic around the Triangle is consequently very heavy and rush hour delays are usual. Sainsbury's turns its back on the main Bristol Road and, though pedestrian lights at the road junctions suggest a flow of people, the shop and car park do form an area functioning separately from the rest of Selly Oak.

The photograph in Figure 6.8ii shows the junction of the Bristol Road and Chapel Lane, looking towards the old established Birmingham Battery and Metal Company opposite Sainsbury's. The firm is nothing to do with electric batteries. It refines non-ferrous metals, especially nickel and copper, stamps brass, and until recently fabricated tubes. You can read about it below and on page 270.

Figure 6.8 'After a century as a family firm the 1980s recession and pressure from competitors has made survival difficult.' – Battery director

You can read about it below and on page 270.

ENQUIRY

In what ways were plans modified between 1980 and 1985? Why do you think this happened? Who were the losers from the modifications and who gained from them? What other information would you need to fully understand the developments at Selly Oak? How could you get it?

The Battery site

Even in the early 1980s the Battery Company had sold off some marginal land (including the site of the Works Social Club) to the multinational Woolworth Holdings PLC who built a B&Q DIY superstore at the bottom of Chapel Lane.

In 1988 the firm employed over 300 people and had a turnover of £5–20 million. Overproduction on the world market led to the closure of the Tube Mill and the land opposite Sainsbury's was sold to Nairn Property Developments, a subsidiary of Ossory Estates PLC who own four firms in the USA and seven in the UK. 'We doubled production at the Tube Mill in response to management encouragement – but it still closed,' said a Battery worker.

In 1989 the Birmingham Battery Company was taken over by Bromsgrove Industries. The local press stated that they had paid £6.2 million and taken on £2.5 million debts.

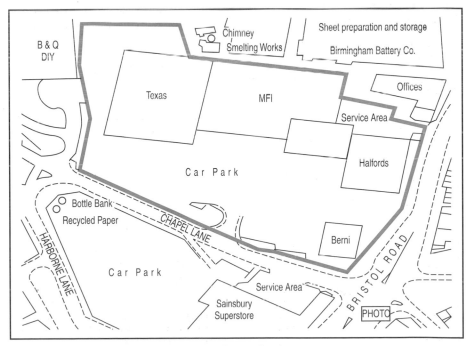

Figure 6.9 Map of the proposals put forward by Nairn Property Developments

Bromsgrove Industries owns 13 firms in the Midlands, all involved in metal industries and engineering, so they intended the factory to continue functioning. 'The first we knew about it was when we read it in the newspaper', said a Battery worker. Nairn Property Developments has put forward a plan to develop their land into a retail site. Figure 6.9 shows the outline of the proposals. Halfords would include a self-service car maintenance area.

The proposed stores will all be owned by large corporations. For example, Halfords is owned by the Ward White Group PLC which has companies in the USA, France and elsewhere, and manufactures shoes, metals insulation materials, etc. Berni Inns is owned by Grand Metropolitan PLC whose interests world-wide include particularly USA and South Africa.

Next to the proposed development there will still be the metal refining and

brass stamping operations. Behind the site the 'land suitable for industrial development' has been declared unsuitable for residential development because of the metal works waste tip and the possibility of methane build-up from the Wimpey Waste Management site by the canal. The traffic build-up in Chapel Lane needs attention and the question of integrating developments with the rest of Selly Oak is important.

PLANNING DECISION EXERCISE

Suppose you have to contribute to a discussion leading to a decision about the development of the Battery site. Prepare yourself a brief on the basis of the information provided here and your own ideas on urban development.

You may take on a specific viewpoint. Actors in the decision-making process could include the managing director of the Battery Company, the representative of the developers, the representatives of the proposed retail outlets, local residents, local traders, local authority planners, local councillors.

In a group, arrange a planning meeting. First, decide whether retailing is a suitable use for this land. Second, make a decision on the proposal from Nairn Property Developments.

ENQUIRY

Explore a development in your own local area. The local press is a useful source, and maps and information can be obtained from your local Planning Office. *Who Owns Whom* and the *Kompass Directories* are a source for company information. Build up a file on the development and follow the decision-making process.

SYNTHESIS

The changes in Selly Oak reflect trends that can be seen in many towns in countries with industrial market economies. Look back at the description of 'post-industrial society' (page 266). Explain how the events and plans in Selly Oak relate to this concept.

Processes of Industrial Change

Linkages and multiplier effects

Most industries are made up of a very complex web of links between places and people. A change in one place, or by one person, affects all the rest. Linkages may involve the transfer of information, materials, money or people. They can be 'seen' (goods, pieces of paper) or 'unseen' (ideas, messages). They may be carried by people, wires, pipes, lorries, radio waves, etc.

The linkages may be organised between firms, departments, individuals or combinations of these. Influences outside the immediate linkages of a firm still affect it – for example, the

Selly Oak company closed their Tube Mill because of world over-capacity. The concept of industrial linkages helps to explain the idea of the *multiplier effect* where the arrival of a new industrial establishment, or the closing down of one, has far-reaching effects on the economy of the area around it.

The 'input → process → output' model of manufacturing is a useful starting point for the study of linkages and multiplier effects. Figure 6.10 is a simplification for manufacturing industry, but there is much more. Before exploring this in the example of the aluminium smelter on page 272, it will be useful to study examples from your own experience.

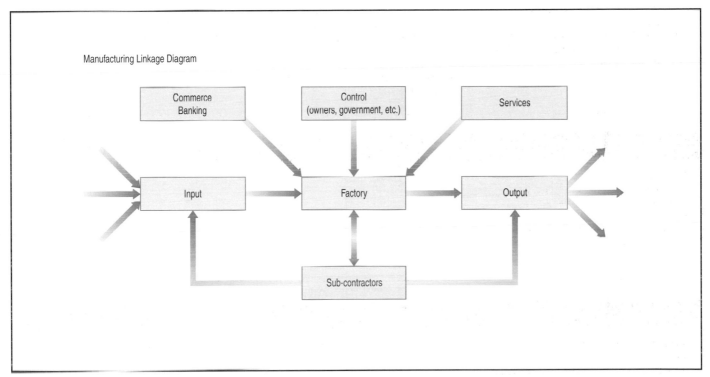

Figure 6.10   Manufacturing linkage diagram

BRAINSTORMING

Choose some simple single product (e.g. a cotton reel or a metal washer). Think of the different links the factory will have – trying to list as many as you can – with raw materials, energy, building materials, labour, customers, machinery, etc.

Take a large piece of paper, put the factory at the centre, and arrange your list around it in a sensible pattern of inputs and outputs, linked by arrows. Keep this part of the diagram at the centre – there is more to come!

Now take the links back a further stage. To what is each linked? For example, labour will be linked to family, home, shops, schools, etc. Add these links around the outside of your diagram.

LOCAL ENQUIRY

Choose a large service industry establishment in your area and consider what the effect of its closure would be. Draw a diagram to illustrate this, and if possible quantify some of the effects.

CASE STUDY *The Australian Aluminium Industry*

The Comalco-sponsored aluminium smelter at Gladstone, Queensland, was the first of six to be proposed by multinational enterprises for Australia. It came from an agreement between Queensland and Comalco to develop the Weipa bauxite deposits in the north of the state. The smelter will eventually produce over 400 000 tonnes of aluminium each year.

The major factors leading to the choice of Australia for new developments were:

1 Australia produces 30% of the world's bauxite, but has a relatively small smelter capacity.

2 Huge amounts of electricity are needed to refine and smelt bauxite. Large quantities of cheap coal are available in Eastern Australia.
3 The market outlook, when decisions were being made, suggested a world shortfall of aluminium.
4 Environmental pressure in the USA, Europe and Japan was against the building of smelters.

Australia's 'competitors' for new smelters are Malaysia, Indonesia, Brazil, Venezuela and the Middle East.

Gladstone has a population of about 20 000 people. Its attractions as one of the sites were:

1 Cheap electricity in bulk from a 1650 MW thermal power station.
2 Supplies of alumina from the 2 million tonne capacity Gladstone alumina refinery already in production.
3 Gladstone's natural deep-water harbour.
4 Gladstone's sub-region could eventually provide housing, infrastructure and community support for further major industry.
5 State government policy supported the development.
6 Flat industrial land was available next to the sea.

Figure 6.11   Aluminium refinery, Gladstone

Figure 6.12   Processing bauxite

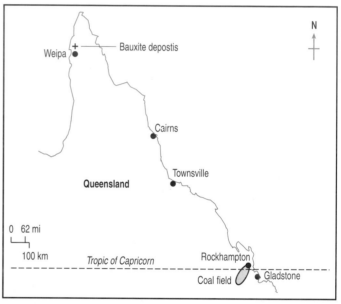

Figure 6.13   Northern Australia

ENQUIRY

The decision to build a new smelter was part of the plan by multinational enterprises to increase production in Australia.

1 Discuss the six attractions of the Gladstone site. Explain each one and put them in a ranked order of importance. How do they link to the national scale factors?

2 Study Table 6.6. In what ways will the smelter have greatest impact at each scale? Explain how 23 000 jobs can be created by a smelter employing 1900 workers. How long would you expect it to take for these changes to work through the system?

3 The following all used the multiplier estimates as evidence in discussions about building the smelter: local and state planning authorities; local business people; Comalco Ltd; Newcastle (NSW) Ecology Centre environmentalists; Builders Workers Industrial Union. How would you expect each to use the information?

4 The smelter has been built. If you lived in Gladstone, would you expect you and your family to be pleased or sorry?

Table 6.6   The multiplier effect of Gladstone Smelter*

	The smelter	Gladstone area	Queensland State	Australia
Industrial output A£ million	595	900 (+250%)	1047 (+7%)	1074 (+1%)
Household income A£ million	28	62 (+74%)	84 (+2%)	95 (+0.3%)
Employment jobs	1900	5084 (+55%)	13 562 (+2%)	23 309 (+0.5%)

* Lowest estimate, per annum full production, not including the power station and alumina refinery which were already in production   Source: Mandeville, 1983

Industrial landscapes and location

What proportion of land must be used for it to be reasonable to call an area 'industrial'? Should an area only be called 'industrial' if its industries are primary and secondary and perhaps warehousing? Terms must be carefully defined to avoid confusion. The landscapes of new light manufacturing industry are certainly different from those of older heavy industry (Figure 6.15). Those of the service industries, like the city centre in Figure 6.14, are completely different again.

Who are the people who have been responsible for creating these environments? Often the present landscape has been created by piece-meal accretion and replacement. Many manufacturing and service enterprises are located on land that is already part of towns. Others may be sited on 'greenfield' sites. In either case, the final building and activity are the result of complex decision-making by a number of people. The lists on page 274 give some idea of the number of people and organisations who might be involved in decisions about the use of a greenfield site (Figure 6.16). Things could be even more complex in an urban area.

The cumulative effects of changes in location pattern – factory closures or new enterprises – can create processes of either decay or growth in specific regions and small areas. In urban areas it is possible to see cycles of decay and growth especially associated with industrial land use. Often periods of dereliction and planning blight seem inevitable before areas are renewed.

Locational decisions and survival

Geographers have studied industrial location at both macro and micro levels. Some studies have concentrated on understanding individual decisions and the power structures and strategies behind them (a behavioural approach). Others have looked at patterns of location over a wide area or in many examples and have developed theories about industrial location based mainly on economic ideas. They have suggested that industrialists look for locations that can satisfy their requirements, rather than the perfect best location – a 'satisficer' location rather than 'optimum' location. The argument continues that market forces would then eliminate firms at badly chosen locations.

In today's world, where environmental, social and political costs are increasingly counted, the traditional 'least-cost' location models emphasising transport are quite inadequate.

Figure 6.14   Keswick town centre

Figure 6.15   Ebbw Valley Steelworks, Wales

Figure 6.16   An industrial development on a greenfield site

CASE STUDY *Micrel Relocates*

A 'greenfield' site next to the M40 south of Warwick is being considered by a company called Micrel for a micro-electronics assembly factory. It will move from an old factory in the Black Country. The new site has been designated by the county council for compulsory purchase.

Factors to consider

Transport costs
Parking facilities
Traffic problems in the local area
Availability of labour locally
Level of rent and rates for factory
Visual impact of factory
Noise and smell from factory and lorries
Increase in local traffic that will be generated
Price and quality of housing nearby
Shopping facilities nearby
Buses to the site

Leisure facilities in local area (golf etc.)
Cost and efficiency of services (gas, water, etc.)
Skills required from employees
Space for expansion in the future
EEC grants available
Local government incentives for new industry
Level of local wages
Waste disposal provision
Government loans and grants for new industry
Attitudes of local people to industry
Strength of trade unions in the area
Quality of building and storage facilities on site

Interested people

A Warwickshire county councillor
Warwick planning officer
Official from the Department of Trade and Industry
Owner of 20% of the shares of Micrel
Chairperson of the board of directors of Micrel
Micrel wholesale customer in Birmingham
Components supplier in Coventry
Farmworker on nearby farm
Owner of land under discussion
Owner of large country house nearby
Unemployed factory worker in Leamington
Manager of proposed factory
Worker employed by Micrel in the Black Country
Owner of village shop nearby
Retired person living in a village nearby
Local construction worker
Local architect

ENQUIRY

What kinds of urban environment are created by high densities of different service industries?

DISCUSSION

Study the list of people who may be interested in the decision, and the list of factors they may think are important.

1 Which of the people do you think will have the strongest influence on the decision and why?

2 Take each person in turn and rank the factors which you think they would consider most important. What do your lists suggest about the value systems of each?

3 What groups of common interest are likely to form?

4 Do any strong conflicts of interest arise? Which viewpoints do you think will carry most weight?

RESEARCH

Make up a similar scenario for the location of another new industrial enterprise (for example, a nuclear power station on the west coast of India, or a hypermarket on derelict land in inner-city Manchester). What information do you need to gather in order to understand the decision-making process?

Making it geographical

The geographical patterns move to centre stage when the impacts of economic and political changes are studied. Figure 6.17 simplifies and generalises a very complex reality. The lists in each 'impact' column are not exhaustive: perhaps you can add some more.

The way in which the impact of industrial change is felt, and the control you have over the impact, depends on who you are and where you are. You can see several sets of 'opposites' listed in the impacts section of the diagram. Often the same industrial change produces impacts at both ends of the scale: the 'yuppy' earning £35 000 a year is part of the same change in industrial structure that has brought unemployment and poverty to many skilled manual workers; the satisfaction of some managers when union power is reduced, because their industry requires less labour, is an impact of the same change that brings, despondency and reduced self-esteem to some union members.

There is no doubt that change and development in industry is often full of tension and conflict, especially between 'capital' and 'labour' when people identify strongly with only one of these elements of industry. This conflict and the variety of impacts experienced by different groups of people in different places should not obscure the enormous benefit brought to many by industrial developments. Read 'Quest for water', a report from an aid charity (Action Aid) which describes an industrial project and its impact in Mozambique and consider the activities on page 276.

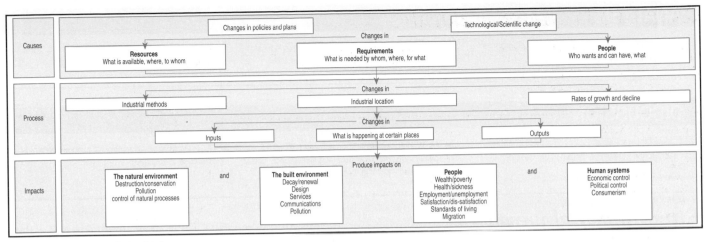

Figure 6.17 The impact of industrial change

QUEST FOR WATER

At independence, the government of Mozambique promised to put a source of fresh water within a kilometre of every home. Any hope of reaching that goal was dashed in 1980 when South African-backed rebels embarked on a scorched earth campaign that has spread terror, famine and homelessness throughout the countryside. One in 3 health centres have been destroyed, over 2,500 schools closed and barely 7% of Mozambican children have access to clean, drinking water.

Their futures – and that of Mozambique – still hang on a political knife edge but one small company in Maputo, the capital, has joined forces with them in the quest for water.

Eusebia was at a pump...near to the city of Maputo

'This is the fourth time I've been here today. It's a 20 minute walk for me and that's much better than it used to be. I would walk 10 km every time I needed water and always with a 20 litre can on my head. Now we can stop and talk when we get here. Of course, my dream is to have water in my own house but this is fine for now.'...

The bright, blue handpump, emblazoned with the word RURAL, is the fruit of an unusual partnership between the government of Mozambique and the embryonic private sector, now re-emerging from a long period of enforced dormancy.

Fresh water requires iron sheets, brass linings and round, cold, rolled steel and those cost good, hard cash. For nearly 10 years, UDAAS, the national water authority, had tried to establish a local handpump industry to save on foreign exchange but also to stop the proliferation of different models – many from South Africa – which aid agencies were importing to bring water to their project areas.

A domestic supplier would not only prevent the duplication of types, it could also provide a more reliable supply of spare parts in the event of breakdowns...

In 1984, the Collinson brothers had paid £600,000 for a workshop abandoned by the Portugese which had subsequently fallen upon hard times under a Workers Commission.

'We reorganized,' recalled Antonio Collinson, a 46 year old former graduate of Maputo's Industrial School, 'We took on 60 more workers and we started up new lines'...

Five years ago, Industrias Collinson began to manufacture handpumps. UDAAS asked them to concentrate on the India Mark II, a cheap and easy-to-fix model widely used in Africa...The firm adapted the pump for use over shallow wells...

'We only started making water pumps to make life a little easier for people in the rural areas,' Collinson relates. 'So far we've produced over 800 and the government buys them all but we only make a small profit because it's a state project. We've been able to keep the unit cost down because we had some old, raw materials left over – steel from Sweden, Spanish pipes and other parts from West Germany.'...

Most pumps serve hundreds of households and so work a busy, 12 hour day. In the humid, coastal regions, the salty air speeds up corrosion in the pump's working parts, thus increasing the likelihood of breakdown.

One way to combat that is galvanisation, a process which coats the pumprod with a rustproof film of zinc and doubles their working life to nearly 20 years. But the equipment was only available abroad and the Collinsons could not afford that scale of investment.

In 1987, Action Aid offered to buy Industrias Collinson a galvanizing unit if the company would pay off the loan by supplying the government with 240 handpumps free of charge. The Collinsons agreed and having fulfilled their side of the bargain, are now galvanizing all new pumps that they manufacture for UDAAS.

The result has been a marked improvement in the quality of handpump manufacture and a small but vital step towards the goal of a low-cost, Mozambican industry capable of meeting – and maintaining – its national water needs...

Source: *Common cause* (No. 1), June 1989

ANALYSIS

1 Draw an 'input → process → output' diagram for Industrias Collinson.

2 Make a list of who has benefited from this industrial development and from the Aid project in 1987.

DISCUSSION

1 How far is Industrias Collinson a profit orientated enterprise? Does this influence the development?

2 This is a very positive report written in a funding agency magazine. Are there negative aspects that are glossed over or ignored?

3 What seems to be necessary for such a worthwhile enterprise to succeed?

Environmental impacts

The obvious impact of industry on the environment is nearly always negative (see page 277). At a global scale, changes in the composition of the atmosphere and oceans are mainly the result of industrialisation and industrial processes. Over-exploitation of natural resources like wood or minerals may lead to many problems. At a regional scale, pollution from waste products and from industrial accidents is widespread, and especially associated with the chemical and energy industries. Close to industrial establishments, visual and noise pollution are common, and the industrial environment itself is often dangerous.

The positive effects on the environment are less immediate and often several stages removed from the industry and its processes. They reflect factors such as increased affluence, the investment of money earned by industry, and the widespread use of industrial products. Think about almost any part of the built environment that you particularly like and see what part industry has played in its creation. The development of electricity and water supplies, sewerage and drainage systems and transport networks have depended on the technology and products of modern industry.

Industrial change can also bring about improvements in the environment, for instance through the application of new processes to keep the air cleaner or to reduce water pollution. The increase in service industries has produced changes that are not all environmentally bad – for example, cleaner industrial landscapes; shopping centres designed for shopper comfort as well as to maximise consumerism; leisure facilities on lakes and seashores that can blend in with the natural environment. These less obvious positive impacts should be balanced against the more immediate impacts with which the rest of this section is mainly concerned.

ANALYSIS

1 Decide for each of the following reports whether the impacts mentioned are mainly local, national or global.

2 Classify each example of pollution quoted by its cause (accident, pollution by waste, by-product or side-effect of an industrial process, etc.). You may wish to make your own classification of causes.

3 Choose one example where industrial change is a factor in the impact (e.g. the increase in the production of pesticides, the obsolescence of electrical equipment, the building of new establishments) and work through the model on page 275 to put the impact in an overall context.

ENQUIRY

Select two different kinds of environmental impact from the examples. Explore possible ways of rectifying or controlling negative impacts, and how to deal with processes that lead to harmful results.

Figure 6.18 Smog

TAX THE POLLUTERS Sean Ryan

THE public could be paying 'pollution tax' on a wide range of everyday items within four years.

The idea is aimed at forcing shoppers and producers to switch to more environment-friendly goods – and paying the price if they don't.

So pesticides and fertilisers blamed for polluting Britain's water supplies would be taxed, making the vegetables and fruit they help produce more expensive, and giving a boost to those which are organically grown.

Similarly, the tax on unleaded petrol could be cut still further as an incentive to drivers to get their cars converted...

The plan, which represents the most concrete series of proposals yet to solve the Government's dilemma over the environment, drawing on market forces to provide the green way forward, was welcomed by environment groups last night.

Under the scheme, the tax would also be levied on coal and electricity, which fuel the greenhouse effect; refrigerators with ozone-eating CFCs; cars and oil, with the aim of conserving energy; and paper and disposable nappies, the products of trees.

Source: *Daily Mail*, 16 October 1989

BHOPAL VICTIMS TO BACK DRIVE AGAINST TOXIC WASTE FIRM
Anne Cunningham

SURVIVORS from the Bhopal chemical disaster are to fly to Britain to support campaigners calling for the closure of Walsall toxic waste disposal firm Leigh Interests.

The Bhopal survivors – still suffering long-term effects from the 1984 tragedy – will visit the Walsall site and meet MPs, environmentalists and local residents.

Their three-day visit to the West Midlands is being co-ordinated by Friends of the Earth and Birmingham's Health and Safety Advice Centre.

Advice centre worker, Tommy Harte said: 'We hope their visit will focus attention on the Leigh Interests campaign and help build international links for better laws on chemical waste and pollution.'...

Claim

Leigh Interests were at the centre of an international row last year when they offered to treat waste from the controversial Karin B cargo ship.

Protesters against the firm claim it is damaging their health and fails to treat poisonous waste safely.

But the company deny the plant is dangerous...

Source: *Daily News*, 1 September 1989

FACELIFT FOR DERELICT LAND
Kevin Palmer

TOP international architects and design consultants will arrive in Birmingham tomorrow to start planning a super development to change the face of the city.

The ambitious scheme could include a 40-storey skyscraper as a 21st century landmark that would dominate the sky-line for miles around.

The specialists are being asked to produce a design for a multi-million pound transformation of the Star site – almost 80 acres of land in the Heartlands development zone...

Most of the site, based on the old Nechells B power station, is derelict

The International Business Exchange, as the project is called, envisages three million square feet of top quality offfices, up to 450 square feet of shopping, and two hotels of 250–300 bedrooms, one of them international standard.

These could include an ice rink, cinemas, sports/health clubs, pubs, restaurants and nightclubs.

Source: *Daily News*, 24 October 1989

PCB THREAT TO OCEAN MAMMALS
Paul Brown

SEALS, polar bears and some whales could face extinction unless there is urgent international action to stop PCBs being released into the atmosphere, a leading geneticist said yesterday after gathering information from around the world.

Recent tests on dead marine mammals found around the world have shown a rising quantity of PCBs in blubber. Seals, sea lions, walruses, and polar bears were all at risk because they were meat-eaters at the end of the food chain, according to Professor Joseph Cummins, a geneticist at the University of Western Ontario, in Cananda.

The world's ocean fisheries could become so contaminated that it would be unsafe for people in countries such as Japan, where fish is an important part of the diet...

The PCBs collected in oily fish and fat and then concentrated in the mammals that preyed upon them. 'We are getting to the point that I fear that many of the wild species will not be able to reproduce and only the ones in zoos will survive,' he said.

Marine mammals were liable to reproductive failure when exposed to even moderate levels of PCBs...

Source: *Guardian*, 31 August 1989

Human impacts

'The nightmare of nothing to do' describes the hopelessness, as Paul Theroux sees it, of a region hit by industrial decline and unemployment. The impact of industrial change on employment patterns is striking and gives cause for great concern. At the moment the world's modern industrial economy seems to give rise to a pool of unemployed people, both in the fully industrialised nations and in the developing nations, that is unacceptable in terms of human rights and justice. When the effects of IT and computerisation are fully felt in service industries, the situation could become far worse.

But all is not doom and gloom. At a local scale the example of new industry in Jamaica has a positive impact on some women's lives (see 'The Hanover Street Project'). Likewise, many of the long-term effects of increased industrialisation are beneficial for many people, as the Figures 6.19–21 show.

The distribution of the wealth, created partly by industry, leaves much to be desired. Figure 6.21 shows the inequality of distribution within some nations. Figure 6.20 shows the tendency for regions on the periphery of an economic unit to be less wealthy than the regions in the core. This 'core-periphery' pattern is a generalised 'model' – it is not a detailed description of every area of the real world, but the idea is useful at many levels (national, regional and global) in the capitalist world. This suggests that there are economic forces which, left to themselves, lead to an unequal distribution of wealth both spatially and within society.

The Hanover Street Project, Jamaica

The Hanover Street Project, formally known as the United Women's Woodworking and Welding Project, is an experiment in training women for jobs usually held only by men. Begun in 1976, the project is still developing. It has demonstrated that low-income women can learn non-traditional skills and can work together to improve their lives.

'I feel better about myself because I now have a trade. Things I would have given out to have made or fixed, I now can do myself. My family life has improved because now I know more about family living.
– Maud Lawrence, welder

'In my community people have a better feeling about me. They know I made my own bed.'
– Delta McFarlane, woodworker

'At first I felt I would not have been able to manage the machine work. I am fine at that now.'
– Myrtle Lawrence

'I feel better in my community because everybody calls me a "welder". Sometimes people come to visit me who are unsure of my exact address and ask for the welder-girl.'
– Cynthia Anderson, welder

Source: Antrobus and Rogers, 1980

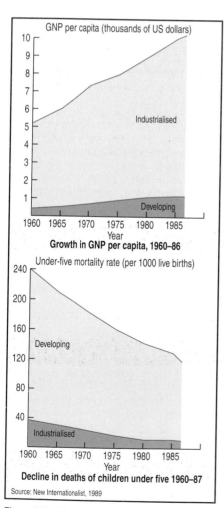

Figure 6.19   The wealth and health of the world

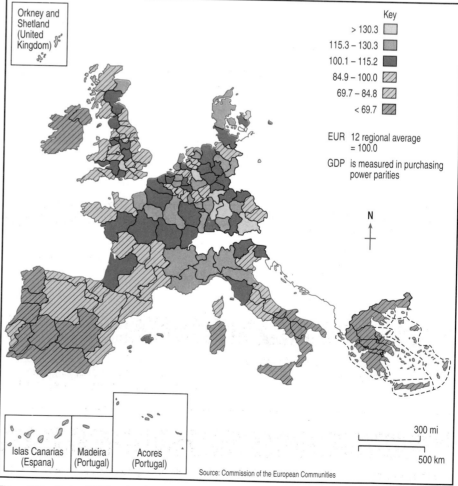

Figure 6.20   Regional GDP per head, 1983

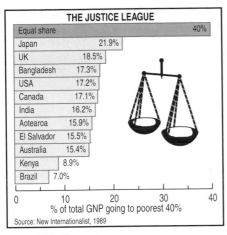

THE JUSTICE LEAGUE

	%
Equal share	40%
Japan	21.9%
UK	18.5%
Bangladesh	17.3%
USA	17.2%
Canada	17.1%
India	16.2%
Aotearoa	15.9%
El Salvador	15.5%
Australia	15.4%
Kenya	8.9%
Brazil	7.0%

% of total GNP going to poorest 40%

Source: New Internationalist, 1989

Figure 6.21 The justice league

SAFER WATER

Real progress has been made since 1970 in providing safe water and adequate sanitation. In rural areas the percentage of people with safe water has trebled. In urban areas access to adequate sanitation has doubled.

Access to safe water 1970–85

Urban: 66% → 74.5% → 77%
Rural: 13.2% → 31.7% → 42.9%

1970 — Year — 1980 — 1985

Access to adequate sanitation 1970–85

Urban: 29.8% → 53.7% → 58.3%
Rural: 11.6% → 13.8% → 15.6%

1970 — Year — 1980 — 1985

Source: New Internationalist, 1989

Figure 6.22 Safer water

THE NIGHTMARE OF NOTHING TO DO

This part of England had the highest rate of unemployment, and today in the sudden shower of rain at Jarrow ('whose name recalls unemployment and the hunger marches of the twenties') it had the poisoned and dispirited look of a place that had just lost a war. It was an area of complex ugliness – not just the dumps full of gulls and crows, and the weak defiance in the faces of the teenagers I saw at Boldon Colliery; it was also the doomed attempts at survival: the farmer ploughing a small strip of field behind an abandoned factory, and the garden allotments of shacks and overgrown enclosures, cabbages and beans, geese and pigs, vegetables and animals alike dusted with fine smut and looking cancerous.

It was hideous and fascinating. We crossed the River Wear and instead of continuing I got off at Sunderland in order to verify its desolation. People said business was terrible, the place was dying on its feet. And Sunderland, because it was so depressed, had a dangerous look: the unrepaired buildings and the shabby streets, and the gangs of boys with spiky hair, and long ragged coats, or else leather jackets painted over with fists and swastikas.

A man named Begbie who was a clerk at Binns Department Store said, 'Some of the kids who left school six or seven years ago have never had a job. There are jobs in the paper, but these kids stay on the dole. They left school at sixteen and they developed what I call a dole-queue mentality. They're unemployable! They don't want to work, and they've discovered they don't really have to. They've learned how to do without it. That's the main difference between the present and other times in British industrial history. We've produced a whole generation of kids who are unemployable!'

Begbie had a grudge, but whether there was any truth in what he said or not, there really was no work here. I looked in the local paper at the situations vacant ads. Very few jobs were listed and most of them asked for people with experience.

Source: Theroux, 1982

ANALYSIS

1 List the effects of changes in industry on the people described in 'The nightmare of nothing to do' and 'The Hanover Street Project'.

2 How strong is the evidence of an unequal distribution of the wealth generated by industry?

DISCUSSION

1 How 'unequal' must the distribution of wealth be before it is unaccepatable?

2 Do you think Paul Theroux's description of north-east England is fair? In what ways is it biased or incomplete? Can you identify the values behind his judgements on the north-east? Could you write an alternative description?

ACTIVITY

With a partner prepare an application to the British government for the funding of a project like Hanover Street in either Trinidad or Gloucester.

Changes at Local Scale

CASE STUDY *A Carpet Factory in the Tapti Valley, Gujarat*

Shashla was ten years old in 1984 when the workshop was built. Her mother had been taken on a visit to a carpet factory some months before by the project team, but Shashla had never seen a carpet. Even so, she was quite pleased that her mother agreed to her joining fifty other young girls at the carpet centre for training. Her two older sisters could help her mother around the house and work in the fields. Shashla picked up the skills quickly, and at the end of a year she could tie knots and read pattern maps. Her team of five girls could produce high quality wool-woven Persian designs on the big loom. During the training year Shashla was paid 150 rupees per month, 25 rupees were compulsorily saved and the rest handed over to her family. The sum of 150 rupees was worth about £10 at that time, but this has to be judged against local wages (national minimum weekly wage about £2) and the low cost of basic requirements. Each day there were literacy classes of one hour in the morning, and recreation in the evening. Shashla looked forward to each day.

In 1985 another 50 girls came for training, and Shashla and her group moved on to ten new looms for commercial production. The carpets are sold to dealers in Delhi through another local co-operative set up by the project.

The Carpet Centre project was set up by a non-governmental organisation as part of a small rural development project for Gammit tribal women. The building was paid for by a local Forestry Co-operative. The 20 looms and materials for two years were bought by Swiss Aid.

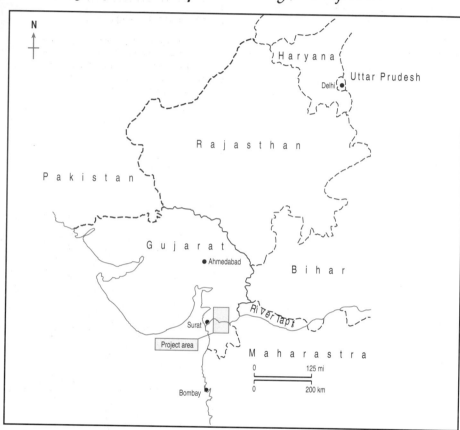

Figure 6.23   Location of the Tapti Valley, Gujarat

The challenges

Third World peasant women generally suffer a triple burden – as citizens in under-developed countries, as peasants living in the most impoverished regions of the country, and as women living in male-dominated communities. Rural women have to bear the brunt of the workload. In addition to their child-rearing and child-caring duties they usually run the family household and work on the land. They receive little or no recognition for this work. They are also excluded when it comes to making decisions or plans. The men remain dominant, often preventing women from exploiting their potential and skills. The project team firmly believes that a stronger, self-supporting community can be created by boosting the confidence and the economic well-being of the rural women.

Another aim of the project team is to encourage the tribal members to value and protect their own traditions and values. Too often urban Indians tend to disparage tribal customs, equating them with backwardness, and urge new city values on people.

The women in the Gammit tribe, for example, still retain a relatively strong sense of dignity and influence in the local community of the kind that no longer exists in urban environments. However the Gammit women have lacked the opportunity and knowledge to improve the quality of their lives and those of their families while retaining their distinctive customs and lifestyle. The project team has set out to help them achieve this.

There is very little paid work available in the region. With men able to find jobs in local forestry cooperatives, sometimes for four months at a time, it is the landless women who really suffer from unemployment. Widows unable to lay claim to their husband's land suffer the most. The 1971 Census figures put female unemployment in the region at 59 per cent, and male unemployment at 39 per cent.

Source: *Indian Tribal Women's Trust, 1985*

DISCUSSION AND ROLE PLAY

Consider this industrial development from one of the following points of view: a member of the development project team; Shashla; Shashla's mother; a local person not involved in the project; a Swiss Aid official; a local government official.

Discuss the Carpet Centre with a group including all the above roles. What does your group think are the project's good and bad features? Will it succeed?

Progress report

By 1987 the carpet factory was independent of outside funding and was making a profit. Seeing this success, other carpet factories were set up by individuals in the region, using girls aged 10–14. These factories provide no basic education or recreation activities. With a full day's work, more carpets are produced and the girls can earn more money.

Educational activities became less popular at the original Carpet Centre since they reduced potential production. Gradually the motivation of the girls declined, and a system of payment by results was developed to reduce absenteeism. Some girls were then forced by their parents to go to work all the time and keep production up because the parents need the money. Facing such parental pressure, some girls have run away from home to other carpet centres, or got married.

It is a time of crisis for the Carpet Centre, with a seeming conflict between the girls' continued education and the running of an economically successful production unit.

Earning or learning?

'A major aim of this development project is to include women in the planning and running of co-operatives, fostering local female leadership so that the project becomes self-sufficient.'
– Project development worker

'These carpet factories should be licensed by the State government and closed if they do not devote a reasonable proportion of their time to properly staffed education projects for the girls. They should be earn-and-learn centres.'
–South Indian development worker

'When the unit started there was no intention to turn the girls from farm labour into factory labour.'
– Project leader

'To an outsider arriving in the region now the carpet industry looks like a case of exploitation of child labour.'
– Visitor to Gujarat

'The Carpet Centre must be subsidised if it is not to lose its girls to other factories where no time is given to education.'
– European visitor

Figure 6.24 Carpet weaving

GROUP DISCUSSION

1 What have been the main social and economic impacts of the carpet factory in the region?

2 From the description of developments and the comments quoted on this page, how far do you think this attempt to raise the awareness and self-confidence of women and children is successful? What else could be done?

3 Suggest strategies for the future from the point of view of each of the 'roles' in 'Discussion and role play' above.

4 Does this case suggest anything about the conflict between a free market and controlled industrial development?

SYNTHESIS

1 Job and wealth creation schemes play a big part in grassroots development projects around the world. How far can industrial development be instrumental in bringing about the emancipation and independence of rural women?

2 Make a list of criteria by which a small-scale industrial development in a rural area should be judged with reference to its effect on women.

CASE STUDY *Development in Western Ireland*

The core-periphery model of development is very useful in studying Ireland. Dublin and the east form a core of industrialisation, affluence and high productivity, with the west and north-west a traditionally rural and poorer periphery. In 1983 the per capita incomes in regions in the west ranged from 43% to 71% of the average in the east.

Nested within this regional scale periphery are local core-periphery patterns. For example, the town of Sligo (population 29 000) is a core area within County Sligo, and towns like Galway and Limerick are similar focuses (Figure 6.25).

Industrialisation

There has been a trend towards industrialisation in the West since 1960, and since 1970 this has been supported by the government with its Industrial Development Authority (IDA) offering tax incentives and assistance grants. The *advance factory programme* (that is, building factories for later purchase or renting) provided new factories in 75 different places between 1972 and 1981. A quarter of this factory floor space was in rural villages with populations of less than 1500 people, and all have been occupied. When Ireland joined the EEC in 1973, industrialisation accelerated and global trends brought transnational companies in search of new locations for de-skilled industrial processes. Since 1981 over half the investment in the West has been by foreign firms, especially export-orientated USA multinationals.

Labour is cheaper in Western Ireland. Many women and part-time farmers were available for work and provided a non-militant workforce. Companies could also hope to monopolise a local workforce and so decrease the possibility of militancy. The available cheap floor space was another attraction.

Economic impacts

The factories give new employment opportunities at a time of reduction in the agricultural workforce, and the foreign firms pay higher wages. This has not led, however, to local farmers giving up. Not all the employment goes to local people. Near Limerick, for example, most of the new housing built within the Shannon Industrial Zone is occupied by people from Dublin, and 45% of the workers in the new factories come from outside the region.

One dimension added to the local economy is the provision of food processing locally, especially for meat and dairy products. About 25% of the factories are in this sector. The economic impact of the other 75% is more limited, apart from employment. Most of their service payments (transport, energy, etc.) go to large towns, and only 5% of their purchases are from within 20 miles of the factory.

Demographic impacts

Emigration has been reduced throughout the West, and in some areas the trend has been reversed. The move from the land to the towns continues, and a commuter population has been created.

Socio-cultural impacts

Women have become a more important part of the wage-earning workforce. On the other hand, local factories tend to be taken seriously only when they employ a substantial number of local male heads of households. The social adaptation to factory work is sometimes slow, with part-time farmers not interested in over-time and work often judged as 'women's work' because of its product (e.g. cosmetics).

Environmental impact

The following reports highlight concern over the environmental impact of chemical factories.

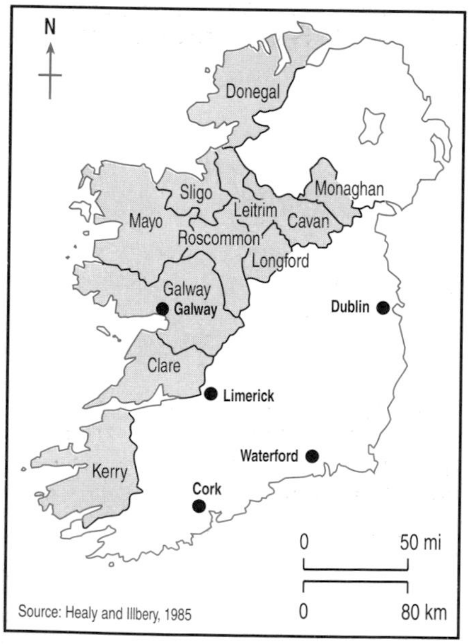

Figure 6.25   Designated areas and planning regions

POLLUTERS TO LOSE GRANTS IN NEW CURBS ON INDUSTRY   Dick Cross

NEW environmental controls on industry were spelled out yesterday by Minister for Industry and Commerce Des O'Malley. The new measures include withholding state grants from persistent offenders...

It was the Government's most positive statement yet on the environment, as Mr. O'Malley announced in Cork that the IDA and Shannon Development would be told to adopt a new approach to chemical and pharmaceutical industries in the process of setting up or in receipt of grants.

Source: *Irish Independent*, 12 September 1989

Western Ireland: rural industrialisation statistics

Increase in primary, manufacturing and public service industry
1961–71   44%
1971–81   45%
(Half this growth was in public services)

Increase in number of women in paid workforce
1971–81   48%

Core location within a peripheral region:
Sligo Town within Sligo County
Sligo Town accounted for 73% of the government aided jobs and 66% of the increase in employment in Sligo County as a whole.

THE HANRAHAN CASE

Ireland has rapidly become a base for toxic waste producing pharmaceuticals plants. In the early 1970s, Ireland exported practically no pharmaceuticals products, but is presently one of the top ten producers in the world.

On-site incineration in the absence of effective controls on air pollution has resulted in serious pollution by toxic solvent vapours and various other noxious and toxic substances. Syntex's County Clare plant and Smith Kline French's plant in Cork have been causing serious pollution since their operations commenced ten years ago. The worst case by far however – one that has become a watershed in Irish environmental history – is that of Merck, Sharpe and Dhome's plant in County Tipperary.

The factory began production in 1976.

Two years later, John Hanrahan, a farmer living about a mile from the factory, lodged a complaint with Tipperary County Council. He claimed that he had difficulty breathing and that his cows had streaming eyes, which he blamed on emissions from Merck. Others living in the vicinity also complained of problems with their livestock.

In 1980, the County Council reluctantly commissioned a report to monitor the atmosphere in the vicinity of the factory. In the meantime, 70 of Hanrahan's cattle had died of mystery illnesses and there was a continuing high incidence of stillbirths and deformities among his calves.

Hanrahan initiated legal proceedings against Merck at this stage...

The Court found that atmospheric pollution, mainly in the form of hydrogen chloride and hydrochloric acid mists, was present in the region and that it was an unquestionable fact that the Merck factory was the source of that pollution.

Source: Keohane, K., *Ecologist* (Vol. 9, No. 4), 1989

Figure 6.26a A stillborn calf. Two hundred and twenty-five of the Hanrahan's cattle died due to emissions of hydrogen chloride and hydrochloric acid from the nearby Merck, Sharpe and Dhome pharmaceuticals factory

SECOND MAJOR CHEMICAL FIRM IN PULL-OUT

Tony O'Brien

A SECOND chemical company has decided not to proceed with a controversial new plant. And its decision means a loss of 55 potential jobs for Limerick City.

Hydrochlor Manufacturing Ltd., had applied to Limerick Corporation for planning permission to build a £3m hydrochloric acid plant at Dock Road in the city.

The plan drew protests from local people and environmentalists but the company insisted yesterday it decided to withdraw its planning application because the site had proved unsuitable.

Source: *Irish Independent*, 13 September 1989

SANDOZ 'MUST COME'

Dick Cross

THE Government yesterday came down strongly in favour of allowing Swiss pharmaceutical company Sandoz to locate at Ringaskiddy, Co. Cork, on an industrial estate owned and serviced by the IDA...

It was vital not just for the very substantial benefits it would bring in its own right but because of the impact a negative decision on its part could have on our future job creation drive in the Cork area and nationally.

Source: *Irish Independent*, 12 September 1989

Figure 6.26b   Chemical pollution

IDA ATTACKS ENVIRONMENT PROTESTORS

PRESSURE groups must not be allowed to dictate where new factories are sited if the drive for jobs and industrial development is to be successful, IDA managing director Padraig White warned yesterday in the wake of the Merrell Dow pull-out from Cork.

He insisted that the central role of the local government planning authority and An Bord Pleanala needed to be reasserted in making decisions on developments, because he claimed this had been one of the 'casualties' of the Merrell Dow case.

But last night the group which opposed the Merrell Dow project rejected Mr. White's charges. 'We are absolutely astounded at his allegations,' stated Ms. Jill Bell of the Concerned Citizens of East Cork and West Waterford.

Source: *Irish Independent*, 15 September 1989

ISSUE

Does government action help or harm?

DEBATE

1   Divide into two groups A and B.
    Group A: Use the information about recent changes in Western Ireland to prepare a case in favour of more industrialisation in peripheral zones.
    Group B: Critically examine the evidence of recent changes in Western Ireland to identify the dangers and problems of rural industrialisation in peripheral zones.

2   Join with the other group. Group A present their case and Group B respond.

3   Consider the chemical industry as a separate case. What policy do you think the government should pursue?

SYNTHESIS

The issue of development in peripheral areas is world-wide. There is concern to improve living standards and there are worries about the use and misuse of the areas by transnational enterprises within the global capitalist system.

Peripheral areas exist in a nested system: at a global scale the economically less-developed world can be seen as peripheral; at a continental scale, Ireland is peripheral to the EEC; at a national scale, the west and north-west to the eastern core; and at a local scale, Sligo County to the town of Sligo.

Change at National Scale

The case of Western Ireland leads our enquiry from local-scale to national-scale perspectives. In this section there are three case studies. For each study an important issue is selected, the people and organisations involved are identified, and reports and information about the issue are presented. You are asked to use the material to enquire into the decision-making processes and into the conflicts of values and interests that arise.

An industrialised country

ISSUE

Should the UK government encourage foreign investment?

CASE STUDY *The Toyota Investment*

On Tuesday, 18 April 1989, Toyota announced plans to invest £700 million at Burnaston near Derby. The British press responded to the event.

THE ONLY word of Japanese known to Mr David Bookbinder, Labour leader of Derbyshire County Council, was the one he least wanted to use during negotiations with Toyota about their possible move into the county. *Sayon-ara*, after all, means 'Good-bye.'

Derbyshire County Council has offered to invest £20 million from its pension fund as a sign of goodwill and will spend a further £12 million on improving roads and other infrastructure.

Source: *Financial Times*, 19 April 1989

Figure 6.26c   David Bookbinder on the flying club airfield in Derbyshire chosen as the site

3,000-JOB CAR PLANT IN DERBY

Philip Johnston

TOYOTA, Japan's biggest motor company, announced plans yesterday to build a £700 million car plant at Burnaston, near Derby, in the biggest single Japanese investment in Europe.

At its peak it will produce 200,000 cars a year, employ 3,000 people and create a further 3,000 jobs in component manufacturing. The company – the 100th Japanese firm to invest in Britain – is also planning an engine plant for its European production, probably in Britain. An announcement will be made in two months.

Toyota's choice of Britain rather than the other EEC countries bidding for the project was hailed by Ministers as 'a vote of confidence in the UK' and a recognition of international confidence in the strength of the economy.

But Mr Bryan Gould, Labour trade spokesman, while welcoming the factory said it marked the final phase of a process 'which has seen the replacement of an indigenous car industry with one controlled from Detroit, Paris and Tokyo'.

Source: *Daily Telegraph*, 19 April 1989

The plant will be built along-side the A38 on a 334 acre grass airfield, half a mile south of the select, ridge-top village of Burnaston.

It will mean the demise of Derby Aerodrome, whose 350 flying club members have recently been summoned to lobby Mr Bookbinder 'to take his factory somewhere else'.

Leading factors in Toyota's decision appeared to be the availability of workers and components in the West Midlands and the county's potential cash injection.

Derbyshire has almost 32 000 people seeking jobs; 7.5 per cent of the working population. Around 7,500 redundancies have been announced in the coal industry since 1983. Toyota said local management would seek a single-union deal.

Source: *Guardian*, 19 April 1989

THE HUNT by Toyota, the world's third biggest car maker, for a European production plant may have ended yesterday in the unglamorous surroundings of a disused airstrip south-west of Derby, but it in fact began as long ago as 1986.

Executives in Toyota's home city of Nagoya had witnessed the strategy being developed by their two smaller Japanese rivals – Nissan and Honda – and decided to act for fear of being frozen out of the European Community market and its 320 million consumers in 1992.

Source: *Independent*, 19 April 1989

TOYOTA WILL BRING 6,000 EXTRA JOBS

Kevin Eason

Toyota, the third biggest car maker in the world, confirmed last night it is to build a £700 million manufacturing plant in the Midlands, creating 6,000 jobs...

The plant ... will have 3,000 workers when production starts in late 1992.

Lord Young of Graffham, the Secretary of State for Trade and Industry, said there would be another 3,000 jobs in component manufacturing. Construction of the factory will start next year. By 1995, it will make 200,000 cars a year.

Source: *The Times*, 19 April 1989

INVESTMENT COUP OF THE DECADE

Russell Hotten

The Midlands was last night celebrating the investment coup of the decade after Toyota said it would build a £700 million car assembly plant 35 miles north of Birmingham.

South Wales and Humberside competed fiercely for the Toyota plant, but the company's president, Dr Shoichiro Toyoda, said he chose Burnaston after 'an overall review of transport, communications, and related infrastructure'.

Source: *Birmingham Post*, 19 April 1989

CAR INDUSTRY FEAR OVER TOYOTA PLAN

Roland Main

TOYOTA'S £700m move to the Midlands will upset the delicate economic balance of the European motor industry, worried analysts predicted last night.

Some analysts believe the flood of 100,000 new cars in the showrooms will result in huge over-capacity.

At present car firms are producing record numbers of vehicles.

But the Society of Motor Manufacturers and Traders is predicting a big downturn in sales by the end of the year...

Last night, the powerful West Midlands TUC motor industry committee called on Trade and Industry Secretary Lord Young to seek assurances from Toyota that it would bring research and development work to Britain.

Chairman Sid Platt said: 'It is vital we get more than a nuts and bolts assembly operation.

'There is a danger that if economic conditions became unfavourable, Toyota could pull out and go off to somewhere like Greece. We need them to demonstrate a clear commitment to the plant's long-term future.'

The Japanese car makers – the second biggest in the world – could do that by siting its £100m engine plant near Derby.

Source: *Daily News*, 20 April 1989

THERE is no question that the formal confirmation of Japan's Toyota to build its European car manufacturing plant here is good news for GB plc. It marks another step in Britain's long climb back to respectability as a car-making country, and will help to close one of the more dismal holes in our balance of payments. Should Toyota also choose to build engines near a British golf course too, the story will be even better.

Source: *Daily Telegraph*, 20 April 1989

DEMOLISHING THE MIRACLE

WE ARE often told that Mrs Thatcher has worked some sort of economic miracle during her tenure of office. Such claims are easily demolished by the facts.

In the past 10 years, British manufacturing has gone through a sea change. Many British plants are now run as remote branch divisions of giant transnational corporations.

At the end of 1986, for example, US-owned companies employed almost 530,000 workers in Britain and accounted for almost 12 per cent of Britain's manufacturing output.

Total investment by Japanese manufacturers is now worth well over £1 billion, mostly in consumer electronics.

This week's announcement that Japanese car giant Toyota is to invest £700 million in a major new plant in Derbyshire marks a new wave of Japanese investment in the run-up to the Single European market in 1992.

Earlier this week, it was announced that Japanese electronics group Fujitsu is to build a £400 million semiconductor plant in County Durham.

Meanwhile, Robert Bosch of West Germany is to establish a motor component plant in South Wales, partly to service the growing number of Japanese car producers in Britain.

The new jobs that will be created from these developments are of course to be welcomed, although the numbers involved are but a fraction of the jobs that have been lost in the process of de-industrialisation over the past few years.

The workforce in British motor production has been cut by 49 per cent in less than five years. In 1988, just seven firms accounted for 79 per cent of British output. Just one of them, the hived-off Austin Rover, was British owned.

Source: *Morning Star*, 20 April 1989

THE NEXT BEST NEWS

YESTERDAY'S confirmation by Toyota that it intends to build a £700 million plant on a former airfield at Burnaston in Derbyshire, generating 6,000 new jobs, completes an impressive week for inward investment. Fujitsu, the Japanese electronics group, has announced a £400 million semiconductor plant in County Durham; and Robert Bosch of West Germany is to set up a motor component plant in South Wales, partly to service the growing number of Japanese car producers (Nissan and Honda are here already) using the UK as a springboard into Europe ahead of 1992. Britain has become a magnet for inward investment which could feed on itself as suppliers scamper to cluster as close as possible to the new car plants to meet Japanese criteria for 'just in time' sourcing of components...

Britain's balance of payments in motor components changed from a favourable balance of £84 million in 1985 to a deficit of £880 million in 1987. In 1988 the deficit worsened to £1.02 billion.

Source: *Guardian*, 19 April 1989

ANALYSIS

1 The news (pages 285–87): what 'facts' are commonly reported? How did each reporter find out the "facts"? Do you think they have been verified? How far is the reporting biased?

2 Editorial comment: what viewpoint is each editorial presenting? Which viewpoints get little coverage in the British press? What kinds of evidence do the editors cite to justify their views?

3 What factors seem to have led to the choice of:
a the UK and
b Burnaston for the factory?

DISCUSSION

Take one of the following roles: a national union official from the AEU; the UK Prime Minister; the West German President; the managing director of Austin Rover; an unemployed engineer in Derby; a Japanese banker; a retired person living in a cottage near Burnaston airfield.

Consider your reaction to the news, bearing in mind both short- and long-term implications. Prepare a statement about the investment plan and contribute to a news sheet presenting alternative viewpoints.

ANALYSIS AND RESEARCH

1 Describe the pattern of investment taking place.

2 Monitor the media for reports of further projects.

VICTORY FOR THE BRITISH WORKER

THE decision by Toyota to build a £700m car plant near Derby is extremely encouraging. For decades, British commentators have bemoaned the decline of this country as a manufacturing centre. The motor industry seemed to symbolise the collapse. From being, by a huge margin, a net exporter of cars, we dwindled into a net importer. We might have a future in financial services, but not, it appeared, in making things.

Yet Toyota chose the UK for its European plant. The fact that English is the European language with which the Japanese are most familiar helps, but the investment has not been won by offering the company enormous bribes of the sort once needed to persuade anyone to build a car factory here. No subsidy is being paid. Nor is Toyota's choice unexpected. Nearly 30 per cent of Japanese investment in Europe in the last 20 years has come to the UK...

Such investments are the free market's equivalent of regional policy. Instead of the state attempting, by means of heavy subsidies, to persuade industrialists against their better judgement to set up plants in areas of high unemployment, those areas compete. They offer cheaper, more plentiful labour and land, and a less congested infrastructure. The investments in Derbyshire and County Durham might have been made anywhere in Western Europe: these are not just victories over other regions of Britain.

Source: *Independent*, 19 April 1989

DECISION SWAYED BY LOVE OF GOLF

Derby's excellent communications network, plus the Japanese love of golf, appear to have been the major factors in Toyota's choice of Derby.

Part of the package included offering 18th century Allestree Hall, near Derby, rent-free for five years.

The hall, set in 63 acres of parkland, was offered as executive accommodation – with the added attraction of a full-sized golf course...

Burnaston is also close to the A38 route back to the motor industry heartland in the West Midlands...

The A38 is also a good connection south to Birmingham International Airport.

Source: *Birmingham Post*, 19 April 1989

Several reports in the press at the time and later included comment on the general spread of Japanese investment in the UK.

MITSUBISHI SEEKS UK FOOTHOLD

Clare Dobie

MITSUBISHI Corporation, the £10bn Japanese trading company, is considering investing in nine projects in the UK, adding to the recent rush of Japanese investment ahead of 1992. It is also applying for its shares to be listed in London. The listing follows similar moves by other Mitsubishi companies including Mitsubishi Bank, Mitsubishi Electric and Mitsubishi Trust and Banking Corporation.

Mitsubishi Corporation's plans for the UK signal its determination to become a larger player in Europe before 1992 when it fears trade with the EC could become more difficult.

Nobuo Kobayashi, chairman of the company's Euro-Africa region who recently moved to London, said last week that the company had not decided which investments it would make in the UK. It is considering 20 projects for the EC.

The UK projects are in machinery, metals, food, chemicals and the service sector. The range reflects the spread of the company's activities.

As well as trading, the company invests on its own account in long-term projects such as coal in Australia, copper in Chile (with RTZ) and space satellites...

Its existing UK businesses include Princes Foods, which it acquired from Nestlé earlier this year, a London Metals Exchange trader and Dia-plastics, a joint venture in Wales.

Mitsubishi Corporation also has an arrangement with Aquascutum, the English clothing company, helping to sell its products in Japan.

Source: *Independent*, 23 September 1989

NEWCOMERS WHO ARE WELCOMED BUT FEARED　Terry Dodsworth

Toyota this week, Fujitsu last. Total investment of £1bn over a five-year period. About 4,500 jobs in employment black spots. These are figures which demonstrate beyond all doubt the scale of the new wave of Japanese investment in the UK – one that is bound to have a lasting impact on the local economy.

But they are also figures which raise a variety of reactions, not all positive. Set against the jobs they create and the new capital they provide is the fear that indigenous companies are losing their technology base or being crowded out of new markets.

Critics argue that the build-up of Japanese investment is a further step in the colonisation of British manufacturing by foreign companies. And while the Government contends that ownership is irrelevant, there is a widespread fear that these new UK plants will be run as remote branch divisions, far from the seat of power. British industry, it is said, may well be losing control over its own destiny...

As yet, many of these fears look far-fetched, simply because Japanese investment in Britain is still at a very low level. Whereas US investors began coming to Britain last century, the first Japanese company, a plastic sheet producer called Takiron, put down roots in South Wales only in 1972. Since then, total investment by Japanese manufacturers has risen to about £1.5bn – before Fujitsu and Toyota – employing 25,000 people.

By the standard of US companies, or those from other European countries, this is small beer. At the end of 1986, for example, US-owned companies employed almost 530,000 workers in Britain, and accounted for almost 12 per cent of the country's manufacturing output; and US companies generated 15 per cent of corporate capital investment against 0.5 per cent by the Japanese...

The Japanese invasion has been mainly centred on visible, consumer-goods industries such as cars, televisions and video-cassette recorders. The arrival of the Japanese in these sectors has been accompanied by the well-documented story of the collapse of UK and European competitors. Japanese expansion has alerted Europeans to the region's declining industrial competitiveness.

A great deal of the argument over local content levels is related to this question of local commitment: 'screwdriver' plants do not transfer technology or generate it locally, and they require only relatively unskilled labour. But the issue also extends to research and development. Inward investors that set up local research and engineering development centres can build integrated operations with a high level of local value added. In due course, that should mean less dependence on imports or even a move into net exports.

There has been some fear that the UK will lose out in in the race for Japanese research and design centres to West Germany. Japanese companies are impressed by West Germany's large pool of skilled engineers. Sony, for example, has set up its engineering centre there, although it does development work in some areas such as satellites in the UK...

Mr Nigishi's model for the future Europeanised Japanese corporation is International Business Machines, the world's largest computer company. 'IBM has a huge advertising campaign running about 1992,' he says, 'giving the message that the company is part of the local European community. But we've only had 10 years and they've had 70. It takes time.'

Source: *Financial Times*, 19 April 1989

Japanese investment: twenty views (from the BBC's 'File on 4', 30 May 1989)

More jobs are created in certain regions of UK.

The Japanese feel obstructed by the EEC, especially by France and Italy.

Imports to the UK are reduced.

UK becomes a colony of an economic super-power.

Good wages are paid.

The designs arrive from Japan.

There is more competition for companies in the EEC.

There will be no restrictions on imports from the UK to the EEC after 1992.

The UK government gives subsidies so that new foreign companies have a 25% cost advantage.

UK industrialists have the chance to see Japanese industry at close quarters.

The benefits go back to Japan.

The labour force is docile, skilled and willing.

Declining manufacturing industry is bolstered up.

There is competition to employ the best graduates.

Imaging technology and engine technology stay in Japan.

The latest plant is built on greenfield sites.

Japan plans to have 25% of the EEC market by 1995.

UK electronics overproduction could overwhelm EEC companies.

The Japanese play one EEC country off against another.

Plants state that eventually 80% of the content of cars will be from local sources.

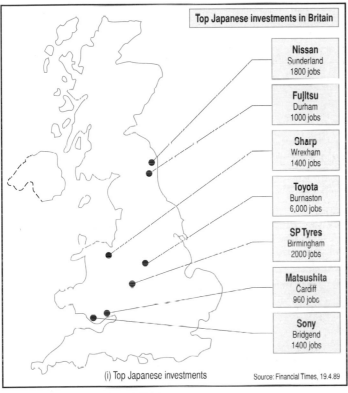

Top Japanese investments in Britain

Nissan Sunderland 1800 jobs

Fujitsu Durham 1000 jobs

Sharp Wrexham 1400 jobs

Toyota Burnaston 6,000 jobs

SP Tyres Birmingham 2000 jobs

Matsushita Cardiff 960 jobs

Sony Bridgend 1400 jobs

(i) Top Japanese investments

Source: Financial Times, 19.4.89

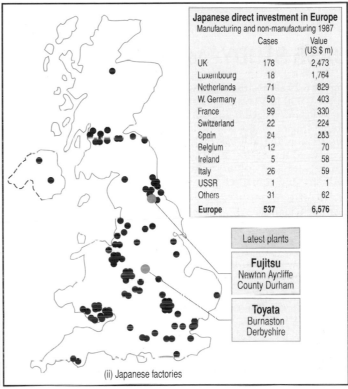

Japanese direct investment in Europe
Manufacturing and non-manufacturing 1987

	Cases	Value (US $ m)
UK	178	2,473
Luxembourg	18	1,764
Netherlands	71	829
W. Germany	50	403
France	99	330
Switzerland	22	224
Spain	24	283
Belgium	12	70
Ireland	5	58
Italy	26	59
USSR	1	1
Others	31	62
Europe	**537**	**6,576**

Latest plants

Fujitsu Newton Aycliffe County Durham

Toyota Burnaston Derbyshire

(ii) Japanese factories

Figure 6.27 Japanese industry in Britain

SYNTHESIS

Two key questions are 'Who benefits or suffers?' and (from the point of view of long-term independence and development) 'Who controls the technology?'. The twenty points about the impact of Japanese investment in the UK were made on 'File on 4'.

1 Read each statement and consider what evidence you know of to support it.

2 Make a card for each statement. Draw a Venn diagram with three overlapping circles, one for each of UK, EEC, and Japan (Figure 6.28). Place each card in an appropriate sector according to which area or areas it fits best.

3 Use your classification of the 'cards', and your studies of the newspaper items, to answer the two key questions.

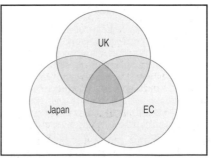

Figure 6.28 Template for the Venn diagram

A centrally planned economy

How desirable is modernisation of industry? Could it be achieved with centralised Research and Development (R&D)? In the Soviet Union a large proportion of the R&D energies went into the defence industries. The aerospace industry, for example, was supported by at least thirty technical schools that give six years training to young people in specialist skills, who then work in the 35 national R&D establishments. There are four times as many graduate engineers and technicians as the USA, but more than 60% of them go into defence.

The Soviet Union's R&D was centralised and government-controlled. R&D programmes had to be put in rank order, and with space and defence taking so much there was little time or resources left over. Industries at the bottom of the list, like services, distribution, transport, retailing and many consumer goods, got little attention.

There is no doubt that in spite of high investment in education and R&D, Soviet technology lagged behind most other industrialised nations. A general measure of this is its relatively low productivity per person in manufacturing – only 60% of that in the USA. Observers in the USA suggest that the time lag was due to the centralised R&D system. In spite of this, the USSR was the world's largest industrial producer and was third by GNP behind the USA and Japan.

CASE STUDY *Modernisation of the Tractor Industry*

Figure 6.29 shows the dominant position of the USSR in 1989 and Figure 6.30 includes information on both the age of Soviet tractor plants and their production. In the USSR many tractors were used outside farming as small trucks, and many others were used in industry and construction.

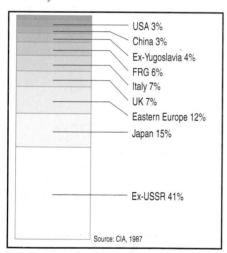

Figure 6.29   World tractor production, 1985

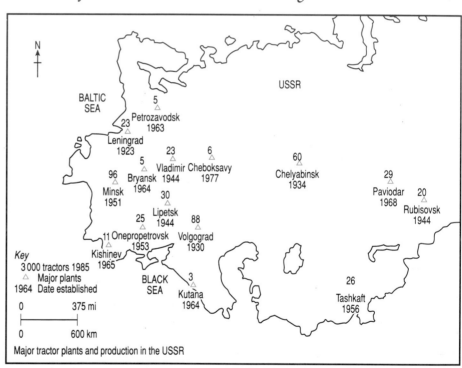

Figure 6.30   Major tractor plants and production in the former USSR

Engineering is a key sector in modern industry. It is the engineering industries that provide most of the national economy sectors with advanced technology. In the period between 1986 and 1990, priority will be given to manufacturing digital programme-controlled metal-cutting machine-tools, the 'processing centre' types of machines, heavy machine-tools and presses, equipment for assembling mass-produced engineering items, of rotary and rotary-conveyor lines and other types of automated equipment, and of high-precision machine-tools.

Plans are for 320 brands of new-generation machines to be serially produced in the USSR by 1990 when at least 90 per cent of Soviet-made engineering products will meet world standards.

People's well-being occupies a central place in the policy of reforms which are taking place in industry. Many enterprises have built themselves sports-and-health facilities, sanatoria, holiday homes and farming areas.

During the 1986–1990 period, priority is being given to micro-electronics, computer technology and high-precision instrument-making. More instruments and equipment will be produced to automate scientific experimentation work. There will be changes in the nature of engineering and design work. New systems for automated designing of manufacturing processes will save time in creating new technology. By the end of the five-year plan period, the level of automation in design work will reach 25–40 per cent.

Source: Lyusor, 1988

The 'problems'

Many Soviet tractors are unreliable and too heavy. They contribute to low crop yields and inefficient farming and industry. New tractors are sometimes delivered lacking basic components.

The main reasons for this situation are the old factories, antiquated machine tools and the late or incomplete delivery of components to assembly plants. There are also problems with poor quality materials and a shortage of metal sheets. Proper maintenance of these older factories is difficult.

Recent farm reorganisation, with the emphasis on smaller units, has created new demands for smaller tractors. A programme of modernisation has been in progress since 1970, and by 1987, 80 out of 224 tractor plants had been modernised to some extent.

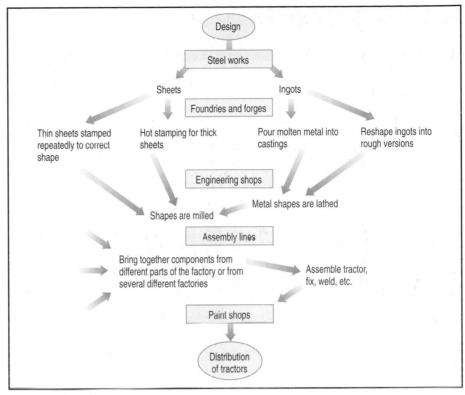

Figure 6.31   Tractor production process

Work in progress: improvements and technological changes

1   Improve and enlarge forges and foundries.

2   Replace old wooden floors which vibrate in machine shops and make precision difficult.

3   Introduce computer-assisted design.

4   Improve machine tool production.

5   Introduce automated control systems for machine tools (i.e. machines that stamp, lathe, mill, assemble, weld, etc.). These are being developed by Eastern European suppliers.

6   Improve machine shops.

7   Import foreign technology. This has been done at Cheboksary, but some problems were created matching into existing plant.

8   Manufacture from thin steel sheets which are faster to stamp, make less waste, need less milling and produce parts of more exact dimensions that reduce friction when the tractor runs.

9   Improve inter-plant transport.

10   Introduce more robotics. So far these are limited to single repetitive operations (e.g. welding, transporting equipment), and there have been flaws in 40% of the robots. In the USA robots also assemble and paint, and so increase the speed and precision of manufacture. This is difficult without programming the complete process.

11   Expand floor space as has already been done at Minsk, where 45% of exports are manufactured, and at Rostov.

12   Replace complete production lines and mechanise intra-factory transport, as has been done at Minsk, Volgograd and Kutaisi.

13   Improve quality of components.

14   Co-ordinate assembly plants with suppliers. Tyres, paint, clutches, batteries, etc., are usually produced outside.

15   Improve quality control by increasing the testing of equipment during manufacture. To do this, the pressure of meeting production targets must be reduced.

ANALYSIS

1   Which part or parts of the production process described on this page does each proposed improvement affect?

2   Create a diagram showing the links between processes and improvements.

3   How does each improvement help to solve problems of quality, quantity and cost?

DISCUSSION

1   Should Russia go all out to replace the present processes with technology imported from abroad?

2   What effects do national value systems and ideologies (e.g. communism, capitalism) have on the process of modernisation?

A newly-industrialising country

ISSUE

Is industrialisation possible without exploitation?

CASE STUDY *Brazil's Economic Miracle*

'In the 1960s and the 1970s, Brazilian industry made a huge leap forward. New factories were established, workers were trained, and production increased on an annual basis at a rate unparalleled in the entire world.'

Source: Shichor and Shichor, *Brazil*, 1988

'Brazil has transformed itself from a rural to an urban society in 25 years. Britain took 200 years and Russia took 70. In 1965, 50 per cent of the population lived in rural areas; by 1985 only 27 per cent did. In Western terms Brazil has had an economic miracle.'

Source: *Food Matters*, October 1989

But:

'The masterminds of this boom neglected to lay a suitable infrastructure – in particular with regard to energy sources, the utilisation of raw materials and the development of transport routes. As a result, a sharp recession ensued in the 1980s. Economic growth slackened off considerably, and many industrial plants ran into financial difficulties.'

Source: Shichor and Shichor, *Brazil*, 1988

'Inflation was 432 per cent in 1987, with devastating effects on the two thirds of Brazilians marginalised from the

Figure 6.32 Car factory in São Paolo

industrial boom. Sixty-six per cent of them have insufficient calorie intake (FAO criteria).'

Source: *Food Matters*, October 1989

These quotations and this statistical summary provide a background for the comments that follow about conditions in Brazil's industries.

Statistical summary 1987
Population: 141 500 000; 73% urban.
Income per capita: £2030; poorest 50% receive only 13% of total income.
National debt: £120 000 million; interest = 35% of export earnings.
GDP is 11% agriculture, 50% services, 39% other industry.
Agriculture employs 27% of working people.
Industrial production (world rankings): arms, 5; IT, 5; steel, 7; textiles, 7; machinery, 9; cars, 11; chemicals, 11.

ANALYSIS

How far is Brazil an industrialised nation? Why is it classified as a Third World nation?

BANKS

The computerisation of the Bank of Brazil provoked not only tenosynovitis but a range of psychological problems. Isolated work under increased pressure and external control increased complexes of persecution, according to psychologist Edith Seligman Silva, from the University of São Paulo Department of Preventative Medicine. Data processors became unable to concentrate or learn after a day at the keyboard – a result of working in a 'language' they cannot understand, without the time to make sense of it and usually in social isolation.

Source: *Brazil network newsletter*, Summer 1989

METAL INDUSTRIES

In February 1989 two British trade unionists, Micky Whitly and Josephine Jewel, attended the Metalworkers' National Conference in São Paulo. Here are some of their impressions.

We're supposed to feel that Brazilian comrades steal our jobs and futures by undercutting us, or being more compliant with management. These conferences help stop such strategies from working – solidarity grows from dialogue.

They are just starting to adopt new technologies now, some of the machinery being used in Brazilian factories is very antiquated. But the main problem is that of health and safety at work. The record in Brazil is the worst in the world for fatalities and injuries. Trade unionists there ... are campaigning for appropriate legislation to improve the situation. For example, here all new plants have to operate below certain noise levels. In Brazil you enter a factory and you are overwhelmed right away by the noise. Another thing, there is no legislation that ensures compensation for industrial injury; there is no recourse to the courts...

The car industry in Brazil ... was about three times bigger than in the UK. Capacity is huge. In the Volkswagen plant there were forty thousand workers. Every major car manufacturer has got a base in Brazil, and they are exporting the bulk of the product, mainly to the States, but we take engines from Brazil, gearboxes, axles. The difference is that they are getting their technology a bit behind us, but they'll get it.

I found it really exhilarating in Brazil. Ordinary workers had a clear understanding of questions like that of Third World debt ... how that relates to their society, the structure of the economy and the way they are working. What the debt means for the diversion of money away from social programmes like housing.

Labour law is embraced by the criminal law. Workers can get jailed for union activities. Since 1985, eight hundred trade unionists have been murdered.

We need this solidarity because capitalism knows no frontiers. Companies can organise much more quickly than we can, and multinationals can transfer their capital.

Source: *Brazil network newsletter*, Summer 1989

PESTICIDES

The most important New Technology, in Brazilian health terms, is pesticides, according to Angelo Trape of the University of Campinas (SP). The use (and manufacture) of pesticides rose enormously during the 1970s; Brazil comes second only to the USA and Japan in terms of its market in pesticides, with over 10,000 commercial products on sale.

Pesticides brought an increase in productivity, but the hoped-for social benefits never appeared. 'When a banker like Olacir de Morais plants 50,000 hectares with soya, the well-being of the Brazilian poor is not his main worry.'

The hazardous technologies of pesticide manufacture and usage were exported to Brazil but the sophisticated technologies to measure worker exposure or contamination of agricultural products were not. Typically in São Paulo plantations, pesticides are mixed by children, who not only suffer illness but may also help provoke it out in the fields if they get the mix wrong.

Multinational firms like Bayer showed films at Masses throughout Brazil to encourage greater pesticide consumption by peasant farmers, including share-croppers who are loaned ground and given seeds by the landowners and in return typically keep one third of the harvest. What chance for health and safety with such labour relations?

Source: *Food Health*, October 1989

'When the time came I bought *Difolatan*, a pesticide made by Chevron in the US, distributed by Hokko, a Japanese company, and sold by Toyomenka, a Brazillian company. But each time I sprayed I felt ill. There were other brands, but they were all toxic.'
– Brazilian farmer

Shoe industry

Shoe manufacture is a global industry, with most high street shops belonging to multinational corporations that organise shoe-making around the world.

In Brazil the shoe industry is notorious for employing child labour.

On 23 January 1989 a BBC programme 'Child Slaves' reported how the glue used for making shoes is associated with aneuria, heart and breathing problems, and how child labour schemes were linked to prostitution rackets. Many shoes are exported from Brazil to Europe.

ENQUIRY

Do a survey of your local shoe shops. Find out where the shoes are made. Consult *Who Owns Whom?* in a library to confirm which multinational owns each shop.

DEBATE

The information on these pages points to some of the dangers of rapid industrialisation and modernisation. How can the exploitation of workers and of consumers be controlled or limited by the efforts of people both inside and outside Brazil? You may like to consider specifically the viewpoints of workers managers, owners, consumers, politicians and law–makers, both in Brazil and in the UK. What links between Brazil and other countries can be helpful?

Global Industrial Organisation

Newly industrialising countries (NICs)

One direct result of investment by transnational corporations has been the growth of industries in many countries around the world that were previously not industrialised. In a few cases the industrialisation has been very rapid since 1960. In Latin America, Brazil, and to a lesser extent Mexico have developed manufacturing industries to provide over 30% of their GNP, and in Southern Europe, Greece, Yugoslavia and Portugal have shown similar growth.

These countries have all been classified by the World Bank as NICs, but the really rapid industrialisation has been in the Asian NICs – South Korea, Taiwan, Hong Kong and Singapore. These four countries raised their industrial production from almost nothing in 1960 to 2% of world production in the 1980s. Their manufactured exports have grown consistently at rates of over 25% per annum and they are now world competitors in textiles, clothing, electronics and light electrical goods.

Two main national aims are common for such rapid industrialisation. One is *import substitution*, that is, the manufacture of goods previously imported for sale on the national market. The second is *export promotion*. This second aim is dominant in the Asian NICs, and the strategy of Free Trade Zones (FTZs) and Export Processing Zones (EPZs) (discussed later in this section) is seen as particularly appropriate. Both national aims should increase GNP and improve the balance of payments for the industrialising country.

Figure 6.33   Inside a modern factory

TNCs move into developing world countries

Cheap labour makes the developing world an attractive place for foreign companies. Low wages for long hours mean that it costs less to produce an item than it would in Europe, Japan or North America. This effect of cheap labour is being felt all around the world. For example, the transnational corporation BSR, an electronics giant with a large factory in Birmingham, has increased the number of people it employs overseas. Between 1978 and 1984 it engaged 8000 more people in Hong Kong, Taiwan and Singapore. At the same it reduced employment in Britain by 15 000!

It is argued that many people are better off because TNCs open factories in the developing world. On the other hand TNCs can shop around for the cheapest deals regardless of the welfare of the families of the people they employ. The TNCs might be forced to improve working conditions and wages if the workers in the developing world were better organised and there were fewer unemployed people waiting to step into their shoes. As it is, it is up to the TNC management and directors to make sure they are not taking advantage of the people of the developing world.

The statistical data in Table 6.7 provides a picture of the rapid industrial growth in some countries.

Table 6.7   Asian NICs, industrial growth 1967–80 (average % growth per annum)

Manufacturing production	South Korea	Singapore	Taiwan
1967–73	21.0	17.9	22.1
1973–80	18.0	8.9	12.8
Manufactured exports			
1967–73	52.4	33.4	37.8
1973–80	28.1	28.1	23.7
GDP			
1967–73	10.9	13.0	10.6
1973–80	8.6	8.5	8.7

Source: UN, *Yearbooks of industrial statistics*

Growth and inequality

Tables 6.8a and 6.8b give an indication of whether economic growth in a country leads to the removal of relative poverty and more equal distribution of wealth.

Table 6.8a Growth and equality: GDP per capita, 1985 (US$)

	1960	1970	1980	1990
Taiwan	619	1189	2489	6573
Brazil	233	450	1977	2540
USA	2851	4922	11 805	18 265
UK	1387	2212	9518	14 226

Source: UN National accounts, *World Development Report*

Table 6.8b Percentage of national income earned by lowest 20% of households

	1960	1970	1980	1986
Taiwan	5.0	8.7	8.8	8.1
Brazil	3.8	3.2	(2.7)	
USA	4.4	4.8	5.3	
UK	6.4	6.6	7.4	5.9

Source: World tables, regional trends, *Taiwan statistical data book*

ANALYSIS

From a study of Tables 6.8a and 6.8b, describe the main features of economic growth and changes in the distribution of wealth in the sample countries.

Figure 6.34 Investment and profit in the Third World

Source: CAFOD, 1985

THIRD WORLD

CASE STUDY *Free Trade Zones in East Asia*

Many light industries have been attracted to FTZs and EPZs. A zone may be anything from a few hundred square metres to several square kilometres. Figure 6.35 shows the proliferation of such zones in East Asia. Figure 6.36 shows how a zone works. The idea has certainly attracted foreign firms to the developing world. In Malaysia, for example, over 60 000 people are employed in the zones. The list of advantages (see box) suggests some of the reasons for this success. High technology has been attracted in the form of the electronics industry, though the low-technology (and labour-intensive) parts of the electronics industry dominate.

Much of the wealth created in these zones goes straight back to parent companies and shareholders in Japan, the USA and Western Europe. The CAFOD report summarised below looks at FTZs from a humanitarian perspective.

Advantages of FTZs for foreign companies

Cheap labour
No customs duties
No import controls
No foreign exchange controls
Unlimited profits may be sent back
Long tax holidays
Cheap loans
Subsidised services
No local taxes
Anti-strike laws
100% foreign ownership

CAFOD report on FTZs (a summary)

A million people are employed in FTZs around the world, 70% of them in Asia. Most of them are girls or young women between the ages of 15 and 25. Prized for their nimble fingers, supposed tolerance of boring yet strenuous work, their docility and lower expectations of workers' rights, they make up at least 80% of the workforce in Malaysia, Taiwan, Mexico and the Philippines.

An FTZ is often a site of great contrasts. The machines are in immaculate, modern, air-conditioned buildings set in landscaped green lawns. The zone is often surrounded by high barbed-wire fences and patrolled by armed guards.

The workers in the same factories, on the other hand, often rent no more than 'body space', that is space enough to lie down on the floor of a room in the local town. A small house may be rented by 10 to 20 people, have only one toilet, a dirt floor, no plumbing and no electricity.

FTZs do practically nothing for long-term male unemployment, and only employ females for a small part of their working life.
Source: Cafod, 1982

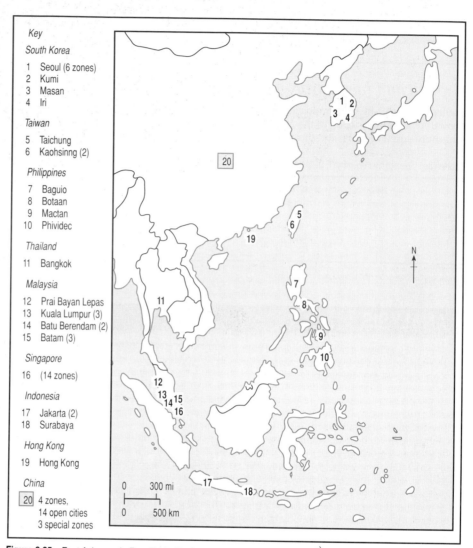

Key

South Korea

1   Seoul (6 zones)
2   Kumi
3   Masan
4   Iri

Taiwan

5   Taichung
6   Kaohsinng (2)

Philippines

7   Baguio
8   Botaan
9   Mactan
10 Phividec

Thailand

11 Bangkok

Malaysia

12 Prai Bayan Lepas
13 Kuala Lumpur (3)
14 Batu Berendam (2)
15 Batam (3)

Singapore

16 (14 zones)

Indonesia

17 Jakarta (2)
18 Surabaya

Hong Kong

19 Hong Kong

China

20 4 zones,
    14 open cities
    3 special zones

Figure 6.35   East Asia – main Free Trade Zones

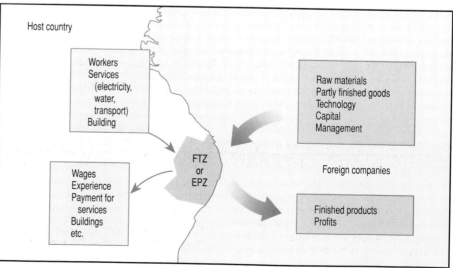

Figure 6.36   The functioning of an FTZ or EPZ

Figure 6.37   Third World TV exports

ROSARIA'S STORY

Rosaria Gutierrez is 22. In two or three years her working life in the Philippines will probably be over, and her present company will terminate her employment and replace her with someone much younger. Since there are four unemployed girls in the locality for every Rosaria with a job, the company will not find this very difficult. Rosaria has been working on and off since she was fifteen and has only been made 'permanent' once, for nine months, before the electronics company she was working for laid her off due to 'shortage of work'. Rosaria thinks this happened because she was not able to complete her 'quota' of work some days, due to recurrent eye-strain. Before that, she worked for four years for a garment company which should have made her permanent after six months' probation (doing work which took her less than a fortnight to learn) but kept her on only as a casual. Being 'casual', therefore, the company only had to pay her less than half a permanent worker's wage. But Rosaria preferred even this to not having a job at all.

Compulsory overtime
At the moment Rosaria works for another garment manufacturer from 8 am to 4.30 pm, Monday to Friday, and 7 am to 2 pm on Saturdays. She is allowed a ten-minute break in the morning and half an hour for lunch. She is not allowed to talk to her colleagues or visit the toilet except during her breaks. There are only four toilets for 350 employees. Compulsory overtime, often resulting in a twelve-hour working day, is common; the workers are locked in, and refusal to work overtime would result in dismissal. Working Saturday afternoon and Sunday morning – at 'plain time' rate – has also been insisted upon, and recently the factory worked a seven-day week for five weeks with no days off allowed, in order to complete a particular batch of work for a customer in the USA.

Unions prohibited
No union activities are allowed; recently four girls known to Rosaria tried to start a union but were soon discouraged. They were set upon outside the factory, beaten and smeared with human excrement. There is no established mechanism by which the workers can air their grievances with the management. Several of the supervisors harass the girls, and humiliate them for making mistakes. Sexual harassment is not unknown and if sexual advances are refused a girl may well lose her job. There is always someone unemployed eager to take each girl's place.

Rosaria's story is common to many thousands of workers around the world involuntarily caught up in the latest industrial innovation – the Free Trade Zone.

Source: *Free Trade Zones*, CAFOD, 1982

ENQUIRY

1 The list of advantages on page 296 is compiled from the viewpoint of a foreign company's management. Use the other information here, and any other sources you have, to compile similar lists of both advantages and disadvantages from other people's viewpoints. You may like to include local women and men, local government officials, local companies and workers and consumers in other countries among your sample.

2 What advantages overlap? What major disadvantages emerge? How often is one person's advantage another's disadvantage? How should such conflicts be resolved?

3 What suggestions would you like to make to the directors of any British multinational company using FTZs in East Asia?

CASE STUDY *Taiwan – growth with equality?*

Taiwan is often held up as the shining example of capitalist development overcoming its own tendency to increase the wealth of the rich at a much faster rate than that of the poor. Table 6.8b on page 295 shows that there is a more equal distribution of wealth in Taiwan than in the UK.

In the 1960s the share of the poorest increased. Since then the share has at least been maintained while the GNP has nearly quadrupled. It is, however, a reflection of the gross inequality acceptable in the world that only 8% of the wealth going to 20% of the people is claimed as 'success'!

In many developing countries, especially those wedded to the import substitution strategy, great spatial inequalities develop between core urban industrial areas and rural peripheral areas. Even when investment is directed at peripheral areas the improvements in production and income often polarise into a few localised centres, bypassing most of the periphery. We have seen something of this in Western Ireland (page 282). Taiwan, with its export orientated strategy and attention to development throughout the country, has to some extent avoided this problem. Figure 6.38 shows the difference between the actual number of jobs created during the ten years 1975 to 1985, and the number of new jobs that would have been a 'fair share' for each place. Thus, for example, Hsinchu (site of a new science-based industrial park) gained 6663 jobs more than its 'fair share'.

The extracts on these pages provide a sample of views about Taiwan's development. None of the extracts mention the pollution, overcrowding and traffic problems associated with rapid industrialisation.

What is so special about Taiwan, an island only half the size of Ireland and some 100 miles off the coast of China? The answer lies in the remarkable success it achieved in transforming itself from colony to prosperous industrial nation in a mere 25 years. Furthermore, this was a transformation characterised by the *equitable participation* of all her peoples. It is the kind of success wished for by all developing nations as they became independent after the Second World War, but which so few have attained.

When Japan was defeated in 1945 it had been the intention of the Americans to return Taiwan to China. In the event, the civil war in China, culminating in the victory of the Peoples' Army under Mao Tse Tung, led to the flight of the government of Chiang Kai Shek to Taiwan with the intention of using it as a base for the reconquest of China. A million Chinese refugees settled on the island, bringing with them in some cases their commercial and technical experience. This new human resource proved to be one important factor in the post-war transformation of Taiwan; another, at least initially, was the economic and technical aid given by the United States.

The situation in Taiwan called for urgent action. Her whole economy had been developed as a colonial tributary of Japan. Japan was now gone and with it her market for Taiwanese produce. China herself had become a belligerent nation opposed to the new regime which had taken over the island. A new and entirely different economy would have to be constructed. The fact that Taiwan's new government was in many respects alien meant that its local-vested interests were small and it acted with considerable impartiality.

Why has Taiwan's development been both different and preferable? The answer seems to lie in the way in which the distinction between town and country, industry and agriculture, was kept to a minimum.

Source: Simpson, 1988

Taiwan's growth since the early 1950s: gains in agricultural labour productivity of nearly 250 per cent, which financed rapid growth, industrialisation, and reallocation of the labour force out of agriculture; growing external orientation of the economy, with industrial exports increasing fourteenfold; changing export composition, shifting from primarily agricultural goods to over 90 per cent industrial; investment in labour-intensive industries including electrical machinery, chemicals, and textiles; the end of the labour surplus around 1968, followed by rising wage shares in national income; and high and growing rural industrialisation.

What kinds of economic development policies and strategies produced these outcomes? There are four key elements:

1 Strategy of decentralised development: Taiwan inherited from colonial days the start of a network of roads, railways, irrigation systems, and industrial estates...

2 Balanced rural development strategy: The development of rural Taiwan combined the standard concern with agriculture with unusually heavy attention to non-agricultural activities. Taiwan made major efforts towards agricultural development, with land reform a key ingredient. Between 1949 and 1953, Taiwan compelled the sale of land by landlords, sold public lands for cultivation, and imposed rent controls.

3 Industrial and trade strategies: Around 1960, Taiwan chose export promotion. Exchange rates were made more realistic, interest rates were reformed, and barriers to trade were reduced...

4 Human resource development: For a country at its stage of development, Taiwan has invested exceptionally large sums from her own resources in education. Many would regard Taiwan's investments in education and the consequent high skill level of the labour force as important factors contributing to both the modern sector enlargement and the traditional sector enrichment as components of the country's rapid economic growth.

Source: Fields, 1980

Taiwan nowadays tends to disdain the image of a labour-intensive, low-cost producer, which accounted for its initial foray into industrialisation; instead [it] embraces a vision of future development rooted in high-technology activities. What remains clear, however, is its commitment to manufacturing and export promotion.

The government has steered industrial development to sites outside of the Taipei core region. To some extent, this action was motivated by strategic considerations: the establishment of an aerospace complex at Taichung, for example. On the whole, however, it was mindful of the need to develop the island's potential. Representative of this thinking are the Ten Major Development Projects scheme, a 5-year programme initiated in 1974, and its successor, the Fourteen Major Projects, implemented at a cost of US $7 billion after 1979...

Source: Todd and Hsueh, 1988

What really alarms many Taiwanese are the high costs of growth, which burst into the open in the last few years.

A farmer's protest on May 20, 1988, which ignited Taipei's worst riot since the late 1940s, drove home the reality that one of the costs of the primacy of export-oriented industrialisation was the erosion and, increasingly, the extinction of Taiwan's agriculture. A burgeoning environmental movement underlined the reality that unregulated industrialisation had created an environmental nightmare, with most of the island's rivers suffering from serious pollution, agricultural produce manifesting high levels of contamination by heavy metals, and air that was considered unfit to breathe for nearly 62 days out of one year. Scores of strikes broke out in the aftermath of the KMT government's lifting of martial law in July 1987, emphasising the workers' point that the 'miracle' had been built on their exploitation and that it was time to claim the benefits that were rightfully theirs.

Source: Bello and Rosenfeld, 1990

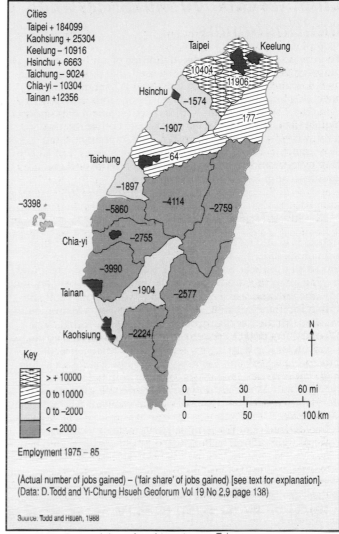

Cities
Taipei + 184099
Kaohsiung + 25304
Keelung – 10916
Hsinchu + 6663
Taichung – 9024
Chia-yi – 10304
Tainan +12356

Key

> + 10000
0 to 10000
0 to –2000
< – 2000

Employment 1975 – 85

(Actual number of jobs gained) – ('fair share' of jobs gained) [see text for explanation].
(Data: D.Todd and Yi-Chung Hsueh Geoforum Vol 19 No 2,9 page 138)

Source: Todd and Hsueh, 1988

Figure 6.38   Pattern of share of employment across Taiwan

ANALYSIS

Use Table 6.9 and Figure 6.38 to assess the extent to which Taiwan has avoided spatial inequality of development between core and peripheral areas.

Table 6.9   Taiwan employment 1975–85 (millions) and output 1975–88

	1975	1985	1990
Employment			
Manufacturing	1.51	2.48	2.64
Total	5.52	7.42	8.28
Output			
Artificial fibre (mt)	283 695	1 327 771	2 573 573
Steel (mt)	1 173 540	6 199 295	11 071 991
Machine tools	41 738	827 797	755 597
Integrated circuits (000s)	373 565	1 152 121	2 488 127

Source: *Taiwan statistical data book*

SYNTHESIS

Write a report on the success of industrial development in Taiwan using the observers' comments and presenting the statistical data.

High technology industries and multinationals

There is no generally accepted definition of a high technology industry. Several criteria might be used, like those suggested by E. J. Malecki in 'High tech industry'. What is a high technology industry today may not be one tomorrow.

In the USA one definition used by government departments requires an industry to be above average both in its use of technical workers and in its expenditure on research and development. This definition accounts for about 7% of all US employment and includes, for instance, aircraft and guided missiles, computers, drugs and plastics.

High tech in the USA

Figures 6.40 and 6.41 show the concentration of the US high technology industry into a few locations. California leads in almost all products, but certain high tech industries are found in other areas that are favourable to their research or marketing.

Semiconductors, essential for all electronic equipment, are important in the sun belt, where firms like Texas Instruments are sited. Medical and surgical instruments are found more often in the frost belt. Most major medical research centres are found in the north east: New Jersey, Ohio, Massachusetts, Illinois, New York and Pennsylvania follow California in this field. The software industry is found in both the sun belt and the frost belt. After California and Texas come Virginia and Maryland, both close to the Federal government who are major customers.

The location of defence industries is a major factor in the concentration of high tech industry, but so are the preferences of the highly skilled professional workers it employs. They are mobile and choose the place where they will live according to the quality of life it offers.

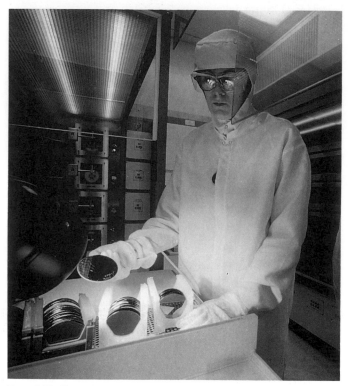

Figure 6.39   Trays of wafers at a Digital Equipment semiconductor facility in Massachusetts

HIGH TECH INDUSTRY

We all have an idea of what high tech is: robots, miracle drugs, computerised home appliances, space vehicles. But to define 'high tech' is much more difficult. Is the nature of the product the determining factor? We tend to consider each new generation of computers as 'high tech,' but not a new, improved version of detergent. Is it the manufacturing process? Highly automated production lines churn out mundane products such as paper and fabrics with little human input. Or is it the skills of a labour force which can vary from engineers and scientists with Ph.D.s to unskilled assemblers? The problem of definition is all the more difficult when a single product is made up of distinct components. Electronics is especially problematic in this regard. Circuit design and fabrication are exacting tasks that are performed by engineers and skilled technicians. Semiconductor assembly, on the other hand, requires few skills, and so is done primarily by young women in countries like Taiwan, Malaysia, and Mexico, where wages are much lower than in the USA. The 'low tech' portion of high tech, then, employs the largest part of the electronics labour force but is most likely to be done overseas, where wage rates are low.

Source: Malecki, 1985

ENQUIRY

1   List as many examples as you can of high technology industries that might be identified by the criteris suggested by Malecki.

2   In what way do the criteria suggested by the US government reflect that an industry is 'high tech'?

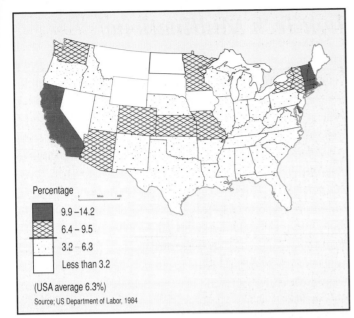

Figure 6.40 High technology employment as a percentage of nonagricultural employment, 1983

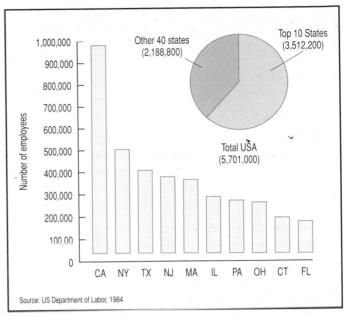

Figure 6.41 USA: employment in high technology industries.

HIGH TECH SITE SELECTION

One of the most visible locational decisions by a high technology firm was that made by the Microelectronics and Computer Technology Corporation (MCC). A joint venture of a dozen major computer and semi-conductor firms, MCC was founded to do research on advanced technologies such as new generations of supercomputers, artificial intelligence, and robotics. As a consortium created in 1982 by several firms, it had no home base or locational inertia, and began its search for a site by examining 57 cities around the country. The cities made polished sales pitches to lure the firm's eventual 400 engineers and scientists. The four finalists in the chase – Atlanta, Austin, San Diego, and Raleigh-Durham – had some things in common. All four areas were in the sun belt, and all had major universities. Except for Raleigh-Durham, in the Research Triangle area of North Carolina, none was particularly well-noted for high tech activity.

When Austin was chosen, its attractions to MCC were widely analysed by other would-be Silicon Valleys. Austin, the state capital, is the site of the main campus of the University of Texas, a school that ranks among the top twenty in the country in research funding. The university's reputation, state commitments of further support, and the city's proven quality-of-life attractiveness for high tech people were the deciding factors. Austin and the State of Texas added to these attractions a package of financial and other incentives, including a favorable lease on land in the University's research park and subsidised mortgages for relocating employees.

In return, Austin has gotten not only MCC. In the typical snowballing manner of high tech areas, several other companies have decided to move research and other advanced technology facilities there. Lockheed Missiles and Space Company, 3M Corporation, and Motorola are among the firms which have added to the agglomeration of technical workers there, at the expense of cities like Minneapolis and Phoenix, where the companies have other facilities. In fact, the entire 100-mile corridor between Austin and San Antonio is nicknamed 'Silicon Gulch.' San Antonio is the site of several computer, biotechnology, and electronics companies. Whether or not the 'Gulch' will rival the San Francisco Bay and Boston regions in high technology will depend on its ability to spawn a succession of new firms as technology advances and changes.

Source: Malecki, 1985

CASE STUDY *The World's Largest High Tech Multinational*

Most high tech industry in the world is controlled by multinational companies like IBM. These giant business enterprises (multinational companies or corporations [MNCs], or enterprises [MNEs], or transnational companies/enterprises [TNCs or TNEs]) often enjoy annual sales that are greater than many a nation's GNP.

They have branches and subsidiary companies, often trading under different names, in countries all around the world. Their allegiance is to their shareholders and to financers, and to the global market place. The parent company may have links with one nation where the headquarters will be located. The directors and executives are likely to be dominantly of one nationality, and the subsidiaries (like IBM(UK)) may be linked to specific nations or regions.

The nature of this expanding sector of global economic activity leads to the concentration of decision-making into the hands of a very few, very affluent middle/upper class men (only five of the 90 'Directors and Officers' of IBM are women) mainly from the USA, Japan and Western Europe. The giant organisations generate employment and high wage levels for those at the top.

Table 6.10 IBM, 1992

Total revenue ($ million)		64 523	
from:			
	Processors	13 916	
	Peripherals	9 285	
	Workstations	10 558	
	Software	11 103	
	Maintenance service	7 635	
	Other	4 674	
	IT total	57 171	
	Services	7 352	
	Total	$64 523	
Net earnings before tax		$9 026	million
Tax		$2 161	million
Net earnings after tax		$6 865	million
Cash dividend paid		$2 765	million
Investment		$4 698	million
Total assets		$86 705	million
Number of stockholders		764 630	
Regional breakdown of revenue			
USA (156 802 employees)		24 633	million
Rest (144 740 employees)		39 892	million
of which Europe/Middle East/Africa		24 971	million
Asia/Pacific		9 672	million
Americas		5 247	million

Source: IBM, 1992 Annual Report

ENQUIRY

1 Find a list of the world's nations ranked by GNP or GDP. Where on this list would IBM rank with its revenue of $64 523 million for 1992?

2 Where on a ranked list of GDP per capita would IBM appear with its revenue of $214 000 per employee (or, if shareholders are included, $60 500 per person)?

3 What are the differences around the world in the revenue generated per employee?

ANALYSIS

Write to a multinational corporation asking for their most recent annual company report. Compare their returns with those of IBM. Consider total revenue, global distribution of business, revenue per employee and revenue in relation to total assets. How do the directors' comments compare with those in the IBM 'Letter to Stockholders'? Are other multinationals now encouraging the independence of their constituent businesses?

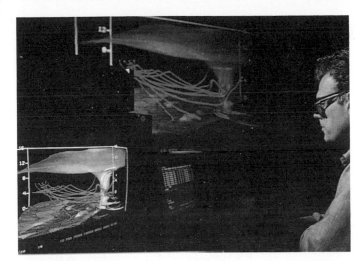

Figure 6.42 IBM computers at the University of Wisconsin are helping researchers analyse vast amounts of meteorological data. The information is used by the National Weather Service, NASA, universities and companies like Federal Express

Figure 6.43 When Wal-Mart Stores, Inc. opened its first hypermart in Garland, Texas, the company selected IBM RT systems to help manage the large amounts of data generated by the store

Figure 6.44 IBM instructor Roger Midgette explains the operation of an IBM product to customers in classrooms across the country from an IBM television studio in Washington, DC. Coursework transmitted over IBM's satellite education networks can be viewed by more than 1200 students simultaneously

Dear Stockholder,

During 1992, the changes that are fundamentally reshaping the worldwide computer industry accelerated. Customers showed a growing preference for smaller computers and open systems, and placed growing value on software, services, and integration skills. The increasing pace of our participation in these opportunities was not enough to offset generally weakened business conditions around the world and severe competitive pressure.

As a result, revenues declined and earnings from operations were down sharply.

To improve IBM's competitiveness and profitability, we are taking the aggressive action required by the rapidly changing marketplace – reallocating resources to growth businesses, reducing costs, increasing the autonomy of our business units.

Intensifying focus on growth areas

We are reallocating resources and increasing our investments in the growth areas of client/server computing, net-working, RISC technology and multimedia, together with the essential software that underpins all of these areas. Our 1993 investments in research, development, and engineering will maintain IBM's leadership.

Reducing costs

Advances in technology are placing more function, power, and memory in ever-smaller chips and devices. At the same time, customers have established world-class quality at competitive prices as the starting requirement to earn their business.

During 1992, we reduced IBM's worldwide workforce by more than 40,000 people, for a reduction of more than 100,000 since 1986. In parallel, we have eliminated layers of management, reduced support and overhead staff, and moved people into revenue-producing jobs.

And, since 1985, ten out of 40 plants have been taken out of our manufacturing base. These and other actions helped to produce a decline in IBM's operating expenses last year.

Increasing autonomy of individual business units

In a diverse and fast-moving industry, with thousands of specialized competitors, clear focus and speed to market are essential for competitive advantage. Increasingly, and at a faster pace, each IBM business is shaping itself to the marketplace disciplines.

As we continue to create more autonomous and responsive businesses, we are creating greater financial and investment flexibility for IBM, including varying forms of ownership. Each business must be competitive in its own right – sufficiently independent so that the possibility of separate ownership can be evaluated against the test of business logic and the prospects for enchancing stockholder value. And, certain of our businesses are already well along the path to more independent operation.

There is no easy way through this period of wrenching transition for IBM. The long-term health of the business, and the interests of all those with a stake in it, requires choices – sometimes, very difficult choices.

That is the case with the decision by the Board of Directors to reduce the dividend on IBM's common stock. This action came only after serious deliberation and careful consideration. We are confident in the long-term strategy for our company – confident that it will result in a more competitive and successful IBM.

John F. Akers, Chairman of the Board
January 26, 1993

Conclusion

Causes and trends

This section takes a step back to look at some of the major causes and trends that are helping to create the kind of changes that you have studied.

There is a temptation for geographers to ignore the causes of change and concentrate on its effects. Such an approach encourages the acceptance of things as they are. If geographers are to contribute to debate and action to create a better world, they need to understand some of the major causes of present patterns and developments and to be able to envisage possible alternatives. In the study of industry, this requires an awareness of economic and historical processes as well as geographical ones.

There are four sets of information here: Causes (1–6); Subsequent causes (1–4); Results (1–4); and statistical data.

Causes of change in industry

Long-term trends

1 *Growth of GNP*, which depends on technological development and innovation. It has been suggested that this growth comes in spurts (Kondratiev waves) with each major development. So, for instance, electricity brought a spurt, followed by a slowing down; then the micro-computer and robotics brought a spurt, which will now run down until the next major innovation.

2 *Growth of consumer and service markets*, which follows the growth of GNP.

3 *Techological developments* in production, distribution and communications allow for *spatial separation*. This means that manufacturing, marketing, research and management can each take place in a different location, even in a different country.

4 *Increased internationalisation* of production and finance and the concentration of ownership into a few hands, largely multinational corporations, in a few countries.

Shorter-term trends

5 *Accelerating mechanisation and computerisation* which reduce the labour needed in manufacture.

6 *Recession and decreasing profits* since 1960, when the post-war (1945) boom ended.

Results of change seen on the ground

1 High unemployment, unequally distributed.

2 Move from manufacturing to service industries.

3 Increased contrast between prosperous core areas and poorer peripheral areas.

4 New firms created in response to high unemployment, using local potential.

GROUP DISCUSSION

1 Make a 'card' for each of the main causes (1–6) suggested for change in industry. Discuss each and put the cards in a pattern with the most important at the top.

2 Use your pattern as a basis for a diagram on a large piece of paper to show the main links between these 'causes' and the subsequent 'causes' (1–4), and the eventual results of change as seen on the ground (1–4).

Subsequent causes of change

Long-term trends

1 *Rapid growth of size and number of multinational enterprises (MNES).*

2 *Growth of international trade*, partly due to movements between branches and subsidiaries of MNES which account for over 39% of world trade.

Trends accelerating since 1975

3 *New International Division of Labour* (NIDL) suggests a whole world view which is 'affluent-centric', seeing the world in terms of an affluent core area exploiting a poor periphery. For this to be possible three things were necessary:
(i) a pool of cheap and unorganised labour in the periphery.
(ii) the development of processes in manufacturing which did not need skilled labour.
(iii) technological innovation in transport and communications to enable the dispersal of manufacturing processes from the core, but without the core losing control of them.
As the core produced more it had difficulties in finding ways to invest profitably all the capital it was accumulating, so this super-exploitation of labour at the periphery was one way to overcome the problem.

4 *New Regional Division of Labour* (NRDL) pays more attention to regional and national influences within the global system. It suggests core/periphery patterns within regions and countries. It sees three kinds of area developing in industrially advanced countries:
(i) areas of high standards of living, high wages, and high capital accumulation where new production forces have produced planning and management centres.
(ii) areas of lower wages and standards of living where the actual manufacture takes place needing relatively few workers.
(iii) areas with a highly skilled labour force that worked in the past but is now no longer required.

STATISTICAL WORK

1 Represent some of the statistical data in Tables 6.11–6.15 graphically. To which of the statements on this page does each set of data relate? Do they confirm the suggestions in the texts?

2 Look back at the statistical data you studied on page 267. Which statements in this section do the earlier data confirm?

Table 6.11   Unemployment trends (% of workforce)

	1960	1970	1976	1985	1987	1992
EUR9	2.5	2.1	6.0	10.8	10.3	9.4
UK	1.6	2.5	4.9	12.0	10.8	10.7
Birmingham	n	n	5.9	15.7	19.0	17.4
Central Birmingham	n	n	n	24.0	30.0	26.4

n – Comparable data not available   Source: *Eurostat* and Birmingham City Council

Table 6.12   Trade (imports/exports, 1983 US$000 million)

	1975	1983	1990
World	907/877	1885/1811	2580/2452
N. America and Europe	589/548	1196/1058	1924/1830
USSR	36/33	80/91	–
Asia and S. America	219/239	492/563	485/486
[World Population	4076 m	4685 m	5315 m]

Source: UN, *Statistical yearbook*, 1990

Table 6.14   Manufacturing job losses and gains, 1982–85

Losses through improved productivity, gains through increased demand

		Loses	Gains
USA	Electrical machinery	− 128 000	+ 213 000
	Cars	− 73 000	+ 150 000
Japan	Cars	− 35 000	+ 53 000
France	All manufacturing	− 162 000	+ 16 000

Source: OECD, 1989

Table 6.13   Installed industrial robots

	1980	1986	1985 per 10 000 employees in manufacturing
Japan	5500	56 000	38
USA	4500	25 000	11
West Germany	1255	12 400	13
UK	371	3683	6
Korea	0	454	1

Source: OECD, 1989

Table 6.15   Growth of MNEs indicated by global foreign direct investment (FDI)

	1960	1970	1975	1981
FDI US$000 m	50	130	140	200

Source: *Economist*, 19 February 1983

The future

Signs of the times. Figures 6.46 and 6.45 (employment changes in the EEC) show how quickly things have moved. Earlier in this chapter you have seen that even greater changes are taking place in other parts of the world. There is no evidence of a slow-down of the changes – indeed, with the break-up of the Communist power bloc in Eastern Europe there is even more uncertainty.

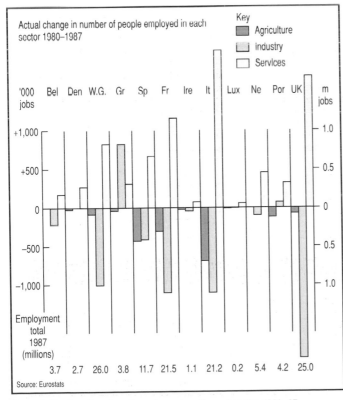

Figure 6.45   Actual number of people employed in each sector, 1980–87

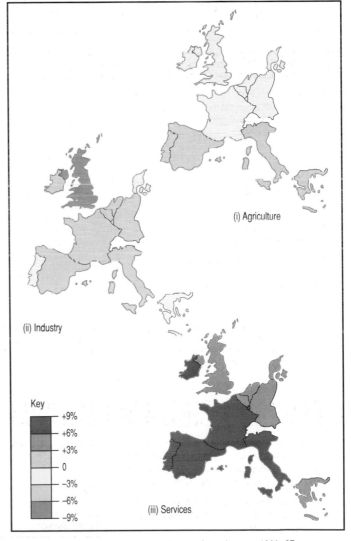

Figure 6.46   Percentage change in employment in each sector 1980–87

The report on 1992 ('EC report...') points to potential difficulties in the UK, while the extract on 'kicking the military habit' ('Can a world...') suggests great opportunities on a global scale. The issue of equal opportunities for women is often pushed into the background by day-to day crises and events, but it is a continuing universal issue with enormous implications for social and economic development. Projects like the one in Grenada ('Equal opportunities...') are small-scale, but by such means the conscientisation and politicisation of women can progress the world over.

Control

The issues of control and power in industrial change are very complex, and are therefore not often subject to explicit media analysis. The transcript from 'File on 4' does show how multinationals make decisions with reference to the well-being of mainly one group – the owners of industry. Together with national governments and international banking, they hold most power over economic development in the world. The question of the role of communities and groups other than owners in deciding the future must be at the top of our agenda. The philosopher André Gorz has suggested a middle way between capitalism and Marxism that tries to use the ideas of each in the areas of life where they are effective and acceptable. The extracts include some of his other ideas.

EQUAL OPPORTUNITIES

Women in Grenada have been training as mechanics since 1988.

'In a sense these women are pioneers who helped to break new ground,' says Ms Neckles. Along with helping the trainees acquire the skills of their new trade, the project also focused on breaking down psychological roadblocks that could hinder the women in their new pursuit. Personal development workshops were offered by the Women and Development Unit of the University of the West Indies in Barbados. 'These were of crucial importance in strengthening the women's determination,' says UNIFEM's (United Nation's Development Fund for Women) Claudine Correira.

Such determination came in handy as the women struggled to overcome negative attitudes by male counterparts in the workplace. 'At first the men seemed somewhat threatened, but as soon as the women showed themselves to be competent they were accepted,' Ms Neckles says. 'They had to prove themselves.'

The idea has proved to be catching. The government of Grenada has now begun training women at the Grenada National College in other non-traditional skills, including plumbing, refrigeration and electrical wiring. 'A lot of women approach me and want to know how they can get the same training,' says Ms Belgrave. 'Now the biggest challenge is adjusting to the life of being a mechanic. It's not that hard. You act like a man in the shop and like a lady at home.'

Source: *World development*, September 1989

Figure 6.47   Margaret Neckles (left), with former students

CAN A WORLD CONVERTED TO THE CAUSE OF PEACE KICK THE MILITARY HABIT?

Anthony Sampson

CAN THE world really adjust to an economic system no longer based on military confrontation? Will the 'peace dividend' be available to finance world development and the alleviation of poverty?

The discussions once confined to disarmers and idealists are now urgently relevant to politicians, investors and planners in both East and West.

Many Western defence companies, including British Aerospace, are having to rethink strategy. This week the Ford motor company announced its intention to sell off its defence division. Moscow is to host a world conference this summer on converting arms factories to peaceful production.

But the first high expectations are facing practical problems. Can the superpowers disarm without massive unemployment and political backlashes? Can they persuade Third World arms makers and buyers to follow their lead?

Source: *Observer*, 14 January 1990

EC REPORT SAYS BRITAIN FACES 1992 JOB LOSSES

Catherine Pepinster

BRITAIN'S industrial areas are set for a sharp decline and a massive increase in job losses because of the introduction of the European Single Market, according to an unpublished report prepared for the European Commission in Brussels.

Areas dominated by coal and steel will suffer high unemployment as a result of competition and will be blighted by a brain drain, it claims. Unless drastic action is taken to create a more diverse spread of industries and introduce new technologies, the report warns that areas like Strathclyde, South Yorkshire, West Yorkshire, Greater Manchester and Merseyside will become the poor relations of Europe, as the move of economic power out of the regions 'will strengthen and accelerate'.

The report, written by the Catholic University of Louvain, in Belgium, will be published later this year.

Source: *Observer*, 14 January 1990

WHO CONTROLS?
(BBC Radio 4, 'File on 4', 21 November 1989)

In 1980 83% of multinational Lucas Industries' business was in car components. Now they have moved into high tech total systems for aerospace and automotive industries, and only 23% of their sales are in the UK. In 1980 Lucas employed some 84 000 people, about one-fifth abroad. By 1990 they have 58 000 people, two-fifths abroad.

Tony Gill, Chairman and Chief Executive of Lucas, is interviewed by Stuart Simon.

S S The jargon name of the game for big business today is 'critical mass'. If you are not big enough in any particular sector to be a world player, get out and regroup in one where you are.

T G With some of what I would describe as the commodity-type businesses, we realised we were getting too small in those businesses to be in the world league, and had to decide either to invest heavily in them to expand enough to have enough, in fact the critical mass, or to pass those businesses to other people. We wished to concentrate on high value-added products; we divested those commodity-type products.

S S Not all the companies that are being closed down, though, are being bought by other people. Some of them are just disappearing. Is that something to worry about?

T G Well, it is very worrying especially if you happen to work for one of those companies, but our employees are important to us but so are our shareholders, and we attempt to do whatever we perceive as in the best interest of the people who own the company.

If we find that we are in a situation where to become competitive, or stay competitive, we have to find out ways and means of employing less people for any particular amount of the business sales, then that's what we have to do, and we have to put up with the unpleasantness of saying goodbye to some people who have perhaps been with the organisation for some time.

André Gorz wrote this in 1974:

ECONOMIC growth which was supposed to ensure the affluence and well-being of everyone, has created needs more quickly than it could satisfy them and has led to a series of dead-ends which are not solely economic in character: capitalist growth is in crisis not only because it is capitalist but also because it is encountering physical limits... The current crisis also possesses a number of new dimensions which Marxists, with rare exceptions, have not foreseen and for which what has been understood as 'socialism' does not contain answers.

It is a crisis in the relation between the individual and the economic sphere as such: a crisis in the character of work; a crisis in our relations with nature, with our bodies, with our sexuality, with society, with future generations, with history; a crisis of urban life, of habitat, of medical practice, of education, of science... We know that *our* world is ending; that if we go on as before, the oceans and the rivers will be sterile, the soil infertile, the air unbreathable in the cities... We know that for 150 years industrial society has developed through the looting of reserves whose creation required millions of years.

Source: *Guardian*, 9 December 1989

From Critique of Economic Reason:

FROM THE point of view of economic rationality, the working time saved across the whole of society, thanks to increasing efficiency of the means used, constitutes working time made available for the production of additional wealth... But the main question we have to ask, then, is what meaning *we* wish to give this new-found free time, and what content we wish to give it.

Economic reason is fundamentally incapable of providing an answer to this question... 'Advances in technology' inevitably pose the question of the meaning and content of free time; better still, of the nature of a society in which there is far more free time than working time and in which, therefore, economic rationality ceases to govern everyone's time...

I cannot emphasise this too strongly: a job whose effect and aim are to save work, cannot at the same time glorify work as the essential source of personal identity and fulfilment.

Source: A. Gorz, *Critique of economic reason*

DISCUSSION

1 In sub-groups, use the evidence on these pages (and other sources you may have) to identify what you see as the three main issues of industrial change facing the world.

2 Compare your suggestions with those of other groups, and agree two issues to explore further.

3 With reference to these two issues, how can individuals, local communities, political parties, national governments, groups of nations, multinational corporations and trade unions influence developments and ensure justice?

Source: CAFOD, 1989

Figure 6.48   Progress?

Further Reading

Chapter One

Baillie, K., *Coastline* (Kingfisher Books, 1987)

Barnes, R. S. K., *The coastline* (J. Wiley & Sons, 1977)

Carter, R. W. G., *Coastal Systems* (Academic Press, Harcourt Brace, 1988)

Chaffey, J., *A New View of Britain* (Hodder and Stoughton, 1994)

Clowes, A. and Comfort, P., *Process and Land Form* (Oliver & Boyd, 1982)

Hansom, J. D., *Coasts* (Cambridge University Press, 1988)

Hilton, K., *Processes & patterns in physical geography*, 2nd ed. (University Tutorial Press, 1985)

Lenon, B. and Cleves, P., *Techniques and Fieldwork in Geography* (University Tutorial Press, 1992)

Thames Water, *The Lower Colne Plan*

Warn, S., *Fieldwork Investigation 1: Landforms* (Nelson, 1986)

Chapter Two

Brown, Lester R. et al., *State of the World – 1988. A Worldwatch Institute report on progress towards a sustainable society* (W. W. Norton and Co., 1988)

Conacher, A., 'Environmental management implications of intensive forestry practices in an indigenous forest ecosystem: a case study from SW Australia' in O'Riordan, T. and Turner, R. K. (eds), *Progress in resource management and environmental planning*, vol. 4 (1983)

Dowdeswell, W. H., *Practical Ecology* (Heinemann, 1984)

Gradwohl, J. and Greenberg, R., *Saving the tropical forests* (Earthscan, 1988)

Kershaw, K. A., *Quantitative and dynamic ecology*, 2nd ed. (E. J. Arnold, 1987)

King, T. J., *Selected Topics in Biology: Ecology* (Nelson, 1980)

Lenan, P. and Cleves, P., *Teaching of fieldwork in Geography* (University Tutorial Press, 1987)

Mottershead, R., *Biogeography* (Basil Blackwell, 1984)

Myers, N. (ed.), *The Gaia Atlas of Planet Management* (Pan Books, 1985).

Slingsby, D. and Cook, C., *Practical Ecology* (Macmillan, 1986)

Steinbeck, J., *Grapes of wrath* (Heinemann, 1983)

Tait J. (ed.), *Practical conservation series* (Open University/Hodder and Stoughton, 1988)

Friends of the Earth publications on sustainable timber resources

Rainforests: Land Use Options for Amazonia (OUP/WWF/Survival International, 1989)

World Wildlife Fund literature on sustainable timber resources

CD-Rom sources from the *Independent*, the *Guardian* and *The Times*

Chapter Three

Aitchinson, J. W. and Heal, P. W., *Geography*, (1987)

Allen, J., *Energy Resources for a Changing World* (Cambridge University P, 1992)

Brown, G. and Skipsey, E. (eds.), *Energy resources: Geology, supply and demand* (Open University Press, 1989)

Chapman, J. D., *Geography and energy* (Longman, 1989)

Davies, G. R. et al., 'Energy for Planet Earth', *Scientific American*, Special Issue (September, 1990)

Flood, J., *Energy without end* (Friends of the Earth, 1991)

Foley, G., *The energy question* (Pelican, 1992)

King, P., *Nuclear power: The facts and the debate* (Macmillan Press, 1990)

Kozlov, I., *The world energy problem* (Progress Publishers, Moscow, 1987)

McLachlan, K. and A., *Oil and development in the Gulf* (John Murray, 1989)

McVegh, J. C., *Energy around the world* (Pergamon Press, 1984)

Moxon, J., *Volta, man's greatest lake* (André Deutsch, 1964)

Neal, P., *Energy, power sources and electricity* (Dryad Press, 1988)

Ramage, J., *Energy: A guidebook* (OUP, 1983)

Raw, M., *Resources in the environment* (Unwin Hyman, 1989)

Souzssan, J., *Primary resources development in the Third World* (Routledge, 1988)

Toke, D., *Green energy: Non nuclear response to the greenhouse effect* (Green Print, 1990)

Woodfield, J. and Bensley, G., *16–19 options: Hawkhurst Moor*, Naish, M. and Warn, S. (eds) (Longman, 1993)

Atlas showing physical features and precipitation

BP world statistics

Geographical digest

Up-to-date news and views on energy issues can be researched using CD-Rom *Guardian*, *The Times* and *Independent*.

Literature is available from the following addresses (either free or at minimal cost) to help your group with research into alternative energy resources.

- British Nuclear Fuels Information Offices, Risley, Warrington WA3 6AS, or from Sellafield.
- Public Relations Officer, CEGB Environment Programme, Marshwood Engineering, Soton SO44 2B.
- Electricity Council, 30 Millbank, London SW18 4RD. International Solar Energy Society, Kings College, London W8 7AH.
- National Centre for Alternative Technology, Machynlleth, Powys.
- Intermediate Technology Development Group, Myson House, Railway Terrace, Rugby CV12 3HT.
- British Wind Energy Association, 4 Hamilton Place, London W1V OBQ.
- ETSU Renewable Energy Enquiry Bureau, Building 156, Harwell Laboratory, Oxfordshire OX11 0RA.

Chapter Four

Bater, J. H., *The Soviet City* (Edward Arnold, 1980)

Bater, J. H., *The Soviet Scene* (Edward Arnold, 1989)

Bristol City Council, *Final Report on Poverty* (1985)

Chaffey, J., *A New View of Britain* (Hodder and Stoughton, 1994)

Dwyer, D. J., *People and Housing in Third World Cities* (Longman, 1975)

Drakakis-Smith, D., *The Third World City* (Methuen, 1987)

French, R. A. and Hamilton, F. E. I. (eds), *The Socialist City* (John Wiley, 1979)

Gilbert, A. and Gugler, J., *Cities, Poverty and Development* (Oxford University Press, 1981)

Hall, P., *London 2001* (Unwin Hyman, 1989)

Harpham, P., Lusty, T. and Vaughan P., *In the Shadow of the City* (Oxford University Press, 1988)

Pryor, E. G., *Housing in Hong Kong* (Oxford, 1983)

Smith, D. M., *Human Geography: A Welfare Approach* (Edward Arnold, 1977)

Smith, D. M., *Where the Grass is Greener* (Penguin, 1979)

Smith, D. M., *Geography. Inequality and Society* (Cambridge University Press, 1987)

United Nations Centre for Human Settlements (Habitat, 1987)

Global Report on Human Settlements (Oxford)

Ward, P. M. (ed.), *Self-Help Housing: A Critique* (Mansell, 1982)

Chapter Five

Bayliss-Smith, T., *The ecology of agricultural systems* (Cambridge University Press, 1982)

Bradford, M. and Kent, W., *Human Geography: theories and their applications* (Oxford University Press, 1982)

Briggs, D., Agriculture and Environment (Longman, 1989)

Blunden, J. and Curry, N., *The Changing Countryside* (Open University Press, 1985)

Bowler, I., The Geography of Agriculture (Longman, 1992)

Bull, D., *Pesticides in the third world: A growing problem* (Oxfam, 1982)

Bull, C., Daniel, P., Hopkinson, M., *The Geography of Rural Resources* (Oliver & Boyd, 1986)

Dudley, N., *This Poisoned Earth: the Truth about Pesticides* (Piatkus, 1987)

Harrison, P., *Inside the Third World* (Penguin Books, 1986)

Harrison, P., *The Third World Tomorrow* (Penguin Books, 1988)

Harrison, P., *The Third Revolution* (Penguin Books, 1993)

Huckle, J. Ed., United Kingdom Agriculture (WWF)

Ilbery, B. W., *Agricultural Geography: a social and economic analysis* (Oxford University Press, 1985)

Mellanby, K., *Farming and Wildlife* (William Collins, 1981)

Pierce, J. T., The food Resource (Longman, 1990)

Shoard, M., *The Theft of the Countryside* (Temple Smith, 1982)

Slater, F., *People and Environments: issues and enquiries* (Longman, 1988)

Tivy, J., Agricultural Ecology (Longman, 1990)

Chapter Six

Bello, W. and Rosenfeld, S., *Dragons in distress* San Francisco (Institute for Food and Development Policy, 1990)

Bradford and Kent, Understanding Human Geography (Oxford University Press, 1993)

Buckley, P. J. and Casson, M., *The future of the multi-national enterprise* (Macmillan, 1991)

Dixon, C. J., Drakakis-Smith, D. and Watts, H. D. (eds), *Multinational corporations and the third world* (Croom Helm, 1986)

Dunning, J. H., *Multinationals and the European Community* (Basil Blackwell, 1988)

Dunning, J. H., *Structural change in the world economy* (Routledge, 1990)

Dunning, J. H., *Multinational enterprises and the global economy* (Addison-Wesley, 1993)

Hamilton, F. E. I. (ed.), *Industry in developing and peripheral regions* (Croom Helm, 1986)

Hamilton, F. E. I. (ed.), *Industrial change in advanced economies* (Croom Helm, 1987)

Hamilton, F. E. I. and Linge, G. J. R. (eds), *Spatial analysis, industry and the industrial environment* Vol. 3 'Regional economics and industrial systems' (Wiley, 1983)

Healey, M. J. and Ibery, B. W. (eds), *The industry of the countryside* (Geo Books, 1985)

Healey, M. J. and Ibery, B. W. Location and change (Oxford University Press, 1990)

Keeble, D. *et al.*, Business success in the countryside (HMSO, 1990)

Law, N. and Smith, D., *Decision-making geography* (Hutchinson, 1987)

General

The World Environment 1972–1992 (UNEP, 1993)

Acknowledgements

1.1 From 'Coasts' J. D. Hansom. Cambridge University Press
1.2 Dorset County Council
1.4a From 'Coasts', J. D. Hansom. Cambridge University Press
1.7 From 'Systematic Geography', B. Knapp. Allen & Unwin, an imprint of HarperCollins Publishers Limited
1.8a © Crown Copyright
T1.3 NCC Oxwich National Nature Reserve
1.15 NCC Oxwich National Nature Reserve
1.16 NCC Oxwich National Nature Reserve
1.20 From 'Coasts', J. D. Hansom. Cambridge University Press
1.21 United States Department of Commerce
1.22 United States Department of Commerce
1.23 United States Department of Commerce
T1.4 Geography Dept., University of Chicago
1.24 Geography Dept., University of Chicago
T1.5 Geography Dept., University of Chicago
T1.6 Geography Dept., University of Chicago
1.29 Geography Dept., University of Chicago
1.32 Geography Dept., University of Chicago
T1.8 University of London Examinations and Assessment Council
1.33 From 'World Resources 1988–89', Basic Books and 'The Natural Geochemistry of our Environment', D. F. Speidel and A. F. Agnew
1.35 Friends of the Earth
1.36 Adapted with permission from 'Global Changes in the Geosphere-Biosphere: Initial Priorities for an IGBP', National Academy of Sciences, 1986. Courtesy of the National Academy Press, Washington DC
1.37 From 'Process and Pattern in Physical Geography', Keith Hilton. University Tutorial Press, an imprint of HarperCollins Publishers Limited
1.38 From Human impact on the hydrological cycle. 'Geofile', Foskett. Mary Glasgow Publications Ltd, London
T1.10 From 'Human Impact', Andrew Goudie. Basil Blackwell Ltd
1.41 From 'Human Impact', Andrew Goudie. Basil Blackwell Ltd
1.42 From 'Human Impact', Andrew Goudie. Basil Blackwell Ltd
T1.13 From 'Process and Pattern in Physical Geography', Keith Hilton. University Tutorial Press, an imprint of HarperCollins Publishers Limited
1.44 From 'Process and Pattern in Physical Geography', Keith Hilton. University Tutorial Press, an imprint of HarperCollins Publishers Limited
1.45 From 'Geographical', September 1987
1.47 Lower Colne Study – J. L. Gardiner, Thames Water, reproduced with the agreement of the National Rivers Authority, Thames Region
1.48 Lower Colne Study – J. L. Gardiner, Thames Water, reproduced with the agreement of the National Rivers Authority, Thames Region
1.49 Lower Colne Study – J. L. Gardiner, Thames Water, reproduced with the agreement of the National Rivers Authority, Thames Region
1.50 Lower Colne Study – J. L. Gardiner, Thames Water, reproduced with the agreement of the National Rivers Authority, Thames Region
1.54 Lower Colne Study – J. L. Gardiner, Thames Water, reproduced with the agreement of the National Rivers Authority, Thames Region
T1.16 Lower Colne Study – J. L. Gardiner, Thames Water, reproduced with the agreement of the National Rivers Authority, Thames Region
1.56 Science Photo Library
2.5 From 'An Introduction to Heathland Ecology', C. H. Gimingham. Oliver & Boyd
T2.2 From 'Ecology: The Experimental Analysis of Distribution and Abundance', Charles J. Krebs, 1985. Harper & Row. Reprinted by permission of HarperCollins Publishers Inc.
T2.4 Countryside Commission and Forestry Commission
2.16 From 'Natural Vegetation of the Member Countries of the European Community and the Council of Europe', Commission of the European Communities
2.18a From 'Process and Pattern in Physical Geography', Keith Hilton. University Tutorial Press, an imprint of HarperCollins Publishers Limited
2.18b 'Forestry in Crisis', S. Tomkins. A & C Black.
T2.5 From 'Soil & Vegetation Systems: Contemporary Problems in Geography', Stephen T. Triedgill, 1977. Oxford University Press
2.20 From 'Progress in Resource Management & Environmental Planning', Arthur Conacher, 1983. John Wiley & Sons Ltd
2.21 Ardea
2.22 From 'Progress in Resource Management & Environmental Planning', Arthur Conacher, 1983. John Wiley & Sons Ltd
T2.7 From 'Rainforests: Land Use Options for Amazonia', 1989. Oxford University Press
2.23b From 'Introduction to World Vegetation', A. S. Collinson. Allen & Unwin, an imprint of HarperCollins Publishers Limited
2.24a From 'Process and Pattern in Physical Geography', Keith Hilton. University Tutorial Press, an imprint of HarperCollins Publishers Limited
2.25 A-Z Botanical
2.26 NHPA
2.27 NHPA
2.28 Sue Cunningham Photographic
2.29 From 'People and Environmental Issues', Brian Knapp. Collins, an imprint of HarperCollins Publishers Limited
2.32 NHPA
2.38 Broads Authority
2.42 From 'Greenhouse World'. New Scientist, 6 May 1989
3.1 From 'The Adventures of X. Ployt. R', Schools Council 1980
3.2 Shell International Petroleum

3.3   BP Statistical Review
3.4   BP Statistical Review
3.5   BP Statistical Review
3.6   BP Statistical Review
T3.1   BP Statistical Review
3.7   BP Statistical Review
3.8   BP Statistical Review
T3.2   From 'Geography' 72(3) 1987, Geographical Association/J. W. Aitchison and D. W. Heal, and 'Climate and Man', J. H.Illiott, 1969. McGraw-Hill Book Company
3.13   Reprinted with permission from 'Origins of Oil in the Sea', ©1985 by National Academy of Sciences, courtesy of National Academy Press, Washington D. C., USA
3.14   Shell International Petroleum
3.15a   Tropix
3.15b   Greenpeace
3.17   From 'Global Climate Change', Shell Briefing Service. Shell International Petroleum
T3.5   IPCC
3.20   Shell International Petroleum
3.23   Norwegian Water Resources and Energy Administration
T3.6   United Nations
T3.7   Norwegian Water Resources and Energy Administration
T3.8   Norwegian Water Resources and Energy Administration
3.27   From 'Volta: Man's Greatest Lake' James Moxon. Andre Deutsch
3.29   Hutchison Library
3.31   United Kingdom Atomic Energy Authority
3.32   Japan Information and Cultural Centre
3.33   Associated Press
3.34   From 'Prospects for Renewable Energy in the NORWEB Area'. NORWEB Generation/ETSU
T3.10   From 'Prospects for Renewable Energy in the NORWEB Area'. NORWEB Generation/ETSU
T3.11   From 'Prospects for Renewable Energy in the NORWEB Area'. NORWEB Generation/ETSU
3.36   From 'Energy, A Guidebook', J. Ramage. Oxford University Press
3.41   From 'Applied Geography', Vol. 6, No. 4, October 1986. Reproduced with permission of Butterworth-Heinemann, Oxford
T3.12   From 'Petroleum Economist', July 1983, February 1984 and 'Geography' 71(2) 1986, Geographical Association/J. Baker.
T3.14   UN Statistical Yearbook, 1985/86
T3.15   'Cambridge Encyclopedia of Latin America and Caribbean', S. Collier. Cambridge University Press
3.47   J. Allan Cash Photolibrary
4.1   From 'Global Report on Human Settlements', 1986. Oxford University Press
T4.1   From 'Urban and Rural Population Projections 1950–2025', United Nations
4.2   Clarke Homes
4.5   The Independent
4.7   Sue Cunningham Photographic
4.9   Doug Brunner/UNICEF
4.12   From 'Decision Making', Norman Law and David Smith, 1987. Stanley Thornes
4.13   J. Allan Cash Photolibrary
4.14   From 'Geographical', April 1988
T4.5   From 'Global Report on Human Settlements', 1986. Oxford University Press

T4.10   APUR (Atelier Parisien d'Urbanisme)
4.18   Hutchison Library
4.19   From 'Geography: Inequality and Society', D. Smith, 1987. Cambridge University Press
4.20   From 'Geography: Inequality and Society', D. Smith, 1987. Cambridge University Press
T4.11   From 'Geography: Inequality and Society', D. Smith, 1987. Cambridge University Press
4.23   From 'The Soviet Scene', J. Bater. Edward Arnold Publishers
4.28   From 'Geography: Inequality and Society', D. Smith, 1987. Cambridge University Press
4.29   From 'Geography: Inequality and Society', D. Smith, 1987. Cambridge University Press
4.30   From 'Geography: Inequality and Society', D. Smith, 1987. Cambridge University Press
4.31   Bristol United Press
4.32   © Bristol City Council
4.33   © Bristol City Council
4.39   J. Allan Cash Photolibrary
4.41   From 'Housing in Hong Kong', Pryor, 1983. Oxford University Press
4.44   From 'Housing in Hong Kong', Pryor, 1983. Oxford University Press
T4.13   From 'Housing in Hong Kong', Pryor, 1983. Oxford University Press
T4.14   From 'Housing in Hong Kong', Pryor, 1983. Oxford University Press
4.45   From 'Housing in Hong Kong', Pryor, 1983. Oxford University Press
4.46   From 'Housing in Hong Kong', Pryor, 1983. Oxford University Press
4.47   From 'Housing in Hong Kong', Pryor, 1983. Oxford University Press
4.50   J. Allan Cash Photolibrary
4.51   Architectural Association
T4.20   From 'The Socialist City', French & Hamilton (eds.). John Wiley & Sons Ltd
T4.21   From 'The Socialist City', French & Hamilton (eds.). John Wiley & Sons Ltd
T4.22   From 'The Socialist City', French & Hamilton (eds.). John Wiley & Sons Ltd
4.52   L'Institut d'Amenagement et Urbanisme de la Région
4.53   L'Institut d'Amenagement et Urbanisme de la Région
T4.23   APUR (Atelier Parisien d'Urbanisme)
4.56   From 'House France: An Applied Geography', 1978. Methuen
4.58   From 'House France: An Applied Geography', 1978. Methuen
4.60   Presse-Infor
4.64   Etablissement Public d'Amenagement de Sairt Quentin en Yvelines
4.66   Etablissement Public d'Amenagement de Saint Quentin en Yvelines
4.67   Etablissement Public d'Amenagement de Saint Quentin en Yvelines
4.68   From 'London Zoo', P. Hall, 1989. Unwin Hyman
4.70   From 'London Zoo', P. Hall, 1989. Unwin Hyman
4.73   From 'Counterurbanisation', 1986. Geo Books
4.74   From 'Counterurbanisation', 1986. Geo Books
T4.25   From 'Counterurbanisation', 1986. Geo Books
T4.26   From 'Counterurbanisation', 1986. Geo Books
T4.27   From 'Counterurbanisation', 1986. Geo Books
4.75   Streetscape looking towards Market Square, by Robin O' Donnell of Alan Baxter & Associates, copyright Duchy of Cornwall

4.77	Sue Cunningham Photographic
5.1	Andes Press Agency
5.4	Hutchison Library
5.6	University of London Examinations and Assessment Council
5.7	New Internationalist
5.10	South American Pictures
5.11	Tropix
5.28	Shell International Petroleum
5.29i	T. P. Bayliss-Smith/Cambridge University Press
5.29ii	Piatkus Books
5.30	From 'Agriculture' 1983. Basil Blackwell Ltd
5.32	From 'What Future for Broadland', Broads Authority
5.35	Fertilizer Manufacturers Association
5.36	Topham Picture Source
5.38	Bayer PLC
5.39	From 'A Growing Problem: Pesticides in the Third World', D. Bull, 1982. Oxfam
5.40	From 'A Growing Problem: Pesticides in the Third World', D. Bull, 1982. Oxfam
T5.13	From 'A Growing Problem: Pesticides in the Third World', D. Bull, 1982. Oxfam
T5.14	From 'A Growing Problem: Pesticides in the Third World', D. Bull, 1982. Oxfam
5.41	Topham Picture Source
5.44a	Geography Dept., Leicester University
5.46	From 'Agricultural Geography', 1985. Oxford University Press
5.48	From 'Hertfordshire Grassland'. Hertfordshire & Middlesex Wildlife Trust/Countryside Management Service/The Body Shop/Hertfordshire County Council
5.49	Open University
5.50	Fertilizer Manufacturers Association
6.1	International Monetary Fund
6.2	Financial Times
6.3	UNDP/D. Kinley
6.4	Greenpeace
6.5	New Scientist
T6.2	From 'Service Industries', P. Daniels 1982. Cambridge University Press
T6.3	From 'Statistical Yearbook', United Nations
T6.4	From 'Statistical Yearbook', United Nations
6.7	City of Birmingham Development Dept.
6.9	City of Birmingham Development Dept.
6.11	Australian Overseas Information Service
6.14	Powerstock
6.15	J. Allan Cash Photolibrary
6.16	Powerstock
6.18	© 24 Heures, Lausanne
6.19	New Internationalist
6.20	Commission of the European Communities
6.21	New Internationalist
6.22	New Internationalist
6.25	From 'The Industrialisation of the Countryside', 1985. Geo Books
6.26a	Ecoscene
6.26b	Greenpeace
6.26c	Financial Times
6.27	Financial Times, 19th April 1989
6.28	Financial Times, 19th April 1989
6.36	Nissan
T6.7	From 'Yearbook of Industrial Statistics'. United Nations
T6.8a	From 'UN National Accounts World Development Report'. United Nations and World Bank
6.39	Digital Equipment Corporation
6.40	US Department of Labor
6.41	Dept. of Geography, University of Minnesota
T6.10	IBM
6.42	IBM
6.43	IBM
6.44	IBM
T6.11	Eurostat and Birmingham City Council
T6.12	From 'Statistical Yearbook', United Nations
T6.13	OECD
T6.14	OECD
T6.15	Economist
6.51	UNDP/Sid Kane

We are grateful to the following for permission to reproduce copyright material:

The American Geographical Society for extracts from 'The Geography of High Technology' by E. J. Malecki in *Focus* October, 1985; the editor, Birmingham Post for an extract from 'Decision swayed by love of golf' in *Birmingham Post* 19.4.89; British Broadcasting Corporation for an extract from *File on 4* broadcast 21.11.89; British Broadcasting Corporation & Lucas Industries plc for an extract from an interview with Sir Anthony Gill by Stuart Simon in *File on 4* broadcast 30.5.89; BBC Enterprises Ltd for an extract from *The Quiet Revolution* by Quentin Seddon; the author, P. Brown for an extract from 'PCB threat to ocean mammals' in *The Guardian* 31.8.89; The Catholic Fund for Overseas Development for an extract from *Free Trade Zones* (CAFOD 1982); Cambridge University Press for an adapted extract from *Ecology of Agricultural Systems* by Bayliss-Smith and an extract from *Poverty, Inequality and Development* by G.S. Fields (CUP 1980); the editor, Common Cause Magazine for an extract from 'Quest for Water' by Action Aid in *Common Cause* No. 1, June 1989; the author, John Cunningham for an extract from 'Mountain Madness' in *The Guardian* June, 1986; Duchy of Cornwall for an extract from *Poundbury Planning Weekend*. (c) 1989 The Keeper of the Records of the Duchy of Cornwall; the editor, The Ecologist for an extract from 'The Hanrahan Case' in *The Ecologist* Vol. 19 No. 4; the author, Rob Edwards for an extract from 'CEGB Uranium venture in Artic upsets Eskimos' in *The Guardian* 3.12.89; Elsevier Science Publishers Ltd for an extract from 'Land fragmentation & consolidation in Cyprus' in *Agricultural Administration* Vol. 2, 1982; Express Newspapers plc for 'Wildlife at Risk as Oil Pours from Ship' by Martin Charlesworth in *Daily Express* 18.9.89; The Financial Times Ltd for extract from 'Newcomers who are welcomed but feared' in *Financial Times* 19.4.89; Guardian News Services Ltd for extracts from *The Guardian Third World Report* Summer 1988. by Ed Vuilliamy & Alan Rusbridger, 'Sheel to pay a high price for Mersey slick' *The Guardian* 22.8.89. and 'Rainforest fact file' by David Pearce in *The Guardian* 8.12.89; Harper Collins/World Resources Institute for an extract from page 159 in *World Resources 1988–1989* by World Resources Institute and International Institute for Environment and Development. Copyright (c) 1988 by the World Resources Institute and the International Institute for Environment and Development in collaboration with the United Nations Environment

Programme. Reprinted by permission of Basic Books; the author's agent, on behalf of Paul Harrison for an extract *Inside the Third World* (Penguin 1982); Indian Tribal Womens Trust for an extract from 'Report 1985 and Progress report 1987–88' in *Development Project Report* 1985; IBM UK Ltd for extracts from *IBM 1992 Annual Report*; Independent Newspapers Ltd for extracts from 'Polluters to lose grants. . .' & 'Sandoz must come' by Dick Cross in *Irish Independent* 12.9.89, 'Second major chemical firm in pull-out' by Tony O'Brien in *Irish Independent* 13.9.89, and an edited extract from 'IDA attacks environment protestors' in *Irish Independent* 15.9.89; the author, Vic Keegan for an extract from 'Poor pay the price' in *The Guardian* 6.12.85; University of London Examinations & Assessment Council for an extract by Vijay Singh in *A-Level Paper, 16–19 Geography* 1990; Morning Star Cooperative Society Ltd for 'Star Comment' in *Morning Star* 20.4.89; John Murray Ltd for 'Harvest Hymn' by John Betjeman in *Collected Poems*; IPC Magazines Ltd for an extract from 'The delicate balance that builds a delta' in *New Scientist* 14.4.90. and an abridged extract from 'American nuclear industry may have a future yet' in *New Scientist* 24.2.90; Newspaper Publishing plc for extracts from 'Fifty nuclear power stations needed every year by 2000' by Tom Wilkie in *The Independent* 25.9.93, 'Barrage on Severn will help reduce pollution' in *The Independent* 24.10.89, 'Conservationists begin legal fight to save health' by Nicholas Schoon in *The Independent* 14.7.90, 'Ceausescu's legacy that won't go away' by Gavin Stamp in *The Independent* 5.1.90, 'Villages win back the right to life' by Victoria Clark in *The Independent* 5.1.90, 'Cholera strikes at boat people camp' by Kevin Hamlin & John Bulloch in *The Independent* 31.8.89, 'Electronic requiem for our cities' by Peter Kellner in *The Independent* 14.8.89, 'The hunt by Toyota' in *The Independent* 19.4.89, 'Victory for the British worker' 14.4.89, 'Mitsubishi seeks UK foothold in Europe' by Clare Dobie in *The Independent* 23.9.89; The Observer Ltd for extracts from 'EC report says Britain faces 1992 job losses' by C. Pepinster in *The Observer* 14.1.90, 'Can a world converted to the cause of peace kick the military habit?' by A Sampson in *The Observer* 14.1.90. and 'French nuclear power threat' in *The Observer* 18.3.90; Oxwich National Nature Reserve for an edited extract from *Site Management Guide NCC*; Penguin Books Ltd for an extract from *Kingdom by the Sea* by Paul Theroux. Copyright (c) Paul Theroux, 1983; Pergamon Press plc for an extract from 'Taiwan: some special implications' by D. Todd & Yi-Chung Hseuch in *Geoforum* Vol 19, No. 2; Judy Piatkus Ltd for extracts from *This Poisoned Earth* by Nigel Dudley (Piatkus Books 1987); the author, Jonathan Porritt for an adapted extract from 'Farming, the limits to reason' in *Daily Telegraph* 10.2.90; Reed Consumer Books Ltd for an extract from *France Today* by J. Ardagh, published by Martin Secker & Warburg 1987;

Review Group Newspapers Ltd for extracts from 'Hedged out by progress' by C. Richmond in *Hemel Hempstead Review* & 'New move for countryside' in *Gazette & Express* (Herts) 1.1.91; the author, Walter Schwartz for an extract from 'Just let nature do the work' in *Weekend Guardian* 7–8.10.89; Solo Syndication for an extract from 'Tax the polluters' by Sean Ryan in the *Daily Mail* 16.10.89; Ewan McNaughton Ltd for an extract from '3000 Job car plant in Derby' by Philip Johnston in *Daily Telegraph* 19.4.89. 'Real facts of our rustic past' by Charles Moore in *Daily Telegraph* 19.8.89, and '32m budget to save England's landscape' by Toby Moore in *Daily Telegraph* 28.3.91. (c) The Telegraph plc 1989/89/91; Thomson Regional Newspapers Ltd for 'Any Old Iron' by M. Cavalori in *Luton Herald and Post* 25.1.90; the author, Simon Tisdall for an extract from 'Grand Canyon smog crisis proves test for Bush pledge' in *The Guardian* 3.12.89; Times Newspapers Ltd for extracts from 'Rogue ship blamed for oil disaster' by Ian Birrell & Tom Revill in *Sunday Times* 8.1.89, 'Two views of a disaster' by Richard North in *Sunday Times* 12.4.91, 'Acid rain from the Mexico Oilfields damaging treasures' by Norman Hammond in *The Times* 2.8.89, 'Free power from beneath the waves' by Nick Nuttall in *The Times* 18.10.90, 'Tidal power pushes forward' by Nick Nuttall in *The Times*, 'Plants confirm air is cleaner' by R. Caseby in *Sunday Times* 18.6.89, 'Toyota will bring 6,000 extra jobs' by Kevin Eason in *The Times* 19.4.89, and 'Bitter Harvest' by Diana Winsor in *Sunday Times Magazine* 1.11.92. (c) Times Newspapers Ltd 1989/90/91/92; United Nations Development Programme for an extract from 'An innovative Philippine rehabilitation programme creates new entrepeneurs' in *World Development Magazine* Sept. 1988 and an extract by Margaret Neckles in *World Development Magazine* Sept. 1989; West Midlands Arts Board and the author, Jez Vanes for an extract from 'Postmark to the Black Country' in *People to People* No.7, January 1989; World Development Movement for an extract from 'Outcry as West dumps toxic wastes in Africa' by Ben Jackson in *Spur* magazine, July/August 1988; World Publications Ltd for an extract from 'Taiwan's success story' by E. S. Simpson in *Geographical Magazine* No.13, Nov. 1988.

No Trace Clause
We have been unable to trace the copyright holders of the following: 'Farmers pay price of rich harvest' in *Daily Telegraph* 10.8.91, 'Community Response' in *Sunday Telegraph Magazine* 1989, 'Fruits of the Forest' by M. Myers, 'Akosombo' by H. Robinson, Fig. 1.1, Fig. 4.76, Fig. 6.40, Fig. 6.52. We would appreciate any information which would enable us to trace the copyright holders of these and any other unacknowledged items in this book.

Index